Y0-CBR-772

Mathematics

ESSENTIALS AND APPLICATIONS

Authors

Glen Vannatta served as Supervisor of Mathematics for the Indianapolis Public Schools in Indianapolis, Indiana from 1966 to 1982. He is currently a Mathematics Consultant for Special Projects for the Indianapolis Public Schools. He previously was a secondary mathematics teacher in Indianapolis. Dr. Vannatta received his M.S. and Ed.D. from Indiana University. He has authored numerous mathematics textbooks, mathematics programs, and articles for professional mathematics journals. He is a member of several state and national professional organizations and a past president of the Indiana Council of Teachers of Mathematics.

John H. Stoeckinger is currently a mathematics teacher and department head at Carmel High School in Carmel, Indiana. He is a former teacher of seventh and eighth grade mathematics in Indiana. While teaching in the Indianapolis Public Schools, he wrote mathematics programs for students of sixth, seventh, and eighth grade ability. Mr. Stoeckinger received his B.S. at Indiana State Teacher's College and his M.S. at Indiana State University. He is co-author, with Dr. Vannatta, of *Basic Mathematics* Kits A, B, and C and is a member of state and national professional organizations.

CHARLES E. MERRILL PUBLISHING CO.
A Bell & Howell Company
Columbus, Ohio
Toronto • London • Sydney

ISBN 0-675-05775-2
Published by
CHARLES E. MERRILL PUBLISHING CO.
A Bell & Howell Company
Columbus, Ohio 43216

Printed in the United States of America

Consultants

Alice R. Garr
Mathematics Department Head
Herricks Middle School
Albertson, New York

Michael Mahaffey
Associate Professor of
Mathematics Education
University of Georgia
Athens, Georgia

Reviewers

Nancy Chisholm Biggs
Secondary Mathematics Consultant
Memphis City Schools
Memphis, Tennessee

Gerald N. Gambino, Jr.
Coordinator of Mathematics
East Penn School District
Emmaus, Pennsylvania

Margaret A. Jelsma
District Mathematics Chairperson
Utica Community Schools
Utica, Michigan

Sheila Dolgowich
Talented and Gifted Coordinator
Berne-Knox-Westerlo High School
Berne, New York

Margaret Snethen Gibson
Math Department Chairman
Madison Middle School
Tulsa, Oklahoma

Fred R. Stewart
Mathematics Supervisor
Neshaminy School District
Langhorne, Pennsylvania

Editorial Staff

Series Editor: Arthur L. Block
Project Editor: Garnet A. Lewis
Book Editors: Darlene Lewis, Patricia Travnicek
Photo Editors: Lindsay Gerard, Russ Lappa

Art Staff

Project Artist: Lewis H. Bolen
Book Designer: William Walker
Artists: Jeffrey A. Clark, Joan Shaull
Illustrator: Jim Shough

Preface

The second edition of *Mathematics: Essentials and Applications* is designed to meet the needs of today's junior high or middle school student.

As with the highly successful first edition, this edition contains many colorful and high-interest illustrations. These illustrations coupled with the relevant real-life applications capture and maintain student interest. Thus, learning is improved.

Highlights of the program include the following.

Essential Skills The program includes a thorough treatment of the 10 *Basic Skills* as defined by the position paper of the National Council of Supervisors of Mathematics.

Problem Solving Learning to solve problems is the principal reason for studying mathematics. *Mathematics: Essentials and Applications* presents a sequential and comprehensive development of problem solving in which students examine various components and aspects of solving problems.

Ample Practice This program presents a blend of essential skills and applications. Each text contains nearly 10,000 problems with many provisions for review, enrichment, and maintenance of skills and concepts.

Applications Research has shown that learning and retention are greatly improved when the student understands the value of the material and applies the skills learned in life-related situations. This program is based upon these findings.

Easy-to-Read Presentation An appropriate reading level, concise format, and interesting applications invite students to read and use these texts.

Diagnostic Skills Review This comprehensive review of the basic computational skills involving whole numbers, decimals, fractions, and percents appears at the end of the text. Separated into subskill levels, this material enables teachers to readily determine skill weaknesses. Ample problems provide necessary practice to improve skills.

BASIC Appendix This appendix provides instructions on understanding and writing programs using the BASIC computer language.

Each chapter of *Mathematics: Essentials and Applications* has a central theme which emphasizes how mathematics articulates with other subject areas. Each chapter is organized into easily managed one-or-two page lessons. Daily routine is enhanced by the periodic inclusion of enrichment, review, and special features. This design allows flexibility in structuring a program to meet individual student needs. The variety of features holds student interest and improves learning.

Each chapter contains the following features:

Cumulative Reviews

One-to-two pages of each chapter provide students a review of all the material presented to that point in the program. Research has proven this to be the most effective method for increasing student retention of mathematical skills.

Skills Reviews, Chapter Reviews, and Tests

These reviews and tests are provided to allow the student and the teacher to assess progress.

Skills Tests

These two-page cumulative tests at the end of Chapters 3, 7, 11, and 14 allow students to practice taking a test in a standardized format.

Applications

Optional features including Mathematics and Consumers and Mathematics and Careers highlight the relevance of mathematical skills to the student's present and future life.

Enrichment

Selected topics from the chapter are extended in a special enrichment feature at the end of each chapter.

Mathematics: Essentials and Applications contains the blend of essential skills, applications, enrichment, review, and practice needed for a thorough and comprehensive seventh- and eighth-grade mathematics program.

Contents

1 Whole Numbers

1–1 Rounding **3**
1–2 Basic Operations **4**
1–3 Exponents and Expanded Notation **6**
1–4 Properties of Addition and Multiplication **8**
1–5 Estimation **10**
1–6 Addition **12**
1–7 Subtraction **14**
Skills Review 15
Cumulative Review 16
1–8 One-digit Multipliers **18**
1–9 Two- and Three-digit Multipliers **20**
1–10 One-digit Divisors **22**
1–11 Two- and Three-digit Divisors . . **24**
1–12 Problem Solving: Choose the Operation **26**
Skills Review 27 **Chapter 1 Review 29**
Chapter 1 Test 30

SPECIAL FEATURES

Drive Carefully **11** Mathematics and Consumers: Checking Account **17** Patterns **19** Short Division **23** Sprouts **25** Mathematics and Consumers: Income Tax **28** Enrichment: Base Two **31**

2 Decimals

2–1 Decimals **33**
2–2 Comparing and Ordering Decimals **34**
2–3 Rounding Decimals **36**
2–4 Addition and Subtraction **38**
2–5 Multiplication **40**
2–6 Zeros in Multiplication **42**
Skills Review 43
Cumulative Review 44
2–7 Division **46**
2–8 Problem Solving: Multi-step Problems **48**
2–9 Multiplication and Division by Powers of Ten **50**
2–10 Division by Decimals **52**
2–11 Estimation **54**
2–12 Focus on Problem Solving: Too Many Facts **56**
Skills Review 57 **Chapter 2 Review 59**
Chapter 2 Test 60

SPECIAL FEATURES

Least and Greatest **35** Traveling Time **37** Mathematics and Consumers: Time Card **45** Moving Towers **51** Calculators and Estimation **55** Mathematics and Careers: Credit Manager **58** Enrichment: Modular Arithmetic **61**

3 Number Theory, Fractions, and Mixed Numerals

3–1 Factors and Divisibility **63**
3–2 Prime Factorization **64**
3–3 Common Factors and Common Multiples **66**
3–4 Problem Solving: Using Factors and Multiples **68**
Skills Review 69

Cumulative Review 70
3-5 Equivalent Fractions and Simplest Form ... 72
3-6 Mixed Numerals ... 74
3-7 Fractions, Mixed Numerals, and Decimals ... 76
3-8 Comparing and Ordering Fractions and Mixed Numerals ... 78
Skills Review 79 Chapter 3 Review 81
Chapter 3 Test 82
Skills Test, Chapters 1-3 84
SPECIAL FEATURES
Divisibility by 4 and 8 65 What's My Number? 67 Mathematics Lab: Figurate Numbers 71 One Third 75 Sevenths 77 Mathematics and Consumers: Mileage Chart 80 Enrichment: Euclidean Algorithm 83

4 Operations with Fractions and Mixed Numerals

4-1 Addition of Fractions with Like Denominators ... 87
4-2 Addition of Fractions with Different Denominators ... 88
4-3 Addition with Mixed Numerals ... 90
4-4 Subtraction of Fractions ... 92
4-5 Subtraction with Mixed Numerals ... 94
4-6 Problem Solving: Using Fractions and Mixed Numerals ... 96
Skills Review 97
Cumulative Review 98
4-7 Multiplication of Fractions ... 100
4-8 Multiplication with Mixed Numerals ... 102
4-9 Reciprocals and Division of Fractions ... 104
4-10 Division with Mixed Numerals ... 106
4-11 Focus on Problem Solving: Too Few Facts ... 108
Skills Review 109
Chapter 4 Review 111
Chapter 4 Test 112
SPECIAL FEATURES
Magic Squares 93 Mathematics Lab: Pictographs 99 Cross-Number Puzzle 107 Mathematics and Consumers: Rule of 78 110 Enrichment: Logical Reasoning 113

5 Geometry

5-1 Basic Geometric Terms ... 115
5-2 Angles ... 116
5-3 Angle Relationships ... 118
5-4 Perpendicular and Parallel Lines ... 120
5-5 Congruent Figures ... 122
5-6 Polygons ... 124
5-7 Triangles and Quadrilaterals ... 126
Skills Review 127
Cumulative Review 128
5-8 Constructions: Line Segments and Angles ... 130
5-9 Constructions: Perpendicular and Parallel Lines ... 132
5-10 Constructions: Congruent Triangles ... 134
5-11 Constructions: Regular Polygons ... 136
Skills Review 137 Chapter 5 Review 139 Chapter 5 Test 140
SPECIAL FEATURES
Four Lines 119 Line of Symmetry 123 Mathematics Lab: Paper Folding 129 Point of Symmetry 135 Mathematics and History: Golden Rectangle 138 Enrichment: Special Circles 141

6 Equations

6-1 Order of Operations 143
6-2 Variables and Expressions 144
6-3 Formulas 146
6-4 Using Variables 148
6-5 Solving Equations Using Subtraction 150
6-6 Solving Equations Using Addition 152
Skills Review 153
Cumulative Review 154
6-7 Solving Equations Using Division 156
6-8 Solving Equations Using Multiplication 158
6-9 Problem Solving: Using Equations 160
6-10 Solving Two-step Equations . . . 162
6-11 Sequences 164
6-12 Focus on Problem Solving: Look for a Pattern 166
Skills Review 167 Chapter 6 Review 169 Chapter 6 Test 170

SPECIAL FEATURES

Number Puzzle **145** Calculator Palindromes **151** Mathematics Lab: Making a Calendar **155** Magic Squares **157** Using Formulas **163** Mathematics and Careers: Loan Officer **168** Enrichment: Repeating Decimals **171**

7 Ratio, Proportion, and Percent

7-1 Ratios 173
7-2 Proportions 174
7-3 Using Proportions 176
7-4 Rates 178
7-5 Problem Solving: Using Rates and Proportions 180
7-6 Scale Drawings 182
Skills Review 183
Cumulative Review 184
7-7 Percents and Decimals 186
7-8 Percents and Fractions 188
7-9 Percents, Decimals, and Fractions 190
Skills Review 191 Chapter 7 Review 193 Chapter 7 Test 194
Skills Test, Chapters 1-7 196

SPECIAL FEATURES

A Famous Race **177** Mathematics Lab: Scale Drawings **185** Mathematics and Consumers: Utility Bills **192** Enrichment: Fibonacci Sequence **195**

8 Using Percents

8-1 Percents and Proportions 199
8-2 Finding the Percent of a Number 200
8-3 Finding the Percent One Number is of Another 202
8-4 Finding a Number When a Percent of It is Known 204
8-5 Percent of Increase or Decrease 206
8-6 Problem Solving: Using Percent 208
Skills Review 209
Cumulative Review 210
8-7 Percent and Tax 212
8-8 Percent and Business 214
8-9 Percent and Interest 216
8-10 Focus on Problem Solving: Guess and Check 218
Skills Review 219 Chapter 8 Review 221 Chapter 8 Test 222

SPECIAL FEATURES

Inflation **203** A Shortcut **207** Mathematics Lab: 100% Bar Graph **211** Compound Interest **217** Mathematics and Consumers: Earnings Statement **220** Enrichment: Successive Discounts **223**

9 Rational Numbers

9-1 Integers and Rational Numbers 225
9-2 Comparing Rational Numbers . . 226
9-3 Adding Rational Numbers 228
9-4 Subtracting Rational Numbers . 230
Skills Review 231
Cumulative Review 232
9-5 Multiplying Rational Numbers . . 234
9-6 Dividing Rational Numbers 236
9-7 Solving Equations 238
9-8 Solving Two-Step Equations . . . 240
9-9 Problem Solving: Using Rationals 242
9-10 Integers as Exponents 244
9-11 Scientific Notation 246
Skills Review 247 Chapter 9 Review 249 Chapter 9 Test 250

SPECIAL FEATURES

Windchill Factor **227** Mathematics Lab: Stock Listing **233** An Integer Puzzle **237** Density of Rational Numbers **241** Decimals in Expanded Form **245** Mathematics and Science: Temperature Formulas **248** Enrichment: Distributive Property **251**

10 Measurement

10-1 Metric Units of Length 253
10-2 Measuring Length 254
10-3 Changing Metric Units 256
10-4 Precision and Error 258
10-5 Mass and Capacity 260
10-6 Problem Solving: Using Metric Measurements 262
Skills Review 263
Cumulative Review 264
10-7 Time 266
10-8 Customary Units 268
10-9 Using the Customary System . . 270
10-10 Focus on Problem Solving: Working Backwards 272
Skills Review 273 Chapter 10 Review 275 Chapter 10 Test 276

SPECIAL FEATURES

History of Measurement **255** Tasty Recipes **257** Significant Digits **259** Mathematics Lab: Bar Graph **265** Computer Time **267** Boxes of Cereal **271** Mathematics and Computers: Universal Product Code **274** Enrichment: Accuracy **277**

11 Perimeter, Area, and Volume

11-1 Perimeter 279
11-2 Area of Rectangles and Parallelograms 280
11-3 Area of Triangles and Trapezoids 282
11-4 Circumference and Area of Circles 284
11-5 Surface Area of Prisms and Pyramids 286
11-6 Surface Area of Cylinders and Cones 288
Skills Review 289
Cumulative Review 290
11-7 Volume of Prisms and Pyramids 292
11-8 Volume of Cylinders and Cones 294
11-9 Problem Solving: Using Perimeter, Area, and Volume 296

Skills Review 297 **Chapter 11 Review 299** **Chapter 11 Test 300** **Skills Test, Chapters 1–11 302**

SPECIAL FEATURES

Converting Metric Units of Area **281** Calculator π **285** Mathematics Lab: Approximating π **291** Volume, Capacity and Mass **295** Mathematics and Science: Density **298** Enrichment: Spheres **301**

12 Probability and Statistics

12–1 Counting Outcomes Using Tree Diagrams **305**
12–2 Counting Outcomes Using Multiplication **306**
12–3 Probability **308**
12–4 Multiplying Probabilities **310**
12–5 Adding Probabilities **312**
12–6 Odds **314**
Skills Review 315
Cumulative Review 316
12–7 Statistics **318**
12–8 Using Statistical Graphs **320**
12–9 Problem Solving: Using Statistics **322**
12–10 Range, Mean, Median, and Mode **324**
12–11 Focus on Problem Solving: Using Venn Diagrams **326**
Skills Review 327 **Chapter 12 Review 329** **Chapter 12 Test 330**

SPECIAL FEATURES

Pascal's Triangle **309** Conditional Probability **311** Mathematics Lab: Probability Experiment **317** Normal Curve **319** Percentiles **325** Mathematics and Careers: Insurance Agent **328** Enrichment: Scattergrams **331**

13 Real Numbers and Graphing

13–1 Squares and Square Roots . . . **333**
13–2 Approximating Square Roots . . **334**
13–3 Real Numbers **336**
13–4 Inequalities **338**
13–5 The Coordinate System **340**
13–6 Using Coordinates **342**
Skills Review 343
Cumulative Review 344
13–7 Equations with Two Variables . . **346**
13–8 Graphing Equations **348**
13–9 Graphing Two Equations **350**
13–10 Curved Graphs **352**
13–11 Problem Solving: Using Graphs **354**
Skills Review 355 **Chapter 13 Review 357** **Chapter 13 Test 358**

SPECIAL FEATURES

Mathematics and Science: Formulas Involving Square Root **337** What Is It? **341** Mathematics Lab: Divide-and-Average Method **345** Write an Equation **349** Inequalities with Two Variables **351** Curve Stitching **353** Mathematics and Consumers: Certificate of Deposit **356** Enrichment: Slope **359**

14 Right Triangles

14–1 Right Triangles **361**
14–2 The Pythagorean Theorem. . . . **362**
14–3 Using the Pythagorean Theorem **364**
14–4 30°-60° Right Triangles **366**
14–5 Similar Triangles **368**
14–6 Indirect Measurement **370**
14–7 Problem Solving: Right Triangles **372**
Skills Review 373
Cumulative Review 374

14-8 Tangent, Sine, and Cosine Ratios **376**
14-9 Using Tangent, Sine, and Cosine. **378**
14-10 Focus on Problem Solving: Solve a Similar Problem **380**

Skills Review 381 Chapter 14 Review 383 Chapter 14 Test 384 Skills Test, Chapters 1-14 386

SPECIAL FEATURES

Pythagorean Triples **363** Constructing Irrational Numbers **365** Mathematics Lab: Stadia **375** Interpolation **379** Mathematics and Geography: Latitude and Longitude **382** Enrichment: Dilations **385**

Appendix: BASIC 388
Diagnostic Skills Review 398
Squares and Approximate Square Roots 422
Trigonometric Ratios 423
Glossary 424
Symbols and Formulas 431
Index 432

1 Whole Numbers

In a recent year, each passenger car in the United States was driven an average of 9,839 miles. Depending on the accuracy desired, a reporter may express 9,839 as about 9,840, about 9,800, or about 10,000.

1-1 Rounding

The numbers 9,840, 9,800, and 10,000 result when 9,839 is rounded in different ways.

The chart shows the place-value position of each digit in 9,839.

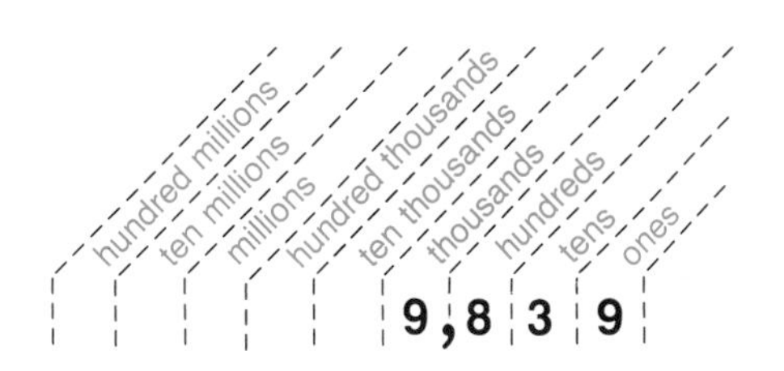

Suppose you round 9,839 to the nearest thousand. You know that 9,839 is between 9,000 and 10,000.

You can round numbers using the following rules.

- Look at the digit to the right of the place-value position being rounded.
- Round *up* if this digit is *5 or greater.*
- Round *down* if this digit is *less than 5.*

To the nearest thousand, $\underline{9}$,839 is 10,000 since 8 is *5 or greater.* What is 9,839 to the nearest ten? To the nearest hundred?

EXERCISES ***Choose the correct answer for rounding to the underlined place-value position.***

1. $\underline{5}8$	50	60	**2.** $3\underline{5}4$	350	360
3. $\underline{2}$,898	2,000	3,000	**4.** \$9,$\underline{6}45$	\$9,600	\$9,700
5. 2$\underline{7}$,653	27,000	28,000	**6.** $\underline{9}6$,524	90,000	100,000

Round each of the following to the underlined place-value position.

7. $\underline{7}4$	**8.** $8\underline{0}5$	**9.** \$$\underline{6}35$	**10.** 1,8$\underline{9}$3
11. 4,$\underline{3}$48	**12.** 8,6$\underline{2}$5	**13.** $\underline{7}$,642	**14.** $\underline{9}$,555
15. \$4,$\underline{4}$98	**16.** 1$\underline{6}$,924	**17.** 36,$\underline{3}$47	**18.** $\underline{2}$9,096
19. 327,9$\underline{6}$2	**20.** $\underline{8}$60,724	**21.** $\underline{9}$62,445	**22.** 3$\underline{2}$6,789
23. $\underline{4}$,589,927	**24.** 3,2$\underline{8}$9,650	**25.** 15,$\underline{4}$89,622	**26.** 2$\underline{7}$,342,567

1-2 Basic Operations

The express train has 12 cars. The local train has 7. The subtraction sentence $12 - 7 = 5$ shows that the express train has 5 more cars than the local train. This subtraction sentence and the addition sentence $5 + 7 = 12$ are related as shown.

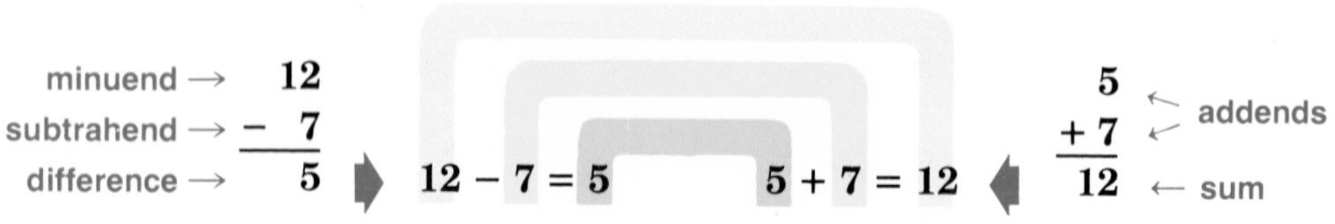

minuend → 12
subtrahend → − 7
difference → 5

$12 - 7 = 5$ $5 + 7 = 12$

5 ← addends
+ 7
12 ← sum

The multiplication sentence $6 \times 4 = 24$ and division sentence $24 \div 4 = 6$ are related as follows.

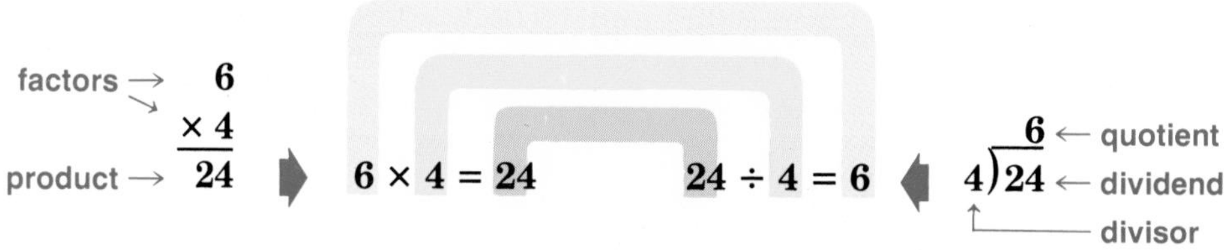

factors → 6
× 4
product → 24

$6 \times 4 = 24$ $24 \div 4 = 6$

6 ← quotient
4)24 ← dividend
divisor

EXERCISES ***Write a related subtraction sentence for each addition sentence. Write a related addition sentence for each subtraction sentence.***

1. $2 + 1 = 3$ **2.** $8 + 9 = 17$ **3.** $2 + 0 = 2$

4. $4 = 2 + 2$ **5.** $1 + 9 = 10$ **6.** $9 = 5 + 4$

7. $20 + 40 = 60$ **8.** $400 + 300 = 700$ **9.** $9{,}000 = 1{,}000 + 8{,}000$

10. $7 - 2 = 5$ **11.** $11 - 5 = 6$ **12.** $9 - 0 = 9$

13. $3 = 10 - 7$ **14.** $12 - 8 = 4$ **15.** $7 = 14 - 7$

16. $50 - 10 = 40$ **17.** $600 - 300 = 300$ **18.** $1{,}200 - 300 = 900$

Write a related division sentence for each multiplication sentence. Write a related multiplication sentence for each division sentence.

19. $6 \times 2 = 12$ **20.** $2 \times 1 = 2$ **21.** $18 = 2 \times 9$

22. $72 = 9 \times 8$ **23.** $0 \times 5 = 0$ **24.** $7 \times 7 = 49$

25. $7 \times 40 = 280$ **26.** $100 \times 9 = 900$ **27.** $5 \times 900 = 4{,}500$

28. $12 \div 3 = 4$ **29.** $32 \div 8 = 4$ **30.** $54 \div 6 = 9$

31. $8 = 40 \div 5$ **32.** $7 \div 7 = 1$ **33.** $0 \div 3 = 0$

34. $360 \div 6 = 60$ **35.** $100 \div 5 = 20$ **36.** $8{,}100 \div 9 = 900$

Replace each ▒ with a number to make a true sentence.

8 = ▒ − 5

8 = 13 − 5

The missing number is 13.

48 ÷ ▒ = 6

48 ÷ 8 = 6

The missing number is 8.

37. 2 + 3 = ▒

38. 16 − 8 = ▒

39. 0 + 0 = ▒

40. ▒ = 18 − 9

41. 0 + 7 = ▒

42. 2 − 1 = ▒

43. ▒ + 3 = 4

44. 10 − ▒ = 8

45. 16 = ▒ + 9

46. 6 − ▒ = 6

47. ▒ − 6 = 6

48. ▒ = 56 ÷ 8

49. ▒ = 8 × 3

50. ▒ = 6 × 7

51. 18 ÷ ▒ = 9

52. 2 + ▒ = 11

53. ▒ × 9 = 63

54. 3 ÷ ▒ = 1

55. 8 × ▒ = 0

56. ▒ ÷ 1 = 0

57. ▒ ÷ 5 = 3

58. 8 × ▒ = 32

59. ▒ = 2 × 6

60. 8 = ▒ ÷ 8

61. ▒ = 3 + 8
▒ = 30 + 80
▒ = 300 + 800
▒ = 3,000 + 8,000

62. 15 − ▒ = 9
150 − ▒ = 90
1,500 − ▒ = 900
15,000 − ▒ = 9,000

63. 14 − 8 = ▒
140 − 80 = ▒
1,400 − 800 = ▒
14,000 − 8,000 = ▒

64. 1 = 10 − ▒
10 = 100 − ▒
100 = 1,000 − ▒
1,000 = 10,000 − ▒

65. 1 × 5 = ▒
10 × 5 = ▒
100 × 5 = ▒
1,000 × 5 = ▒

66. ▒ = 6 ÷ 3
▒ = 60 ÷ 3
▒ = 600 ÷ 3
▒ = 6,000 ÷ 3

67. 7 × ▒ = 28
7 × ▒ = 280
7 × ▒ = 2,800
7 × ▒ = 28,000

68. ▒ ÷ 5 = 7
▒ ÷ 5 = 70
▒ ÷ 5 = 700
▒ ÷ 5 = 7,000

69. 9 = ▒ ÷ 3
90 = ▒ ÷ 3
900 = ▒ ÷ 3
9,000 = ▒ ÷ 3

Write four related sentences using the numbers in each of the following.

70. A small airplane has 4 passengers in first class and 9 in coach. There are 13 passengers in all.

71. Tickets to the school play cost \$3 each. The cost of 7 tickets is \$21.

72. Sid buys two shirts for \$17. One shirt costs \$8, the other \$9.

1-3 Exponents and Expanded Form

There are about 10,000 private airports in the United States. The number 10,000 is expressed in **standard form.** Another way to express 10,000 is as the product $10 \times 10 \times 10 \times 10$.

You can also express $10 \times 10 \times 10 \times 10$ using exponents. An **exponent** tells how many times a number, called the **base,** is used as a factor. Numbers that can be expressed using exponents are called **powers.**

$$\underbrace{10 \times 10 \times 10 \times 10}_{\text{4 factors}} = 10^4$$

exponent: 4; base: 10

Read 10^4 as *ten to the fourth power.*

Read 4^2 as *four to the second power* or *four squared.*

$$4^2 = 4 \times 4 \text{ or } 16$$

Read 2^3 as *two to the third power* or *two cubed.*

$$2^3 = 2 \times 2 \times 2 \text{ or } 8$$

First and Zero Powers

$5^1 = 5$ Any number to the first power is that number.

$3^0 = 1$ Any number (other than zero) to the zero power is 1.

EXERCISES Express each of the following as a product of factors. For example, express 5^4 as $5 \times 5 \times 5 \times 5$.

1. 6^2 **2.** 10^3 **3.** 2^5 **4.** 4^3 **5.** 11^4

6. 4 cubed **7.** 14 squared **8.** 15 cubed **9.** 10 squared

Express each of the following in standard form.

10. 9^2 **11.** 3^3 **12.** 5^2 **13.** 10^2 **14.** 2^1

15. 15^1 **16.** 10^3 **17.** 10^5 **18.** 3^0 **19.** 12^0

Express each of the following as a power of 10 using exponents.

20. 100 **21.** 10 **22.** 1,000 **23.** 1 **24.** 10,000

25. 100,000 **26.** 1,000,000 **27.** 10,000,000

28. For powers of 10, describe the relationship between the exponent and the number of zeros in the standard form numeral.

The chart below shows how powers of 10 are related to place value.

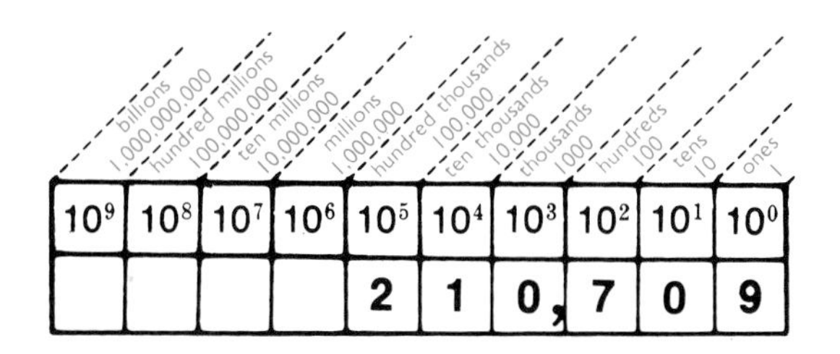

The place-value chart can help you to write the **expanded form** of 210,709.

$$\mathbf{200{,}000 + 10{,}000 + 700 + 9}$$

$$\mathbf{(2 \times 100{,}000) + (1 \times 10{,}000) + (7 \times 100) + (9 \times 1)}$$ Using 1, 10, 100, and so on.

$$\mathbf{(2 \times 10^5) + (1 \times 10^4) + (7 \times 10^2) + (9 \times 10^0)}$$ Using 10^0, 10^1, 10^2, and so on.

EXERCISES ***Express each of the following in standard form.***

29. $80 + 7$

30. $800 + 10 + 4$

31. $2{,}000 + 400 + 50$

32. $(7 \times 10) + (6 \times 1)$

33. $(2 \times 10{,}000) + (4 \times 1{,}000)$

34. $(4 \times 10^5) + (2 \times 10^1)$

35. $(1 \times 10^4) + (1 \times 10^0)$

36. $(7 \times 100{,}000) + (5 \times 10{,}000) + (9 \times 1{,}000) + (2 \times 10) + (2 \times 1)$

37. $(4 \times 10^8) + (3 \times 10^6) + (4 \times 10^5) + (8 \times 10^4) + (5 \times 10^2)$

Express each of the following in expanded form using 1, 10, 100, and so on.

38. 734

39. 4,602

40. 16,000

41. 50,000

42. 908,000

43. 4,000,000

44. 3,040,000

45. 4,205,400,000

Express each of the following in expanded form using 10^0, 10^1, 10^2, and so on.

46. 865

47. 1,260

48. 9,000

49. 85,000

50. 400,500

51. 8,000,000

52. 17,049,690

53. 19,470,000,000

54. The total cost of transportation in the United States is more than 500 billion dollars a year.

55. In a recent year, there were 300 million vehicles on the world's highways.

1-4 Properties of Addition and Multiplication

Gasoline is a very important fuel. Properties of gasoline include that it is lighter than water and it burns easily. Like gasoline, addition and multiplication have properties.

Identity Property of Addition (Addition Property of 0)
When zero is added to a number, the sum is that number.

$$400 + 0 \stackrel{?}{=} 400$$
$$400 = 400 \ \checkmark$$

Identity Property of Multiplication (Multiplication Property of 1)
When a number is multiplied by 1, the product is that number.

$$8 \times 1 \stackrel{?}{=} 8$$
$$8 = 8 \ \checkmark$$

Commutative Properties The order in which numbers are added or multiplied does not change the answer.

$$8 + 5 \stackrel{?}{=} 5 + 8 \qquad 30 \times 5 \stackrel{?}{=} 5 \times 30$$
$$13 = 13 \ \checkmark \qquad 150 = 150 \ \checkmark$$

Associative Properties The way in which addends or factors are grouped does not change the answer. *Parenthesis* ( ) tell which operation to do first.

$$(20 + 30) + 40 \stackrel{?}{=} 20 + (30 + 40)$$
$$50 + 40 \stackrel{?}{=} 20 + 70$$
$$90 = 90 \ \checkmark$$

$$(2 \times 3) \times 10 \stackrel{?}{=} 2 \times (3 \times 10)$$
$$6 \times 10 \stackrel{?}{=} 2 \times 30$$
$$60 = 60 \ \checkmark$$

EXERCISES ***Name the property illustrated by each of the following.***

1. $7 + 5 = 5 + 7$
2. $1 \times 16 = 16$
3. $0 + 1{,}000 = 1{,}000$
4. $2 \times (3 \times 10) = (2 \times 3) \times 10$
5. $(6 + 4) + 2 = 6 + (4 + 2)$
6. $0 + 10 = 10 + 0$
7. $200 + 500 = 500 + 200$
8. $(7 \times 6) \times 3 = 3 \times (7 \times 6)$
9. $5 \times (20 \times 3) = (5 \times 20) \times 3$

10. Write a sentence to illustrate each property of addition.
11. Write a sentence to illustrate each property of multiplication.

Distributive Property of Multiplication over Addition The product of a number and a sum is equal to the sum of the products.

There are 14 dots in each arrangement.

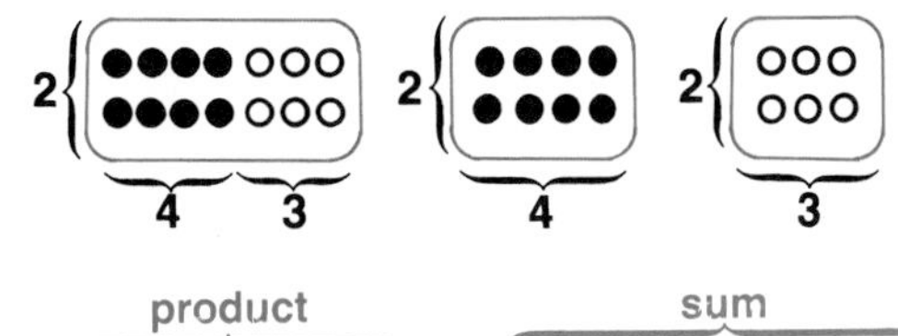

product: number × sum; sum: product + product

$$2 \times (4 + 3) \stackrel{?}{=} (2 \times 4) + (2 \times 3)$$

$$2 \times 7 \stackrel{?}{=} 8 + 6$$

$$14 = 14 \checkmark$$

EXERCISES ***Name the property illustrated by each of the following.***

12. $7 + 0 = 0 + 7$

13. $(9 \times 1) \times 4 = 4 \times (9 \times 1)$

14. $(5 \times 4) \times 8 = 5 \times (4 \times 8)$

15. $1 \times 4{,}205 = 4{,}205$

16. $2 \times (8 + 1) = (2 \times 8) + (2 \times 1)$

17. $190 + (6 + 200) = (6 + 200) + 190$

18. $(10 + 11) \times 2 = 2 \times (10 + 11)$

19. $(4 \times 30) + (4 \times 7) = 4 \times (30 + 7)$

Replace each ▒ with a number to make a true sentence.

20. 2 + ▒ = 2

21. ▒ = 1 × 8

22. 15 = ▒ × 1

23. 2 + 3 = ▒ + 2

24. 4 × 1 = ▒ × 4

25. 429 = ▒ + 0

26. (6 + 4) + ▒ = 2 + (6 + 4)

27. 6 × (5 + 4) = (6 × ▒) + (6 × 4)

28. (2 × 6) × 18 = 2 × (▒ × 18)

29. 25 + (▒ + 59) = (25 + 75) + 59

30. (8 × 30) + (8 × ▒) = 8 × (30 + 7)

31. 5 × (100 + 8) = (▒ × 100) + (▒ × 8)

Use one of the properties to help you compute answers for each of the following without paper and pencil.

32. $40 + (60 + 239)$
Hint: $(40 + 60) + 239$

33. $20 \times (5 \times 13)$
Hint: $(20 \times 5) \times 13$

34. $(24 \times 4) + (24 \times 6)$
Hint: $24 \times (4 + 6)$

35. $(14 \times 2) \times 500$

36. $(28 \times 2) + (28 \times 8)$

37. $(821 + 700) + 300$

State whether each of the following is true or false.

38. $12 - 5 = 5 - 12$

39. $16 \div 8 = 8 \div 16$

40. $(8 - 4) - 2 = 8 - (4 - 2)$

41. $(12 \div 6) \div 2 = 12 \div (6 \div 2)$

42. Subtraction is commutative.

43. Division is commutative.

44. Subtraction is associative.

45. Division is associative.

1-5 Estimation

The largest cable car carries 121 passengers. About how many passengers can be carried in 9 trips?

Multiply to find the number of passengers. Since you only need to know *about* how many, estimate.

Estimate 121×9 as follows. Round 121 to its greatest place-value position, hundreds. Do *not* change 1-digit factors like 9.

$$\begin{array}{r} 121 \\ \times \quad 9 \\ \hline \end{array} \rightarrow \begin{array}{r} 100 \\ \times \quad 9 \\ \hline 900 \end{array}$$

121 rounds to 100

In 9 trips, the cable car can carry about 900 passengers.

When you estimate, use the following rules.

Addition and Subtraction Round each number to its greatest place-value position. Then add or subtract.

Multiplication Round each factor to its greatest place-value position. Do *not* change 1-digit factors. Then, multiply.

Division Round the divisor to its greatest place-value position. Do *not* change 1-digit divisors. Then, round the dividend so it is a multiple of the divisor. Then divide.

EXERCISES ***Copy. Then complete the estimation.***

1. $4,387 + 8,965 ➧ $4,000 + 9,000 = $▒▒,▒▒▒

2. 28,045 − 3,860 ➧ 30,000 − 4,000 = ▒▒,▒▒▒

3. 623 × 77 ➧ 600 × 80 = ▒▒,▒▒▒

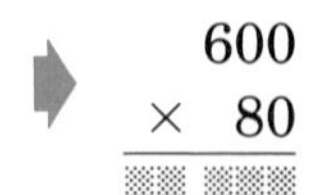

4. 5)3,021 ➧ 5)3,000 = ▒▒▒

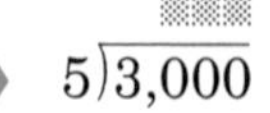

5. 22)13,406 ➧ 20)14,000 = ▒▒▒

Estimate.

6. 430 + 315

7. $807 + 791

8. 2,465 + 8,140

9. 19,364 − 12,988

10. 723,619 − 181,000

11. 9,382 − 724

12. 79,850 + 4,461

13. 53,180 − 6,912

14. $650 + 2,333 + 9,410

15. 151,522 + 80,500 + 8,205

16. 71 × 8

17. 137 × 6

18. 8,500 × 7

19. $95 × 13

20. 810 × 56

21. 4)$78

22. 8)234

23. 6)4,290

24. 17)650

25. 91)4,469

26. 210,500 − 68,800

27. 8,140 + 771 + 2,440 + 16,895

28. $29,500 ÷ 3

29. 5,124 × 74

30. 1,221 ÷ 38

31. 265 × 314

32. 67,800 ÷ 83

33. 330,481 ÷ 587

Estimate. Use the line graph. Round times to the nearest hour and distances to the nearest 10 kilometers.

34. How far does Sheila ride in 2 hours?

35. How far does she ride in 6 hours?

36. How long does it take Sheila to ride 40 kilometers? 90 kilometers?

37. Predict how far she can ride in 10 hours.

38. Predict how long it would take Sheila to ride 150 kilometers.

Sheila's Bike Hike

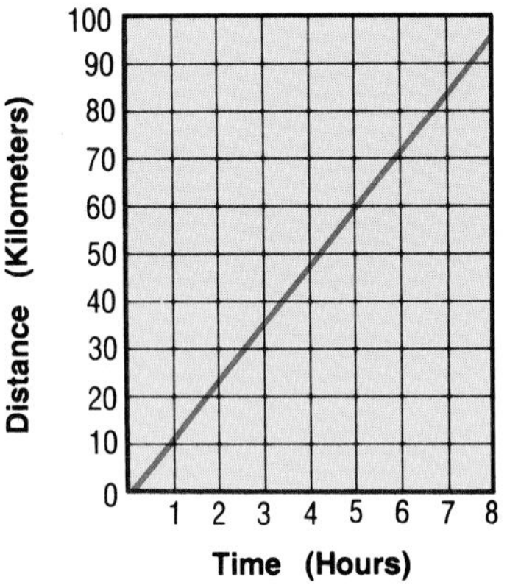

Distance (Kilometers): 0, 10, 20, 30, 40, 50, 60, 70, 80, 90, 100

Time (Hours): 1, 2, 3, 4, 5, 6, 7, 8

DRIVE CAREFULLY

Copy. Then use estimation to find the message.

B	37 + 14	**A**	510 − 289	**T**	190 × 6	**N**	435 ÷ 7
L	6,100 − 795	**F**	2,608 + 803	**S**	63 × 42	**E**	14,294 ÷ 22

___ ___ ___ ___ ___ ___   ___ ___ ___ ___   ___ ___ ___ ___ ___

3,800 200 2,400 1,200 700 60   2,400 700 200 1,200   50 700 5,200 1,200 2,400

1-6 Addition

In two recent years, 3,805 and 2,437 transit buses were delivered in the United States. To find the total number of buses delivered, add.

Estimate as shown.

$$\begin{array}{r} 3{,}805 \\ +\ 2{,}437 \\ \hline \end{array} \quad \Rightarrow \quad \begin{array}{r} 4{,}000 \\ +\ 2{,}000 \\ \hline 6{,}000 \end{array}$$

4,000 ← 3,805 rounds to 4,000
2,000 ← 2,437 rounds to 2,000
6,000 ← estimate

To find the exact answer, add in each place-value position as follows.

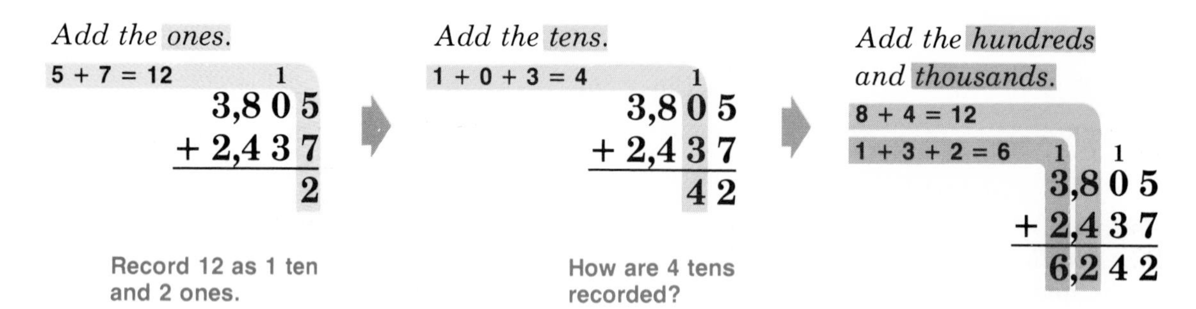

There are 6,242 buses. Based on the estimate this answer makes sense. As a check, add the numbers in reverse order. Which property of addition is this?

$$\begin{array}{r} {}^{1\ \ 1} \\ 2{,}437 \\ +\ 3{,}805 \\ \hline 6{,}242 \end{array} \checkmark$$

EXERCISES ***Add. Check your answers.***

1. 37 + 61	**2.** 85 + 79	**3.** 506 + 80
4. 372 + 29	**5.** 213 + 174	**6.** 482 + 526
7. \$9,510 + 494	**8.** 2,376 + 2,689	**9.** 8,705 + 655
10. 2,042 + 1,209	**11.** 2,619 + 4,385	**12.** 6,495 + 8,195

When you add three or more numbers, look for a way to group the digits so you can add to make a 10. Which property of addition is used?

```
  11 11
  18,678
   2,435
+ 15,272
  36,385
```

Add 8 + 2 to make 10.
Then, 10 + 5 is 15.

EXERCISES ***Add. Check your answers.***

13. 7,246 + 8,465	**14.** 8,243 + 2,737	**15.** 13,525 + 4,277	**16.** 18,692 + 5,323	**17.** 4,264 + 26,543

18. 13,961 + 24,732	**19.** 62,033 + 78,359	**20.** 276,485 + 79,735	**21.** 862,761 + 735,839
22. \$4,243 1,304 + 467	**23.** 4,542 3,240 + 1,811	**24.** 18,652 7,859 + 4,806	**25.** 5,987 24,007 + 8,633
26. \$1,234 20,044 5,271 + 6,307	**27.** 7,650 721 13,428 + 75,263	**28.** 47,165 8,634 60,041 + 36,980	**29.** \$41,084 605,500 9,361 + 86,284

30. 283 + 16 + 922

31. \$263 + \$174 + \$30

32. 23,000 + 1,440 + 179

33. 37,000 + 7,650 + 11,907

34. \$7,268 + \$24,112 + \$65,040

35. 23,655 + 10,981 + 4,405

36. 203,490 + 50,997 + 2,437

37. 51,526 + 275,687 + 47,895

Copy and complete.

38. 5▒8 + ▒7▒ 827	**39.** 2,▒4▒ + 153 ▒,2▒1	**40.** ▒5,73▒ + 24,▒32 ▒2▒,5▒7	**41.** 4▒6,2▒7 + 7▒,83▒ ▒46,▒02

Solve. Use the circle graph.

42. Write each number of passengers in standard form.

43. Find the total number of passengers.

Passenger by Vehicle Type

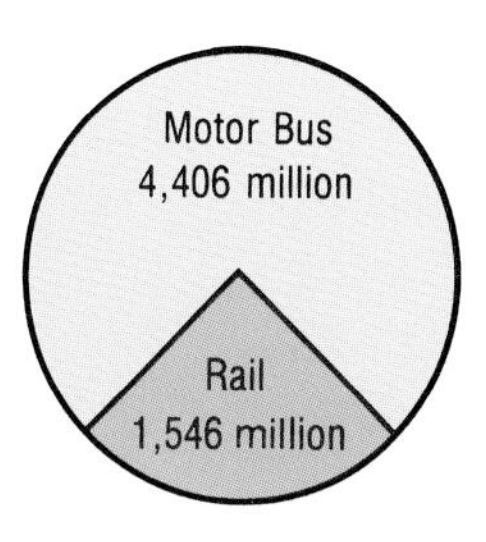

1-7 Subtraction

John Solis drives a truck from Charleston to Boston, a distance of 746 miles. After driving 285 miles, he subtracts to find how many more miles he has to drive.

The estimate is 400.

$$\begin{array}{r} 746 \\ -\ 285 \\ \hline \end{array} \rightarrow \begin{array}{r} 700 \\ -\ 300 \\ \hline 400 \end{array}$$

746 rounds to 700
285 rounds to 300
estimate

To find the exact answer, subtract in each place-value position as follows.

Subtract the ones.

6 − 5 = 1

$$\begin{array}{r} 746 \\ -\ 285 \\ \hline 1 \end{array}$$

Rename 74 tens as 6 hundreds and 14 tens.

$$\begin{array}{r} \overset{6\ 14}{\cancel{7}\cancel{4}}6 \\ -\ 285 \\ \hline 1 \end{array}$$

Subtract the tens and hundreds.

14 − 8 = 6

6 − 2 = 4

$$\begin{array}{r} \overset{6\ 14}{\cancel{7}\cancel{4}}6 \\ -\ 285 \\ \hline 461 \end{array}$$

There are 461 miles to be driven. Based on the estimate, does this answer seem reasonable? You can check the answer using addition.

$$\begin{array}{r} \overset{1}{2}85 \\ +\ 461 \\ \hline 746 \end{array} \checkmark$$

EXERCISES ***Subtract. Check your answers.***

1. 86 − 54	**2.** 97 − 48	**3.** 182 − 54	**4.** 998 − 56	**5.** 243 − 78
6. \$499 − 156	**7.** 528 − 327	**8.** 946 − 149	**9.** 645 − 186	**10.** 822 − 573
11. 1,586 − 323	**12.** 4,296 − 267	**13.** 1,966 − 549	**14.** 8,645 − 264	**15.** \$6,145 − 411
16. 3,371 − 2,180	**17.** 8,624 − 4,875	**18.** 1,564 − 1,088	**19.** 6,295 − 3,496	**20.** 7,536 − 2,748
21. 24,623 − 8,490	**22.** 67,981 − 8,291	**23.** 86,912 − 28,851	**24.** 74,652 − 54,738	

Study the following example.

$$\begin{array}{r} 2{,}106 \\ -\ \ 428 \\ \hline \end{array}$$

Rename 106 as 0 hundreds, 9 tens, and 16 ones. Subtract the ones and tens.

$$\begin{array}{r} {\scriptstyle 0\ 9\ 16} \\ 2{,}\not{1}\not{0}\not{6} \\ -\ \ 4\,2\,8 \\ \hline 7\,8 \end{array}$$

Rename 2 thousands as 1 thousand and 10 hundreds. Then, subtract.

$$\begin{array}{r} {\scriptstyle 10} \\ {\scriptstyle 1\ \not{0}\ 9\,16} \\ \not{2}{,}\not{1}\not{0}\not{6} \\ -\ \ 4\,2\,8 \\ \hline 1{,}6\,7\,8 \end{array}$$

EXERCISES ***Subtract. Check your answers.***

25. 100 − 32	**26.** \$706 − 79	**27.** 851 − 83	**28.** 810 − 264	**29.** 900 − 207
30. 2,408 − 214	**31.** 1,614 − 786	**32.** 4,000 − 2,156	**33.** \$8,100 − 5,940	**34.** 14,307 − 1,209
35. 13,250 − 2,163	**36.** 78,004 − 29,406	**37.** 106,940 − 27,685	**38.** 215,670 − 112,795	

39. 57,984 − 38,977 **40.** 306,141 − 85,909 **41.** 626,910 − 200,046

Solve.

42. An auto plant assembles 940 cars Friday and 741 Monday. How many fewer cars are assembled Monday?

43. After 288 miles of pipeline have been inspected, there are 492 miles to go. How long is the pipeline?

Skills Review: Pages 3-15

Round each of the following to the underlined place-value position.

1. $1\underline{4}6$ **2.** $1\underline{2},596$

5. Express 7^2 in standard form.

Estimate.

7. 84×12 **8.** $47\overline{)4,651}$

Replace each ■ with a number to make a true sentence.

3. 16 − ■ = 8 **4.** ■ ÷ 4 = 9

6. Name the property illustrated by $(8 + 6) + 4 = 8 + (6 + 4)$.

Add or subtract.

9. 2,461 + 97 **10.** 12,784 − 4,286

11. 41,206 + 8,480 + 29,845

Cumulative Review

Round each of the following to the underlined place-value position.

1. $1\underline{8}5$
2. $2,8\underline{0}6$
3. $12\underline{6},482$
4. $1,\underline{2}28,400$

Replace each ■ with a number to make a true sentence.

5. ■ = 11 − 5
6. 20 + 40 = ■
7. 2 × 400 = ■

Name the property illustrated by each of the following.

8. (5 + 18) + 6 = 6 + (5 + 18)
9. (2 × 10) + (2 × 8) = 2 × (10 + 8)

Estimate.

10. $\begin{array}{r} 20,064 \\ -\ 2,141 \\ \hline \end{array}$
11. $\begin{array}{r} 65,960 \\ +\ 8,321 \\ \hline \end{array}$
12. $\begin{array}{r} \$478 \\ \times\ 18 \\ \hline \end{array}$
13. $58\overline{)18,486}$

Add or subtract. Check your answers.

14. $\begin{array}{r} 47 \\ +\ 85 \\ \hline \end{array}$
15. $\begin{array}{r} 216 \\ +\ 48 \\ \hline \end{array}$
16. $\begin{array}{r} 422 \\ +\ 769 \\ \hline \end{array}$
17. $\begin{array}{r} 2,464 \\ +\ 695 \\ \hline \end{array}$
18. $\begin{array}{r} 12,045 \\ +\ 2,958 \\ \hline \end{array}$
19. $\begin{array}{r} \$2,816 \\ 285 \\ +\ 5,489 \\ \hline \end{array}$
20. $\begin{array}{r} 82,406 \\ 17,218 \\ +\ 4,706 \\ \hline \end{array}$
21. $\begin{array}{r} 211,050 \\ 78,580 \\ +\ 124,694 \\ \hline \end{array}$
22. $\begin{array}{r} 428,800 \\ 19,486 \\ +\ 122,895 \\ \hline \end{array}$
23. $\begin{array}{r} \$92 \\ -\ 75 \\ \hline \end{array}$
24. $\begin{array}{r} 263 \\ -\ 94 \\ \hline \end{array}$
25. $\begin{array}{r} 990 \\ -\ 644 \\ \hline \end{array}$
26. $\begin{array}{r} \$2,140 \\ -\ 620 \\ \hline \end{array}$
27. $\begin{array}{r} 4,610 \\ -\ 3,750 \\ \hline \end{array}$
28. $\begin{array}{r} 19,000 \\ -\ 8,035 \\ \hline \end{array}$
29. $\begin{array}{r} 51,265 \\ -\ 2,846 \\ \hline \end{array}$
30. $\begin{array}{r} 314,210 \\ -\ 142,160 \\ \hline \end{array}$
31. $\begin{array}{r} 414,800 \\ -\ 225,284 \\ \hline \end{array}$
32. 519 + 86 + 4,375
33. \$209,655 + \$822,500
34. 2,454 − 658
35. 775,100 − 235,600

Solve.

36. Charles Lindbergh used all but 18 of his 450 gallons of fuel when he flew across the Atlantic. How many gallons did he use?
37. There are 164,225 cars registered in Alaska. Hawaii has 450,687. How many cars do the two states have?

Mathematics and Consumers

Jean Finley uses checks to pay some of her expenses. Checks are safer and often more convenient than paying cash. A **check** directs a bank or savings and loan to pay a certain amount from the money you deposit in a **checking account.**

Railroad Savings Bank Number 204
21-432/987
Date Sept. 10, 19 ~~
Pay to the order of Rivere Auto Parts $26.07
Twenty-six and 07/100 ~~~~ Dollars
memo Muffler Jean Finley
4:0441...0813 90104410...

The amount of the check is written in two ways: \$26.07 and twenty-six and $\frac{07}{100}$ dollars. Explain why a line is drawn between $\frac{07}{100}$ and *dollars.*

CHECK NO.	DATE	CHECK ISSUED TO	BALANCE BROUGHT FORWARD	✓	27	19
~	9/4	TO Deposit FOR	AMOUNT OF CHECK OR DEPOSIT BALANCE		68	50
204	9/10	TO Rivere Auto Parts FOR muffler	AMOUNT OF CHECK OR DEPOSIT BALANCE		26	07
205	9/18	TO Cash FOR lunch	AMOUNT OF CHECK OR DEPOSIT BALANCE		15	00
206	9/27	TO AJ Hardware FOR sander	AMOUNT OF CHECK OR DEPOSIT BALANCE		18	65
~	9/27	TO Deposit FOR	AMOUNT OF CHECK OR DEPOSIT BALANCE		15	93

A **check register** is used to record checks and deposits. The **balance** is the amount left in the account.

In early October, Jean receives the bank statement for September. Some checks and deposits are outstanding since they do not appear on the statement. To be sure no mistakes have been made, Jean **reconciles** her account as follows.

A Add any **outstanding deposits** to the statement *ending balance.*

B Subtract any **outstanding checks** and any service charges.

C If the ending balances agree, the account is reconciled.

ENDING BALANCE	
\$54.62	
CHECK NUMBER	**AMOUNT**
CHECKS	
204	26.07
205	15.00
DEPOSITS	
	68.50

STATEMENT

EXERCISES ***Express each amount in words as you would on a check.***

1. \$10.85 **2.** \$14 **3.** \$23.16 **4.** \$106.06

Find the balance on the check register after each issued check or deposit.

5. deposit made 9/4 **6.** check 204 **7.** check 205

8. check 206 **9.** deposit made 9/27 (register ending balance)

10. Describe any outstanding checks and/or deposits.

11. Follow steps A, B, and C to reconcile Jean Finley's checking account.

1-8 One-digit Multipliers

A passenger jet flies at an average speed of 854 kilometers per hour. To find the total distance flown in 7 hours, multiply.

Estimate as shown below.

$$\begin{array}{r} 854 \\ \times \quad 7 \\ \hline \end{array} \rightarrow \begin{array}{r} 900 \\ \times \quad 7 \\ \hline 6{,}300 \end{array}$$

854 rounds to 900

estimate

To find the exact distance, multiply in each place-value position as shown.

Multiply the ones.
7 × 4

$$\begin{array}{r} {}^{2} \\ 854 \\ \times \quad 7 \\ \hline 8 \end{array}$$

Record 28 as 2 tens and 8 ones.

Multiply the tens.
7 × 5 tens

$$\begin{array}{r} {}^{3\,2} \\ 854 \\ \times \quad 7 \\ \hline 78 \end{array}$$

How are 37 tens obtained?

Multiply the hundreds.
7 × 8 hundreds

$$\begin{array}{r} {}^{3\,2} \\ 854 \\ \times \quad 7 \\ \hline 5{,}978 \end{array}$$

How are 59 hundreds obtained?

The jet flies 5,978 kilometers. Based on the estimate, is this result reasonable?

***EXERCISES* Multiply. Check to be sure your answers are reasonable.**

1. 30 × 3
2. 40 × 7
3. 53 × 2
4. 24 × 4
5. 19 × 6
6. 35 × 5
7. $22 × 9
8. 28 × 5
9. 86 × 6
10. 63 × 8
11. 210 × 3
12. 621 × 2
13. 204 × 4
14. 306 × 7
15. 406 × 8
16. 639 × 4
17. 142 × 6
18. 280 × 7
19. $193 × 9
20. 462 × 8

Multiply. Check to be sure your answers are reasonable.

21. 268×5 **22.** 286×3 **23.** $1,487 \times 5$ **24.** $9,140 \times 8$ **25.** $\$2,609 \times 7$

26. $8,009 \times 6$ **27.** $6,455 \times 9$ **28.** $9,384 \times 4$ **29.** $6,677 \times 2$ **30.** $9,816 \times 9$

31. 541×7 **32.** 4×244 **33.** 608×9

34. $3 \times 1,046$ **35.** $\$6,763 \times 8$ **36.** $8,321 \times 6$

Copy and complete.

37. ▒0 × 8 = ▒8▒

38. 5▒ × 5 = ▒75

39. ▒0▒ × 7 = ▒,1▒9

40. 1▒6 × ▒ = ▒16

41. 1▒6 × ▒ = ▒,▒16

Express each of the following in standard form.

42. 4^3 **43.** 3^4 **44.** 8^3 **45.** 2^{10} **46.** 5^6

Solve. Use the bar graph.

47. What is the average subway trip length?

48. For which method of transport is the average trip 9 miles long?

49. Rank the methods of transport from 1 through 5. The method of transport with the longest average trip length gets a rank of 1.

50. The manager of a taxi company expects about 275 fares a day. How many miles long should the manager expect the 275 fares to be?

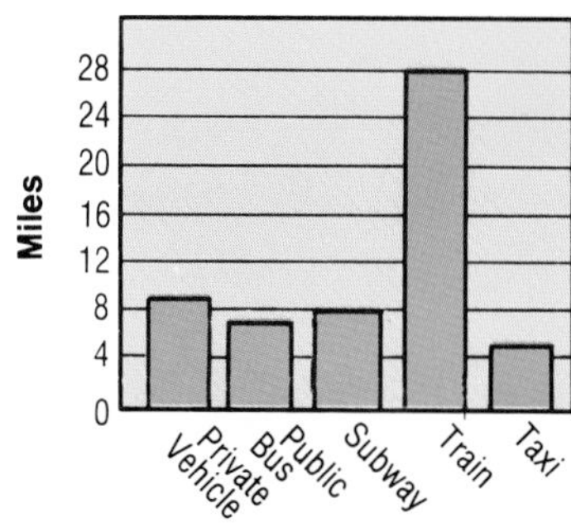

PATTERNS

Copy and complete the following. Do not compute.

$5^2 = 25$ $15^2 = 225$ $25^2 = 625$

$35^2 = 1,225$ $45^2 = 2,025$ $55^2 =$ ▒

$65^2 =$ ▒ $75^2 =$ ▒ $85^2 =$ ▒ $95^2 =$ ▒

1-9 Two- and Three-digit Multipliers

An auto parts store has tires on sale for $46 each. During the sale, 128 tires are sold. To find the total amount of sales, multiply.

Estimate as shown at the right.

$$\begin{array}{r} 128 \\ \times \$46 \\ \hline \end{array} \quad \Rightarrow \quad \begin{array}{r} 100 \\ \times \$50 \\ \hline \$5{,}000 \end{array}$$

128 rounds to 100
$46 rounds to $50
estimate

To find the exact amount, multiply by the digit in each place-value position as follows.

Multiply by the ones.

6 × 128

$$\begin{array}{r} 128 \\ \times \$46 \\ \hline 768 \end{array}$$

Multiply by the tens.

4 tens × 128

$$\begin{array}{r} 128 \\ \times \$46 \\ \hline 768 \\ 512 \end{array}$$

Note: Place the 2 tens under the 6 tens.

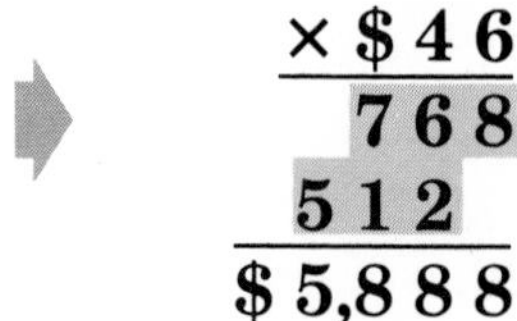

Now, add.

$$\begin{array}{r} 128 \\ \times \$46 \\ \hline 768 \\ 512 \\ \hline \$5{,}888 \end{array}$$

The total amount spent on tires is $5,888. Based on the estimate, is this answer reasonable?

EXERCISES Multiply. Check to be sure your answer is reasonable.

1. 49 × 11	**2.** 32 × 23	**3.** 21 × 12
4. 75 × 70	**5.** 89 × 20	**6.** 68 × 80
7. $47 × 12	**8.** 28 × 16	**9.** 63 × 21
10. 82 × 62	**11.** 71 × 68	**12.** 64 × 82
13. 52 × 37	**14.** 83 × 25	**15.** 95 × 73

Be sure that partial products are recorded in the proper place-value positions. Study these examples.

$$\begin{array}{r l} 541 & \\ \times\ 218 & \text{partial products} \\ \hline 4\ 328 & 541 \times 8 \\ 5\ 41\ \ & 541 \times 1 \text{ ten} \\ 108\ 2\ \ \ \ & 541 \times 2 \text{ hundreds} \\ \hline 117{,}938 & \end{array}
\qquad
\begin{array}{r l} 736 & \\ \times\ 509 & \\ \hline 6\ 624 & 736 \times 9 \\ 368\ 00 & 736 \times 0 \text{ tens} \\ & 736 \times 5 \text{ hundreds} \\ \hline 374{,}624 & \end{array}$$

EXERCISES ***Multiply. Check to be sure your answer is reasonable.***

16. 423×26 **17.** 654×15 **18.** 902×48 **19.** 723×80 **20.** 802×50

21. 625×82 **22.** 509×43 **23.** $\$728 \times 92$ **24.** $2{,}841 \times 64$ **25.** $1{,}659 \times 57$

26. $4{,}060 \times 21$ **27.** $2{,}008 \times 17$ **28.** $6{,}026 \times 31$ **29.** $8{,}142 \times 65$ **30.** $9{,}575 \times 44$

31. 124×200 **32.** 651×300 **33.** 126×104 **34.** 440×440 **35.** $1{,}230 \times 420$

36. 409×211 **37.** 547×324 **38.** 862×415 **39.** $\$729 \times 183$ **40.** 692×679

41. 450×836 **42.** $1{,}206 \times 204$ **43.** $\$106 \times 9{,}641$

44. $8{,}319 \times 249$ **45.** $6{,}811 \times 2{,}412$ **46.** $3{,}947 \times 659$

Solve. Use the pictograph.

47. How many of the H/JR × 15 tires were sold during the week?

48. Which size tire sold 30 tires?

49. The BR78 × 13 tire sold for $49 each. How much was spent on this tire size?

50. The tires sold for $49, $62, $65, $67, $70, and $76 each respectively. Find the total amount of sales on all six size tires.

Tire Sales by Size
Week of September 5

BR 78 x 13
FR 78 x 14
GR 78 x 14
GR 78 x 15
H/JR x 15
LR 78 x 15

Each O means 4 tires.

1-10 One-digit Divisors

A discount store buys bicycle tires at \$4 each. How many tires can the store buy for \$350? To find the number of tires, divide \$350 by \$4. The remainder will tell how many dollars are left.

Estimate as shown at the right. Since 360 is a multiple of 4, round 350 to 360.

\$4)\$350 → \$4)\$360, quotient 90 ← estimate

Do *not* change 1-digit divisors when estimating.

To find the exact answer, divide. Since you multiply in each place-value position from right to left, divide from left to right.

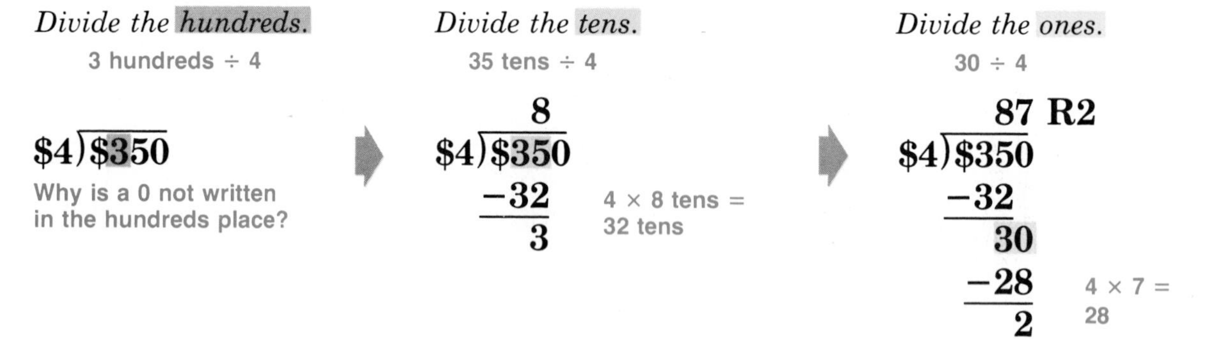

The exact answer is 87 R2. This answer means that 87 tires are bought with \$2 remaining.

Based on the estimate, 90, this answer makes sense. Check division as shown.

Check

87	← quotient
× 4	← divisor
348	
+ 2	← remainder
350	← dividend ✓

EXERCISES ***Divide. Check your answers.***

1. 7)28	**2.** 2)19	**3.** 5)26	**4.** 9)50	**5.** 8)71
6. 4)48	**7.** 3)39	**8.** 2)46	**9.** 6)77	**10.** 7)93
11. 8)648	**12.** 7)\$119	**13.** 8)151	**14.** 6)118	**15.** 8)184
16. 5)280	**17.** 4)150	**18.** 6)216	**19.** 2)234	**20.** 9)741

Divide 1,870 by 9.

$$\begin{array}{r} 20 \\ 9\overline{)1,870} \\ -1\,8 \\ \hline 07 \end{array}$$

Why is 0 written in the tens place of the quotient?

$$\begin{array}{r} 207 \text{ R7} \\ 9\overline{)1,870} \\ -1\,8 \\ \hline 070 \\ -\ 63 \\ \hline 7 \end{array}$$

EXERCISES ***Divide. Check your answers.***

21. $7\overline{)490}$ **22.** $9\overline{)324}$ **23.** $2\overline{)402}$ **24.** $3\overline{)\$300}$ **25.** $8\overline{)314}$

26. $4\overline{)803}$ **27.** $\$5\overline{)\$462}$ **28.** $7\overline{)745}$ **29.** $6\overline{)417}$ **30.** $3\overline{)922}$

31. $4\overline{)2,500}$ **32.** $6\overline{)2,132}$ **33.** $8\overline{)4,000}$ **34.** $5\overline{)4,912}$

35. $7\overline{)7,605}$ **36.** $9\overline{)9,468}$ **37.** $4\overline{)7,843}$ **38.** $3\overline{)4,821}$

39. $5\overline{)11,575}$ **40.** $8\overline{)28,960}$ **41.** $7\overline{)10,560}$ **42.** $9\overline{)33,306}$

43. $24,012 \div 4$ **44.** $\$18,140 \div 2$ **45.** $24,077 \div 8$

46. $48,022 \div 6$ **47.** $65,692 \div 9$ **48.** $24,278 \div 3$

Solve.

49. During each class period, 4 students use the computer terminal. How many class periods are needed so that each of 55 students uses the terminal once?

50. Spark plugs are packed 8 to a box. Suppose 1,500 spark plugs are packed. How many boxes are filled?

SHORT DIVISION

Divide using short division. Check your answers.

$$\begin{array}{r} 4 \\ 7\overline{)3,0_{2}16} \end{array}$$

$_{2}1$ means 21 tens

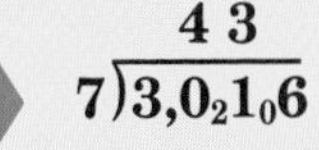

$$\begin{array}{r} 4\,3 \\ 7\overline{)3,0_{2}1_{0}6} \end{array} \qquad \begin{array}{r} 4\,3\,0 \text{ R6} \\ 7\overline{)3,0_{2}1_{0}6} \end{array}$$

1. $783 \div 8$ **2.** $3,509 \div 6$ **3.** $13,355 \div 7$ **4.** $38,708 \div 9$

1-11 Two- and Three-digit Divisors

The weekly payroll for the 28 office workers at a truck terminal is \$6,636. To find the average weekly earnings, divide \$6,636 by 28.

Estimate as shown at the right. Since 6,000 is a multiple of 30, round 6,636 to 6,000.

28)\$6,636 → 30)\$6,000 = \$200 ← estimate

↑ Round 28 to 30.

To find the exact answer, divide \$6,636 by 28 as follows.

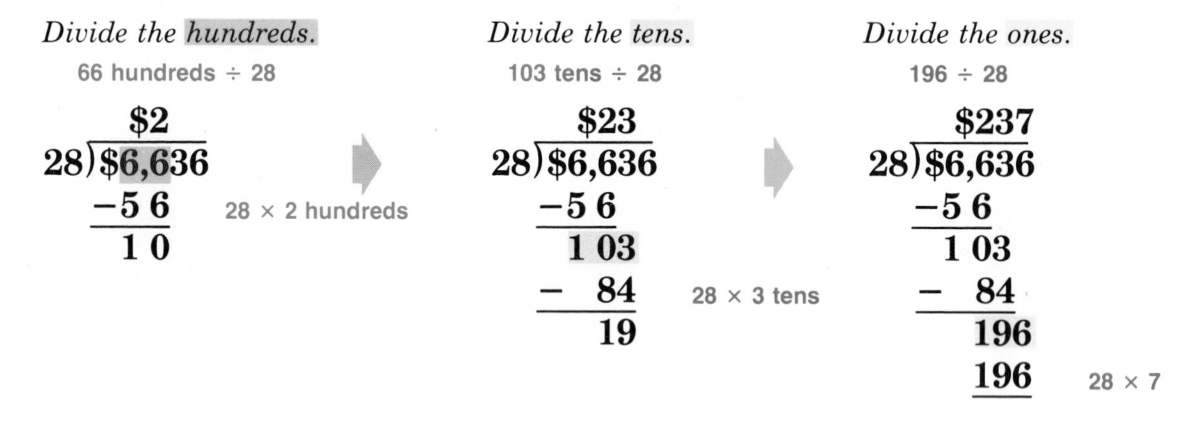

The average weekly earnings are \$237.
Based on the estimate, is this amount reasonable?
To check the answer, multiply \$237 by 28. Is the answer correct?

EXERCISES ***Divide. Check your answers.***

1. 10)90	**2.** 11)66	**3.** 15)75
4. 30)\$150	**5.** 20)43	**6.** 14)85
7. 62)372	**8.** 22)198	**9.** \$40)\$355
10. 24)140	**11.** 36)288	**12.** 48)371
13. 53)302	**14.** 87)723	**15.** 16)160
16. 24)245	**17.** 36)720	**18.** 51)564

When dividing, you may have to correct a digit in the quotient. Copy and complete each example.

$$\begin{array}{r} 5 \\ 36\overline{)2{,}232} \\ -1\,80 \\ \hline 43 \end{array}$$

Note that the remainder 43 is greater than the divisor 36. So, change the digit in the quotient from 5 to 6.

$$\begin{array}{r} 8 \\ 242\overline{)1{,}925} \\ -1\,936 \\ \hline \end{array}$$

Since 1,936 is greater than 1,925, change the digit in the quotient from 8 to 7. Explain why.

EXERCISES ***Divide. Check your answers.***

19. $13\overline{)234}$ **20.** $29\overline{)676}$ **21.** $46\overline{)983}$ **22.** $33\overline{)920}$

23. $43\overline{)2{,}606}$ **24.** $39\overline{)1{,}560}$ **25.** $65\overline{)4{,}652}$ **26.** $97\overline{)3{,}521}$

27. $74\overline{)7{,}844}$ **28.** $82\overline{)9{,}400}$ **29.** $53\overline{)8{,}600}$ **30.** $62\overline{)52{,}130}$

31. $49\overline{)10{,}045}$ **32.** $95\overline{)\$20{,}515}$ **33.** $45\overline{)14{,}371}$ **34.** $58\overline{)52{,}251}$

35. $200\overline{)600}$ **36.** $224\overline{)896}$ **37.** $300\overline{)1{,}800}$ **38.** $165\overline{)1{,}178}$

39. $560\overline{)5{,}600}$ **40.** $274\overline{)5{,}916}$ **41.** $\$406\overline{)\$13{,}000}$ **42.** $895\overline{)22{,}375}$

43. 42,690 ÷ 702 **44.** 124,220 ÷ 526 **45.** 396,000 ÷ 976

Solve. Use the chart.

1 year	=	52 weeks
1 week	=	7 days
1 day	=	24 hours
1 hour	=	60 minutes
1 minute	=	60 seconds

46. How many weeks are in 30 years?

47. How many days are in 1,440 hours?

48. How many hours are in 10,080 minutes?

49. How many seconds are in an hour?

50. How many hours old were you on your tenth birthday?

51. Make up a problem involving your age expressed in seconds.

SPROUTS

Play sprouts with 2 or more players. Start with 3 to 10 dots. In turn, each player draws a curve connecting a dot to a dot *and* placing another dot on the curve. A dot can be connected to *no more than* 3 curves. The winner is the last player to draw a curve and a dot.

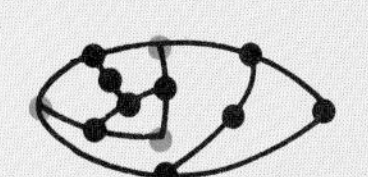

1-12 Problem Solving: Choose the Operation

There are 358 students signed up to take driver's education. If possible, each class should have 28 students. How many classes are needed to include all the students?

To help choose the operation, study the meaning of each operation.

Add	join, combine, or put things together
Subtract	remove or compare to determine the number left, the number needed, or how many more are in one group than another
Multiply	join, combine, or put together a number of equal-sized groups
Divide	separate into same-sized groups to find the number of groups

Then use the plan below to solve the problem.

Read the problem. You need to find the number of classes. You know the number of students signed up and the number in each class.

Decide what to do. To find the number of classes, separate the number of students into groups of equal size. So, divide.

Solve the problem.

```
    12 R22
28)358
  -28
    78
   -56
    22
```

The quotient 12 R22 means there are 12 classes of 28 with 22 students remaining. There need to be 13 driver's education classes. One class will have 22 students.

Examine the solution. The solution is reasonable since an estimate for 358 ÷ 28 is 300 ÷ 30 or 10.

Check

```
   28      336
 × 12     + 22
  336      358 √
```

Choose the operation needed to solve each of the following.

1. A jet can fly ▒ miles per hour. How far can it fly in ▒ hours?

2. An average car uses ▒ gallons of fuel a year. How many more gallons would make ▒ gallons?

3. Janet Kolenda works ▒ hours. How much does she earn if she earns ▒ dollars an hour?

4. A bus travels ▒ miles on each gallon of fuel. How far can the bus travel on ▒ gallons?

Solve.

5. The world's fastest airplane can go 7,488 meters in 8 seconds. How far does it go each second?

6. The Kingdome holds 59,059 fans. If Royals stadium holds 18,297 fewer fans, what is its capacity?

7. The longest regularly scheduled bus route takes 82 hours to drive. The average speed is 63 kilometers per hour. How long is the bus route?

8. In a recent year, there were 315,471 automotive retailers in the United States. Of these, 24,135 were in Texas. How many were in the rest of the country?

9. Each day, an average of 585 vehicles use the airport parking lot. How many vehicles use the lot in a week?

10. Steve Caner buys wallpaper at $12 a single roll. How many rolls can he buy for $200? How much money is left over?

11. Quarts of oil are packed 24 to a case. How many cases are filled by 5,000 quarts of oil?

12. The record for walking 20,000 meters is 84 minutes. Estimate the walking speed.

Solve. Use the mileage chart.

	Atlanta	Dallas	Louisville	Memphis	Miami	New Orleans
Atlanta		795	382	371	655	479
Dallas	795		819	452	1,300	496
Louisville	382	819		367	1,037	685
Memphis	371	452	367		997	390
Miami	655	1,300	1,037	997		856
New Orleans	479	496	685	390	856	

13. Which trip is shorter, a trip from Louisville to Miami via Atlanta or a trip from Louisville to Miami via Memphis?

14. John Semall's car gets 25 miles per gallon. The fuel tank holds 14 gallons and is full. Can he drive from Memphis to Atlanta on one tank of fuel?

15. How many miles longer is a trip from Dallas to Miami than a trip from Louisville to Atlanta?

16. A trip from Memphis to New Orleans takes 13 gallons of fuel. Find the miles per gallon.

Skills Review: Pages 18-27

Multiply or divide.

1. $2,172 \times 3$
2. 425×62
3. $117 \div 9$
4. $1,562 \div 58$
5. $25,706 \div 205$

Solve.

6. A department store buys bicycles at $75 each. Find the cost of 45 bicycles.

Mathematics and Consumers

Milt Thomas earned $19,316 last year driving a truck. A table is used to find federal income tax.

Milt is single and claims 1 exemption. For each exemption, subtract $1,000 from the yearly earnings. Then, find the tax using the table.

earnings		1 exemption		taxable income
$19,316	−	**$1,000**	=	**$18,316**

On the table, $18,316 is at least $18,300 *but not over* $18,350. Milt owes $3,233 in taxes.

If line 37 (taxable income) is—		And you are—			
At least	But less than	Single	Married filing jointly *	Married filing sepa-rately	Head of a house-hold
		Your tax is—			
8,000					
8,000	8,050	867	614	1,012	790
8,050	8,100	876	622	1,023	798
8,100	8,150	884	630	1,034	806
8,150	8,200	893	638	1,045	814
8,200	8,250	901	646	1,056	822
8,250	8,300	910	654	1,067	830
8,300	8,350	918	662	1,078	838
8,350	8,400	927	670	1,089	846
15,000					
15,000	15,050	2,337	1,828	2,812	2,228
15,050	15,100	2,350	1,837	2,828	2,239
15,100	15,150	2,364	1,847	2,845	2,251
15,150	15,200	2,377	1,856	2,861	2,262
15,200	15,250	2,391	1,866	2,878	2,274
15,250	15,300	2,404	1,875	2,894	2,285
15,300	15,350	2,418	1,885	2,911	2,297
15,350	15,400	2,431	1,894	2,927	2,308
15,400	15,450	2,445	1,904	2,944	2,320
15,450	15,500	2,458	1,913	2,960	2,331
18,000					
18,000	18,050	3,147	2,459	3,827	2,918
18,050	18,100	3,160	2,470	3,847	2,929
18,100	18,150	3,174	2,481	3,866	2,941
18,150	18,200	3,187	2,492	3,886	2,952
18,200	18,250	3,202	2,503	3,905	2,965
18,250	18,300	3,217	2,514	3,925	2,979
18,300	18,350	3,233	2,525	3,944	2,993
18,350	18,400	3,248	2,536	3,964	3,007
18,400	18,450	3,264	2,547	3,983	3,021
18,450	18,500	3,279	2,558	4,003	3,035

***EXERCISES** Find the tax for a single person with 1 exemption and each yearly earnings.*

1. $16,452 **2.** $19,204 **3.** $9,300

Find the tax for a married couple with 4 exemptions and each yearly earnings.

4. $19,250 **5.** $12,057 **6.** $22,424

Solve.

7. Kim Heuer's yearly income as a legal aide is $17,310. He is the head of a household and claims 2 exemptions. Find Kim's tax.

8. Kim Heuer (problem 7) had $210 withheld in each of 12 months. Find the amount of tax he owes or the amount of refund he is due.

9. Sara Ripken's annual income as a department store supervisor is $21,480. She is married and files separately. Find the tax she owes if she claims 3 exemptions.

10. The yearly earnings of Robert and Caroline Miller are $8,300 and $15,128. They are married, file jointly, and claim 5 exemptions. Find the amount of tax.

11. Katie Guiteau is single, self-employed, and expects to earn $19,400 this year. She claims 1 exemption. Based on her expected earnings and taxes, how much should she save each month in order to be able to pay her taxes?

Chapter 1 Review

VOCABULARY

exponents (6)
expanded form (7)
place value (3)
base (6)
properties (8–9)
standard form (6)
powers (6)

EXERCISES ***Round each of the following to the underlined place-value position. (3)***

1. $\underline{7}6$ **2.** $5{,}4\underline{9}6$ **3.** $8\underline{5}{,}243$ **4.** $2{,}\underline{5}87{,}200$

Replace each ▒ with a number to make a true sentence. (4)

5. $5 \times$ ▒ $= 30$ **6.** ▒ $\div 6 = 4$ **7.** $11 -$ ▒ $= 2$

Express each of the following in standard form. (6)

8. 12^2 **9.** 9^3 **10.** $(4 \times 10^6) + (8 \times 10^3)$

Name the property illustrated by each of the following. (8)

11. $4{,}321 \times 1 = 4{,}321$ **12.** $6 \times (10 + 7) = (6 \times 10) + (6 \times 7)$

Estimate. (10)

13. $9{,}876 + 5{,}231$ **14.** 286×74 **15.** $4{,}329 \div 67$

Add, subtract, multiply, or divide. (12–15, 18–25)

16. $\begin{array}{r} 545 \\ +\ 79 \\ \hline \end{array}$ **17.** $\begin{array}{r} 1{,}862 \\ -\ 371 \\ \hline \end{array}$ **18.** $\begin{array}{r} \$5{,}124 \\ +\ 28{,}209 \\ \hline \end{array}$ **19.** $\begin{array}{r} 24{,}102 \\ -\ 19{,}864 \\ \hline \end{array}$ **20.** $\begin{array}{r} 224{,}342 \\ 96{,}689 \\ +\ 1{,}634 \\ \hline \end{array}$

21. $\begin{array}{r} 86 \\ \times\ 9 \\ \hline \end{array}$ **22.** $\begin{array}{r} 5{,}284 \\ \times\ 5 \\ \hline \end{array}$ **23.** $\begin{array}{r} \$98 \\ \times\ 46 \\ \hline \end{array}$ **24.** $\begin{array}{r} 9{,}163 \\ \times\ 38 \\ \hline \end{array}$ **25.** $\begin{array}{r} 413 \\ \times\ 207 \\ \hline \end{array}$

26. $4\overline{)57}$ **27.** $6\overline{)238}$ **28.** $24\overline{)1{,}080}$ **29.** $87\overline{)5{,}655}$ **30.** $175\overline{)13{,}125}$

Solve. (26)

31. New York City has 636 miles of subway. Suppose you travel through 332 miles. How many more miles are there?

32. The World Trade Center tower has 104 elevators. Suppose each elevator were to carry 15 people. How many people can be carried at one time?

Chapter 1 Test

Round each of the following to the underlined place-value position.

1. $\underline{8}7$ **2.** $2\underline{5}6$ **3.** $6{,}\underline{8}40$ **4.** $\underline{1}5{,}896{,}000$

Replace each ▒ with a number to make a true sentence.

5. ▒ − 9 = 7 **6.** 56 ÷ ▒ = 7 **7.** ▒ = 5 × 6

Express each of the following in standard form.

8. 3^4 **9.** 2^6 **10.** 13^2 **11.** 6^3 **12.** 30^2

13. $(4 \times 100) + (8 \times 10) + (4 \times 1)$ **14.** $(8 \times 10^3) + (9 \times 10^2) + (2 \times 10^0)$

Name the property illustrated by each of the following.

15. $15 + 0 = 15$ **16.** $8 \times 6 = 6 \times 8$

Estimate.

17. $\begin{array}{r} 7{,}643 \\ +\ 18{,}974 \\ \hline \end{array}$ **18.** $\begin{array}{r} \$19{,}675 \\ -\ 11{,}246 \\ \hline \end{array}$ **19.** $\begin{array}{r} 87 \\ \times\ 76 \\ \hline \end{array}$ **20.** $\begin{array}{r} 289 \\ \times\ 92 \\ \hline \end{array}$ **21.** $78\overline{)16{,}542}$

Add, subtract, multiply, or divide.

22. $\begin{array}{r} 8{,}606 \\ +\ 1{,}233 \\ \hline \end{array}$ **23.** $\begin{array}{r} 5{,}165 \\ -\ 484 \\ \hline \end{array}$ **24.** $\begin{array}{r} \$33{,}106 \\ +\ 75{,}900 \\ \hline \end{array}$ **25.** $\begin{array}{r} \$80{,}014 \\ -\ 24{,}700 \\ \hline \end{array}$ **26.** $\begin{array}{r} 465{,}043 \\ -\ 72{,}853 \\ \hline \end{array}$

27. 864 − 223 **28.** \$16,128 + \$494 **29.** 114,018 − 11,699

30. 461 + 1,984 + 27,205 **31.** 116,926 + 45,094 + 57,090

32. $\begin{array}{r} 58 \\ \times\ 5 \\ \hline \end{array}$ **33.** $\begin{array}{r} 718 \\ \times\ 4 \\ \hline \end{array}$ **34.** $\begin{array}{r} \$56 \\ \times\ 30 \\ \hline \end{array}$ **35.** $\begin{array}{r} 3{,}184 \\ \times\ 74 \\ \hline \end{array}$ **36.** $\begin{array}{r} 416 \\ \times\ 209 \\ \hline \end{array}$

37. $8\overline{)\$70}$ **38.** $6\overline{)604}$ **39.** $9\overline{)2{,}088}$ **40.** $70\overline{)406}$ **41.** $28\overline{)1{,}026}$

42. 7,042 × 38 **43.** 14,720 ÷ 21 **44.** 12,818 ÷ 493

Solve.

45. The 14 employees of Ace Leasing earn an average of \$1,118 a month. Find the total monthly earnings of the 14 employees.

46. Defiance County in Ohio has a population of 39,987 and an area of 412 square miles. Estimate the population per square mile.

Enrichment

Most computers use a **base-two** or **binary** numeration system. In this system, powers of 2 determine the place values. The only digits are 0 and 1. In a computer, 0 represents *no* or a switch in the *off* position. The digit 1 represents *yes* or a switch in the *on* position.

The place-value chart shows the value of each digit of the base-two numeral 101101_{two}. Read this numeral as *one zero one one zero one base two.*

one hundred twenty-eights	sixty-fours	thirty-twos	sixteens	eights	fours	twos	ones
128	64	32	16	8	4	2	1
2^7	2^6	2^5	2^4	2^3	2^2	2^1	2^0
		1	0	1	1	0	1

Determine the value of 101101_{two} as follows.

$$\begin{aligned} \mathbf{101101_{two}} &= (1 \times 2^5) + (0 \times 2^4) + (1 \times 2^3) + (1 \times 2^2) + (0 \times 2^1) + (1 \times 2^0) \\ &= (1 \times 32) + (0 \times 16) + (1 \times 8) + (1 \times 4) + (0 \times 2) + (1 \times 1) \\ &= 32 + 0 + 8 + 4 + 0 + 1 \\ &= \mathbf{45_{ten}} \end{aligned}$$

Change 20 to a base-two numeral as follows. The powers of 2 are 1, 2, 4, 8, 16, and so on. Ask "what is the greatest power of 2 in 20?" There is 1 sixteen with 20 − 16 or 4 remaining. In 4, there are 0 eights, 1 four, 0 twos, and 0 ones. So, $20_{ten} = 10100_{two}$.

***EXERCISES** Determine the value of each of the following.*

1. 1_{two} **2.** 10_{two} **3.** 111_{two} **4.** 1010_{two}

5. 1000_{two} **6.** 10011_{two} **7.** 100111_{two} **8.** 10100010_{two}

Write each of the following as a base-two numeral.

9. 3 **10.** 4 **11.** 11 **12.** 14

13. 20 **14.** 32 **15.** 68 **16.** 224

17. the number of months in one year

18. your age in years

19. the number of days in the month of August

20. the boiling point of water in degrees Celsius

2 Decimals

The highest average speed for a motorcycle on a closed track is 160.289 miles an hour. Many records in sports, including this one, are expressed using decimals.

2-1 Decimals

Decimal fractions, commonly called **decimals,** are a way of expressing numbers that have a denominator of 10, 100, 1,000, or any power of ten. The fractions named by the following can be expressed as decimals.

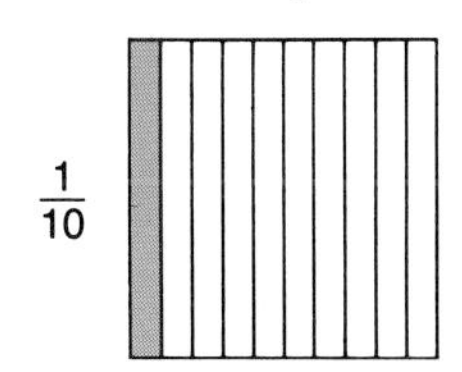

one tenth or 0.1

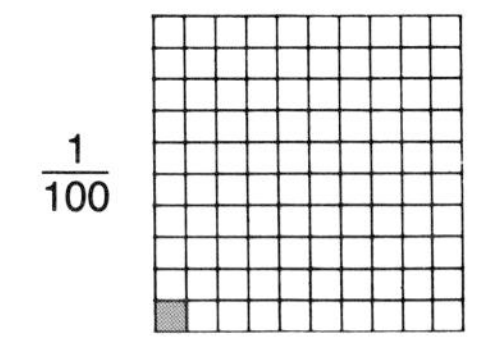

one hundredth or 0.01

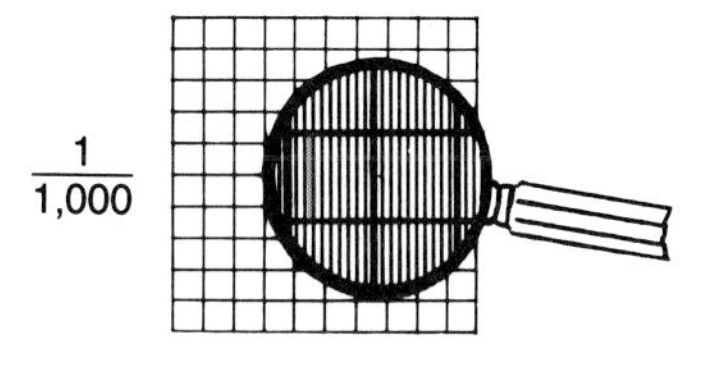

one thousandth or 0.001

160.289 **is read** one hundred sixty and two hundred eighty-nine thousandths

Read the decimal point as *and.*

The place-value chart can be extended in either direction. The decimal point separates the ones and the tenths places.

The digit 9 and its place value name the number nine thousandths, 0.009.

EXERCISES ***Write the number named by each of the following digits in 160.289.***

1. the 8 **2.** the 1 **3.** the 0 **4.** the 6 **5.** the 2

Express each of the following as a decimal.

6. $\frac{9}{10}$ **7.** $\frac{13}{100}$ **8.** $\frac{165}{1,000}$ **9.** $\frac{5}{100}$ **10.** $\frac{23}{1,000}$

11. $\frac{251}{10,000}$ **12.** $\frac{6}{100}$ **13.** $2\frac{53}{1,000}$ **14.** $57\frac{3}{1,000}$ **15.** $9\frac{42}{10,000}$

16. seven tenths **17.** thirteen hundredths **18.** forty-five thousandths

19. six hundredths **20.** five thousandths **21.** twelve thousandths

22. four and three tenths **23.** seventy-five and nine thousandths

24. fifty-one ten-thousandths **25.** eighty-nine and sixteen millionths

2-2 Comparing and Ordering Decimals

Olympic events in swimming, track, and speed skating are 400 meters or 0.4 kilometers long. You can express 0.4 as 0.40.

The shading in the figures below indicate that 0.4 and 0.40 have the same value. Decimals that have the same value are **equivalent.**

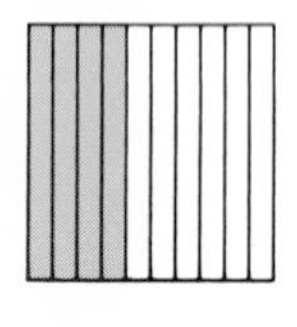

$\frac{4}{10}$ **or 0.4**

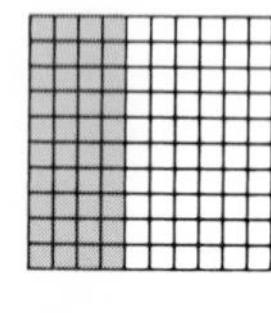

$\frac{40}{100}$ **or 0.40**

You can *annex* zeros to the right of a decimal without changing its value. Study the examples at the right.

0.4 = 0.40

5.6 = 5.60

7 = 7.0

To compare decimals like 6.35 and 6.359, annex zeros so that the decimals have the same number of decimal places.

6.35 = 6.350 **6.359**

Both have 3 decimal places

Now, compare as with whole numbers. Since $6{,}350 < 6{,}359$, it follows that $6.350 < 6.359$. So, $6.35 < 6.359$.

EXERCISES ***State whether each of the following is true or false.***

1. 0.30 = 0.3 **2.** 0.04 = 0.4 **3.** 9.8 = 9.800

4. 6 = 6.00 **5.** 2 = 2.00 **6.** 7.06 = 7.060

7. 1.001 = 1.010 **8.** 153 = 153.000 **9.** 0.201 = 0.20100

Write two decimals equivalent to each of the following.

10. 0.8 **11.** 0.9 **12.** 0.50 **13.** 1.1 **14.** 5.5

15. 0.03 **16.** 4 **17.** 59 **18.** 2.07 **19.** 0.008

Replace each ▒ with $<$, $>$, or $=$ to make a true sentence.

20. 0.2 ▒ 0.5
21. 0.88 ▒ 0.85
22. 0.02 ▒ 0.20
23. 0.20 ▒ 0.200
24. 0.014 ▒ 1.013
25. 4.0 ▒ 4.00
26. 0.103 ▒ 0.094
27. 10.6 ▒ 10.60
28. 0.8 ▒ 0.88
29. 5 ▒ 0.61
30. 12 ▒ 12.6
31. 0.612 ▒ 0.6
32. 0.010 ▒ 1.0100
33. 8.04 ▒ 8.4
34. 0.204 ▒ 0.20
35. 0.05 ▒ 0.052
36. 2.68 ▒ 2.689
37. 4.105 ▒ 4.1
38. 40.4 ▒ 40.44
39. 9.006 ▒ 9.06
40. 0.102 ▒ 0.602

Order the numbers in each list from greatest to least.

41. 0.2, 0.02, 2.0, 0.002
42. 8.4, 8.41, 8.406, 8.442
43. 0.65, 0.605, 0.5, 0.61
44. 12.003, 12, 11.9, 12.103
45. 9.063, 8.063, 9.062, 9.026
46. 41.7, 40.7, 44.2, 41.08

Solve.

47. The chart at the right lists professional basketball players with the best free-throw percentages. Rank the players in order from 1 through 9. The player with the highest percentage gets a rank of 1.

Player	Percentage
Bird	86.3
Bridgeman	88.4
Criss	86.4
Long	87.0
McKinney	86.2
Murphy	95.8
Newlin	88.8
Sobers	93.5
Spanarkel	88.7

48. The chart below lists golfers and their average number of strokes per round. Rank the golfers in order from 1 through 5. The golfer with the lowest average gets a rank of 1.

Golfer	Post	Blalock	Bradley	Lopez	Higuchi
Average	72.3	72.15	72.31	71.2	72.17

LEAST AND GREATEST

Use each digit in each set once to write the least decimal possible. Then write the greatest decimal possible that is less than one.

1. 5 7
2. 6 3 0
3. 7 9 8 2
4. 0 1 7 9 0

2-3 Rounding Decimals

The record speed for a rocket-powered car is 739.666 miles an hour. In each report of this record, the speed was rounded in a different way as shown at the right.

Report	Miles per Hour
Newpaper	739.67
Radio	739.7
Television	740

To round 739.666 to the nearest whole number, you need to determine whether 739.666 is closer to 739 or to 740.

Look at the digit to the right of the place being rounded. Then follow the same rules used when rounding whole numbers.

Round down if the digit to the right is 4 or less.

To the nearest whole number $73\underline{9}.666$ rounds to 740.

Round up if the digit to the right is 5 or greater.

The television report rounded to the nearest whole number. Explain how the radio and newspaper rounded the speed.

***EXERCISES* Round each of the following to the underlined place-value position. Then, choose the correct answer.**

	a.	b.	c.	d.
1. $0.\underline{0}54$	**a.** 0.05	**b.** 0.1	**c.** 0	**d.** none
2. $2.7\underline{6}9$	**a.** 2.7	**b.** 2.77	**c.** 3.0	**d.** none
3. $5.\underline{0}99$	**a.** 5	**b.** 5.1	**c.** 5.09	**d.** none
4. $4\underline{5}.6432$	**a.** 45.6	**b.** 46	**c.** 45	**d.** none
5. $134.0\underline{8}43$	**a.** 130	**b.** 134.1	**c.** 134.08	**d.** none

Round each of the following to the nearest whole number (or nearest dollar).

6. 5.8 **7.** 2.4 **8.** 8.4 **9.** 7.43

10. 0.85 **11.** $8.95 **12.** $29.59 **13.** 99.865

Round each of the following to the nearest tenth.

14. 0.24 **15.** 0.48 **16.** 0.95 **17.** 42.07

18. 0.916 **19.** 94.98 **20.** 2.64 **21.** 0.951

Round each of the following to the nearest hundredth (or nearest cent).

22. 0.051 **23.** 1.069 **24.** 7.657 **25.** $2.095

26. $8.0455 **27.** 3.463 **28.** $29.6588 **29.** 2.8764

Round each of the following to the nearest thousandth (or nearest tenth of a cent).

30. 0.0038 **31.** 19.0141 **32.** $0.3254 **33.** 0.00657

34. 6.2704 **35.** $0.6095 **36.** $16.0048 **37.** 2.0996

Round each of the following to the underlined place-value position.

38. $\underline{8}.7649$ **39.** $8.\underline{7}649$ **40.** $8.7\underline{6}49$ **41.** $8.76\underline{4}9$

42. $0.0\underline{4}8$ **43.** $0.00\underline{8}5$ **44.** \$$9.2\underline{6}7$ **45.** \$$\underline{6}.05$

46. $0.1\underline{0}8$ **47.** $4.01\underline{0}9$ **48.** $16.\underline{0}8$ **49.** \$$13.7\underline{9}1$

Each number below has been rounded to a certain place-value position. Name that place-value position.

50. 0.0945 → 0.09 **51.** 4.6406 → 5

52. 7.657 → 7.7 **53.** 6.053 → 6.1

54. 182.948 → 180 **55.** 0.999 → 1.00

Solve. Use the chart.

Mountain	Height in Miles
Mt. Bona	3.1100
Mt. Blackburn	3.1042
Mt. Foraker	3.2955
Mt. McKinley	3.8485
Mt. St. Elias	3.4106
Mt. Sanford	3.0752

56. Rank the mountains from 1 through 6. The highest mountain gets a rank of 1.

57. How will rounding each height to the nearest tenth of a mile affect the ranking?

TRAVELING TIME

Two trucks are 405 kilometers apart. At 11:00 A.M., they start traveling toward each other at speeds of 65 and 70 kilometers an hour. At what time will they meet?

2-4 Addition and Subtraction

A weightlifter lifts 46.8 kilograms in the first event. The next two lifts are 53.6 and 67.2 kilograms. To find the total lifted, add.

First align the decimal points. Then, add as with whole numbers. That is, add in each place-value position from least to greatest.

46.8 + 53.6 + 67.2 ➡

```
  11
  46.8
  53.6
+ 67.2
 167.6
```

When you add, group digits to make a 10. For example, 8 + 2 = 10. Then, 10 + 6 = 16.

The total lifted is 167.6 kilograms. Use the commutative property to check this answer.

EXERCISES ***Add. Check your answers.***

Add 7.3, 9, and 8.45. Annex zeros to help align the decimal points.

```
  7.30   7.3 = 7.30
  9.00     9 = 9.00
+ 8.45
 24.75
```

1. 0.1 + 0.6
2. \$2.14 + 1.04
3. 9.51 + 8.39
4. 27.06 + 7.06
5. 1.034 + 0.08
6. 68.7 + 1.47
7. 42.6 + 8.41
8. 93.7 + 21.919
9. 7.65 + 0.4 + 1.07
10. 2.009 + 21.26 + 8.744
11. 17 + 8.7 + 0.66
12. 402.1 + 83 + 62.09 + 4.88
13. 55.07 + 2.65 + 47.7 + 98.03

14. 0.6 + 0.3
15. \$0.42 + 68¢ (68¢ = \$0.68)
16. 24.6 + 7.4
17. \$6.05 + \$0.05
18. 9.76 + 10.46
19. 0.38 + 18.8
20. 0.836 + 0.77
21. 0.95 + 0.097
22. 4.06 + 206
23. \$0.43 + \$1.86 + \$5.79
24. 0.046 + 0.25 + 6.6
25. 17 + 8.7 + 0.98
26. \$1.17 + \$52 + 88¢
27. 23 + 0.09 + 6.8 + 0.74
28. 2.06 + 7.89 + 54 + 4.063

Subtract 20.7 from 371.
To subtract decimals, align the decimal points. Then subtract as with whole numbers.
Note that 371 = 371.0.

Rename 1 one as 10 tenths.

$$\begin{array}{r} \overset{0\ 10}{37\not{1}.\not{0}} \\ -\ 20.7 \\ \hline 350.3 \end{array} \qquad \text{Check} \qquad \begin{array}{r} \overset{1}{20.7} \\ +\ 350.3 \\ \hline 371.0 \end{array} \checkmark$$

EXERCISES ***Subtract. Check your answers.***

Subtract 6.703 from 17.
Annexing zeros helps you to properly align the decimal points.

$$\begin{array}{r} \overset{6\ \ 9\,9\,10}{1\not{7}.\not{0}\not{0}\not{0}} \\ -\ 6.703 \\ \hline 10.297 \end{array}$$

17 = 17.000

29. 0.6 − 0.2	**30.** 2.11 − 1.02	**31.** 8.6 − 7.3	**32.** 0.497 − 0.168	**33.** \$2.83 − 0.95
34. \$1.36 − 0.48	**35.** 0.721 − 0.045	**36.** 1.006 − 0.189	**37.** 4.053 − 3.355	**38.** 19.143 − 8.477
39. 9 − 1.7	**40.** 15.1 − 6.34	**41.** 0.81 − 0.682	**42.** 46 − 0.493	**43.** 23 − 4.093

44. \$1.84 − 41¢ **45.** 0.47 − 0.25 **46.** 2.91 − 0.93
47. 12.043 − 3.166 **48.** 82.007 − 3.218 **49.** 2.003 − 1.487
50. 4.16 − 0.5 **51.** 91.11 − 43.6 **52.** 2.616 − 0.96
53. 11.264 − 8.2 **54.** 10.111 − 7 **55.** 42 − 7.6
56. \$81 − \$4.83 **57.** 210 − 56.765 **58.** 67 − 8.082

Solve. Use the line graph.

59. In 1975, what percent of income was saved (to the nearest tenth)?

60. What is the difference between the percent saved in 1970 and 1980?

61. During which five years did the percent saved increase the most? What was this increase?

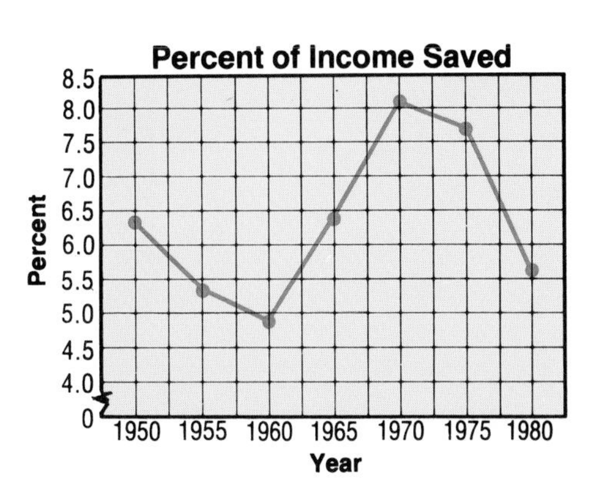

2-5 Multiplication

Todd Garrau buys three souvenirs at the baseball park for $4.75 each. To find the total cost, you can add or multiply.

Addition helps show how to place the decimal point when you multiply. As shown, the souvenirs cost $14.25.

```
  2 1
 $4.75              2 1
  4.75     ▶       $4.75   2 decimal places
+ 4.75            ×    3
$14.25            $14.25   2 decimal places
```

Multiply two decimals as with whole numbers as shown at the right.

Answer the following questions to determine how to place the decimal point in the product.

```
   1.94   2 decimal places
 ×  8.2   1 decimal place
    388
  15 52
 15.908   3 decimal places
```

A How many decimal places are in 1.94? How many are in 8.2?

B From your answers to A, can you determine the number of decimal places in the product?

From these and other examples, you can conclude this rule.

The number of decimal places in the product is the same as the sum of the number of decimal places in the factors.

***EXERCISES* Answer the following to justify the rule above.**

1. An estimate for 1.94 × 8.2 is 2 × 8 or what number?
2. Which possible product for 1.94 × 8.2 is most reasonable?

   0.15908   1.5908   15.908
   159.08   1,590.8   15,908
3. What is the sum of the decimal places in 1.94 and 8.2? Is this sum the same as the number of decimal places in the most reasonable product?

Copy. Then place the decimal point in the product.

4. $\begin{array}{r} 0.5 \\ \times\ 3 \\ \hline 15 \end{array}$ **5.** $\begin{array}{r} 4.1 \\ \times\ 2 \\ \hline 82 \end{array}$ **6.** $\begin{array}{r} \$5.81 \\ \times\ 7 \\ \hline \$4067 \end{array}$ **7.** $\begin{array}{r} 12 \\ \times\ 2.6 \\ \hline 312 \end{array}$ **8.** $\begin{array}{r} \$8.45 \\ \times\ 24 \\ \hline \$20280 \end{array}$

9. $0.2 \times 0.8 = 16$

10. $8.6 \times 0.1 = 86$

11. $0.049 \times 265 = 12985$

12. $\$1.04 \times 255 = \$26520$

13. $23.6 \times 0.704 = 166144$

14. $2.89 \times 0.808 = 233512$

Multiply.

15. $\begin{array}{r} 9.2 \\ \times\ 2 \\ \hline \end{array}$ **16.** $\begin{array}{r} 0.83 \\ \times\ 7 \\ \hline \end{array}$ **17.** $\begin{array}{r} 421 \\ \times\ 0.5 \\ \hline \end{array}$ **18.** $\begin{array}{r} 214 \\ \times\ 0.3 \\ \hline \end{array}$ **19.** $\begin{array}{r} 4.16 \\ \times\ 5 \\ \hline \end{array}$

20. $\begin{array}{r} \$0.23 \\ \times\ 15 \\ \hline \end{array}$ **21.** $\begin{array}{r} 46.4 \\ \times\ 46 \\ \hline \end{array}$ **22.** $\begin{array}{r} 20.8 \\ \times\ 54 \\ \hline \end{array}$ **23.** $\begin{array}{r} 704 \\ \times\ 0.26 \\ \hline \end{array}$ **24.** $\begin{array}{r} 19.08 \\ \times\ 124 \\ \hline \end{array}$

25. $\begin{array}{r} 0.7 \\ \times\ 0.6 \\ \hline \end{array}$ **26.** $\begin{array}{r} 0.8 \\ \times\ 0.5 \\ \hline \end{array}$ **27.** $\begin{array}{r} 0.5 \\ \times\ 9.7 \\ \hline \end{array}$ **28.** $\begin{array}{r} 0.416 \\ \times\ 3.3 \\ \hline \end{array}$ **29.** $\begin{array}{r} \$8.16 \\ \times\ 0.75 \\ \hline \end{array}$

30. $\begin{array}{r} 87.031 \\ \times\ 4.2 \\ \hline \end{array}$ **31.** $\begin{array}{r} 7.004 \\ \times\ 4.31 \\ \hline \end{array}$ **32.** $\begin{array}{r} 406.1 \\ \times\ 1.65 \\ \hline \end{array}$ **33.** $\begin{array}{r} 90.514 \\ \times\ 0.875 \\ \hline \end{array}$ **34.** $\begin{array}{r} 326.04 \\ \times\ 79.8 \\ \hline \end{array}$

35. 187×0.004

36. 204×0.015

37. 8.003×97

38. 1.7×0.8

39. 4.5×0.6

40. 2.61×2.4

41. $\$10.42 \times 1.5$

42. 24.03×0.141

43. 27.06×81.1

44. 4.903×2.97

45. 6.145×0.916

46. 0.418×9.05

Solve. Use the chart.

47. What is the total cost for a 3-line and a 6-line ad if both are run for 7 days?

48. How much less does a 3-line ad run for 4 days cost than a 4-line ad run for 3 days?

49. What is the cost of twelve 3-line ads if 7 run for 5 days and 5 run for 10 days?

WANT AD RATES

Lines	1 time Sunday	1 time Daily	3 Days	4 Days	5 Days	6 Days	7 Days	10 Days
2	3.42	3.42	9.84	12.32	14.90	17.88	19.32	27.60
3	5.13	5.13	14.76	18.48	22.35	26.82	29.98	41.40
4	6.84	6.84	19.68	24.64	29.80	35.76	38.64	55.20
5	8.55	8.55	24.60	30.80	37.25	44.70	48.50	69.00
6	10.26	10.26	29.52	36.96	44.70	53.44	57.96	82.80
7	11.97	11.97	34.44	43.12	52.15	62.58	67.62	96.60
8	13.68	13.68	39.36	49.28	59.60	71.52	77.28	110.40
9	15.39	15.39	44.28	55.24	67.05	80.46	86.94	124.20
10	17.10	17.10	49.20	61.60	74.58	89.60	96.60	138.00

2-6 Zeros in Multiplication

It is often necessary to write extra zeros in order to correctly place the decimal point in products. Study this example.

$$\begin{array}{r} 1.14 \\ \times\, 0.056 \\ \hline 684 \\ 570 \\ \hline 6384 \end{array}$$

1.14 — 2 decimal places
× 0.056 — 3 decimal places
6384 → ▒.▒▒▒▒▒ — 5 decimal places

The factors have a total of 5 decimal places. So, the product must have 5. Possible answers are 0.63840 and 0.06384.

Since 1.14 is close to 1, the product 1.14 × 0.056 should be close to 0.056. Do you see why the product is 0.06384?

EXERCISES ***Copy. Then place the point and necessary zeros in the product.***

1. $\begin{array}{r} 0.8 \\ \times\ 4 \\ \hline 32 \end{array}$ **2.** $\begin{array}{r} 0.08 \\ \times\ 4 \\ \hline 32 \end{array}$ **3.** $\begin{array}{r} 0.008 \\ \times\ 4 \\ \hline 32 \end{array}$ **4.** $\begin{array}{r} 0.08 \\ \times\ 0.04 \\ \hline 32 \end{array}$ **5.** $\begin{array}{r} 0.1 \\ \times\ 0.1 \\ \hline 1 \end{array}$

6. 0.002 × 0.1 = 2 **7.** 0.006 × 0.5 = 3 **8.** 0.09 × 0.01 = 9

Multiply.

9. $\begin{array}{r} 0.3 \\ \times\ 0.3 \\ \hline \end{array}$ **10.** $\begin{array}{r} 0.1 \\ \times\ 0.2 \\ \hline \end{array}$ **11.** $\begin{array}{r} 0.01 \\ \times\ 0.1 \\ \hline \end{array}$ **12.** $\begin{array}{r} 0.16 \\ \times\ 0.5 \\ \hline \end{array}$ **13.** $\begin{array}{r} 0.23 \\ \times\ 0.2 \\ \hline \end{array}$

14. $\begin{array}{r} 0.703 \\ \times\ 0.5 \\ \hline \end{array}$ **15.** $\begin{array}{r} 63 \\ \times\ 0.006 \\ \hline \end{array}$ **16.** $\begin{array}{r} \$10.08 \\ \times\ 0.5 \\ \hline \end{array}$ **17.** $\begin{array}{r} 0.001 \\ \times\ 0.01 \\ \hline \end{array}$ **18.** $\begin{array}{r} 0.08 \\ \times\ 0.11 \\ \hline \end{array}$

19. $\begin{array}{r} 0.033 \\ \times\ 1.1 \\ \hline \end{array}$ **20.** $\begin{array}{r} 0.003 \\ \times\ 0.4 \\ \hline \end{array}$ **21.** $\begin{array}{r} 0.715 \\ \times\ 0.002 \\ \hline \end{array}$ **22.** $\begin{array}{r} 0.00009 \\ \times\ 12 \\ \hline \end{array}$ **23.** $\begin{array}{r} 0.356 \\ \times\ 0.007 \\ \hline \end{array}$

24. 2.6 × 0.2 **25.** 0.9 × 0.008 **26.** 1.4 × 0.007
27. 0.615 × 0.005 **28.** 0.27 × 0.003 **29.** 2.546 × 0.001

Multiply. Round each product to the indicated place-value position.

30. 0.12 × 0.3, hundredths **31.** 6.7 × 0.8, whole number
32. 0.354 × 0.01, thousandths **33.** 0.14 × 1.6, tenths
34. 32 × 0.085, tenths **35.** 0.56 × 0.56, hundredths
36. 805 × 0.0044, whole number **37.** 0.0625 × 0.632, thousandths

Solve. Use the chart.

Vitamin Content of Fresh Fruits (milligrams)			
Fruit	Vitamin B_1 (thiamin)	Vitamin B_2 (riboflavin)	Vitamin C
Apple	0.04	0.03	6
Banana	0.06	0.07	12
Peach	0.02	0.05	7
Orange	0.13	0.05	66
Grapefruit	0.10	0.04	88

38. How many milligrams of vitamin B_1 does a peach provide?

39. How many milligrams of vitamin C does a banana provide?

40. Andrea has two oranges in one day. How many milligrams of riboflavin does she receive from the oranges?

41. Hernando has a grapefruit and two peaches during the day. How many milligrams of thiamin does he receive from the fruits?

42. The minimum daily requirement of vitamin B_2 for Theresa is 1.2 milligrams. Would three bananas fulfill that requirement?

Skills Review: Pages 33-43

Express each of the following as a decimal.

1. $\frac{4}{10}$ **2.** $3\frac{5}{100}$

Round the following to the underlined place-value position.

4. $0.\underline{6}68$ **5.** $6.08\underline{3}4$

Replace the ▒ with <, >, or = to make a true sentence.

3. 2.05 ▒ 2.046

Add or subtract.

6. $\begin{array}{r} \$23.04 \\ -\ \ 6.98 \\ \hline \end{array}$ **7.** $\begin{array}{r} 2.03 \\ +\ 8.075 \\ \hline \end{array}$

Multiply.

8. $\begin{array}{r} 8.7 \\ \times\ \ 8 \\ \hline \end{array}$ **9.** $\begin{array}{r} 109 \\ \times\ 0.7 \\ \hline \end{array}$ **10.** $\begin{array}{r} 6.8 \\ \times\ 0.3 \\ \hline \end{array}$ **11.** $\begin{array}{r} 10.8 \\ \times\ 0.45 \\ \hline \end{array}$ **12.** $\begin{array}{r} 0.102 \\ \times\ 0.59 \\ \hline \end{array}$

Cumulative Review

Replace each ▒ with <, >, or = to make a true sentence.

1. 4.6 ▒ 4.9 **2.** 2.100 ▒ 2.1 **3.** 2.06 ▒ 2.08

Round each of the following to the underlined place-value position.

4. $\underline{9},465$ **5.** $\underline{2}47.62$ **6.** $0.0\underline{2}9$ **7.** $0.90\underline{9}9$

Estimate.

8. $\begin{array}{r} 2{,}496 \\ +\ 8{,}487 \\ \hline \end{array}$ **9.** $\begin{array}{r} 19{,}024 \\ -\ \ 9{,}659 \\ \hline \end{array}$ **10.** $\begin{array}{r} 204 \\ \times\ \ 21 \\ \hline \end{array}$ **11.** $78\overline{)651}$

Add or subtract. Check your answers.

12. $\begin{array}{r} 12{,}946 \\ +\ \ 8{,}487 \\ \hline \end{array}$ **13.** $\begin{array}{r} 8{,}100 \\ -\ 4{,}683 \\ \hline \end{array}$ **14.** $\begin{array}{r} \$8.29 \\ +\ \ 0.46 \\ \hline \end{array}$ **15.** $\begin{array}{r} 6.51 \\ -\ 0.432 \\ \hline \end{array}$ **16.** $\begin{array}{r} 7.069 \\ +\ 4.07 \\ \hline \end{array}$

17. 2.04 + 8.3 **18.** 9.18 − 0.46 **19.** 12 − 4.061

20. \$12 + \$8.96 + 89¢ **21.** 6.06 + 0.842 + 14.008

Multiply or divide. Write any remainders with an R.

22. $\begin{array}{r} 206 \\ \times\ \ \ 5 \\ \hline \end{array}$ **23.** $\begin{array}{r} 4{,}316 \\ \times\ \ \ \ 3 \\ \hline \end{array}$ **24.** $\begin{array}{r} 43 \\ \times\ 12 \\ \hline \end{array}$ **25.** $\begin{array}{r} 462 \\ \times\ \ 37 \\ \hline \end{array}$ **26.** $\begin{array}{r} 876 \\ \times\ 240 \\ \hline \end{array}$

27. $\begin{array}{r} 0.88 \\ \times\ \ \ 7 \\ \hline \end{array}$ **28.** $\begin{array}{r} 4.061 \\ \times\ \ \ \ 9 \\ \hline \end{array}$ **29.** $\begin{array}{r} 4.1 \\ \times\ 0.2 \\ \hline \end{array}$ **30.** $\begin{array}{r} \$0.05 \\ \times\ \ \ 6.4 \\ \hline \end{array}$ **31.** $\begin{array}{r} 0.38 \\ \times\ 0.015 \\ \hline \end{array}$

32. $4\overline{)252}$ **33.** $6\overline{)\$247}$ **34.** $3\overline{)2{,}745}$ **35.** $8\overline{)48{,}344}$

36. $20\overline{)680}$ **37.** $18\overline{)130}$ **38.** $47\overline{)752}$ **39.** $183\overline{)2{,}950}$

40. 8,012 × 8 **41.** 24 × 6.5 **42.** 2.403 × 0.19

43. 384 ÷ 5 **44.** \$23,402 ÷ 9 **45.** 2,262 ÷ 87

Solve.

46. Tony drives 651.3 miles. Elizabeth drives 293.6 miles farther than Tony. How many miles does Elizabeth drive?

47. Aletea averages 79.5 strokes for four rounds of golf. What is her total number of strokes?

Mathematics and Consumers

A **time card** is a record of the hours worked. Phil Bowen's time card is shown at the right.

Phil Bowen					Hourly Rate: $4.65
	Date	In	Out	In	Out	Daily Hours

	Date	In	Out	In	Out	Daily Hours
11						
10	11-17	07:00	11:30	12:45	16:00	7.75
9	11-16	07:00	11:30	12:15	15:15	7.5
8	11-15	06:45	11:30	12:15	15:00	7.5
7	11-14	07:00	11:30	12:15	15:30	7.75
6	11-13	07:15	11:30	12:15	15:30	7.5

To determine how many hours Mr. Bowen worked from November 13 through November 17, add the daily hours.

$$\begin{array}{r} {\scriptstyle 3\ 1} \\ 7.75 \\ 7.50 \\ 7.50 \\ 7.75 \\ +\ 7.50 \\ \hline 38.00 \end{array}$$

To find Mr. Bowen's total earnings, multiply his hourly rate, $4.65, by the number of hours worked, 38.

$$\begin{array}{rl} \$4.65 & \text{hourly rate} \\ \times\ \ 38 & \text{hours worked} \\ \hline 37\ 20 & \\ 139\ 5 & \\ \hline \$176.70 & \text{total earnings} \end{array}$$

Mr. Bowen's total earnings for the week are $176.70.
Explain why Mr. Bowen's paycheck is probably for less than $176.70.

EXERCISES ***Find the total hours worked and weekly earnings for each time card.***

1.

Serves					Hourly Rate: $5.00
	Date	In	Out	In	Out	Daily Hours

	Date	In	Out	In	Out	Daily Hours
6						
5	3-5	6:15	10:30			4.25
4	3-4	6:30	11:00			4.5
3	3-3	6:00	10:15			4.25
2	3-2	6:00	11:00			5
1	3-1	6:00	10:30			4.5

2.

Beal					Hourly Rate: $7.05
	Date	In	Out	In	Out	Daily Hours

	Date	In	Out	In	Out	Daily Hours
6						
5	3-5	9:15	1:45			4.5
4	3-4	9:00	2:30			5.5
3	3-3	9:30	2:15			4.75
2	3-2	9:30	2:00			4.5
1	3-1	9:30	1:15			3.75

Solve.

3. Chris Lewis works for 17 hours and earns $6.50 an hour. On another job, he is paid $7.25 an hour for 26 hours. How much does he earn for working 43 hours?

4. Ron Alexander works 37.5 hours a week and earns $5.28 an hour. What are his total yearly earnings?

2-7 Division

Sheila McAuliffe buys five pairs of wrist bands for \$4.45. To find the cost of each pair, divide \$4.45 by 5.

To divide a decimal by a whole number, place the decimal point as shown at the right. Then, divide as with whole numbers.

$5\overline{)\$4.45}$ ➡ $5\overline{)\$4.45}$ (decimal point placed directly above)

Divide the ones.

4 ones ÷ 5

$$\begin{array}{r} \$0. \\ 5\overline{)\$4.45} \end{array}$$

Write a 0 in the ones place to help place the decimal point.

Divide the tenths.

44 tenths ÷ 5

$$\begin{array}{r} \$0.8 \\ 5\overline{)\$4.45} \\ -4\,0 \\ \hline 45 \end{array}$$

Divide the hundredths.

45 hundredths ÷ 5

$$\begin{array}{r} \$0.89 \\ 5\overline{)\$4.45} \\ -4\,0 \\ \hline 45 \\ \underline{45} \end{array}$$

Sheila pays \$0.89 for each pair. How can you check the answer?

EXERCISES ***Copy. Then place the point and necessary zeros in the quotient.***

1. $\begin{array}{r} 4 \\ 7\overline{)2.8} \end{array}$ **2.** $\begin{array}{r} 321 \\ 6\overline{)19.26} \end{array}$ **3.** $\begin{array}{r} 27 \\ 4\overline{)10.8} \end{array}$ **4.** $\begin{array}{r} 16 \\ 8\overline{)0.128} \end{array}$ **5.** $\begin{array}{r} 8 \\ 5\overline{)0.040} \end{array}$

Divide. Check your answers.

> Annex zeros until the remainder is zero.
>
> $$\begin{array}{rl} 0.5 & \\ 24\overline{)12.0} & \text{annex a 0} \\ -12\,0 & \\ \hline 0 & \text{remainder is 0} \end{array}$$

6. $6\overline{)2.4}$ **7.** $5\overline{)3.5}$ **8.** $6\overline{)6.6}$

9. $8\overline{)40.8}$ **10.** $2\overline{)8.6}$ **11.** $3\overline{)10.8}$

12. $7\overline{)43.05}$ **13.** $9\overline{)14.67}$ **14.** $4\overline{)2.0}$

15. $8\overline{)\$6.00}$ **16.** $6\overline{)9.0}$ **17.** $2\overline{)5.0}$

18. $2\overline{)1}$ **19.** $4\overline{)37}$ **20.** $8\overline{)46}$ **21.** $11\overline{)46.2}$

22. $18\overline{)9.9}$ **23.** $26\overline{)\$52.78}$ **24.** $32\overline{)7.36}$ **25.** $38\overline{)77.9}$

26. $66\overline{)29.7}$ **27.** $45\overline{)92.7}$ **28.** $73\overline{)\$16.79}$ **29.** $86\overline{)215}$

30. $62\overline{)1{,}119.1}$ **31.** $57\overline{)1.311}$ **32.** $46\overline{)46.276}$ **33.** $98\overline{)590.45}$

When a division does *not* result in remainder of 0, the quotient is usually rounded. To round a quotient to a certain place-value position, divide to one extra decimal place. Then round.

Round the quotient of 2 divided by 3 to the nearest tenth. To do this, divide to the hundredths place. Then round to the nearest tenth.

To the nearest tenth, 0.66 rounds to 0.7.

$$\begin{array}{r} \mathbf{0.66} \\ 3\overline{)2.00} \\ -1\,8 \\ \hline 20 \\ -18 \\ \hline 2 \end{array}$$

annex zeros

EXERCISES ***Round each quotient to the indicated place-value position.***

34. $\begin{array}{r} 5.78 \\ 18\overline{)104.1} \end{array}$, tenths **35.** $\begin{array}{r} 1.236 \\ 6\overline{)7.42} \end{array}$, hundredths **36.** $\begin{array}{r} 56.4 \\ 7\overline{)395} \end{array}$, whole number

Divide. Round each quotient to the indicated place-value position.

37. $4\overline{)6.7}$, whole number **38.** $7\overline{)17.68}$, tenths **39.** $5\overline{)5.415}$, hundredths

40. $8\overline{)24.65}$, tenths **41.** $2\overline{)\$196.30}$, dollar **42.** $6\overline{)3.5}$, tenths

43. $9\overline{)\$568}$, cent **44.** $4\overline{)22.87}$, hundredths **45.** $6\overline{)483.7}$, whole number

46. $16.38 \div 12$, tenths **47.** $103 \div 7$, whole number

48. $\$1,175 \div 73$, dollar **49.** $\$580 \div 47$, cent

Solve. Round costs to the nearest tenth of a cent. (Think of $0.99 as 99¢.)

50. Lucille buys 50 paper plates for $0.99. What is the cost of each plate?

51. A 16-ounce can of tomatoes costs 59¢. A 12-ounce can costs 42¢. Which can is the better buy per ounce?

52. Wax paper costs $1.09 for 75 square feet. The 200-square foot box costs $2.83. Which is the better buy per square foot?

2–8 Problem Solving: Multi-step Problems

Marty Zabonik hiked each of the four hiking trails shown at the right. Marty wants to find the average length of the trails.

Find **average** as follows.

- First, add.
- Then, divide the sum by the number of addends.

Solve the problem as follows.

Read the problem. You need to find the average length. You know the length of each trail and the number of trails.

Decide what to do. Find the average distance as follows. Add the trail lengths. Then, divide the total length by the number of trails.

Solve the problem.

Add

$$\begin{array}{r} \scriptstyle 2 \\ 4.8 \\ 7.4 \\ 5.3 \\ +\ 3.9 \\ \hline 21.4 \end{array}$$

4.8, 7.4, 5.3, 3.9: 4 lengths

21.4: total length

Divide

$$\begin{array}{r} 5.35 \\ 4\overline{)21.40} \\ -20 \\ \hline 1\,4 \\ -1\,2 \\ \hline 20 \\ 20 \\ \hline \end{array}$$

The average length is 5.35 miles.

Examine the solution. The solution is reasonable since the average length is between the longest and shortest length.

Check You check the addition. The check for the division is shown.

$$\begin{array}{r} \scriptstyle 1\ 2 \\ 5.35 \\ \times\ \ 4 \\ \hline 21.40 \end{array} \checkmark$$

Solve.

1. The daily high temperatures in degrees Fahrenheit for one week in July were 84.6, 83.5, 89.7, 79.8, 78.4, 81.4, and 83.6. Find the average daily high.

2. The amounts of Sandra Graham's electric bills for six months are $58.74, $59.80, $63.49, $60.88, $74.39, and $79.60. Find the average monthly bill.

Solve.

3. The odometer reading at the start of a trip was 25,199.8 miles. After the trip, the reading was 25,720.1. Find the miles per gallon (to the nearest tenth) if 17 gallons of gasoline were used.

4. Beverly Mock earns $21.80, $29.45, $31.87, $24.50, $35.95, and $31.60 in tips. Her hourly earnings add another $110.85 for the 6 days. Find her average daily earnings.

5. Bill's mathematics test scores are 86, 88, 87, 94, and 56. What is his average score?

6. Suppose 5 pounds of ground beef cost $7.45. How much do 3 pounds cost?

7. Michelle spends $14.95 for cassette tapes and $3.99 for sunglasses. She has to pay 95¢ tax. What is her change from $20?

8. Wally works as a waiter and earns $2.89 an hour plus tips. Suppose Wally works for 7 hours and receives $25.64 in tips. What are his total wages?

9. Elizabeth buys 5 pairs of socks for $2.98 each. The sales tax is $0.82. What is her change from two ten-dollar bills?

10. What score on a third test will give an average of at least 80 after scores of 75 and 79?

11. Joshua makes a 15-minute long-distance call. The charge is $0.47 for the first minute and $0.26 for each additional minute. What is the total cost of the phone call if the tax is $0.18?

12. Jack makes a 25-minute long-distance call. The charge is $0.58 for the first minute and $0.31 for each additional minute. The tax is $0.28. What is the total cost of the call?

Solve. Use the bar graph.

13. What is the average snowfall for the four months?

14. During which months was the snowfall greater than the average?

15. During which months was the snowfall less than the average?

16. Suppose the snowfall during November was 4.6 inches. What was the average monthly snowfall for November through March?

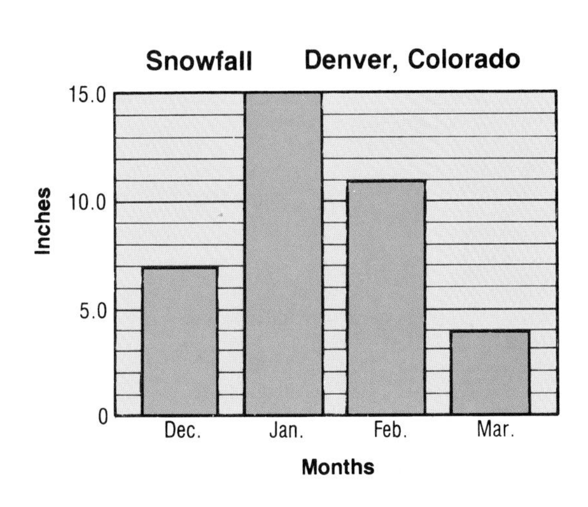

2-9 Multiplication and Division by Powers of Ten

Donna Soto runs 2.5 miles on Monday. For the whole week, she runs 10 times that distance or 25 miles.

To find the total distance run the whole week, multiply 2.5 by 10.

$$\begin{array}{r} 2.5 \\ \times\ 10 \\ \hline 25.0 \end{array} \text{ or } 25$$

2.5 × 10 = 2.5 or 25

Divide 2.5 by 10.

$$\begin{array}{r} 0.25 \\ 10\overline{)2.50} \\ -2\,0 \\ \hline 50 \\ 50 \\ \hline \end{array}$$

2.5 ÷ 10 = 2.5 or 0.25

To multiply by powers of ten, move the decimal point to the right.

0.64 × 10 = 0.64 or 6.4

0.64 × 100 = 0.64 or 64

0.64 × 1,000 = 0.640 or 640

To divide by powers of ten, move the decimal point to the left.

82 ÷ 10 = 82 or 8.2

82 ÷ 100 = 82 or 0.82

82 ÷ 1,000 = 082 or 0.082

State rules for multiplying and for dividing by powers of ten.

EXERCISES ***Copy. Then place the decimal point and necessary zeros in each product or quotient.***

1. 6.6 × 10 = 66

2. 47 ÷ 10 = 47

3. 0.29 ÷ 100 = 29

4. 6.48 × 1,000 = 648

5. 8,906 ÷ 1,000 = 8906

6. 276 × 100 = 276

Multiply or divide.

7. 6.5 × 10

8. 8.3 ÷ 10

9. 94.1 ÷ 100

10. 1,000 ÷ 100

11. 8,610 ÷ 1,000

12. 4.21 × 100

13. 0.681 × 1,000

14. 47 × 10

15. 0.93 × 100

16. 168 ÷ 1,000

17. 4.6 × 1,000

18. 4.4 ÷ 100

19. 6 ÷ 10

20. 9 ÷ 100

21. 5 ÷ 1,000

22. 0.4 × 10

23. 0.03 × 100

24. 0.001 × 1,000

25. 0.6 ÷ 10

26. 0.69 × 10

27. 42.3 × 1,000

28. 8 ÷ 1,000

29. 0.6 ÷ 100

30. 0.84 × 1,000

Study these examples.

$2.5 \times 10^0 = 2.5$	$2.5 \div 10^0 = 2.5$
$2.5 \times 10^1 = 25$	$2.5 \div 10^1 = 0.25$
$2.5 \times 10^2 = 250$	$2.5 \div 10^2 = 0.025$
$2.5 \times 10^3 = 2{,}500$	$2.5 \div 10^3 = 0.0025$

Remember: $10^0 = 1$ $10^1 = 10$ $10^2 = 100$ $10^3 = 1{,}000$

EXERCISES ***Match each of the following with the letter of the correct answer.***

31. 0.84×10^2 **a.** 0.084
32. 0.84×10^1 **b.** 840
33. $0.84 \div 10^1$ **c.** 84
34. 0.84×10^3 **d.** 0.84
35. $0.84 \div 10^0$ **e.** 8.4

Multiply or divide.

36. 2.9×10^1 **37.** 7.06×10^2 **38.** 45.9×10^0
39. $19.4 \div 10^3$ **40.** $8.7 \div 10^2$ **41.** $188 \div 10^1$
42. $\$0.03 \times 10^2$ **43.** $2{,}156 \div 10^0$ **44.** $2{,}010 \times 10^2$
45. 7.64×10^3 **46.** 0.001×10^3 **47.** $9 \div 10^2$
48. $\$9.999 \times 10^2$ **49.** $11 \div 10^3$ **50.** 400×10^0

51. State the relationship between the number of zeros (or the exponent) in a power of ten and the number of places the decimal point is moved for multiplication or division.

MOVING TOWERS

Four disks are stacked on a post as shown at the right. Without placing any disk over a smaller one, move the tower, one disk at a time, to one of the other posts. Find the *minimum* number of moves. Try to discover the pattern between the number of disks and number of moves.

2-10 Division by Decimals

Catherine Varca takes a 37.5-mile boat trip across a lake in 1.5 hours. To find the average speed, divide 37.5 by 1.5.

As shown for 42 ÷ 6, multiplying the divisor and dividend by 10 does *not* change the quotient. Would multiplying both by 100 or by 1,000 change the quotient?

$6\overline{)42} = 7$ ➧ $60\overline{)420} = 7$

6 × 10 = 60
42 × 10 = 420

To divide by a decimal, multiply the divisor and dividend by a power of ten so that the divisor is a whole number. Then, divide as with whole numbers. Use this idea to divide 37.5 by 1.5.

Multiply 1.5 and 37.5 by 10. Why?

1.5)37.5 ➧ **1.5)37.5**

1.5 × 10 = 15
37.5 × 10 = 375

Divide as with whole numbers.

```
      25
1.5)37.5
    30
     75
     75
```

The average speed of the boat is 25 miles an hour. Use multiplication to check this result.

EXERCISES ***Copy. Then complete the following.***

1. 0.9)0.72 ➧ 0.9)0.72 (quotient: 0.▒)

2. 0.07)0.574 ➧ 0.07)0.574 (quotient: ▒.▒)

3. 0.63)2.52 ➧ 0.63)2.52 (quotient: ▒.)

4. 0.075)0.0435 ➧ 0.075)0.04350 (quotient: ▒.▒▒)

Name the appropriate power of ten you would multiply by to change each divisor to a whole number. Use, 10, 100, or 1,000.

5. 6.5 **6.** 0.04 **7.** 6.15 **8.** 0.18 **9.** 0.019

Copy. Then place the decimal point and necessary zeros in the quotient.

10. 0.2)1.68 (84)

11. 0.09)8.73 (97)

12. 0.089)0.01869 (21)

13. 0.05)25.50 (510)

Divide. Check your answers.

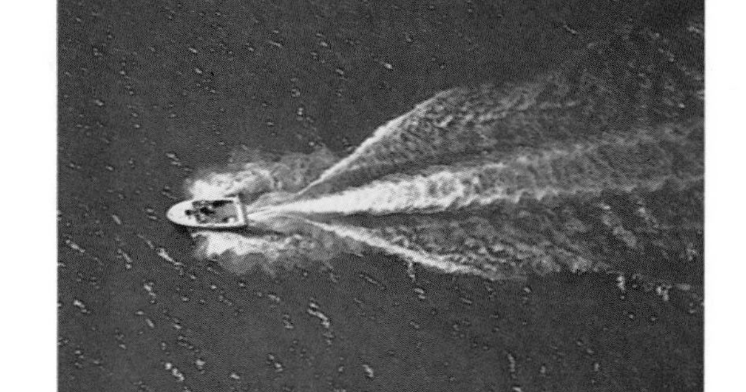

14. $0.8\overline{)2.4}$ **15.** $0.3\overline{)0.201}$

16. $0.04\overline{)0.092}$ **17.** $0.7\overline{)0.245}$

18. $0.008\overline{)0.072}$ **19.** $0.06\overline{)0.204}$

20. $0.021\overline{)0.0504}$ **21.** $0.63\overline{)7.56}$

22. $4.6\overline{)\$115}$ **23.** $0.053\overline{)0.00954}$

24. $0.05\overline{)0.7}$ **25.** $0.024\overline{)0.5064}$

26. $0.91\overline{)0.0546}$ **27.** $8.1\overline{)132.03}$

28. $0.26\overline{)11.102}$ **29.** $4.7\overline{)43.381}$ **30.** $0.087\overline{)2.6448}$ **31.** $0.68\overline{)4.42}$

32. $9.6\overline{)199.68}$ **33.** $0.047\overline{)0.4841}$ **34.** $0.84\overline{)\$25.62}$ **35.** $0.075\overline{)4.35}$

36. $1.54\overline{)3.08}$ **37.** $0.603\overline{)5.8491}$ **38.** $16.8\overline{)756}$ **39.** $0.493\overline{)5.1765}$

40. $0.125\overline{)5.75}$ **41.** $15.8\overline{)790}$ **42.** $2.62\overline{)0.0655}$ **43.** $0.405\overline{)105.3}$

Divide. Round each quotient to the indicated place-value position.

44. $5.98 \div 2.9$, whole number

45. $1.063 \div 0.06$, tenths

46. $0.327 \div 1.4$, hundredths

47. $0.46 \div 8.1$, tenths

48. $12.9 \div 6.3$, whole number

49. $0.4088 \div 0.041$, hundredths

50. $0.015 \div 0.029$, thousandths

51. $1.98 \div 0.71$, thousandths

52. In 9 softball games, Lisa has 14 hits. To the nearest tenth, how many hits is this per game?

53. A fund-raising relay team ran 249.5 kilometers on a 0.4-kilometer track. To the nearest lap, how many laps did the relay team run?

54. A relay team runs 1.6 kilometers in 4.2 minutes. This time is 0.1 minutes slower than the winning time. To the nearest hundredth, find the average kilometers per minute for the winning team.

55. On a 308-mile trip, Mr. Winters' car uses 12.3 gallons of gasoline. To the nearest gallon, how many miles per gallon does the car get?

2-11 Estimation

Renee runs 3.75 laps around a park in 325.3 seconds (5 minutes and 25.3 seconds). About how many seconds per lap does she average?

To find *about* how many, estimate 325.3 ÷ 3.75 as follows.

Round 3.75 to its greatest place-value position, ones. Round 325.3 so it is a multiple of the divisor.

$$3.75\overline{)325.3} \;\Rightarrow\; 4\overline{)320} \quad \text{estimate: } 80$$

3.75 rounds to 4
325.3 rounds to 320

Renee averages about 80 seconds (1 minute and 20 seconds) a lap.

When you estimate, use the following rules for rounding.

Addition and Subtraction	Round each number to its greatest place-value position.
Multiplication	Round each factor to its greatest place-value position. Do *not* change 1-digit factors.
Division	Round the divisor to its greatest place-value position. Do *not* change 1-digit divisors. Then, round the dividend so it is a multiple of the divisor.

EXERCISES ***Copy. Then complete the estimation.***

1. $0.46 + 0.83 \Rightarrow 0.5 + 0.8 = \blacksquare.\blacksquare$
2. $\$14.81 - 2.92 \Rightarrow \$10 - 3 = \$\blacksquare$
3. $\$12.95 + 6.06 \Rightarrow \$10 + 6 = \$\blacksquare\blacksquare$
4. $91.4 \times 6.5 \Rightarrow 90 \times 7 = \blacksquare\blacksquare\blacksquare$
5. $0.63 \times 0.81 \Rightarrow 0.6 \times 0.8 = \blacksquare.\blacksquare\blacksquare$
6. $0.043 \times 0.81 \Rightarrow 0.04 \times 0.8 = \blacksquare.\blacksquare\blacksquare\blacksquare$
7. $0.71\overline{)1.98} \Rightarrow 0.7\overline{)2.1}$ quotient: $\blacksquare.$
8. $0.493\overline{)5.1765} \Rightarrow 0.5\overline{)5.0}$ quotient: $\blacksquare\blacksquare.$

Estimate.

9. $\begin{array}{r} 0.14 \\ +\ 0.38 \\ \hline \end{array}$ 10. $\begin{array}{r} 2.83 \\ -\ 0.95 \\ \hline \end{array}$ 11. $\begin{array}{r} \$9.51 \\ +\ 8.39 \\ \hline \end{array}$ 12. $\begin{array}{r} 0.824 \\ -\ 0.085 \\ \hline \end{array}$ 13. $\begin{array}{r} \$3.14 \\ -\ 0.85 \\ \hline \end{array}$

14. $848.6 - 16.93$ 15. $6.093 - 0.851$ 16. $26.834 + 11.76$

17. $14.26 + 0.65 + 1.987$ 18. $\$23.76 + \$48.61 + \$9.26$

19. $\begin{array}{r} 20.15 \\ \times\ 4.2 \\ \hline \end{array}$ 20. $\begin{array}{r} 86.8 \\ \times\ 10.2 \\ \hline \end{array}$ 21. $\begin{array}{r} 123.7 \\ \times\ 21.4 \\ \hline \end{array}$ 22. $\begin{array}{r} \$2.86 \\ \times\ 1.1 \\ \hline \end{array}$ 23. $\begin{array}{r} 2.04 \\ \times\ 18.7 \\ \hline \end{array}$

24. $9.1\overline{)26.5}$ 25. $8.06\overline{)42.11}$ 26. $5.841\overline{)232.6}$ 27. $1.88\overline{)0.116}$

28. 0.68×0.21 29. $\$26.19 \times 2.6$ 30. 214.5×28.07

31. $44.1 \div 0.71$ 32. $4.35 \div 0.075$ 33. $57 \div 0.07$

34. Suppose you round all factors up. Is the estimate greater than or less than the exact answer?

Choose the best estimate for each of the following.

35. $2.93 + 7.84$ **a.** 9 **b.** 10 **c.** 11

36. $0.875 - 0.128$ **a.** 0.8 **b.** 1 **c.** 0.9

37. 9.3×4.1 **a.** 36 **b.** 45 **c.** 40

38. $27.2 \div 2.85$ **a.** 8 **b.** 10 **c.** 9

Estimate.

39. At one sports store, tee shirts are \$5.79 each. At a second store the cost is \$6.55. Is the difference in cost more than \$1?

40. Grady makes \$4.84 an hour and works 37.5 hours a week. His deductions will be about \$50. Estimate his weekly pay.

CALCULATORS AND ESTIMATION

One of the best uses of estimation is to determine the reasonableness of calculator results. Determine which of the following are not reasonable.

1. $9.84 + 20.65 = 35.89$
2. $29.3 \times 61.2 = 1{,}793.16$
3. $6.045 - 3.88 = 2.165$
4. $8.911 \div 13.3 = 6.7$
5. $\$8.14 + \$1.06 + \$0.98 = \$16.18$
6. $0.55 \times \$86.60 = \$47.63$

Focus on Problem Solving

2-12 Too Many Facts

In 5 years, the stock in an athletic shoe company went up $11.50 to a price of $20.25 a share. What is the average increase each year?

Some problems have more facts than you need. You must choose from the facts in order to correctly solve problems.

Read the problem. You need to find the average increase each year. You know the amount of increase and the number of years. You do not need the current price, $20.25.

Decide what to do. To find the average increase each year, divide the amount of increase by the number of years.

Solve the problem.

$$\begin{array}{r} \$\ 2.30 \\ 5\overline{)\$11.50} \\ -10 \\ \hline 1\,5 \\ -1\,5 \\ \hline 00 \\ 0 \\ \hline \end{array}$$

The average increase each year is $2.30.

Examine the solution. An estimate for $11.50 ÷ 5 is a little more than $2.

Check

$$\begin{array}{r} \overset{1}{\$2}.30 \\ \times\quad 5 \\ \hline \$11.50 \end{array} \checkmark$$

State any facts not needed to solve each of the following.

1. Ken Perez writes checks for $21.78, $43, and $7.08. He makes a $180 deposit. What is the total amount of the checks?
2. A gift costs $7.05. Howard has $45. He gives the clerk a 20-dollar bill. What is his change?
3. A school buys 3 gross of pencils. Each gross (144) cost $10.80. Find the cost of each pencil.
4. Rosalind Lucero paid $1,536 tax in 1982 and $1,623.60 in 1983. For 1982, find the tax paid each month.

Solve. State any facts not needed to solve the problem.

5. Two police radio dispatchers take 104 calls in 8 hours. How many calls is this each hour?

6. An average of 35 cars a minute go through an intersection. How many cars is this in an hour?

7. Eight adult tickets to a game cost $14. Children's tickets cost $0.75 each. What is the cost of each adult ticket?

8. Mr. Cardenas paid $50 down on a set of golf clubs and made 12 payments of $21.50. Find the total amount he paid for the clubs.

9. Joan Alioto earns $4.50 an hour as a fitness advisor. She works 20 hours a week. In how many hours will she earn $180?

10. Amy buys a radio marked down to $19.50 from $25. How much does she pay for the radio if the tax is $1.07?

11. The odometer reading is 4,206.9 miles at the start of a trip and 4,365 at the end. Find the miles per gallon if 6.2 gallons of gasoline are used.

Solve. Use the chart.

High Street Parking Garage	**Rates**
0-30 minutes	**$1.00**
Each additional 30 minutes up to a total of 4 hours	**$0.60**
All day	**$5.50**

12. Carlos Andrews parks his car for 45 minutes. Find the parking charge.

13. Mary Ann Weir parks for 2 hours and 30 minutes, drives for 2 hours, and then parks another 20 minutes. What is her charge for parking?

Skills Review: Pages 46–57

Multiply or divide.

1. 6.4×10

2. $8.806 \times 1{,}000$

3. $4.3 \div 100$

4. $8\overline{)6.4}$

5. $5\overline{)7}$

6. $16\overline{)19.2}$

7. $27\overline{)0.594}$

8. $0.6\overline{)2.76}$

9. $0.09\overline{)1.836}$

10. $0.65\overline{)1.56}$

11. $0.788\overline{)43.34}$

Estimate.

12. $\begin{array}{r} 0.486 \\ +\ 0.94 \\ \hline \end{array}$

13. $\begin{array}{r} 0.84 \\ \times\ 0.11 \\ \hline \end{array}$

Solve. State any facts not needed.

14. The average weight of 7 players is 208.8 pounds. Find the total weight of the players.

Mathematics and Careers

Vicki Johnson is a credit manager at The Stereo Center. She computes the down payment, monthly installment, and finance charges for customers who buy items on credit.

Customers can pay the cash price or in equal monthly payments called **installments.** The installment plan includes a **finance charge,** a fee charged for paying monthly.

Marty Jones buys a stereo for $485. He pays $45.50 a month for 12 months. Find the finance charge as follows.

$45.50	monthly installment	→	**$546**	installment price
× **12**	months		− **485**	cash price
$546.00	installment price		**$61**	finance charge

The finance charge is $61, a little more than $5 a month.

Solve.

1. Anthony Turner buys a radio for $18.97 a month for 6 months. What is the installment price?
2. Theresa Ruben buys a turntable for $33.85 a month for 1 year. What is the installment price?
3. Monthly installments on a television are $21.40 for 24 months. What is the finance charge if the cash price is $425?
4. Joseph pays an installment price of $11.35 a month for 12 months for a speaker. How much would he save by paying $115 cash?
5. Tonya Artusi buys a stereo system at $55.84 a month for 12 months. Her down payment is $125. How much would she save by paying $685 cash?

Solve. Use the payment book.

6. What is the total amount of the loan?
7. How many payments will be made before the loan is paid in full?
8. What is the total finance charge?
9. What is the monthly late payment fee?

ACCOUNT NO 001 3586 133 | DUE DATE Nov 01 | PAYMENT AMOUNT 93 52

If paid after Nov 10 98.19

PATRICIA JAMES | Loan amount 1,765 : 00

FOR BANK USE ONLY: AMOUNT / LATE CHARGE / TOTAL

MAKE CHECKS OR MONEY ORDERS PAYABLE TO MARINE BANK

ADDRESS ALL CORRESPONDENCE TO THE BANK AT PO BOX 555 BUFFALO NEW YORK 14240

1 of 24

Chapter 2 Review

VOCABULARY decimals (33) equivalent decimals (34) average (48)

***EXERCISES* Express each of the following as a decimal. (33)**

1. $\frac{75}{100}$ **2.** $\frac{6}{1{,}000}$ **3.** one and two tenths

Replace each ▒ with <, >, or = to make a true sentence. (35)

4. 0.40 ▒ 0.4 **5.** 1.85 ▒ 1.843 **6.** 2.1065 ▒ 2.106

Round each of the following to the underlined place-value position. (36)

7. $0.\underline{4}5$ **8.** $0.0\underline{6}7$ **9.** $4{,}\underline{5}35$ **10.** $2\underline{9}.91$

Add, subtract, multiply, or divide. (38–39, 40–43, 46–47, 50–53)

11. $\begin{array}{r} 9.75 \\ +\ 5.23 \\ \hline \end{array}$ **12.** $\begin{array}{r} 18.4 \\ +\ 8.63 \\ \hline \end{array}$ **13.** $\begin{array}{r} 45.3 \\ -\ 9.6 \\ \hline \end{array}$ **14.** $\begin{array}{r} 14.5 \\ -\ 2.85 \\ \hline \end{array}$ **15.** $\begin{array}{r} \$9 \\ -\ 5.83 \\ \hline \end{array}$

16. 673.01 − 8.076 **17.** \$12.19 + \$47 + \$0.73

18. $\begin{array}{r} 2.9 \\ \times\ 5 \\ \hline \end{array}$ **19.** $\begin{array}{r} \$7.2 \\ \times\ 0.8 \\ \hline \end{array}$ **20.** $\begin{array}{r} 3.54 \\ \times\ 6.2 \\ \hline \end{array}$ **21.** $\begin{array}{r} 0.43 \\ \times\ 0.06 \\ \hline \end{array}$ **22.** $\begin{array}{r} 30.4 \\ \times\ 0.15 \\ \hline \end{array}$

23. $8\overline{)27.2}$ **24.** $68\overline{)23.12}$ **25.** $0.9\overline{)7.38}$ **26.** $0.26\overline{)202.8}$

27. 4.6 × 100 **28.** 6.65 × 1,000 **29.** 0.24 ÷ 10

30. 97 × 0.9 **31.** 31.5 × 0.6 **32.** 0.077 × 0.2

Estimate. (54)

33. $\begin{array}{r} \$86.22 \\ +\ 43.43 \\ \hline \end{array}$ **34.** $\begin{array}{r} 298.65 \\ -\ 95.84 \\ \hline \end{array}$ **35.** $\begin{array}{r} 39.4 \\ \times\ 8.2 \\ \hline \end{array}$ **36.** $9.1\overline{)648.2}$

Solve. State any facts not needed to solve the problem. (48–49, 56–57)

37. Armondo Aden buys three tennis rackets for \$21.50 each marked down from \$24.99. What does he pay for the three rackets? The tax is \$3.87.

38. A 4-cylinder car uses 8.3 gallons of gasoline on a 205-mile trip. To the nearest tenth, how many miles per gallon is this?

Chapter 2 Test

Express each of the following as a decimal.

1. $\frac{65}{100}$ **2.** $\frac{9}{1{,}000}$ **3.** nine tenths

Replace each ▒ with <, >, or = to make a true sentence.

4. 2.03 ▒ 2.3 **5.** 1.8 ▒ 1.800 **6.** 0.709 ▒ 0.071

Round each of the following to the underlined place-value position.

7. $\underline{1}.83$ **8.** $2.\underline{0}9$ **9.** $\$4.5\underline{8}6$ **10.** $7.7\underline{7}77$

Add, subtract, multiply, or divide.

11. $\begin{array}{r} \$6.46 \\ +\ 5.59 \\ \hline \end{array}$ **12.** $\begin{array}{r} 16.5 \\ +\ 8.42 \\ \hline \end{array}$ **13.** $\begin{array}{r} 23.4 \\ -\ 6.8 \\ \hline \end{array}$ **14.** $\begin{array}{r} 12.7 \\ -\ 1.85 \\ \hline \end{array}$ **15.** $\begin{array}{r} 6.944 \\ -5.98 \\ \hline \end{array}$

16. 17.04 + 0.086 + 27.8 **17.** 43.4 − 16.707

18. $\begin{array}{r} 1.9 \\ \times\ 4 \\ \hline \end{array}$ **19.** $\begin{array}{r} 2.7 \\ \times 0.6 \\ \hline \end{array}$ **20.** $\begin{array}{r} 0.8 \\ \times 0.4 \\ \hline \end{array}$ **21.** $\begin{array}{r} \$4.15 \\ \times\ 0.6 \\ \hline \end{array}$ **22.** $\begin{array}{r} 0.043 \\ \times\ 0.5 \\ \hline \end{array}$

23. $7\overline{)7.28}$ **24.** $19\overline{)68.4}$ **25.** $0.8\overline{)1.864}$ **26.** $0.028\overline{)0.4508}$

27. 24 ÷ 100 **28.** 8.1 ÷ 1,000 **29.** 0.67 × 100

30. $0.25 × 17 **31.** 2.6 × 0.9 **32.** 0.061 × 0.08

33. 48.3 ÷ 46 **34.** 0.135 ÷ 0.05 **35.** 4.1478 ÷ 4.46

Estimate.

36. $\begin{array}{r} \$0.83 \\ +\ 0.78 \\ \hline \end{array}$ **37.** $\begin{array}{r} 46.7 \\ -\ 8.79 \\ \hline \end{array}$ **38.** $\begin{array}{r} 28.6 \\ \times\ 7.6 \\ \hline \end{array}$ **39.** $0.087\overline{)0.26}$

Solve. State any facts not needed to solve the problem.

40. A bus gets 6.5 miles per gallon. The bus is driven about 220 miles a day. How many miles can the bus go on 22.6 gallons of gasoline?

41. The 6 employees at Harris Sports Store work 10, 15, 12, 20, 40, and 40 hours each week. To the nearest tenth of an hour, what is the average weekly working time?

Enrichment

Assign each day of the week a number. Suppose today is day 2, or Tuesday. You can compute what day it will be 18 days from now as follows.

0—Sunday
1—Monday
2—Tuesday
3—Wednesday
4—Thursday
5—Friday
6—Saturday

A Add 2 + 18. $2 + 18 = 20$

B Divide 20 by 7. $20 \div 7 = 2\text{ R}6$

C The remainder 6 means that 18 days after Tuesday is Saturday.

Computing in this way with the digits 0 through 6 is called **modulo 7** arithmetic. In modulo 7, the result is always 0, 1, 2, 3, 4, 5, or 6. Add 2 + 18 in modulo 7 as follows.

$$\mathbf{2 + 18 \equiv 6 \ (mod\ 7)}$$

2 plus 18 is equivalent to 6 modulo 7

Other examples are $7 + 14 \equiv 0 \pmod 7$ and $8 \times 5 \equiv 5 \pmod 7$.

EXERCISES ***Complete the following.***

1. $5 + 23 \equiv$ ▒ (mod 7)
2. $7 \times 6 \equiv$ ▒ (mod 7)
3. $1 + 3 \equiv$ ▒ (mod 7)
4. $4 + 365 \equiv$ ▒ (mod 7)
5. $12 \times 19 \equiv$ ▒ (mod 7)
6. $76 \times 7 \equiv$ ▒ (mod 7)
7. $7 + 2 \equiv$ ▒ (mod 7)
8. $8 \times 5 \equiv$ ▒ (mod 9)
9. $24 + 61 \equiv$ ▒ (mod 12)
10. $9 \times 12 \equiv$ ▒ (mod 12)
11. $9 + 1 \equiv$ ▒ (mod 6)
12. $26 \times 26 \equiv$ ▒ (mod 8)

13. What number in modulo 7 is equivalent to 7?

14. What is an everyday use of modulo 12 arithmetic?

Solve. Use modular arithmetic.

15. Ines works five hours until 3:00 P.M. At what time did she start working?

16. Anton buys a clock on Monday. On what day of the week does the 30-day guarantee run out?

17. Julie buys a television on Friday. What day of the week does the 90-day guarantee run out?

18. Thomas Lynd has a 30-month installment auto loan. The first payment is due in October. In what month is the last payment due?

Number Theory, Fractions, and Mixed Numerals

The 24 rocks in the display are arranged in 3 rows of 8 rocks each. Both 3 and 8 are factors of 24.

3-1 Factors and Divisibility

The **factors** of a whole number divide that number with a remainder of 0.

Divide to find factors. First, divide by 1, then 2, then 3, and so on. The factors of 24, shown in red are 1, 2, 3, 4, 6, 8, 12, and 24.

24 ÷ 1 = 24
24 ÷ 2 = 12
24 ÷ 3 = 8
24 ÷ 4 = 6
24 ÷ 5 = 4 R4
24 ÷ 6

The remainder, shown in blue, is not 0. So, 5 is *not* a factor of 24. Explain why you do not need to divide by 6 to know that 6 is a factor.

A number is **divisible** by its factors. Use these divisibility rules.

2: A number is divisible by 2 if the ones digit is 0, 2, 4, 6, or 8.

5: A number is divisible by 5 if the ones digit is 0 or 5.

3: A number is divisible by 3 if the sum of its digits is divisible by 3.

26	**342**
2 + 6 = 8	3 + 4 + 2 = 9

Explain why 26 is not divisible by 3 and why 342 is divisible by 3.

EXERCISES ***State all the factors of each number.***

1. 4	**2.** 5	**3.** 9	**4.** 10	**5.** 12	**6.** 17
7. 20	**8.** 32	**9.** 40	**10.** 45	**11.** 65	**12.** 72
13. 80	**14.** 91	**15.** 100	**16.** 111	**17.** 128	**18.** 174

For each of the following, determine divisibility by 2, 3, and 5.

19. 6	**20.** 15	**21.** 18	**22.** 21	**23.** 29	**24.** 30
25. 36	**26.** 50	**27.** 60	**28.** 80	**29.** 105	**30.** 140

31. What number is a factor of every number?

32. What number is *not* a factor of any number?

33. State and verify a rule for divisibility by 10.

34. State and verify a rule for divisibility by 9. Hint: This rule is similar to the rule for 3.

3–2 Prime Factorization

Bodies of water can be classified as rivers, lakes, oceans, and so on. Whole numbers (0, 1, 2, 3, 4, 5, . . .) can be classified by the number of factors.

A **prime number** has exactly two different factors, *one* and *itself.*

$$13 = 1 \times 13$$

Since 13 has exactly two factors (1 and 13), it is prime.

A **composite number** has more than two different factors.

$$10 = 1 \times 10 \qquad 10 = 2 \times 5$$

Since 10 has more than two factors (1, 2, 5, and 10), it is composite.

List the factors of 1 and of 0. Are 1 and 0 prime, composite, or neither?

EXERCISES ***State prime, composite, or neither for each of the following.***

1. 3	**2.** 6	**3.** 11	**4.** 9	**5.** 0	**6.** 17
7. 20	**8.** 15	**9.** 19	**10.** 18	**11.** 25	**12.** 23
13. 33	**14.** 41	**15.** 39	**16.** 27	**17.** 21	**18.** 34
19. 45	**20.** 1	**21.** 57	**22.** 68	**23.** 77	**24.** 93

25. List the first fifteen prime numbers.

26. List the first fifteen composite numbers.

27. Name the greatest prime number less than 100.

28. Name the least prime number greater than 100.

29. Research and report on *twin primes* and *Goldbach's Conjecture.*

Even numbers are whole numbers that are divisible by 2. Whole numbers that are not even are called **odd numbers.**

30. List the first ten even numbers.

31. List the first ten odd numbers.

Every composite number can be expressed as a product of prime factors in exactly one way except for order. This product is called the **prime factorization** of a number.

Factor trees, like the one at the right, help you find the prime factorization of a number.

The prime factorization of 18 is $2 \times 3 \times 3$. Expressed using exponents, it is 2×3^2.

18

2 × 9

2 × 3 × 3

Always find the *least* prime factor first. Then, divide by each prime as often as possible until each factor is prime. Write the factors in order from least to greatest.

EXERCISES ***Copy and complete.***

32. 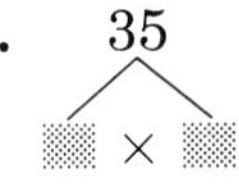

33. 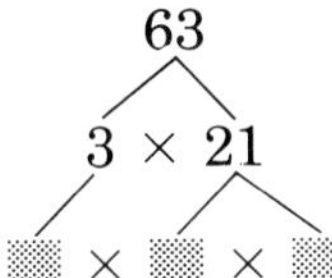

34. 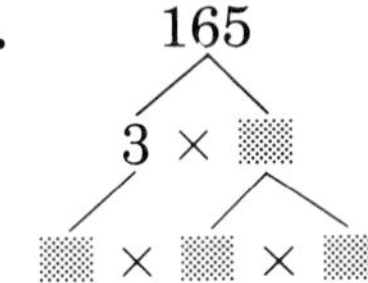

35. 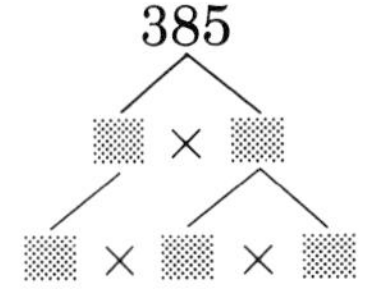

Use exponents to express the prime factorization of each of the following.

36. $2 \times 2 \times 2$ **37.** $2 \times 2 \times 3 \times 5$ **38.** $2 \times 2 \times 2 \times 2$

39. $3 \times 5 \times 5 \times 7$ **40.** $3 \times 3 \times 3 \times 7$ **41.** $5 \times 5 \times 7 \times 7$

42. 15 **43.** 26 **44.** 31 **45.** 36 **46.** 40 **47.** 53

48. 72 **49.** 80 **50.** 81 **51.** 100 **52.** 120 **53.** 169

54. 200 **55.** 250 **56.** 256 **57.** 300 **58.** 900 **59.** 1,694

DIVISIBILITY BY 4 AND 8

4: A number is divisible by 4 if the number formed by its last two digits is divisible by 4. 284 is divisible by 4 because 84 is divisible by 4.

8: A number is divisible by 8 if the number formed by its last three digits is divisible by 8. 1,912 is divisible by 8 because 912 is divisible by 8.

For each of the following, determine divisibility by 2, 3, 4, 5, 8, 9, and 10.

1. 32 **2.** 96 **3.** 200 **4.** 775 **5.** 1,000 **6.** 2,310

3-3 Common Factors and Common Multiples

The minerals pyrite and gold have a common color, metallic yellow. Similarly, groups of whole numbers have **common factors.**

The factors of 20 and 32 are listed at the right. The common factors shown in blue, are 1, 2, and 4. The greatest of these, called the **greatest common factor** (GCF), is 4.

20: 1, 2, 4, 5, 10, 20

32: 1, 2, 4, 8, 16, 32

Note that factors occur in pairs.

Prime factors can be used to find the GCF.
For example, the GCF of 56 and 84 is found as follows.

Write the prime factorization of each number.

$$56 = 2 \times 2 \times 2 \times 7$$
$$84 = 2 \times 2 \times 3 \times 7$$

The common factors are 2, 2, and 7. The GCF of 56 and 84 is $2 \times 2 \times 7$ or 28.

$$2 \times 2 \times 7$$

EXERCISES ***Find the GCF for each group of numbers.***

1. factors of 8: 1, 2, 4, 8
factors of 12: 1, 2, 3, 4, 6, 12

2. factors of 9: 1, 3, 9
factors of 15: 1, 3, 5, 15
factors of 24: 1, 2, 3, 4, 6, 8, 12, 24

3. $5 = 5$
$25 = 5 \times 5$

4. $4 = 2 \times 2$
$8 = 2 \times 2 \times 2$

5. $6 = 2 \times 3$
$12 = 2 \times 2 \times 3$
$18 = 2 \times 3 \times 3$

6. 4, 10	**7.** 12, 15	**8.** 9, 21	**9.** 24, 16
10. 20, 12	**11.** 27, 18	**12.** 24, 18	**13.** 20, 35
14. 15, 21	**15.** 27, 36	**16.** 21, 56	**17.** 54, 36
18. 69, 93	**19.** 72, 45	**20.** 108, 96	**21.** 84, 120
22. 6, 8, 12	**23.** 12, 16, 20	**24.** 12, 18, 30	**25.** 9, 18, 27
26. 36, 48, 56	**27.** 30, 50, 60	**28.** 35, 65, 105	**29.** 72, 81, 90

30. Numbers, such as 9 and 16, whose GCF is 1 are **relatively prime.** Find the two *least* composite numbers that are relatively prime.

The **multiples** of a number result from multiplying that number by the whole numbers 0, 1, 2, 3, and so on. The multiples of 12 and 16 are listed below. Multiples of both numbers, shown in blue, are called **common multiples.**

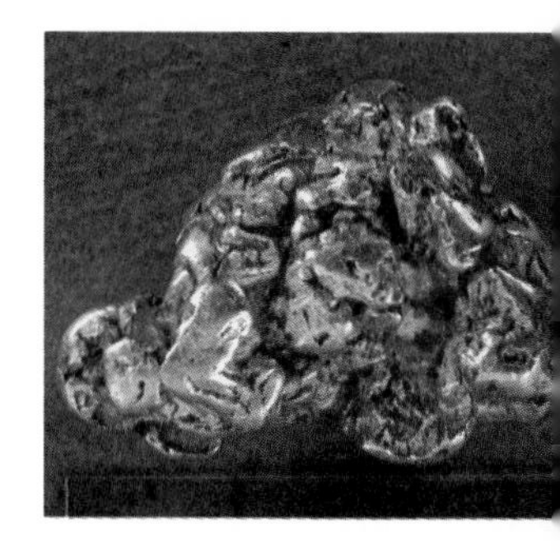

12: 0, 12, 24, 36, 48, . . .

16: 0, 16, 32, 48, 64, . . .

The first two common multiples of 12 and 16 are 0 and 48. What is the next one?

The least nonzero common multiple is called the **least common multiple** (LCM) of the numbers. The LCM of 12 and 16 is 48.

Find the LCM of 6 and 15 using prime factorization.

Write the prime factorization of each number.

6 = 2 × 3
15 = 3 × 5

The LCM contains each factor the greatest number of times it appears in any of the prime factorizations.

The LCM of 6 and 15 is 2 × 3 × 5 or 30.

EXERCISES ***Find the LCM for each group of numbers.***

31. multiples of 6: 0, 6, 12, 18, 24, . . .
multiples of 9: 0, 9, 18, 27, 36, . . .

32. multiples of 4: 0, 4, 8, 12, 16, . . .
multiples of 8: 0, 8, 16, 24, 32, . . .
multiples of 16: 0, 16, 32, 48, 64, . . .

33. 8 = 2 × 2 × 2
12 = 2 × 2 × 3

34. 20 = 2 × 2 × 5
12 = 2 × 2 × 3

35. 5 = 5
10 = 2 × 5
15 = 3 × 5

36. 2, 4 **37.** 3, 6 **38.** 3, 4 **39.** 6, 10

40. 9, 12 **41.** 14, 21 **42.** 36, 9 **43.** 4, 9

44. 4, 10 **45.** 25, 30 **46.** 35, 12 **47.** 21, 28

48. 2, 3, 5 **49.** 2, 4, 10 **50.** 8, 3, 4 **51.** 10, 20, 30

52. What is the LCM of two relatively prime numbers?

WHAT'S MY NUMBER?

Find the least number divisible by 1, 2, 3, 4, 5, 6, 7, 8, and 9.

3–4 Problem Solving: Using Factors and Multiples

A scale has 8-gram metal weights on one side and 6-gram metal weights on the other. Find the least number of each kind of weight needed in order to balance the scale.

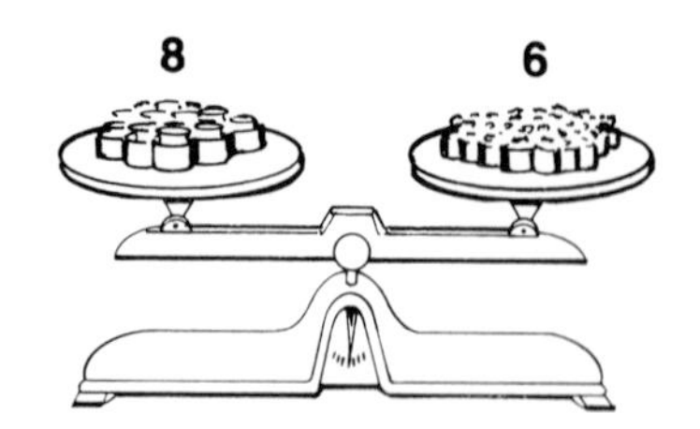

Read the problem. You have to find the least number of weights needed on each side so that the scale balances. You know the mass of each kind of metal weight.

Decide what to do. You can list multiples to find possible masses on each side of the scale. For each common multiple, the scale will balance. The LCM will help you find the *least* number of weights.

Solve the problem. List the nonzero multiples of 6 and 8 to find the LCM.

	6×1	6×2	6×3	6×4	6×5	6×6	6×7
6:	6,	12,	18,	24,	30,	36,	42, . . .

	8×1	8×2	8×3	8×4	8×5	8×6	8×7
8:	8,	16,	24,	32,	40,	48,	56, . . .

The LCM of 6 and 8 is 24. So, the scale will balance with three 8-gram weights on one side and four 6-gram weights on the other. Name two other combinations that will balance.

Examine the solution. It is reasonable that there be more of the smaller weights. The answer is correct since 6×4 and 8×3 both equal 24.

Solve.

1. The math club uses the computer every fourth school day. The computer club uses it every other school day. The last time the clubs used the computer the same day was Monday, April 5. Find all days and dates in April when both clubs use the computer.

APRIL

Sun.	Mon.	Tues.	Wed.	Thurs.	Fri.	Sat.
				1	2	3
4	5	6	7	8	9	10
11	12	13	14	15	16	17
18	19	20	21	22	23	24
25	26	27	28	29	30	

2. Lance has two pieces of cloth. One is 68 inches wide and the other is 84 inches wide. Find the width of the widest strips that each piece can be cut into with nothing left over. (Hint: Use factors.)

3. A softball team needs 10 players and a volleyball team needs 6. The same number of players are in each sport. How many softball and volleyball teams are there?

4. The choir has a concert every other month beginning in October. The band has a concert every third month beginning in September. During which months will both the choir and band have a concert?

5. Jeannie has the same amount of money in each of nickels, dimes, and quarters. What is the least number of each type of coin possible (besides zero)? How much in dollars and cents are the nickels, dimes, and quarters worth?

6. The Science Department replaces slides every 2 years, petrie dishes every 3 years, and microscopes every 4 years. They last replaced all these supplies in 1980. During what year will the department again have to replace *all* these supplies?

7. There are 140, 126, and 154 students in each of three classes. Separate each class into groups having the same number in each group with no students left out. All groups are the same size. What size groups are possible? How many groups are there for each size group?

Skills Review: Pages 63-69

State all the factors of each number.

1. 6 **2.** 23 **3.** 60

Use exponents to express the prime factorization of each of the following.

4. 35 **5.** 175

Find the GCF for each group of numbers.

6. 15, 10 **7.** 8, 10, 12

Find the LCM for each group of numbers.

8. 5, 8 **9.** 27, 9, 3

Solve.

10. The geology club meets every third school day. The biology club meets every fourth school day. The last time the clubs met on the same day was Tuesday, October 22. Find the next day and date both clubs will meet.

Cumulative Review

Replace each ▒ with <, >, or = to make a true sentence.

1. 7.6 ▒ 7.1 **2.** 6.049 ▒ 6.05 **3.** 0.35 ▒ 0.335

Round each of the following to the underlined place-value position.

4. $\$3,\underline{5}62$ **5.** $0.\underline{3}2$ **6.** $0.0\underline{3}4$ **7.** $\$\underline{1}8.45$

Estimate.

8. $\begin{array}{r} 3,120 \\ -\ 1,963 \\ \hline \end{array}$ **9.** $\begin{array}{r} \$34.67 \\ +\ \ 21.10 \\ \hline \end{array}$ **10.** $\begin{array}{r} 7.8 \\ \times\ \ 7 \\ \hline \end{array}$ **11.** $\begin{array}{r} 32.4 \\ \times\ 31.6 \\ \hline \end{array}$ **12.** $79.1\overline{)569.4}$

Add, subtract, multiply, or divide.

13. $\begin{array}{r} 4,672 \\ +\ \ \ 284 \\ \hline \end{array}$ **14.** $\begin{array}{r} 15,638 \\ +\ \ 5,766 \\ \hline \end{array}$ **15.** $\begin{array}{r} 8.6 \\ +\ 0.7 \\ \hline \end{array}$ **16.** $\begin{array}{r} 713 \\ -\ \ 48 \\ \hline \end{array}$ **17.** $\begin{array}{r} 7,500 \\ -\ 3,452 \\ \hline \end{array}$

18. $\begin{array}{r} 4,030 \\ -\ 2,987 \\ \hline \end{array}$ **19.** $\begin{array}{r} \$4.31 \\ -\ \ 0.47 \\ \hline \end{array}$ **20.** $\begin{array}{r} 3.52 \\ -\ 1.6 \\ \hline \end{array}$ **21.** $\begin{array}{r} 7.005 \\ +\ 4.31 \\ \hline \end{array}$ **22.** $\begin{array}{r} 12.36 \\ +\ \ 8.077 \\ \hline \end{array}$

23. 0.575 + 0.38 **24.** 18 − 3.058 **25.** 21.006 − 8.34

26. 89,427 + 326,050 + 119,890 **27.** $4.75 + $3.02 + $11 + $6.14

28. $\begin{array}{r} 308 \\ \times\ \ \ 7 \\ \hline \end{array}$ **29.** $\begin{array}{r} \$4.06 \\ \times\ \ \ \ \ 8 \\ \hline \end{array}$ **30.** $\begin{array}{r} 6.9 \\ \times\ 0.9 \\ \hline \end{array}$ **31.** $\begin{array}{r} 703 \\ \times\ \ 37 \\ \hline \end{array}$ **32.** $\begin{array}{r} 5.508 \\ \times\ \ \ \ 16 \\ \hline \end{array}$

33. $\begin{array}{r} 0.72 \\ \times\ 0.35 \\ \hline \end{array}$ **34.** $\begin{array}{r} 0.014 \\ \times\ \ 0.73 \\ \hline \end{array}$ **35.** $\begin{array}{r} 0.484 \\ \times\ \ \ 2.3 \\ \hline \end{array}$ **36.** $\begin{array}{r} \$0.08 \\ \times\ \ \ 4.5 \\ \hline \end{array}$ **37.** $\begin{array}{r} 72.86 \\ \times\ \ 3.05 \\ \hline \end{array}$

38. $17\overline{)1,343}$ **39.** $4\overline{)\$8.08}$ **40.** $6\overline{)81}$ **41.** $8\overline{)\$40.56}$

42. $7\overline{)0.161}$ **43.** $28\overline{)6,552}$ **44.** $37\overline{)3,996}$ **45.** $0.9\overline{)5.85}$

46. $16\overline{)16.92}$ **47.** $0.47\overline{)2.5004}$ **48.** $80\overline{)60}$ **49.** $33\overline{)2.277}$

50. $1.9\overline{)106.4}$ **51.** $24.1\overline{)1,446}$ **52.** $9.8\overline{)51.94}$ **53.** $0.64\overline{)4.288}$

54. $12.34 × 13 **55.** 4.9 × 0.023 **56.** $365 ÷ 5

Find the greatest common factor (GCF) for each group of numbers.

57. 24, 9 **58.** 18, 12 **59.** 15, 8 **60.** 12, 18, 20

Find the least common multiple (LCM) for each group of numbers.

61. 3, 2 **62.** 8, 16 **63.** 10, 4 **64.** 4, 6, 5

Solve.

65. Janet Guthrie drove a lap at the Indianapolis 500 in 47 seconds. One lap is 13,200 feet. Find the speed to the nearest tenth of a foot per second.

66. Calhoun county in Alabama has a population of 116,936 and an area of 611 square miles. Estimate the population per square mile.

67. After three tests, Lacy has an 86 average. What score must she receive on a fourth test in order to have an average of at least 88?

68. Mrs. Devine pays $1.34 a gallon for gasoline. Her car tank holds 14.5 gallons. Her car gets 27 miles per gallon. Can she drive for 400 miles on one tank of gasoline?

Mathematics Lab

Figurate numbers are numbers whose geometric representations form figures such as triangles and squares.

Triangular Numbers

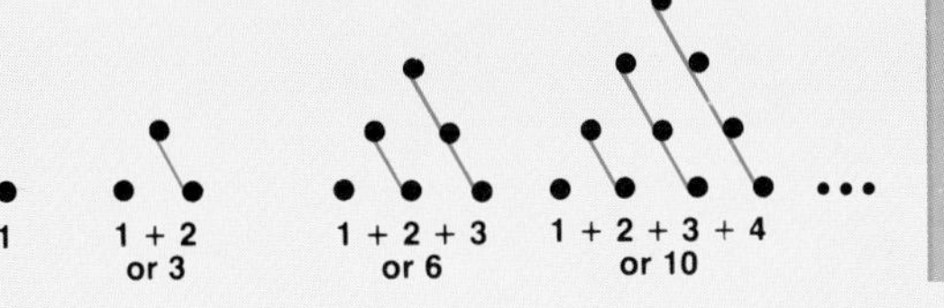

Square numbers

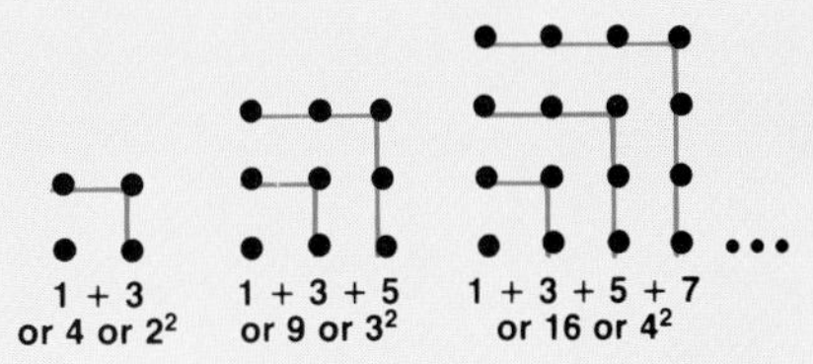

Complete the following.

1. Draw geometric representations and then list the fifth through the tenth triangular numbers.
2. Draw geometric representations and then list the fifth through the tenth square numbers.
3. Show geometrically and with numbers that the sum of two consecutive triangular numbers is a square number.

3–5 Equivalent Fractions and Simplest Form

During July, Phoenix usually gets about $\frac{3}{5}$ of an inch of rain. The number lines below show that the fractions $\frac{3}{5}$ and $\frac{6}{10}$ name the same number. Fractions that name the same number are **equivalent.**

$\frac{3}{5} = \frac{6}{10}$ ← numerator
← denominator

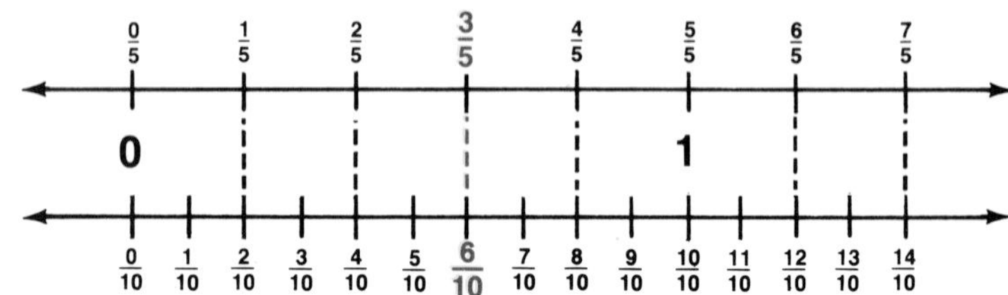

Multiplying or dividing the numerator and denominator of a fraction by the same *nonzero* number gives an equivalent fraction.

$\frac{3}{5} = \frac{6}{10}$ (×2 numerator, ×2 denominator) $\frac{6}{10} = \frac{3}{5}$ (÷2 numerator, ÷2 denominator)

Explain how the shaded regions show that $\frac{3}{5}$ and $\frac{6}{10}$ are equivalent.

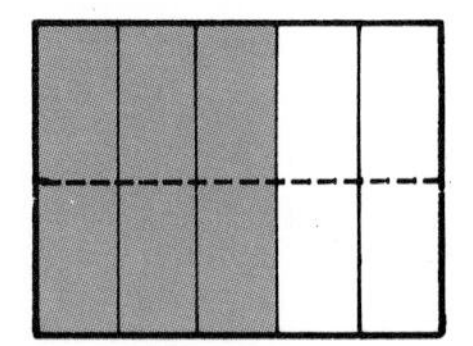

EXERCISES ***Write a pair of equivalent fractions for each of the following.***

1. 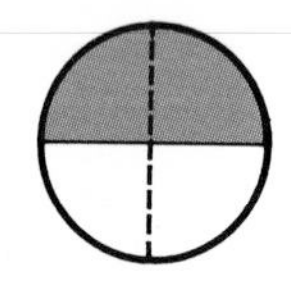
2. 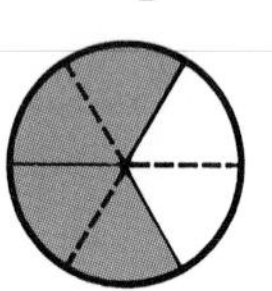
3. 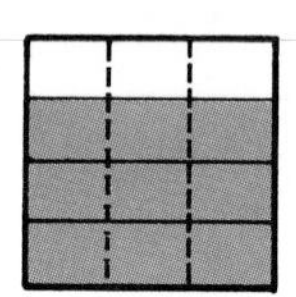
4. 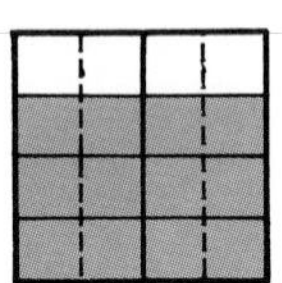

Copy. Then complete the following.

5. $\frac{1 \times 3}{2 \times 3} = \frac{▒}{6}$
6. $\frac{4 \times 2}{4 \times 2} = \frac{▒}{8}$
7. $\frac{4 \times 4}{5 \times 4} = \frac{16}{▒}$
8. $\frac{12 \div ▒}{3 \div 3} = \frac{4}{1}$
9. $\frac{8 \div ▒}{12 \div ▒} = \frac{▒}{3}$
10. $\frac{16 \div ▒}{64 \div ▒} = \frac{1}{▒}$

Replace each ▒ with a number so that the fractions are equivalent.

11. $\frac{2}{5} = \frac{▒}{10}$
12. $\frac{8}{3} = \frac{▒}{9}$
13. $\frac{7}{9} = \frac{14}{▒}$
14. $\frac{8}{15} = \frac{24}{▒}$
15. $\frac{2}{4} = \frac{▒}{2}$
16. $\frac{12}{6} = \frac{▒}{3}$
17. $\frac{20}{24} = \frac{5}{▒}$
18. $\frac{14}{10} = \frac{7}{▒}$

Find three fractions equivalent to each of the following.

19. $\frac{1}{2}$
20. $\frac{2}{3}$
21. $\frac{5}{4}$
22. $\frac{4}{12}$
23. $\frac{24}{36}$
24. $\frac{40}{15}$

A fraction is in **simplest form** when the greatest common factor (GCF) of the numerator and denominator is 1. Follow these steps to write $\frac{60}{160}$ in simplest form.

- Find the GCF of 60 and 160. The GCF is $2 \times 2 \times 5$ or 20.

$$60 = 2 \times 2 \times 3 \times 5$$
$$160 = 2 \times 2 \times 2 \times 2 \times 2 \times 5$$

- Divide 60 and 160 by the GCF.

$$\frac{60}{160} = \frac{3}{8} \quad (\div 20)$$

Explain why $\frac{3}{8}$ is in simplest form.

To write a fraction in simplest form, divide both the numerator and the denominator by their GCF.

EXERCISES ***Write each fraction in simplest form.***

You can write fractions in simplest form as follows.

The GCF of 15 and 18 is 3. $\frac{\not{15}^{\,5}}{\not{18}_{\,6}} = \frac{5}{6}$

The GCF of 20 and 5 is 5. $\frac{\not{20}^{\,4}}{\not{5}_{\,1}} = \frac{4}{1}$ or 4

25. $\frac{6}{8}$ **26.** $\frac{9}{12}$ **27.** $\frac{12}{15}$ **28.** $\frac{16}{14}$ **29.** $\frac{6}{12}$ **30.** $\frac{8}{16}$

31. $\frac{27}{9}$ **32.** $\frac{36}{6}$ **33.** $\frac{12}{18}$ **34.** $\frac{10}{12}$ **35.** $\frac{21}{28}$ **36.** $\frac{12}{16}$

37. $\frac{18}{20}$ **38.** $\frac{20}{32}$ **39.** $\frac{25}{15}$ **40.** $\frac{20}{30}$ **41.** $\frac{25}{40}$ **42.** $\frac{27}{45}$

43. $\frac{36}{64}$ **44.** $\frac{84}{63}$ **45.** $\frac{35}{90}$

Solve. Write fractions in simplest form.

46. Mr. Taylor works 10 months each year. What fraction of a year does he work?

47. Miss Prifogle is on vacation 12 days in June. What fraction of the month is she on vacation?

48. Calvin plays tennis for 75 minutes. What fraction of an hour is this?

3-6 Mixed Numerals

Suppose it snows 8 inches in 5 days. The improper fraction $\frac{8}{5}$ is the average daily snowfall. The numerator of an **improper fraction** is greater than or equal to the denominator. The numerator of a **proper fraction** is less than the denominator.

A **mixed numeral** indicates the sum of a whole number and a fraction. The figures below show that $\frac{8}{5}$ and the mixed numeral $1\frac{3}{5}$ have the same value.

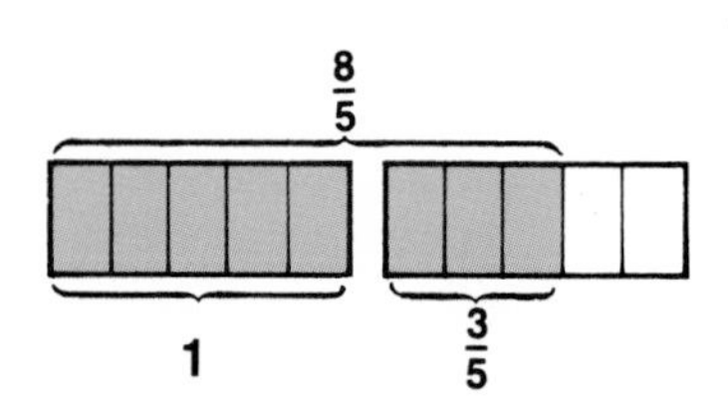

The mixed numeral $1\frac{3}{5}$ means $1 + \frac{3}{5}$.

Read $1\frac{3}{5}$ as *one and three fifths.*

Since a fraction means to divide, $\frac{8}{5}$ means $8 \div 5$.

$$\frac{8}{5} \Rightarrow \begin{array}{r} 1\frac{3}{5} \\ 5\overline{)8} \\ -5 \\ \hline 3 \end{array}$$

Express the remainder as a fraction.

To change an improper fraction to a mixed numeral, divide the numerator by the denominator. Write the remainder as a fraction.

EXERCISES ***Change each fraction to a mixed numeral in simplest form.***

$$\frac{38}{4} \Rightarrow 4\overline{)38} \quad 9\frac{2}{4} = 9\frac{1}{2}$$

A mixed numeral is in simplest form when the fraction part is a proper fraction in simplest form.

1. $\frac{5}{4}$	**2.** $\frac{10}{7}$	**3.** $\frac{9}{5}$	**4.** $\frac{3}{2}$	**5.** $\frac{10}{3}$	**6.** $\frac{7}{6}$
7. $\frac{10}{4}$	**8.** $\frac{12}{8}$	**9.** $\frac{8}{6}$	**10.** $\frac{14}{8}$	**11.** $\frac{9}{6}$	**12.** $\frac{15}{9}$
13. $\frac{15}{10}$	**14.** $\frac{18}{12}$	**15.** $\frac{16}{6}$	**16.** $\frac{18}{4}$	**17.** $\frac{27}{12}$	**18.** $\frac{24}{15}$

The figures at the right show that the fraction $\frac{7}{2}$ and the mixed numeral $3\frac{1}{2}$ are equivalent. You can change any mixed numeral to an improper fraction.

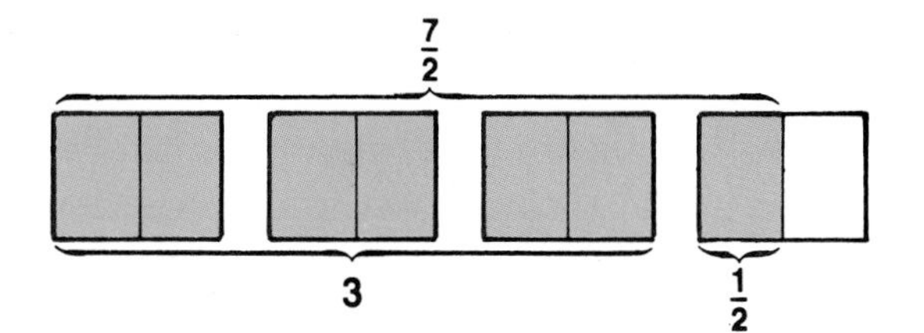

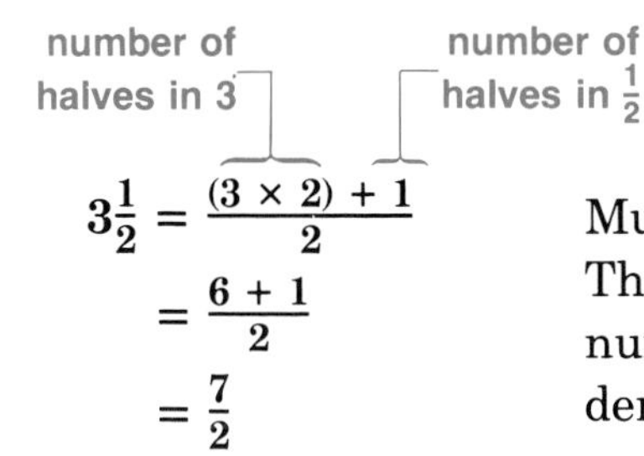

$$3\frac{1}{2} = \frac{(3 \times 2) + 1}{2} = \frac{6 + 1}{2} = \frac{7}{2}$$

Multiply the whole number by the denominator. Then add the numerator. This result is the numerator of the improper fraction. The denominator remains the same.

EXERCISES ***Change each mixed numeral to an improper fraction.***

19. $1\frac{1}{2}$	**20.** $1\frac{1}{4}$	**21.** $2\frac{1}{3}$	**22.** $3\frac{1}{5}$	**23.** $1\frac{5}{6}$	**24.** $1\frac{2}{7}$
25. $2\frac{3}{4}$	**26.** $5\frac{4}{9}$	**27.** $3\frac{2}{3}$	**28.** $7\frac{1}{6}$	**29.** $4\frac{5}{8}$	**30.** $6\frac{4}{5}$
31. $10\frac{3}{8}$	**32.** $12\frac{1}{2}$	**33.** $6\frac{7}{10}$	**34.** $5\frac{5}{12}$	**35.** $11\frac{1}{10}$	**36.** $15\frac{11}{12}$

Solve. Express each result as a mixed numeral in simplest form.

37. How many gallons are there in 25 quarts?

38. How many tons are there in 7,000 pounds?

39. How many feet are there in 75 inches?

40. How many yards are there in 1,000 feet?

41. How many hours are there in 90 minutes?

42. How many minutes are there in 220 seconds?

43. How many days are there in 100 hours?

44. How many weeks are there in a leap year?

ONE THIRD

Find the value as a fraction, of the first six terms of the following sequence. Describe your results.

$$\frac{1}{3}, \frac{1 + 3}{5 + 7}, \frac{1 + 3 + 5}{7 + 9 + 11}, \frac{1 + 3 + 5 + 7}{9 + 11 + 13 + 15}, \ldots$$

3-7 Fractions, Mixed Numerals, and Decimals.

North Dakota produces about $\frac{1}{8}$ of the wheat grown in the United States. The fraction $\frac{1}{8}$ can be changed to a decimal by dividing 1 by 8.

$$\frac{1}{8} \Rightarrow \begin{array}{r} 0.125 \\ 8\overline{)1.000} \\ \underline{-8} \\ 20 \\ \underline{-16} \\ 40 \\ \underline{-40} \\ 0 \end{array}$$

remainder of 0

The fraction $\frac{1}{8}$ changed to a decimal is 0.125. Such a decimal is called a **terminating decimal.** The division ends or terminates because the last remainder is 0.

To change $3\frac{2}{11}$ to a decimal, divide 2 by 11. Then, add 3 to the quotient. In this quotient, the digits 1 and 8 repeat. Such a decimal is called a **repeating decimal.** Write a repeating decimal with a bar placed over the digits that repeat.

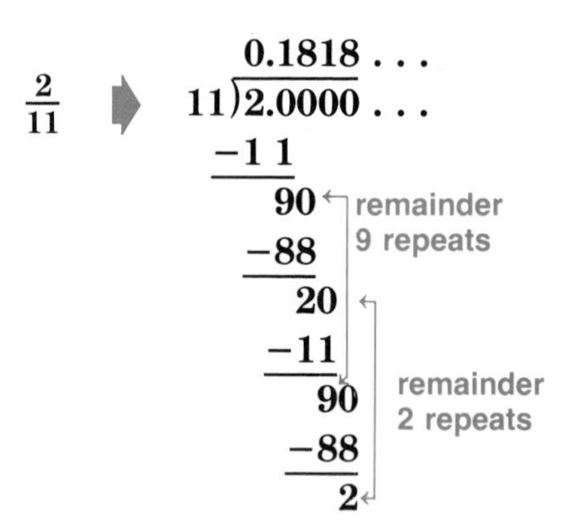

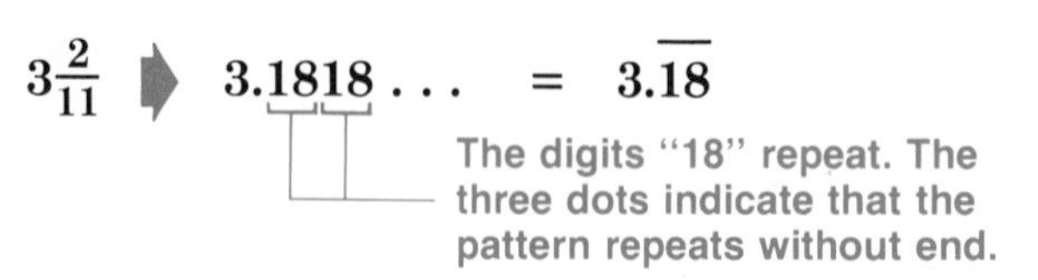

EXERCISES ***Write terminating (T) or repeating (R) for each decimal quotient. Express each repeating decimal using bar notation.***

1. 0.75 **2.** 0.375 **3.** 0.444 . . . **4.** 0.333 . . .

5. 0.272727 . . . **6.** 5.7272 . . . **7.** 4.5625 **8.** 1.83333 . . .

Change each fraction or mixed numeral to a terminating or repeating decimal. Use bar notation for repeating decimals.

9. $\frac{1}{4}$ **10.** $\frac{2}{3}$ **11.** $\frac{3}{5}$ **12.** $\frac{1}{6}$ **13.** $\frac{7}{9}$ **14.** $\frac{11}{10}$

15. $\frac{6}{11}$ **16.** $\frac{11}{15}$ **17.** $\frac{15}{8}$ **18.** $\frac{17}{20}$ **19.** $\frac{5}{9}$ **20.** $1\frac{13}{25}$

21. $\frac{23}{18}$ **22.** $\frac{22}{45}$ **23.** $3\frac{21}{40}$ **24.** $6\frac{5}{12}$ **25.** $\frac{39}{16}$ **26.** $\frac{109}{30}$

State whether each of the following is true or false.

27. $\frac{7}{8} = 0.875$ **28.** $\frac{15}{4} = 3.\overline{7}$ **29.** $\frac{5}{13} = 0.\overline{38}$ **30.** $2\frac{1}{12} = 2.08\overline{3}$

You can change terminating decimals to fractions or mixed numerals.

$0.6 = \frac{\overset{3}{\cancel{6}}}{\underset{5}{\cancel{10}}}$ The GCF of 6 and 10 is 2.

$= \frac{3}{5}$

$0.175 = \frac{\overset{7}{\cancel{175}}}{\underset{40}{\cancel{1,000}}}$ The GCF is 25.

$= \frac{7}{40}$

$3.16 = 3\frac{\overset{4}{\cancel{16}}}{\underset{25}{\cancel{100}}}$ The GCF is 4.

$= 3\frac{4}{25}$

EXERCISES ***Copy and complete.***

31. $0.23 = \frac{▒}{100}$ **32.** $4.9 = 4\frac{▒}{10}$ **33.** $0.077 = \frac{77}{▒}$ **34.** $0.50 = \frac{▒}{100} = \frac{▒}{2}$

Change each decimal to a fraction or mixed numeral in simplest form.

35. 0.33 **36.** 0.69 **37.** 0.97
38. 0.75 **39.** 0.20 **40.** 0.55
41. 0.05 **42.** 0.6 **43.** 0.08
44. 0.15 **45.** 0.36 **46.** 0.88
47. 0.875 **48.** 0.250 **49.** 0.625
50. 0.065 **51.** 0.735 **52.** 0.005
53. 0.437 **54.** 0.034 **55.** 1.10
56. 1.25 **57.** 1.9 **58.** 1.06
59. 1.14 **60.** 2.08 **61.** 3.125
62. 4.050 **63.** 3.375 **64.** 4.018

65. Copy and complete.

Fraction	$\frac{3}{2}$	$\frac{17}{8}$	$\frac{21}{5}$	?	?	?	?	?	?
Mixed Numeral	?	?	?	$3\frac{3}{4}$	$9\frac{1}{2}$	$7\frac{5}{8}$	?	?	?
Decimal	?	?	?	?	?	?	18.8	8.375	7.18

SEVENTHS

Change $\frac{1}{7}$, $\frac{2}{7}$, $\frac{3}{7}$, $\frac{4}{7}$, $\frac{5}{7}$, and $\frac{6}{7}$ to repeating decimals. What pattern do you notice about the repeating digits in each quotient?

3–8 Comparing and Ordering Fractions and Mixed Numerals.

Africa makes up about $\frac{5}{25}$ of the land area of the world. North America makes up about $\frac{4}{25}$ of the land area. To find which continent has the greater area, compare $\frac{5}{25}$ and $\frac{4}{25}$.

To compare fractions with the same denominator, compare numerators.

Since $5 > 4$ it follows that $\frac{5}{25} > \frac{4}{25}$. So, Africa has the greater area.

To compare fractions with different denominators, compare equivalent fractions that have the same denominator. The **least common denominator** (LCD) is the LCM of the denominators. Compare $\frac{4}{9}$ and $\frac{7}{15}$.

Use prime factorization to find the LCD.

$9 = 3 \times 3$

$15 = 3 \times 5$

LCD: $3 \times 3 \times 5$ or 45

Rename each fraction using the LCD.

$\frac{4}{9} = \frac{20}{45}$ (× 5) $\quad \frac{7}{15} = \frac{21}{45}$ (× 3)

The denominators are the same. Since $20 < 21$, it follows that $\frac{20}{45} < \frac{21}{45}$.

So, $\frac{4}{9} < \frac{7}{15}$.

EXERCISES Replace each ▒ with a number so that the fractions are equivalent.

1. $\frac{1}{2} = \frac{▒}{8}$ 2. $\frac{1}{3} = \frac{▒}{9}$ 3. $\frac{3}{4} = \frac{▒}{12}$ 4. $\frac{7}{4} = \frac{▒}{8}$ 5. $\frac{3}{5} = \frac{▒}{15}$

6. $\frac{3}{4} = \frac{▒}{20}$ 7. $\frac{8}{3} = \frac{▒}{9}$ 8. $\frac{7}{10} = \frac{▒}{30}$ 9. $\frac{8}{9} = \frac{▒}{27}$ 10. $\frac{9}{11} = \frac{▒}{33}$

Find the LCD for each of the following pairs of fractions. Then rename each fraction using the LCD.

11. $\frac{1}{4}, \frac{2}{5}$ 12. $\frac{7}{3}, \frac{7}{5}$ 13. $\frac{5}{2}, \frac{21}{8}$ 14. $\frac{3}{4}, \frac{2}{3}$ 15. $\frac{3}{8}, \frac{4}{15}$

16. $\frac{4}{9}, \frac{6}{7}$ 17. $\frac{9}{20}, \frac{7}{15}$ 18. $\frac{17}{12}, \frac{19}{15}$ 19. $\frac{3}{8}, \frac{7}{10}$ 20. $\frac{7}{12}, \frac{2}{9}$

Replace each ▒ with <, >, or = to make a true sentence.

> Compare the whole number part of a mixed numeral first. If the whole numbers are equal, compare the fraction part.
>
> Since $4 > 3$, it follows that $4\frac{3}{4} > 3\frac{7}{8}$.
>
> Since $\frac{5}{16} < \frac{7}{16}$, it follows that $2\frac{5}{16} < 2\frac{7}{16}$.

21. $\frac{3}{5}$ ▒ $\frac{4}{5}$ **22.** $\frac{9}{10}$ ▒ $\frac{7}{10}$ **23.** $6\frac{5}{8}$ ▒ $7\frac{11}{16}$ **24.** $2\frac{7}{9}$ ▒ $2\frac{4}{9}$

25. $\frac{1}{3}$ ▒ $\frac{1}{6}$ **26.** $\frac{3}{2}$ ▒ $\frac{6}{4}$ **27.** $\frac{2}{5}$ ▒ $\frac{3}{10}$ **28.** $1\frac{4}{9}$ ▒ $1\frac{1}{3}$

29. $\frac{5}{6}$ ▒ $\frac{11}{12}$ **30.** $4\frac{1}{2}$ ▒ $4\frac{2}{4}$ **31.** $\frac{3}{2}$ ▒ $\frac{5}{3}$ **32.** $\frac{1}{5}$ ▒ $\frac{1}{4}$

33. $2\frac{3}{6}$ ▒ $2\frac{7}{15}$ **34.** $\frac{5}{9}$ ▒ $\frac{7}{12}$ **35.** $\frac{11}{15}$ ▒ $\frac{33}{45}$ **36.** $\frac{13}{9}$ ▒ $\frac{17}{12}$

Order the fractions or mixed numerals in each list from greatest to least.

> You can order the fractions $\frac{2}{3}, \frac{3}{4}, \frac{3}{5}$, and $\frac{5}{8}$ by using equivalent fractions or decimals. Respectively, the equivalent decimals are $0.\overline{6}$, 0.75, 0.6, and 0.625. From greatest to least, the order is as follows.
>
> decimals: **0.75, $0.\overline{6}$, 0.625, 0.6** fractions: $\mathbf{\frac{3}{4}, \frac{2}{3}, \frac{5}{8}, \frac{3}{5}}$

37. $\frac{1}{2}, \frac{3}{5}, \frac{11}{20}, \frac{7}{10}$ **38.** $\frac{8}{3}, \frac{12}{5}, \frac{19}{8}, \frac{11}{4}$ **39.** $2\frac{5}{6}, 2\frac{7}{8}, 2\frac{3}{4}, 1\frac{2}{3}$

40. $\frac{1}{3}, \frac{1}{2}, \frac{3}{10}, \frac{2}{5}, \frac{1}{4}, \frac{3}{8}, \frac{3}{5}, \frac{5}{12}$ **41.** $3\frac{8}{9}, 2\frac{3}{5}, 2\frac{5}{6}, 2\frac{9}{10}, 3\frac{2}{3}, 2\frac{3}{4}, 2\frac{11}{12}$

Skills Review: Pages 72-79

Write each fraction in simplest form.

1. $\frac{10}{12}$ **2.** $\frac{12}{20}$ **3.** $\frac{65}{100}$

Change each fraction to a mixed numeral in simplest form.

4. $\frac{11}{9}$ **5.** $\frac{24}{10}$ **6.** $\frac{64}{12}$

Change each decimal to a fraction or mixed numeral in simplest form.

7. 0.025 **8.** 4.84

Replace each ▒ with <, >, or = to make a true sentence.

9. $\frac{9}{10}$ ▒ $\frac{18}{20}$ **10.** $4\frac{5}{7}$ ▒ $4\frac{9}{13}$

Mathematics and Consumers

Allison Blank plans a trip to Boston from Cleveland. Her car averages 30 miles per gallon (mpg).

She finds the total cost of gasoline for the trip as follows. She figures the cost of gasoline at $1.40 a gallon and uses the mileage chart.

The distance from Cleveland to Boston is 628 miles.

	Boston	Cleveland	Des Moines	Kansas City	Phoenix	Washington, D.C.
Boston		628	1,280	1,391	2,604	429
Cleveland	628		652	779	1,992	346
Des Moines	1,280	652		195	1,409	984
Kansas City	1,391	779	195		1,214	1,043
Phoenix	2,604	1,992	1,409	1,214		2,256
Washington,D.C.	429	346	984	1,043	2,256	

gallons of gasoline used $= \frac{628}{30}$ ➧ $30\overline{)628.0}$ = 20.9

To the nearest gallon, Mrs. Blank's car will use 21 gallons of gasoline.

cost of gasoline $= 21 \times \$1.40$ ➧ $\$1.40 \times 21 = \$29.40$

To the nearest dollar, the cost of gasoline will be $29.

Solve.

1. Nancy Valdez budgets $20 for gasoline, $3.50 for tolls, and $10 for food for a one way trip of 250 miles. What is the round trip cost?

2. Dolores Alesi does not want to drive more than 10 hours a day. She averages 50 miles an hour. Can she drive from Des Moines to Boston in three days?

3. David Wang plans to drive round trip from Kansas City to Washington, D.C. His car gets 26 mpg. Gasoline costs $1.35 a gallon. How much should he budget for gasoline?

4. Julie Grange has $115 to spend on gasoline for a trip from Phoenix to Washington, D.C. Gasoline costs range between $1.29 and $1.45 a gallon. Her car gets 35 mpg. Does she have enough money for gas?

5. The roundtrip airfare from Cleveland to Kansas City is $340. The company Kim Francis works for pays 24¢ a mile for employees who drive their own car while on business as long as the mileage is *less* than the airfare. Can Miss Francis drive or must she fly on the trip from Cleveland to Kansas City and back? Explain your answer.

Chapter 3 Review

VOCABULARY

prime number (64)
factor tree (65)
(LCM) (67)
mixed numerals (74)
repeating decimal (76)
factor (63)
composite number (64)
(GCF) (66)
equivalent fractions (72)
divisible (63)
prime factorization (65)
multiples (67)
simplest form (73)
terminating decimal (76)
(LCD) (78)

EXERCISES ***State all the factors of each number. (63)***

1. 13 **2.** 25 **3.** 45 **4.** 102 **5.** 110 **6.** 150

Use exponents to express the prime factorization of each of the following. (65)

7. 9 **8.** 28 **9.** 85 **10.** 115 **11.** 196

Find the GCF for each group of numbers. Then find the LCM. (66-67)

12. 2, 5 **13.** 6, 12 **14.** 8, 12 **15.** 5, 10, 20

Solve. (68)

16. Carlos has a mathematics test every third school day. He has a science test every fifth school day. The last day he had both tests was Friday, January 5. Find the next day and date he will have both tests.

Write each fraction in simplest form. (73)

17. $\frac{24}{36}$ **18.** $\frac{25}{30}$ **19.** $\frac{125}{50}$ **20.** $\frac{27}{81}$ **21.** $\frac{65}{130}$

Change each fraction to a mixed numeral in simplest form. (74)

22. $\frac{8}{5}$ **23.** $\frac{27}{2}$ **24.** $\frac{30}{4}$ **25.** $\frac{28}{6}$ **26.** $\frac{54}{8}$

Change each fraction or mixed number to a terminating or repeating decimal. Use bar notation for repeating decimals. (76)

27. $\frac{3}{8}$ **28.** $\frac{1}{6}$ **29.** $\frac{31}{5}$ **30.** $7\frac{1}{3}$ **31.** $3\frac{2}{9}$

Replace each ▒ with <, >, or = to make a true sentence. (79)

32. $\frac{6}{2}$ ▒ $\frac{12}{4}$ **33.** $2\frac{2}{3}$ ▒ $4\frac{1}{3}$ **34.** $\frac{3}{4}$ ▒ $\frac{2}{3}$ **35.** $\frac{4}{3}$ ▒ $\frac{5}{4}$

Chapter 3 Test

State all the factors of each number.

1. 12 **2.** 35 **3.** 51 **4.** 68 **5.** 39 **6.** 108

State prime, composite, or neither for each of the following.

7. 4 **8.** 2 **9.** 0 **10.** 39 **11.** 19 **12.** 67

Use exponents to express the prime factorization of each of the following.

13. 16 **14.** 35 **15.** 78 **16.** 6 **17.** 325

Find the GCF for each group of numbers. Then find the LCM for each group of numbers.

18. 4, 5 **19.** 8, 10 **20.** 7, 21 **21.** 9, 12, 15

Solve.

22. One poster is 36 inches wide and another is 48 inches wide. Find the width of the widest strip that each poster can be cut into with nothing left over.

Write each fraction in simplest form.

23. $\frac{5}{15}$ **24.** $\frac{8}{12}$ **25.** $\frac{9}{21}$ **26.** $\frac{10}{25}$ **27.** $\frac{18}{30}$

Change each fraction to a mixed numeral in simplest form.

28. $\frac{7}{3}$ **29.** $\frac{19}{2}$ **30.** $\frac{42}{8}$ **31.** $\frac{18}{5}$ **32.** $\frac{96}{10}$

Change each fraction or mixed numeral to a terminating or repeating decimal. Use bar notation for repeating decimals.

33. $\frac{15}{12}$ **34.** $\frac{17}{40}$ **35.** $\frac{4}{9}$ **36.** $\frac{17}{3}$ **37.** $6\frac{4}{15}$

Change each decimal to a fraction or mixed numeral in simplest form.

38. 0.36 **39.** 2.18 **40.** 0.410 **41.** 0.825 **42.** 4.095

Replace each ▒ with <, >, or = to make a true sentence.

43. $\frac{1}{4}$ ▒ $\frac{3}{8}$ **44.** $\frac{12}{7}$ ▒ $\frac{5}{3}$ **45.** $6\frac{6}{7}$ ▒ $6\frac{12}{14}$ **46.** $2\frac{9}{16}$ ▒ $2\frac{13}{24}$

Enrichment

The Greek mathematician Euclid wrote about numbers and divisibility in *The Elements*. He gave a method for finding the GCF of groups of numbers. This method is now called the **Euclidean Algorithm.** This algorithm works as follows.

Find the GCF of 30 and 145.

Divide the greater number by the lesser number.

Divide the lesser number by the remainder.

Continue dividing the divisor by the remainder until you get a remainder of 0. The last nonzero remainder is the GCF.

The GCF of 30 and 145 is 5, the last nonzero remainder. Check this using prime factorization.

You can use the GCF to find the least common multiple (LCM). The LCM of 30 and 145 is 870. Check this using prime factorization.

$$\text{LCM of 30 and 145} = \frac{\mathbf{30 \times 145}}{\textbf{GCF of 30 and 145}} = \frac{\mathbf{4{,}350}}{\mathbf{5}} \textbf{ or 870}$$

EXERCISES ***Use the Euclidean Algorithm to find the GCF of each pair of numbers. Then, use the GCF to find the LCM of each pair of numbers.***

1. 9, 75 **2.** 16, 108 **3.** 81, 315 **4.** 110, 63

5. 456, 759 **6.** 136, 232 **7.** 567, 432 **8.** 975, 364

9. Which pair of numbers in exercises 1–8 are relatively prime (GCF of 1)?

Find the GCF of each group of numbers. Use the Euclidean Algorithm with any two numbers. Then apply the algorithm again with the third number and the GCF of the first two.

10. 72, 90, 96 **11.** 312, 468, 1,012 **12.** 714, 2,030, 2,205

Skills Test, Chapter 1-3

Standardized Format

Directions: Work each problem on your own paper. Choose the letter of the correct answer. If the correct answer is not given, choose the letter for *none of the above*. Make no marks in this book.

1. How would you read 47?

- **a** four sevens
- **b** four and seven
- **c** forty-seven
- **d** *none of the above*

2. Which sentence is true?

- **e** $1.8 > 18$
- **f** $1.8 < 1.9$
- **g** $1.80 = 1.08$
- **h** *none of the above*

3. Round 83.84 to the nearest tenth.

- **a** 80
- **b** 83.9
- **c** 84
- **d** *none of the above*

4. Which of the following is another way to express $6 \times 6 \times 6 \times 6$?

- **e** 6^4
- **f** 4×6
- **g** 4^6
- **h** *none of the above*

5. Estimate.

70.4×38.6

- **a** 2,100
- **b** 2,800
- **c** 28,000
- **d** *none of the above*

6. Add.

$87{,}816 + 4{,}207$

- **e** 91,103
- **f** 92,023
- **g** 92,013
- **h** *none of the above*

7. Add.

$$\begin{array}{r} \$87.85 \\ 16.14 \\ 14.06 \\ +\ 9.28 \\ \hline \end{array}$$

- **a** $127.33
- **b** $126.33
- **c** $116.33
- **d** *none of the above*

8. Subtract.

$$\begin{array}{r} 16{,}018 \\ -\ 2{,}749 \\ \hline \end{array}$$

- **e** 13,351
- **f** 14,359
- **g** 13,459
- **h** *none of the above*

9. Subtract.

$12.1 - 9.63$

- **a** 2.42
- **b** 2.47
- **c** 2.57
- **d** *none of the above*

10. Multiply.

805×26

- **e** 6,440
- **f** 6,530
- **g** 20,930
- **h** *none of the above*

11. Multiply.

$$\begin{array}{r} 9.86 \\ \times\ 0.7 \\ \hline \end{array}$$

- **a** 6.902
- **b** 69.02
- **c** 690.2
- **d** *none of the above*

12. Divide.

$186 \div 15$

- **e** 12
- **f** 120
- **g** 12 R6
- **h** *none of the above*

GO ON TO THE NEXT PAGE.

13. Divide.

$2.88 \div 8$

a 36

b 3.6

c 0.36

d *none of the above*

14. Which two decimals are equivalent to 0.1?

e 0.01 and 0.001

f 1.0 and 10

g 0.10 and 0.100

h *none of the above*

15. What is the prime factorization of 18?

a 2×9

b $2 \times 3 \times 5$

c $2 \times 3 \times 3$

d *none of the above*

16. What is the greatest common factor of 10 and 20?

e 10

f 5

g 2

h *none of the above*

17. What is the least common multiple of 6 and 10?

a 2

b 16

c 60

d *none of the above*

18. Which of the following is $\frac{12}{20}$ in simplest form?

e $\frac{3}{5}$

f $\frac{6}{10}$

g $\frac{1}{2}$

h *none of the above*

19. How many prime numbers are in the following list? 8, 10, 17, 21, 29, 49

a 1

b 2

c 3

d *none of the above*

20. The bar graph shows the number of televisions sold during a 4-day sale. How many more televisions were sold on Monday than on Tuesday?

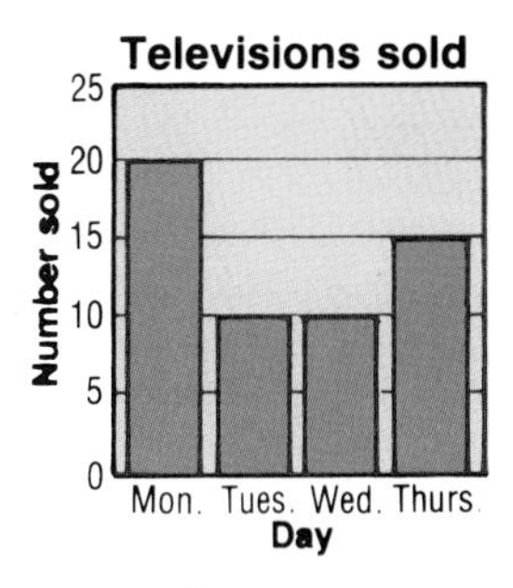

e 10

f 5

g 0

h *none of the above*

21. The school cafeteria sold 406 cartons of milk on Monday, 375 on Tuesday, 423 on Wednesday, 395 on Thursday, and 411 on Friday. What is the average number of cartons of milk sold during the five days?

a 402

b 420

c 2,005

d *none of the above*

22. For a home economics project, Steve buys 2.5 yards of material and two patterns. The material costs \$3.20 a yard and the patterns cost \$1.95 each. The tax on the material and patterns is \$0.48. Which of the following is true?

e The two patterns cost \$2.80.

f The total cost plus tax is \$12.38.

g The change from \$15 is \$2.52.

h *none of the above*

STOP.

4 Operations with Fractions and Mixed Numerals

During the spring, $\frac{3}{8}$ of a garden display is tulips. Another $\frac{1}{8}$ of the display is daffodils.

4-1 Addition of Fractions with Like Denominators

To find how much of the garden is made up of tulips and daffodils, add $\frac{3}{8}$ and $\frac{1}{8}$.

$\frac{3}{8} + \frac{1}{8} = \frac{3+1}{8}$ — The denominators are alike. Add the numerators. Write the sum over the like denominator.

$= \frac{\overset{1}{\cancel{4}}}{\underset{2}{\cancel{8}}}$ — The GCF of 4 and 8 is 4.

$= \frac{1}{2}$ — Tulips and daffodils make up $\frac{1}{2}$ of the garden.

EXERCISES Copy and complete.

1. $\frac{1}{5} + \frac{2}{5} = \frac{1+2}{5} = \frac{■}{5}$
2. $\frac{2}{7} + \frac{4}{7} = \frac{2+4}{7} = \frac{■}{7}$
3. $\frac{5}{9} + \frac{4}{9} = \frac{5+4}{9} = \frac{9}{9} = ■$

Add. Write each sum in simplest form.

4. $\frac{1}{9} + \frac{4}{9}$
5. $\frac{3}{5} + \frac{1}{5}$
6. $\frac{4}{11} + \frac{5}{11}$
7. $\frac{2}{7} + \frac{3}{7}$
8. $\frac{3}{4} + \frac{1}{4}$
9. $\frac{1}{6} + \frac{1}{6}$
10. $\frac{4}{9} + \frac{2}{9}$
11. $\frac{3}{10} + \frac{1}{10}$
12. $\frac{9}{10} + \frac{1}{10}$
13. $\frac{5}{12} + \frac{1}{12}$
14. $\frac{4}{15} + \frac{8}{15}$
15. $\frac{7}{11} + \frac{3}{11}$
16. $\frac{7}{20} + \frac{9}{20}$
17. $\frac{5}{16} + \frac{7}{16}$
18. $\frac{11}{24} + \frac{7}{24}$

Add. Write each sum as a mixed numeral in simplest form.

$\frac{3}{8} + \frac{7}{8} = \frac{10}{8}$ ➡ $8\overline{)10}$ gives $1\frac{2}{8}$ ➡ $1\frac{\overset{1}{\cancel{2}}}{\underset{4}{\cancel{8}}}$ or $1\frac{1}{4}$

19. $\frac{4}{7} + \frac{5}{7}$
20. $\frac{2}{5} + \frac{4}{5}$
21. $\frac{2}{3} + \frac{2}{3}$
22. $\frac{8}{15} + \frac{11}{15}$
23. $\frac{12}{13} + \frac{11}{13}$
24. $\frac{3}{4} + \frac{3}{4}$
25. $\frac{5}{8} + \frac{7}{8}$
26. $\frac{5}{9} + \frac{7}{9}$
27. $\frac{5}{12} + \frac{11}{12}$
28. $\frac{7}{18} + \frac{17}{18}$
29. $\frac{2}{5} + \frac{3}{5} + \frac{4}{5}$
30. $\frac{4}{15} + \frac{8}{15} + \frac{7}{15}$
31. $\frac{1}{8} + \frac{3}{8} + \frac{7}{8}$
32. $\frac{7}{12} + \frac{7}{12} + \frac{1}{12}$
33. $\frac{4}{9} + \frac{1}{9} + \frac{7}{9}$
34. $\frac{20}{21} + \frac{10}{21} + \frac{19}{21}$

4-2 Addition of Fractions with Different Denominators

Myron Cahill plants $\frac{1}{4}$ of his rose garden in red tea roses and another $\frac{1}{6}$ in yellow tea roses. To find the part of the garden he plants in tea roses, add $\frac{1}{4}$ and $\frac{1}{6}$.

$$\begin{array}{r} \frac{1}{4} \\ + \frac{1}{6} \\ \hline \end{array}$$

Find the LCD.

4 = 2 × 2
6 = 2 × 3
LCD: 2 × 2 × 3 or 12

Rename each fraction. Use the LCD.

$$\begin{array}{r} \frac{1}{4} = \frac{3}{12} \\ + \frac{1}{6} = \frac{2}{12} \\ \hline \end{array}$$

Add and simplify if necessary.

$$\begin{array}{r} \frac{1}{4} = \frac{3}{12} \\ + \frac{1}{6} = \frac{2}{12} \\ \hline \frac{5}{12} \end{array}$$

Tea roses are planted in $\frac{5}{12}$ of the rose garden.

EXERCISES Add. Write each sum in simplest form.

1. $\frac{1}{4} = \frac{5}{20}$, $+\frac{1}{10} = \frac{2}{20}$
2. $\frac{1}{5} = \frac{2}{10}$, $+\frac{3}{10} = \frac{3}{10}$
3. $\frac{1}{2} = \frac{3}{6}$, $+\frac{2}{6} = \frac{2}{6}$
4. $\frac{3}{4} = \frac{21}{28}$, $+\frac{1}{7} = \frac{4}{28}$

5. $\frac{3}{10} + \frac{1}{2}$
6. $\frac{2}{3} + \frac{2}{9}$
7. $\frac{1}{3} + \frac{1}{2}$

8. $\frac{1}{5} + \frac{1}{3}$
9. $\frac{2}{5} + \frac{3}{7}$
10. $\frac{5}{8} + \frac{2}{9}$
11. $\frac{1}{6} + \frac{4}{9}$
12. $\frac{3}{8} + \frac{5}{12}$
13. $\frac{5}{6} + \frac{1}{10}$
14. $\frac{5}{9} + \frac{4}{15}$
15. $\frac{5}{12} + \frac{3}{10}$

Rename each fraction as a mixed numeral in simplest form.

16. $\frac{8}{7}$
17. $\frac{7}{5}$
18. $\frac{13}{7}$
19. $\frac{6}{4}$
20. $\frac{10}{8}$
21. $\frac{12}{9}$

Sometimes the sum must be changed to a mixed numeral.

Find the LCD.

$$\begin{array}{r} \frac{7}{9} \\ + \frac{2}{3} \\ \hline \end{array}$$

9 = 3 × 3
3 = 3
LCD: 3 × 3 or 9

Rename.

$$\begin{array}{r} \frac{7}{9} = \frac{7}{9} \\ + \frac{2}{3} = \frac{6}{9} \\ \hline \end{array}$$

Add. Change the fraction to a mixed numeral.

$$\begin{array}{r} \frac{7}{9} = \frac{7}{9} \\ + \frac{2}{3} = \frac{6}{9} \\ \hline \frac{13}{9} = 1\frac{4}{9} \end{array}$$

Note: Since 9 is a multiple of 3, the LCD of 9 and 3 is 9.

EXERCISES ***Add. Write each sum in simplest form.***

22. $\frac{5}{6} + \frac{1}{2}$ **23.** $\frac{3}{4} + \frac{5}{8}$ **24.** $\frac{5}{9} + \frac{2}{3}$ **25.** $\frac{7}{12} + \frac{3}{4}$ **26.** $\frac{4}{7} + \frac{11}{14}$

27. $\frac{4}{5} + \frac{5}{6}$ **28.** $\frac{2}{3} + \frac{3}{4}$ **29.** $\frac{3}{4} + \frac{4}{9}$ **30.** $\frac{7}{8} + \frac{3}{5}$ **31.** $\frac{4}{7} + \frac{7}{9}$

32. $\frac{5}{6} + \frac{5}{8}$ **33.** $\frac{7}{8} + \frac{3}{10}$ **34.** $\frac{7}{9} + \frac{5}{6}$ **35.** $\frac{7}{8} + \frac{5}{12}$ **36.** $\frac{11}{12} + \frac{7}{8}$

37. $\frac{11}{15} + \frac{9}{10}$ **38.** $\frac{3}{10} + \frac{24}{25}$ **39.** $\frac{7}{12} + \frac{11}{18}$ **40.** $\frac{17}{20} + \frac{7}{15}$ **41.** $\frac{9}{16} + \frac{13}{24}$

42. $\frac{2}{5} + \frac{3}{10} + \frac{7}{10}$ **43.** $\frac{2}{3} + \frac{1}{12} + \frac{5}{12}$ **44.** $\frac{1}{2} + \frac{1}{3} + \frac{1}{4}$ **45.** $\frac{3}{4} + \frac{5}{8} + \frac{1}{6}$

46. $\frac{3}{7} + \frac{5}{14} + \frac{11}{28}$ **47.** $\frac{7}{12} + \frac{5}{6} + \frac{13}{24}$ **48.** $\frac{4}{7} + \frac{1}{3} + \frac{1}{4}$ **49.** $\frac{5}{6} + \frac{3}{5} + \frac{2}{9}$

Solve.

50. Phoenix has $\frac{3}{10}$ of the population of Arizona. Tucson has $\frac{3}{20}$ of the population. What part of the population of Arizona do these cities have?

51. Oklahoma City has $\frac{3}{20}$ of the population of Oklahoma. Tulsa has $\frac{3}{25}$ of the population. What part of the population of Oklahoma do these cities have?

52. Alex used $\frac{5}{8}$ of a cord of wood, then bought $\frac{1}{3}$ of a cord to replace it. Did he replace all of the wood that he used?

53. Angie earns $45.50. She saves $\frac{1}{5}$ of her earnings and spends $\frac{1}{6}$ for transportation. What fraction of her earnings has she used?

4–3 Addition with Mixed Numerals

Jennifer Peltier plants two sizes of marigolds. One marigold is $2\frac{3}{8}$ inches taller than the other. The shorter marigold is $3\frac{7}{8}$ inches tall.

To find the height of the taller marigold, add $2\frac{3}{8}$ and $3\frac{7}{8}$.

Add with mixed numerals as follows.

Add the fractions.

$$\begin{array}{r} 2\frac{3}{8} \\ +\,3\frac{7}{8} \\ \hline \frac{10}{8} \end{array}$$

Add the whole numbers.

$$\begin{array}{r} 2\frac{3}{8} \\ +\,3\frac{7}{8} \\ \hline 5\frac{10}{8} \end{array}$$

Rename and simplify.

$$\frac{10}{8} = 1\frac{2}{8} = 1\frac{1}{4}$$

$$5 + 1\frac{1}{4} = 6\frac{1}{4}$$

$$\begin{array}{r} 2\frac{3}{8} \\ +\,3\frac{7}{8} \\ \hline 5\frac{10}{8} = 6\frac{1}{4} \end{array}$$

The taller marigold is $6\frac{1}{4}$ inches tall.

EXERCISES **Rename each mixed numeral.**

$$5\frac{12}{10} = 5 + \frac{12}{10} = 5 + 1\frac{2}{10} = 5 + 1\frac{1}{5} = 6\frac{1}{5}$$

1. $3\frac{4}{3}$ **2.** $6\frac{8}{5}$ **3.** $5\frac{11}{7}$

4. $4\frac{12}{8}$ **5.** $8\frac{8}{6}$ **6.** $12\frac{16}{10}$

Add. Write each sum in simplest form.

7. $4\frac{1}{3} + 5\frac{1}{3}$ **8.** $6\frac{1}{5} + 7\frac{2}{5}$ **9.** $9\frac{3}{8} + 5\frac{1}{8}$ **10.** $8\frac{2}{9} + 7\frac{4}{9}$

11. $14\frac{5}{9} + 7$ **12.** $9\frac{7}{8} + 13$ **13.** $6\frac{1}{4} + 8\frac{3}{4}$ **14.** $12\frac{9}{10} + 7\frac{1}{10}$

15. $11\frac{3}{5} + 13\frac{4}{5}$ **16.** $15\frac{3}{10} + 12\frac{9}{10}$ **17.** $16\frac{5}{8} + 15\frac{7}{8}$ **18.** $23\frac{5}{9} + 17\frac{8}{9}$

19. $3\frac{1}{5} + 8 + 4\frac{2}{5}$ **20.** $2\frac{3}{7} + 1\frac{1}{7} + 5\frac{3}{7}$ **21.** $6\frac{4}{9} + 7\frac{7}{9} + 9\frac{4}{9}$

Add $9\frac{3}{10}$ and $5\frac{1}{5}$. Note that the denominators are unlike.

Find the LCD.

$$\begin{array}{r} 9\frac{3}{10} \\ +\ 5\frac{1}{5} \\ \hline \end{array}$$

The LCD of 10 and 5 is 10. Explain.

Rename the fraction.

$$\begin{array}{rcl} 9\frac{3}{10} & = & 9\frac{3}{10} \\ +\ 5\frac{1}{5} & = & 5\frac{2}{10} \\ \hline \end{array}$$

Add and simplify.

$$\begin{array}{rcl} 9\frac{3}{10} & = & 9\frac{3}{10} \\ +\ 5\frac{1}{5} & = & 5\frac{2}{10} \\ \hline & & 14\frac{5}{10} = 14\frac{1}{2} \end{array}$$

EXERCISES ***Add. Write each sum in simplest form.***

22. $\begin{array}{rcl} 4\frac{1}{4} & = & 4\frac{1}{4} \\ +\ 6\frac{1}{2} & = & 6\frac{2}{4} \\ \hline \end{array}$

23. $\begin{array}{rcl} 8\frac{3}{4} & = & 8\frac{9}{12} \\ +\ 7\frac{1}{6} & = & 7\frac{\square}{12} \\ \hline \end{array}$

24. $\begin{array}{rcl} 8\frac{1}{2} & = & 8\frac{\square}{4} \\ +\ 6\frac{3}{4} & = & 6\frac{\square}{4} \\ \hline \end{array}$

25. $\begin{array}{rcl} 21\frac{1}{3} & = & 21\frac{\square}{12} \\ +\ 6\frac{3}{4} & = & 6\frac{\square}{12} \\ \hline \end{array}$

26. $5\frac{1}{6} + 7\frac{1}{3}$

27. $10\frac{1}{3} + 6\frac{1}{4}$

28. $8\frac{3}{8} + 9\frac{1}{6}$

29. $11\frac{1}{3} + 5\frac{2}{5}$

30. $12\frac{1}{10} + 7\frac{5}{6}$

31. $13\frac{4}{9} + 8\frac{1}{6}$

32. $14\frac{3}{10} + 10\frac{2}{5}$

33. $15\frac{2}{3} + 14\frac{2}{7}$

34. $17\frac{3}{8} + 21\frac{3}{10}$

35. $8\frac{5}{12} + 23\frac{3}{8}$

36. $13\frac{1}{6} + 26\frac{7}{15}$

37. $33\frac{9}{20} + 18\frac{2}{15}$

38. $11\frac{3}{4} + 8\frac{2}{3}$

39. $16\frac{1}{2} + 14\frac{5}{7}$

40. $15\frac{1}{2} + 9\frac{4}{5}$

41. $18\frac{7}{8} + 15\frac{5}{8}$

42. $17\frac{5}{6} + 7\frac{7}{9}$

43. $16\frac{4}{7} + 23\frac{9}{14}$

44. $26\frac{3}{4} + 19\frac{3}{5}$

45. $31\frac{7}{12} + 15\frac{5}{8}$

46. $24\frac{3}{4} + 35\frac{11}{16}$

47. $27\frac{2}{5} + 36\frac{17}{20}$

48. $42\frac{3}{10} + 31\frac{11}{15}$

49. $36\frac{5}{9} + 45\frac{10}{21}$

50. $12\frac{1}{6} + 3\frac{1}{2} + 4\frac{1}{3}$

51. $7\frac{5}{12} + 16\frac{2}{9} + 4\frac{5}{6}$

52. $33\frac{2}{3} + 8\frac{4}{5} + 21\frac{9}{10}$

Solve. Use the diagram.

53. How thick is the insulation and the drywall?

54. How thick are the outside layers of the wall including the wall sheathing and siding?

55. How thick is the entire wall?

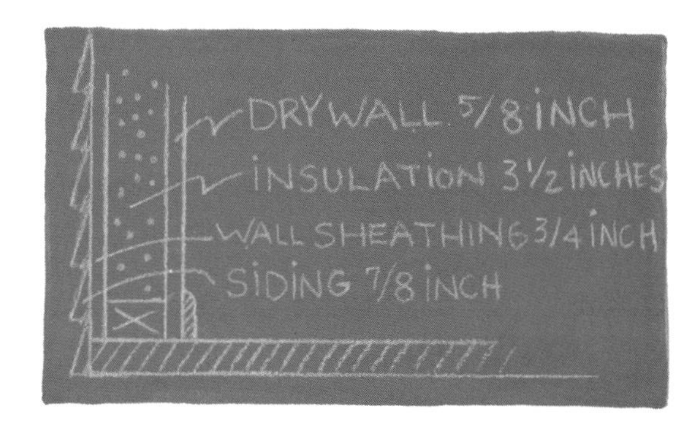

4-4 Subtraction of Fractions

Mike O'Reilly mows grass for $\frac{3}{4}$ of an hour and pulls weeds for $\frac{1}{4}$ of an hour. To find how much more time he spends mowing than weeding, subtract $\frac{1}{4}$ from $\frac{3}{4}$.

$\frac{3}{4} - \frac{1}{4} = \frac{3-1}{4}$ The denominators are alike. Subtract the numerators. Write the difference over the like denominator.

$= \frac{\cancel{2}^{1}}{\cancel{4}_{2}}$ The GCF of 2 and 4 is 2.

$= \frac{1}{2}$ Mike mows grass for $\frac{1}{2}$ hour more than he pulls weeds.

Subtract $\frac{3}{5}$ from $\frac{5}{6}$. These fractions have *unlike* denominators. So, subtract equivalent fractions with a like denominator.

$$\begin{array}{r} \frac{5}{6} \\ -\frac{3}{5} \\ \hline \end{array}$$

Find the LCD.

6 = ② × ③
5 = ⑤

LCD: 2 × 3 × 5 or 30.
Note: The GCF of 6 and 5 is 1.
So the LCD is 6 × 5 or 30.

Rename each fraction.

$$\begin{array}{rcl} \frac{5}{6} & = & \frac{25}{30} \\ -\frac{3}{5} & = & \frac{18}{30} \\ \hline \end{array}$$

Subtract and simplify if necessary.

$$\begin{array}{rcl} \frac{5}{6} & = & \frac{25}{30} \\ -\frac{3}{5} & = & \frac{18}{30} \\ \hline & & \frac{7}{30} \end{array}$$

EXERCISES ***Copy and complete.***

1. $\frac{2}{3} - \frac{1}{3} = \frac{2-1}{3} = \frac{▩}{3}$
2. $\frac{5}{7} - \frac{3}{7} = \frac{5-3}{7} = \frac{▩}{7}$
3. $\frac{4}{5} - \frac{2}{5} = \frac{▩}{5}$

Subtract. Write each difference in simplest form.

4. $\frac{4}{5} - \frac{2}{5}$
5. $\frac{5}{6} - \frac{4}{6}$
6. $\frac{6}{7} - \frac{3}{7}$
7. $\frac{9}{10} - \frac{6}{10}$
8. $\frac{9}{11} - \frac{3}{11}$
9. $\frac{11}{15} - \frac{4}{15}$
10. $\frac{7}{10} - \frac{3}{10}$
11. $\frac{5}{6} - \frac{1}{6}$
12. $\frac{7}{8} - \frac{1}{8}$
13. $\frac{9}{10} - \frac{3}{10}$
14. $\frac{10}{11} - \frac{7}{11}$
15. $\frac{5}{8} - \frac{1}{8}$
16. $\frac{9}{16} - \frac{7}{16}$
17. $\frac{13}{15} - \frac{4}{15}$
18. $\frac{11}{16} - \frac{7}{16}$
19. $\frac{17}{20} - \frac{7}{20}$
20. $\frac{11}{12} - \frac{1}{12}$
21. $\frac{13}{18} - \frac{5}{18}$
22. $\frac{11}{24} - \frac{5}{24}$
23. $\frac{23}{30} - \frac{7}{30}$

24. $\frac{3}{4} = \frac{3}{4}$
$-\frac{1}{2} = \frac{2}{4}$

25. $\frac{5}{6} = \frac{10}{12}$
$-\frac{3}{4} = \frac{9}{12}$

26. $\frac{5}{6} = \frac{\blacksquare}{18}$
$-\frac{4}{9} = \frac{\blacksquare}{18}$

27. $\frac{4}{5} = \frac{\blacksquare}{10}$
$-\frac{1}{2} = \frac{\blacksquare}{10}$

28. $\frac{5}{5} - \frac{1}{3}$
29. $\frac{9}{10} - \frac{2}{5}$
30. $\frac{7}{8} - \frac{1}{4}$
31. $\frac{8}{9} - \frac{1}{3}$
32. $\frac{9}{20} - \frac{1}{4}$

33. $\frac{5}{6} - \frac{3}{8}$
34. $\frac{7}{10} - \frac{3}{8}$
35. $\frac{8}{9} - \frac{5}{12}$
36. $\frac{11}{12} - \frac{7}{10}$
37. $\frac{6}{7} - \frac{1}{2}$

38. $\frac{3}{4} - \frac{3}{7}$
39. $\frac{13}{15} - \frac{3}{5}$
40. $\frac{11}{12} - \frac{1}{6}$
41. $\frac{17}{20} - \frac{7}{10}$
42. $\frac{8}{9} - \frac{5}{6}$

43. $\frac{13}{15} - \frac{7}{10}$
44. $\frac{7}{9} - \frac{5}{12}$
45. $\frac{8}{9} - \frac{11}{15}$
46. $\frac{17}{20} - \frac{3}{5}$
47. $\frac{11}{12} - \frac{7}{15}$

Add and subtract. Write each answer in simplest form.

$$\left(\frac{1}{10} + \frac{2}{5}\right) - \frac{3}{10} = \left(\frac{1}{10} + \frac{4}{10}\right) - \frac{3}{10}$$
$$= \frac{5}{10} - \frac{3}{10} = \frac{2}{10} \text{ or } \frac{1}{5}$$

48. $\left(\frac{7}{9} - \frac{1}{3}\right) + \frac{2}{9}$
49. $\left(\frac{5}{12} + \frac{1}{4}\right) - \frac{1}{12}$

50. $\left(\frac{3}{8} + \frac{3}{4}\right) - \frac{7}{16}$
51. $\frac{14}{15} - \left(\frac{1}{3} + \frac{1}{5}\right)$

52. $\frac{4}{18} + \left(\frac{8}{9} - \frac{1}{6}\right)$
53. $\frac{17}{20} + \left(\frac{9}{10} - \frac{3}{5}\right)$

MAGIC SQUARES

Copy and complete each magic square. Name the magic sum.

1.

?	?	$\frac{8}{11}$
$\frac{9}{11}$	$\frac{5}{11}$	$\frac{1}{11}$
?	?	$\frac{6}{11}$

2.

$\frac{4}{5}$	$\frac{1}{10}$	?
$\frac{3}{10}$	?	?
$\frac{2}{5}$	?	?

3.

$\frac{9}{10}$	?	?	$\frac{3}{4}$
$\frac{7}{20}$	$\frac{13}{20}$	?	$\frac{1}{2}$
$\frac{11}{20}$	?	$\frac{2}{5}$	?
?	?	$\frac{17}{20}$	$\frac{3}{20}$

4-5 Subtraction with Mixed Numerals.

A park ranger takes a group of campers on a $5\frac{1}{2}$-mile hike. After hiking $2\frac{1}{3}$ miles, the ranger subtracts $2\frac{1}{3}$ from $5\frac{1}{2}$ to find the distance left to hike.

Find the LCD.

$$\begin{array}{r} 5\frac{1}{2} \\ -2\frac{1}{3} \\ \hline \end{array}$$

Rename each fraction.

$$\begin{array}{rcl} 5\frac{1}{2} & = & 5\frac{3}{6} \\ -\ 2\frac{1}{3} & = & 2\frac{2}{6} \\ \hline \end{array}$$

Subtract and simplify if necessary.

$$\begin{array}{rcl} 5\frac{1}{2} & = & 5\frac{3}{6} \\ -\ 2\frac{1}{3} & = & 2\frac{2}{6} \\ \hline & & 3\frac{1}{6} \end{array}$$

The campers have to hike another $3\frac{1}{6}$ miles.

EXERCISES Subtract. Write each difference in simplest form.

1. $\begin{array}{rcl} 4\frac{5}{8} & = & 4\frac{5}{8} \\ -\ 2\frac{1}{4} & = & 2\frac{2}{8} \\ \hline \end{array}$

2. $\begin{array}{rcl} 8\frac{5}{6} & = & 8\frac{5}{6} \\ -\ 4\frac{2}{3} & = & 4\frac{4}{6} \\ \hline \end{array}$

3. $\begin{array}{rcl} 10\frac{11}{12} & = & 10\frac{\square}{12} \\ -\ 6\frac{3}{4} & = & 6\frac{\square}{12} \\ \hline \end{array}$

4. $\begin{array}{rcl} 9\frac{4}{9} & = & 9\frac{\square}{18} \\ -\ 5\frac{1}{6} & = & 5\frac{\square}{18} \\ \hline \end{array}$

5. $7\frac{5}{7} - 4\frac{3}{7}$

6. $10\frac{8}{9} - 5\frac{4}{9}$

7. $9\frac{7}{9} - 3\frac{4}{9}$

8. $12\frac{9}{10} - 5\frac{3}{10}$

9. $15\frac{7}{8} - 9\frac{3}{8}$

10. $19\frac{5}{6} - 12\frac{1}{6}$

11. $4\frac{7}{10} - 3\frac{2}{5}$

12. $13\frac{7}{10} - 6\frac{1}{4}$

13. $17\frac{11}{12} - 13\frac{1}{6}$

14. $19\frac{15}{16} - 7\frac{3}{4}$

15. $18\frac{7}{8} - 13$

16. $21\frac{1}{4} - 16$

17. $8\frac{9}{10} - 7\frac{3}{8}$

18. $14\frac{11}{12} - 12\frac{7}{15}$

19. $4\frac{2}{3} - 1\frac{1}{3}$

20. $5\frac{4}{5} - 2\frac{4}{5}$

21. $25\frac{5}{6} - 16\frac{3}{8}$

22. $22\frac{11}{12} - 14\frac{2}{9}$

23. $27\frac{3}{4} - 14\frac{2}{3}$

24. $33\frac{9}{10} - 23\frac{2}{3}$

Subtract $2\frac{3}{4}$ from $5\frac{1}{4}$. Since $\frac{3}{4} > \frac{1}{4}$, rename $5\frac{1}{4}$ as $4\frac{5}{4}$.

$$\begin{array}{r} 5\frac{1}{4} \\ -\ 2\frac{3}{4} \\ \hline \end{array}$$

Rename.

$$5\frac{1}{4} = 4 + 1\frac{1}{4} = 4 + \frac{4}{4} + \frac{1}{4} = 4 + \frac{5}{4} \text{ or } 4\frac{5}{4}$$

$$\begin{array}{rcl} 5\frac{1}{4} & = & 4\frac{5}{4} \\ -\ 2\frac{3}{4} & = & 2\frac{3}{4} \\ \hline \end{array}$$

Subtract.

$$\begin{array}{rcl} 5\frac{1}{4} & = & 4\frac{5}{4} \\ -\ 2\frac{3}{4} & = & 2\frac{3}{4} \\ \hline & & 2\frac{2}{4} = 2\frac{1}{2} \end{array}$$

EXERCISES **Rename.**

25. $4 = 3\frac{\square}{5}$ **26.** $10 = 9\frac{\square}{8}$ **27.** $5\frac{1}{2} = 4\frac{\square}{2}$ **28.** $2\frac{3}{5} = 1\frac{\square}{5}$

29. $3\frac{1}{3} = 3\frac{2}{6} = 2\frac{\square}{6}$ **30.** $6\frac{3}{4} = 6\frac{6}{8} = 5\frac{\square}{8}$ **31.** $9\frac{7}{10} = 9\frac{14}{20} = 8\frac{\square}{20}$

Subtract. Write each difference in simplest form.

32. $\begin{array}{rcl} 8 & = & 7\frac{4}{4} \\ -\ 3\frac{3}{4} & = & 3\frac{3}{4} \\ \hline \end{array}$ **33.** $\begin{array}{rcl} 9\frac{2}{9} & = & 8\frac{\square}{9} \\ -\ 6\frac{4}{9} & = & 6\frac{4}{9} \\ \hline \end{array}$ **34.** $\begin{array}{rcccl} 10\frac{3}{10} & = & 10\frac{6}{20} & = & 9\frac{\square}{20} \\ -\ 5\frac{3}{4} & = & 5\frac{15}{20} & = & 5\frac{15}{20} \\ \hline \end{array}$

35. $\begin{array}{r} 8\frac{2}{5} \\ -\ 4\frac{4}{5} \\ \hline \end{array}$ **36.** $\begin{array}{r} 10\frac{2}{7} \\ -\ 9\frac{5}{7} \\ \hline \end{array}$ **37.** $\begin{array}{r} 9\frac{3}{10} \\ -\ 2\frac{7}{10} \\ \hline \end{array}$ **38.** $\begin{array}{r} 11 \\ -\ 3\frac{5}{9} \\ \hline \end{array}$ **39.** $\begin{array}{r} 9 \\ -\ 3\frac{3}{5} \\ \hline \end{array}$

40. $12\frac{1}{2} - 8\frac{2}{3}$ **41.** $14\frac{5}{8} - 6\frac{5}{6}$ **42.** $16\frac{2}{5} - 13\frac{3}{4}$ **43.** $13\frac{4}{15} - 12\frac{3}{5}$

44. $17\frac{1}{3} - 9\frac{1}{2}$ **45.** $22\frac{2}{5} - 15\frac{2}{3}$ **46.** $14 - 8\frac{3}{8}$ **47.** $24\frac{3}{8} - 19\frac{5}{6}$

48. $32\frac{5}{9} - 24\frac{5}{6}$ **49.** $16\frac{3}{10} - 9\frac{9}{10}$ **50.** $28\frac{9}{14} - 19\frac{6}{7}$ **51.** $38\frac{3}{5} - 26\frac{11}{15}$

52. $30\frac{1}{5} - 28\frac{3}{4}$ **53.** $17\frac{2}{5} - 16\frac{5}{6}$ **54.** $47\frac{2}{9} - 34\frac{4}{7}$ **55.** $64\frac{3}{10} - 41\frac{9}{14}$

Solve.

56. Renee Jones buys a stock at $25\frac{3}{8}$ points (dollars). The stock goes up to $28\frac{1}{4}$ points. Find the number of points the stock increased.

57. A certain stock is at $48\frac{1}{4}$ points. Find the value of the stock after it goes up $1\frac{3}{4}$ points and then goes down $2\frac{5}{8}$ points.

4-6 Problem Solving: Using Fractions

Jayme Haines painted $\frac{1}{3}$ of a fence in the morning. She painted another $\frac{1}{4}$ of the fence after softball practice. What part of the fence does she still have to paint?

Read the problem. You need to find the unpainted part of the fence. You know the fraction painted in the morning and after practice.

Decide what to do.

Step 1 Add the fraction for the part painted in the morning and the fraction for the part painted after practice.

Step 2 Subtract the sum (in step 1) from 1. Explain.

Solve the problem.

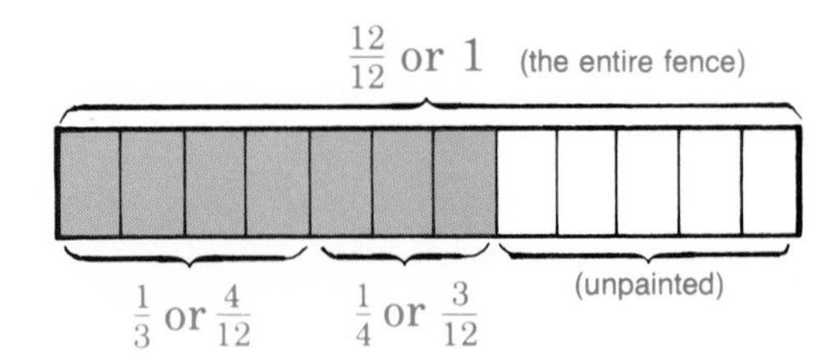

Step 1

$$\frac{1}{3} = \frac{4}{12}$$
$$+\frac{1}{4} = \frac{3}{12}$$
$$\frac{7}{12}$$

Step 2

$$1 = \frac{12}{12}$$
$$-\frac{7}{12} = \frac{7}{12}$$
$$\frac{5}{12}$$

Jayme still has to paint $\frac{5}{12}$ of the fence.

Examine the solution. Since $\frac{5}{12} + \frac{7}{12} = \frac{12}{12}$ or 1, all of the fence (represented by 1) is either painted or unpainted. Also note that the unpainted part of the fence is $\frac{5}{12}$ according to the diagram.

Solve.

1. One-third of the marigolds are light yellow and $\frac{1}{2}$ are deep gold. What fraction of the marigolds are other colors?

2. Bill Harris had $6\frac{1}{2}$ gallons of spray in a tank. He uses $3\frac{7}{8}$ gallon. How many gallons remain in the tank?

3. Pat did $\frac{2}{5}$ of her homework before dinner and $\frac{3}{5}$ after dinner. Does she have her homework completed for the next day?

4. A carpenter cuts $2\frac{1}{2}$-foot and $6\frac{3}{4}$-foot pieces from a 12-foot board. How many feet have been cut from the board all together?

5. John reads $\frac{2}{5}$ of a book on Sunday and $\frac{2}{7}$ of the book on Monday. How much of the book does he still have to read?

6. Mr. Sams buys 5 pounds of ground beef. He uses $2\frac{1}{4}$ pounds for hamburgers and $1\frac{1}{2}$ pounds for spaghetti. How many pounds of ground beef did he use?

7. Maura's first high jump was $57\frac{3}{4}$ inches. Her second jump was 60 inches. How much did she improve?

Solve. Use the chart.

8. Sipe works an additional $4\frac{1}{2}$ hours. Find the total hours worked.

9. How many more hours than McKenna has Postel worked?

10. How many more hours do the four volunteers need to work in order to reach 100 hours?

Hospital Volunteers	Hours Worked
McKenna	$18\frac{1}{2}$
O'Neal	21
Sipe	$17\frac{3}{4}$
Postel	$24\frac{1}{4}$

Skills Review: Pages 87-97

Add or subtract. Write each sum or difference in simplest form.

1. $\frac{1}{4} + \frac{1}{4}$
2. $\frac{1}{5} + \frac{4}{5}$
3. $\frac{3}{4} + \frac{4}{5}$
4. $2\frac{4}{11} + 3\frac{5}{11}$
5. $3\frac{7}{9} + 6\frac{5}{9}$
6. $13\frac{5}{16} + 8\frac{3}{8}$
7. $12\frac{4}{5} + 17\frac{7}{10}$
8. $23\frac{2}{3} + 17\frac{4}{5}$
9. $\frac{7}{8} - \frac{3}{8}$
10. $\frac{7}{9} - \frac{1}{3}$
11. $\frac{11}{12} - \frac{3}{8}$
12. $12 - 5\frac{3}{7}$
13. $10\frac{3}{8} - 4$
14. $23\frac{9}{10} - 16\frac{2}{5}$
15. $24\frac{7}{10} - 15\frac{9}{10}$
16. $21\frac{4}{9} - 17\frac{11}{12}$

Solve.

17. Mexico City had $\frac{7}{10}$ inch of rain in April and $\frac{3}{10}$ inch in February. How much more did it rain in April than in February?

18. A certain stock was sold at $29\frac{7}{8}$ points. The value of the stock went up $2\frac{5}{8}$ points. Find the new value of the stock.

Cumulative Review

Estimate.

1. $\begin{array}{r} 73.7 \\ -\ 10.9 \\ \hline \end{array}$
2. $\begin{array}{r} \$25.98 \\ +\ 13.20 \\ \hline \end{array}$
3. $\begin{array}{r} 8.6 \\ \times\ 9 \\ \hline \end{array}$
4. $\begin{array}{r} 78.3 \\ \times\ 47.1 \\ \hline \end{array}$
5. $6.4\overline{)25.1}$

Add or subtract.

6. $\begin{array}{r} 2,369 \\ +\ 490 \\ \hline \end{array}$
7. $\begin{array}{r} \$16,458 \\ +\ 7,956 \\ \hline \end{array}$
8. $\begin{array}{r} 802 \\ -\ 347 \\ \hline \end{array}$
9. $\begin{array}{r} 0.76 \\ -\ 0.684 \\ \hline \end{array}$
10. $\begin{array}{r} 0.267 \\ +\ 8.03 \\ \hline \end{array}$

11. $0.75 + 0.9$
12. $\$20.56 - \$9.87$
13. $15 - 3.036$
14. $\$16 + \$8.35 + 76¢$
15. $4.37 + 2.7 + 10.7 + 0.08$

Multiply or divide.

16. $\begin{array}{r} 506 \\ \times\ 47 \\ \hline \end{array}$
17. $\begin{array}{r} 503 \\ \times\ 480 \\ \hline \end{array}$
18. $\begin{array}{r} 9.6 \\ \times\ 0.8 \\ \hline \end{array}$
19. $\begin{array}{r} \$17.35 \\ \times\ 14 \\ \hline \end{array}$
20. $\begin{array}{r} 358 \\ \times\ 3.7 \\ \hline \end{array}$

21. $\begin{array}{r} 6.904 \\ \times\ 25 \\ \hline \end{array}$
22. $\begin{array}{r} 12.9 \\ \times\ 5.6 \\ \hline \end{array}$
23. $\begin{array}{r} 0.46 \\ \times\ 0.39 \\ \hline \end{array}$
24. $\begin{array}{r} 0.716 \\ \times\ 6.2 \\ \hline \end{array}$
25. $\begin{array}{r} 0.815 \\ \times\ 0.47 \\ \hline \end{array}$

26. $18\overline{)1,008}$
27. $75\overline{)19,200}$
28. $7\overline{)86.8}$
29. $53\overline{)3.816}$

30. $0.6\overline{)4.38}$
31. $5.6\overline{)25.2}$
32. $0.38\overline{)1.7746}$
33. $13.6\overline{)3,400}$

34. $4.8 \div 16$
35. $77 \div 10$
36. 4.6×100
37. $0.06 \times 1,000$
38. 5.2×0.007
39. $34.9 \div 1,000$

Find the greatest common factor (GCF) for each group of numbers.

40. 8, 12
41. 9, 15
42. 8, 9
43. 5, 10

Find the least common multiple (LCM) for each group of numbers.

44. 5, 10
45. 4, 7
46. 8, 10
47. 14, 21

Write each fraction in simplest form.

48. $\frac{5}{10}$
49. $\frac{9}{21}$
50. $\frac{18}{30}$
51. $\frac{6}{15}$
52. $\frac{14}{36}$

Add or subtract. Write each answer in simplest form.

53. $\frac{2}{9} + \frac{4}{9}$ **54.** $\frac{5}{7} + \frac{6}{7}$ **55.** $\frac{11}{12} - \frac{7}{12}$ **56.** $\frac{7}{9} - \frac{2}{9}$

57. $\frac{4}{5} + \frac{7}{10}$ **58.** $\frac{2}{3} + \frac{2}{7}$ **59.** $\frac{7}{12} - \frac{1}{3}$ **60.** $\frac{7}{8} - \frac{5}{12}$

61. $10\frac{1}{4} + 7\frac{1}{4}$ **62.** $9\frac{5}{8} + 7\frac{7}{8}$ **63.** $9\frac{6}{7} - 4\frac{2}{7}$ **64.** $13\frac{2}{5} - 5\frac{4}{5}$

65. $14\frac{2}{3} + 7\frac{1}{9}$ **66.** $11\frac{3}{4} + 17\frac{7}{16}$ **67.** $15\frac{7}{9} - 9\frac{5}{12}$ **68.** $18\frac{1}{3} - 12\frac{2}{5}$

Solve.

69. Flowering plants make up one-half of the 350,000 kinds of plants. How many kinds of flowering plants are there?

70. Corn gives off 325,000 gallons of water per acre during a growing season. How much water is given off by 90 acres of corn?

71. Twenty pounds of potatoes cost \$2.69. Find the cost per pound to the nearest tenth of a cent.

72. At a grade 6-8 middle school, $\frac{2}{5}$ of the students are in grade 6 and $\frac{1}{3}$ are in grade 7. What fraction of the students are in grade 8?

Mathematics Lab

The **pictograph** compares the amount of copper mined in several states. Usually, the data shown by a pictograph have been rounded.

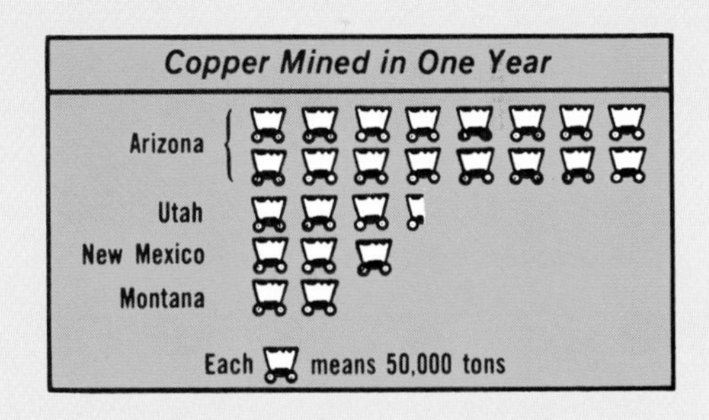

Answer each question. Use the pictograph.

1. About how many tons are mined a year in Arizona?

2. About how many tons are mined a year in Utah?

Make a pictograph for each set of data below.

3. Number of TV Sets Sold

black & white	40
color portable	45
color console	65

4. Pennies Minted in One Year

Denver	5 billion
Philadelphia	5 billion
San Francisco	0.5 billion

4-7 Multiplication of Fractions

Joyce Thomason planted a garden for flowers and vegetables. The garden is $\frac{2}{3}$ vegetables. Tomatoes take $\frac{1}{4}$ of the vegetable part of the garden. What part of the garden is taken by the tomatoes?

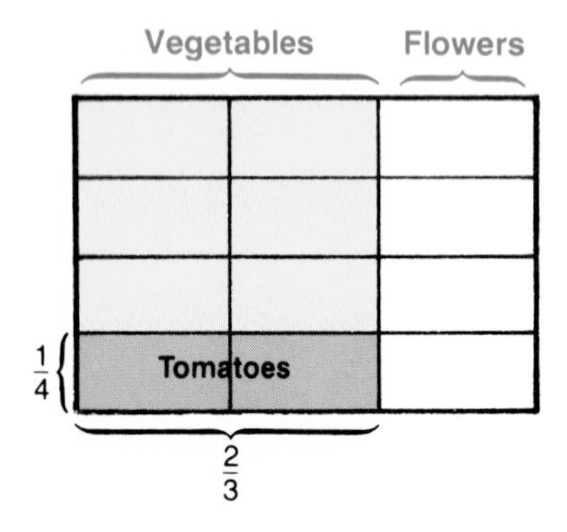

From the sketch of the garden, you can see that $\frac{2}{12}$ or $\frac{1}{6}$ of the garden is taken by tomatoes. You get the same result if you multiply $\frac{1}{4}$ and $\frac{2}{3}$.

$$\frac{1}{4} \times \frac{2}{3} = \frac{1 \times 2}{4 \times 3}$$ Multiply numerators. Multiply denominators.

$$= \frac{\overset{1}{\cancel{2}}}{\underset{6}{\cancel{12}}}$$ The GCF of 2 and 12 is 2.

$$= \frac{1}{6}$$

To multiply fractions, first multiply the numerators. Then multiply the denominators. Write the product in simplest form.

EXERCISES *Copy and complete.*

1. $\frac{1}{2} \times \frac{3}{4} = \frac{1 \times ▒}{2 \times ▒} = ▒$ **2.** $\frac{1}{3} \times \frac{4}{5} = \frac{1 \times ▒}{3 \times ▒} = ▒$ **3.** $\frac{2}{5} \times \frac{2}{3} = \frac{2 \times ▒}{5 \times ▒} = ▒$

Multiply. Write each product in simplest form.

4. $\frac{1}{2} \times \frac{2}{3}$	**5.** $\frac{1}{3} \times \frac{1}{5}$	**6.** $\frac{1}{2} \times \frac{3}{5}$
7. $\frac{2}{3} \times \frac{1}{3}$	**8.** $\frac{1}{4} \times \frac{3}{5}$	**9.** $\frac{5}{6} \times \frac{1}{6}$
10. $\frac{2}{7} \times \frac{2}{5}$	**11.** $\frac{5}{6} \times \frac{7}{8}$	**12.** $\frac{2}{3} \times \frac{3}{5}$
13. $\frac{3}{7} \times \frac{2}{3}$	**14.** $\frac{4}{5} \times \frac{5}{7}$	**15.** $\frac{5}{8} \times \frac{7}{10}$
16. $\frac{2}{3} \times \frac{3}{4}$	**17.** $\frac{2}{5} \times \frac{5}{6}$	**18.** $\frac{5}{8} \times \frac{4}{9}$
19. $\frac{3}{10} \times \frac{5}{7}$	**20.** $\frac{5}{7} \times \frac{7}{10}$	**21.** $\frac{2}{5} \times \frac{5}{8}$
22. $\frac{4}{5} \times \frac{5}{6}$	**23.** $\frac{9}{10} \times \frac{5}{12}$	**24.** $\frac{11}{15} \times \frac{5}{33}$

When multiplying fractions, you can use a shortcut. Study the following examples.

$$\frac{4}{5} \times \frac{7}{8} = \frac{4 \times 7}{5 \times 8} = \frac{\overset{1}{\cancel{4}} \times 7}{5 \times \underset{2}{\cancel{8}}} = \frac{7}{10}$$

The GCF of 4 and 8 is 4.

$$\frac{5}{6} \times \frac{9}{10} = \frac{5 \times 9}{6 \times 10} = \frac{\overset{1}{\cancel{5}} \times \overset{3}{\cancel{9}}}{\underset{2}{\cancel{6}} \times \underset{2}{\cancel{10}}} = \frac{3}{4}$$

The GCF of 5 and 10 is 5. The GCF of 9 and 6 is 3.

Notice that when you use this shortcut, the product is in simplest form.

EXERCISES ***Multiply. Write each product in simplest form.***

25. $\frac{1}{2} \times \frac{2}{3}$ **26.** $\frac{3}{7} \times \frac{1}{3}$ **27.** $\frac{4}{9} \times \frac{1}{4}$ **28.** $\frac{1}{5} \times \frac{5}{12}$ **29.** $\frac{3}{4} \times \frac{4}{7}$

30. $\frac{3}{5} \times \frac{5}{8}$ **31.** $\frac{6}{7} \times \frac{2}{3}$ **32.** $\frac{3}{5} \times \frac{2}{9}$ **33.** $\frac{7}{12} \times \frac{4}{5}$ **34.** $\frac{3}{4} \times \frac{5}{6}$

35. $\frac{7}{8} \times \frac{4}{9}$ **36.** $\frac{2}{5} \times \frac{9}{10}$ **37.** $\frac{5}{12} \times \frac{4}{9}$ **38.** $\frac{5}{6} \times \frac{3}{7}$ **39.** $\frac{4}{5} \times \frac{15}{17}$

40. $\frac{7}{8} \times \frac{9}{14}$ **41.** $\frac{3}{8} \times \frac{2}{3}$ **42.** $\frac{4}{7} \times \frac{7}{8}$ **43.** $\frac{2}{3} \times \frac{3}{10}$ **44.** $\frac{3}{4} \times \frac{4}{9}$

45. $\frac{5}{7} \times \frac{7}{10}$ **46.** $\frac{7}{12} \times \frac{4}{7}$ **47.** $\frac{2}{5} \times \frac{5}{12}$ **48.** $\frac{5}{8} \times \frac{4}{5}$ **49.** $\frac{3}{4} \times \frac{8}{9}$

50. $\frac{2}{3} \times \frac{9}{10} \times \frac{5}{7}$ **51.** $\frac{14}{15} \times \frac{3}{5} \times \frac{20}{21}$ **52.** $\frac{5}{6} \times \frac{21}{25} \times \frac{2}{7}$

53. $\frac{18}{35} \times \frac{5}{12} \times \frac{7}{9}$ **54.** $\frac{16}{25} \times \frac{5}{8} \times \frac{5}{6}$ **55.** $\frac{27}{28} \times \frac{7}{9} \times \frac{4}{5}$

Solve.

56. Dan Westfall's garden is $\frac{4}{5}$ flowers. Of these flowers, $\frac{7}{8}$ are perennials. What part of the garden is planted in perennials?

57. Janet Tudor's garden is $\frac{3}{4}$ flowers. Of these flowers, $\frac{4}{9}$ are tulips. What part of the garden is planted in tulips?

58. Harvey Schmidt's garden is $\frac{7}{10}$ vegetables. Of these vegetables, $\frac{5}{7}$ are beans. What part of the garden is planted in beans?

59. A recipe calls for $\frac{3}{4}$-pound of wax beans. How many pounds of wax beans are needed to make $\frac{1}{2}$ of the recipe?

4-8 Multiplication with Mixed Numerals

The heights of several house plants are given in relation to the wax begonia.

A dracaena grows $4\frac{7}{8}$ times as tall as a wax begonia. The mixed numeral $4\frac{7}{8}$ can be changed to an improper fraction in the following ways.

$$4\frac{7}{8} = 4 + \frac{7}{8}$$
$$= \frac{32}{8} + \frac{7}{8} \qquad 4 = \frac{4 \times 8}{1 \times 8} = \frac{32}{8}$$
$$= \frac{39}{8}$$

number of eighths in 4 — number of eighths in $\frac{7}{8}$

$$4\frac{7}{8} = \frac{(4 \times 8) + 7}{8}$$
$$= \frac{32 + 7}{8}$$
$$= \frac{39}{8}$$

The wax begonia is $1\frac{1}{6}$ feet tall. To find the height of a dracaena, multiply $4\frac{7}{8}$ by $1\frac{1}{6}$.

$$4\frac{7}{8} \times 1\frac{1}{6} = \frac{39}{8} \times \frac{7}{6}$$ Change the mixed numerals to improper fractions.

$$= \frac{\overset{13}{\cancel{39}} \times 7}{8 \times \underset{2}{\cancel{6}}}$$ The GCF of 39 and 6 is 3.

$$= \frac{91}{16}$$ $91 \div 16 = 5$ R11 or $5\frac{11}{16}$

$$= 5\frac{11}{16}$$ The dracaena is $5\frac{11}{16}$ feet tall.

To multiply with mixed numerals, first change the mixed numerals to improper fractions. Then multiply the fractions.

EXERCISES ***Change each of the following to an improper fraction.***

1. $1\frac{1}{5}$ **2.** $1\frac{3}{7}$ **3.** $2\frac{1}{3}$ **4.** $2\frac{1}{4}$ **5.** $2\frac{3}{4}$ **6.** $3\frac{1}{6}$

7. $4\frac{2}{3}$ **8.** $7\frac{7}{9}$ **9.** 5 **10.** $4\frac{3}{10}$ **11.** $5\frac{7}{12}$ **12.** $9\frac{3}{8}$

Multiply. Write each product in simplest form. (Hint: Change a whole number factor like 9 to $\frac{9}{1}$***).***

13. $\frac{3}{4} \times 1\frac{2}{5}$ **14.** $3\frac{3}{4} \times \frac{3}{5}$ **15.** $2\frac{1}{2} \times \frac{2}{3}$ **16.** $\frac{3}{11} \times 3\frac{2}{3}$

17. $4\frac{2}{3} \times 9$ **18.** $5\frac{3}{7} \times 14$ **19.** $6 \times 4\frac{3}{5}$ **20.** $9\frac{1}{4} \times 12$

21. $1\frac{1}{2} \times 3\frac{1}{4}$ **22.** $4\frac{1}{2} \times 2\frac{1}{2}$ **23.** $7\frac{1}{2} \times 3\frac{3}{5}$ **24.** $8\frac{3}{4} \times 3\frac{2}{7}$

25. $9\frac{1}{2} \times 4\frac{1}{2}$ **26.** $6\frac{1}{4} \times 2\frac{2}{3}$ **27.** $2\frac{4}{7} \times 1\frac{5}{16}$ **28.** $2\frac{7}{10} \times 2\frac{1}{12}$

29. $2\frac{2}{9} \times 2\frac{4}{7}$ **30.** $3\frac{1}{8} \times 3\frac{2}{5}$ **31.** $4\frac{1}{8} \times 2\frac{2}{3}$ **32.** $1\frac{9}{16} \times 4\frac{4}{5}$

33. $1\frac{3}{8} \times 2 \times \frac{4}{11}$ **34.** $3\frac{4}{5} \times 1\frac{7}{8} \times 2\frac{7}{19}$ **35.** $1\frac{1}{2} \times \frac{8}{9} \times 2\frac{2}{5}$

Add, subtract, and multiply. Write each answer in simplest form.

36. $\left(\frac{1}{2} - \frac{1}{4}\right) \times \frac{4}{5}$ **37.** $\left(\frac{2}{3} \times \frac{1}{8}\right) + \frac{5}{6}$ **38.** $\frac{3}{4} \times \left(\frac{2}{3} + \frac{2}{3}\right)$

39. $\left(5\frac{1}{2} + \frac{1}{3}\right) \times \frac{6}{7}$ **40.** $8 - \left(1\frac{1}{2} \times 3\frac{2}{3}\right)$ **41.** $\left(10 \times 3\frac{1}{6}\right) + 8\frac{1}{3}$

Solve. Use the diagram on page 102. The wax begonia is $1\frac{1}{6}$ ***feet tall.***

42. Find the height of the African violet.

43. Find the height of a Boston fern.

44. Find the height of a coleus.

Solve. Use the chart.

45. How many words can John type in $9\frac{1}{2}$ minutes?

46. How many words can Joan type in $3\frac{5}{6}$ minutes?

47. Claire types for $7\frac{1}{3}$ minutes and Martha types for $9\frac{1}{4}$ minutes. Who types more words?

Typist	Words per Minute
Claire	44
John	36
Martha	32
Tom	60
Joan	54

4-9 Reciprocals and Division of Fractions

Lester Turner has a flat that holds 12 petunias. He divides the flat in half, with 6 petunias in each half. You can think of this problem as division or as multiplication.

$12 \div 2 = 6$

Dividing by 2 and multiplying by $\frac{1}{2}$ give the same result.

$12 \times \frac{1}{2} = 6$

The numbers 2 and $\frac{1}{2}$ are reciprocals of each other. Two numbers whose product is 1 are called **reciprocals.**

2 and $\frac{1}{2}$ are reciprocals. $\frac{2}{1} \times \frac{1}{2} = 1$

$\frac{2}{3}$ and $\frac{3}{2}$ are reciprocals. $\frac{2}{3} \times \frac{3}{2} = 1$

EXERCISES ***Name the reciprocal of each of the following.***

1. 4 **2.** 7 **3.** $\frac{1}{5}$ **4.** $\frac{1}{8}$ **5.** $\frac{3}{4}$ **6.** $\frac{5}{6}$

7. $\frac{5}{8}$ **8.** $\frac{7}{12}$ **9.** $\frac{1}{6}$ **10.** $\frac{1}{9}$ **11.** 6 **12.** 10

13. $\frac{8}{3}$ **14.** $\frac{7}{5}$ **15.** $\frac{16}{11}$ **16.** $\frac{4}{7}$ **17.** $\frac{9}{2}$ **18.** $\frac{20}{21}$

Answer the following.

19. What is the reciprocal of 7?

20. The reciprocal of $\frac{2}{9}$ is what number?

21. What number is its own reciprocal?

22. What number has no reciprocal?

23. Dividing by 5 gives the same result as multiplying by what number?

24. Multiplying by $\frac{1}{3}$ gives the same result as dividing by what number?

25. Describe the reciprocal of a number less than 1.

Since dividing by a number is like multiplying by its reciprocal, the following rule is true.

To divide by a fraction, multiply by its reciprocal.

Study the following examples.

$\frac{4}{15} \div \frac{4}{5} = \frac{4}{15} \times \frac{5}{4}$ The reciprocal of $\frac{4}{5}$ is $\frac{5}{4}$.

$= \frac{\overset{1}{\cancel{4}}}{\underset{3}{\cancel{15}}} \times \frac{\overset{1}{\cancel{5}}}{\underset{1}{\cancel{4}}}$

$= \frac{1}{3}$

$\frac{5}{6} \div 10 = \frac{5}{6} \times \frac{1}{10}$ The reciprocal of 10 is $\frac{1}{10}$.

$= \frac{\overset{1}{\cancel{5}}}{6} \times \frac{1}{\underset{2}{\cancel{10}}}$

$= \frac{1}{12}$

EXERCISES ***Answer the following.***

26. To divide by $\frac{2}{3}$, you multiply by what number?

27. Multiplying by $\frac{5}{2}$ is the same as dividing by what number?

Copy and complete.

28. $\frac{5}{9} \div \frac{2}{3} = \frac{5}{9} \times \frac{▒}{2} = ▒$

29. $\frac{5}{8} \div \frac{1}{2} = \frac{5}{8} \times \frac{▒}{1} = ▒$

30. $\frac{2}{9} \div \frac{2}{3} = \frac{2}{9} \times \frac{▒}{2} = ▒$

31. $\frac{3}{5} \div 6 = \frac{3}{5} \times \frac{1}{▒} = ▒$

32. $\frac{4}{7} \div 8 = \frac{4}{7} \times \frac{▒}{8} = ▒$

33. $6 \div \frac{3}{10} = \frac{6}{1} \times \frac{10}{▒} = ▒$

34. $\frac{3}{4} \div \frac{1}{4}$ **35.** $\frac{5}{7} \div \frac{1}{7}$ **36.** $\frac{3}{8} \div \frac{1}{2}$ **37.** $\frac{4}{9} \div \frac{1}{3}$ **38.** $\frac{5}{6} \div \frac{5}{12}$

39. $\frac{7}{10} \div \frac{2}{5}$ **40.** $\frac{5}{6} \div \frac{2}{3}$ **41.** $\frac{3}{8} \div \frac{3}{4}$ **42.** $\frac{5}{8} \div \frac{5}{6}$ **43.** $\frac{8}{9} \div \frac{8}{15}$

44. $\frac{2}{9} \div \frac{3}{5}$ **45.** $\frac{5}{9} \div \frac{9}{10}$ **46.** $\frac{4}{9} \div \frac{3}{4}$ **47.** $\frac{15}{16} \div \frac{5}{8}$ **48.** $\frac{11}{12} \div \frac{22}{27}$

49. $\frac{6}{7} \div 6$ **50.** $\frac{8}{9} \div 4$ **51.** $7 \div \frac{7}{10}$ **52.** $9 \div \frac{3}{8}$ **53.** $\frac{9}{10} \div 6$

54. $\frac{11}{12} \div 33$ **55.** $15 \div \frac{5}{7}$ **56.** $18 \div \frac{3}{10}$ **57.** $\frac{9}{10} \div \frac{3}{4}$ **58.** $\frac{7}{8} \div \frac{7}{12}$

59. $\frac{3}{10} \div \frac{9}{20}$ **60.** $\frac{4}{9} \div \frac{8}{21}$ **61.** $\frac{5}{12} \div \frac{25}{36}$ **62.** $\frac{7}{8} \div \frac{21}{32}$ **63.** $\frac{13}{20} \div \frac{39}{40}$

Solve.

64. In $\frac{3}{5}$ ounce of fertilizer, there is $\frac{3}{10}$ ounce nitrogen. What part of the fertilizer is nitrogen?

65. In 4 ounces of fertilizer, there is $\frac{2}{3}$ ounce phosphorus. What part of the fertilizer is phosphorus?

4-10 Division with Mixed Numerals

A $3\frac{1}{2}$-foot row yields $8\frac{2}{5}$ pounds of tomatoes. To find the yield in pounds of tomatoes for each foot, divide $8\frac{2}{5}$ by $3\frac{1}{2}$.

$$8\frac{2}{5} \div 3\frac{1}{2} = \frac{42}{5} \div \frac{7}{2}$$

Rename the mixed numerals as fractions.

$$= \frac{42}{5} \times \frac{2}{7}$$

Multiply by the reciprocal of $\frac{7}{2}$.

$$= \frac{\overset{6}{\cancel{42}}}{5} \times \frac{2}{\underset{1}{\cancel{7}}}$$

$$= \frac{12}{5}$$

$$= 2\frac{2}{5}$$

The yield is $2\frac{2}{5}$ pounds of tomatoes for each foot.

EXERCISES *Copy and complete.*

1. $2\frac{1}{3} \div 4 = \frac{7}{3} \div \frac{4}{1} = \frac{7}{3} \times \frac{▒}{▒} = ▒$
2. $3\frac{3}{5} \div 6 = \frac{18}{5} \div \frac{6}{1} = \frac{18}{5} \times \frac{▒}{▒} = ▒$
3. $3 \div 4\frac{1}{2} = \frac{3}{1} \div \frac{9}{2} = \frac{3}{1} \times \frac{▒}{▒} = ▒$
4. $4 \div 4\frac{3}{4} = \frac{4}{1} \div \frac{19}{4} = \frac{4}{1} \times \frac{▒}{▒} = ▒$
5. $1\frac{1}{5} \div 1\frac{3}{5} = \frac{6}{5} \div \frac{8}{5} = \frac{6}{5} \times \frac{▒}{▒} = ▒$
6. $2\frac{1}{4} \div 1\frac{7}{8} = \frac{9}{4} \div \frac{15}{8} = \frac{9}{4} \times \frac{▒}{▒} = ▒$

Divide. Write each quotient in simplest form.

7. $6\frac{1}{4} \div 5$
8. $1\frac{5}{8} \div 2$
9. $4 \div 1\frac{1}{3}$
10. $5 \div 3\frac{1}{3}$
11. $10 \div 3\frac{3}{4}$
12. $6 \div 1\frac{1}{4}$
13. $8 \div 2\frac{2}{5}$
14. $2\frac{2}{5} \div \frac{3}{10}$
15. $3\frac{1}{8} \div \frac{5}{12}$
16. $1\frac{3}{5} \div \frac{5}{8}$
17. $\frac{7}{8} \div 1\frac{1}{5}$
18. $\frac{8}{9} \div 2\frac{2}{5}$
19. $\frac{5}{6} \div 1\frac{1}{9}$
20. $1\frac{2}{5} \div 2\frac{2}{3}$
21. $1\frac{1}{4} \div 4\frac{1}{2}$
22. $3\frac{1}{5} \div 1\frac{1}{3}$
23. $1\frac{1}{4} \div 7\frac{1}{2}$
24. $3\frac{1}{2} \div 5\frac{1}{2}$
25. $10\frac{1}{2} \div 2\frac{1}{3}$
26. $7\frac{1}{8} \div 3\frac{4}{5}$
27. $4\frac{3}{4} \div 1\frac{7}{8}$
28. $5\frac{1}{2} \div 2\frac{3}{4}$
29. $9\frac{3}{5} \div 4\frac{1}{5}$
30. $3\frac{3}{16} \div 2\frac{1}{8}$

The fraction bar means divide. So, a division like $1\frac{1}{2} \div \frac{3}{4}$ can be expressed as a **complex fraction.** Simplify a complex fraction as shown.

$$\frac{1\frac{1}{2}}{\frac{3}{4}} \quad 1\frac{1}{2} \div \frac{3}{4} = \frac{3}{2} \div \frac{3}{4} = \frac{3}{2} \times \frac{4}{3} = \frac{\overset{1}{\cancel{3}}}{\underset{1}{\cancel{2}}} \times \frac{\overset{2}{\cancel{4}}}{\underset{1}{\cancel{3}}} = \frac{2}{1} \text{ or } 2$$

EXERCISES ***Simplify.***

31. $\dfrac{\frac{7}{9}}{\frac{7}{12}}$ 32. $\dfrac{\frac{11}{15}}{\frac{11}{12}}$ 33. $\dfrac{\frac{4}{7}}{\frac{7}{8}}$ 34. $\dfrac{\frac{8}{25}}{\frac{4}{5}}$ 35. $\dfrac{\frac{4}{5}}{8}$ 36. $\dfrac{5}{\frac{5}{6}}$

37. $\dfrac{2\frac{5}{8}}{14}$ 38. $\dfrac{12}{1\frac{1}{9}}$ 39. $\dfrac{9}{2\frac{1}{4}}$ 40. $\dfrac{2\frac{3}{4}}{\frac{5}{6}}$ 41. $\dfrac{\frac{9}{10}}{5\frac{2}{5}}$ 42. $\dfrac{4\frac{2}{3}}{1\frac{3}{5}}$

Complete. The procedure below leads to the rule on page 105.

43. Why can you multiply both numerator and denominator by $\frac{8}{5}$?

44. Complete the procedure below for $\frac{a}{b} \div \frac{c}{d}$.

$$\frac{4}{7} \div \frac{5}{8} = \frac{\frac{4}{7}}{\frac{5}{8}} = \frac{\frac{4}{7} \times \frac{8}{5}}{\frac{5}{8} \times \frac{8}{5}} = \frac{\frac{4}{7} \times \frac{8}{5}}{1} \text{ or } \frac{4}{7} \times \frac{8}{5}$$

$\frac{5}{8}$ and $\frac{8}{5}$ are reciprocals.

CROSS-NUMBER PUZZLE

Across ***Copy and complete the puzzle.***

1. $7\frac{1}{2} \times 3\frac{3}{5}$
3. $\frac{7}{11} = \frac{▒}{33}$
4. $15\frac{3}{4} + 7\frac{2}{3}$
7. $6\frac{2}{3} \div 2\frac{1}{2}$
8. $7\frac{4}{15} - 2\frac{2}{3}$
10. GCF of 91 and 65
13. $31\frac{1}{3} + 11\frac{1}{4} + 10\frac{1}{4}$
15. $4\frac{2}{3} \div \frac{3}{4}$

1	2			3 2		
		4		5/12		5
6					7	
8			9			
		10				11
	12			13	14	
	15					

Down

3. $12\frac{1}{4} - 9\frac{5}{6}$ (sample)
4. LCM of 3 and 7
5. $1\frac{1}{2} + 1\frac{1}{4} + 1\frac{1}{8} + \frac{19}{24}$
6. $16 \times 2\frac{3}{4}$
9. $5\frac{3}{4} = \frac{▒}{4}$
11. $8\frac{1}{2} \div 3$
12. reciprocal of $\frac{1}{16}$
14. $2\frac{15}{16} - \frac{3}{4}$

Focus on Problem Solving

4-11 Too Few Facts

Mr. Moss plants $\frac{3}{4}$ of his farm in corn, $\frac{1}{8}$ in soybeans, and the rest in oats. How many acres of oats does he plant?

This problem does *not* have all the facts needed to solve it. Why?

Read the problem. Find the acres of oats planted. The fraction planted in corn and the fraction planted in soybeans is given.

Decide what to do. Find the fraction of the farm planted in oats. Multiply this fraction by the total number of acres in the farm.

Solve the problem.

Step 1

fraction planted in oats $= 1 - \frac{3}{4} - \frac{1}{8}$

$= \frac{8}{8} - \frac{6}{8} - \frac{1}{8}$

$= \frac{2}{8} - \frac{1}{8}$ or $\frac{1}{8}$

Step 2

$\frac{1}{8} \times$ total acres in the farm $=$ acres of oats

You need to know the total acres in the farm to solve the problem.

Examine the solution. Since the problem has too few facts, it cannot be solved.

Tell what missing facts are needed in order to solve each of the following.

1. A $6\frac{1}{2}$-foot board is to be cut into pieces of the same length. How long is each piece?
2. Mr. White buys $5\frac{1}{2}$ pounds of cookies. How much change does he receive from a \$10 bill?
3. How much money will Mrs. Kincaid earn in 5 days if she works $7\frac{1}{2}$ hours each day?
4. The Myers family expects to pay \$1.30 a gallon for gasoline. Find the cost of gasoline for a 650-mile trip.

If the problem has enough facts, solve it. If not, state the missing facts.

5. Jane gets $\frac{3}{4}$ of the problems correct on a test. If the test has 20 problems, how many did she get correct?

6. Bob has $6\frac{1}{4}$ bags of plant food. He uses $1\frac{1}{4}$ bag each month. How many months will his supply of plant food last?

7. Maria works $2\frac{1}{2}$ hours a day and 5 days a week. How much does she earn each week?

8. The population of Detroit is 2.36 times the population of Boston. What is the population of Detroit?

9. Jerry uses $1\frac{1}{3}$ square yards of material to make a wall hanging. At $3 a square yard, what is the cost of enough material for 3 wall hangings?

10. A recipe calls for $2\frac{2}{3}$ cups of flour. Charlene has to triple the recipe. How many cups of flour does she need?

Solve if possible. Use the circle graph.

11. What part of the Collins budget is spent on housing and taxes?

12. How much money does the Collins family spend on transportation?

13. Which expense is 5 times as much as the medical expense?

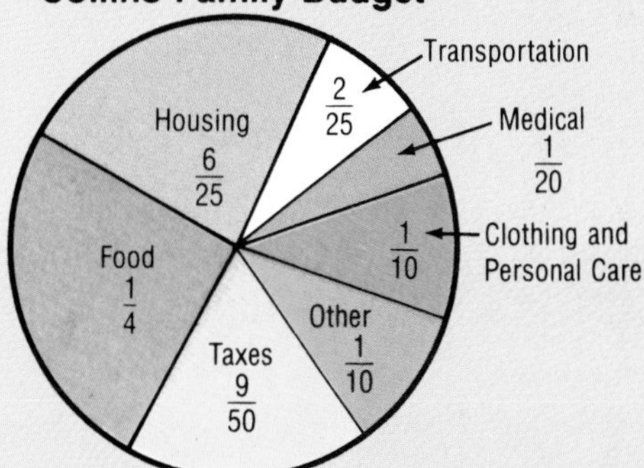

Skills Review: Pages 100-109

Multiply or divide. Write each product or quotient in simplest form.

1. $\frac{1}{3} \times \frac{1}{4}$
2. $\frac{2}{5} \times \frac{4}{5}$
3. $\frac{4}{5} \times \frac{5}{7}$
4. $\frac{7}{10} \times \frac{5}{12}$
5. $\frac{3}{7} \times 1\frac{5}{9}$
6. $2\frac{5}{8} \times 2\frac{2}{7}$
7. $\frac{5}{6} \div \frac{1}{6}$
8. $\frac{3}{5} \div \frac{7}{10}$
9. $\frac{11}{12} \div \frac{5}{9}$
10. $3\frac{3}{4} \div 5$
11. $9 \div 3\frac{3}{5}$
12. $\frac{6}{7} \div 1\frac{5}{7}$

If the problem has enough facts, solve it. If not, state the missing facts.

13. The price of a coat is reduced by $\frac{1}{4}$. Find the amount of price reduction on a $52 coat.

14. Caryn works 8, $7\frac{1}{2}$, $6\frac{1}{4}$, and $4\frac{3}{4}$ hours on 4 weekends. Find the average number of hours worked.

Mathematics and Consumers

Suppose a one-year loan has a total interest charge of \$72. For a one-year loan, the following sum is used to figure the amount of interest each month.

12 + 11 + 10 + 9 + 8 + 7 + 6 + 5 + 4 + 3 + 2 + 1 = 78

You can find the amount of interest paid as follows.

1 month: $\frac{12}{78}$ of interest paid. ➧ $\frac{12}{78} \times \$72 = \$11.08$

3 months: $\frac{12}{78} + \frac{11}{78} + \frac{10}{78}$ or $\frac{33}{78}$ of interest paid. ➧ $\frac{33}{78} \times \$72 = \$30.46$

6 months: $\frac{12}{78} + \frac{11}{78} + \frac{10}{78} + \frac{9}{78} + \frac{8}{78} + \frac{7}{78}$ or $\frac{57}{78}$ of interest paid. ➧ $\frac{57}{78} \times \$72 = \$52.62$

The above method is called the **rule of 78.** Do you see why?

EXERCISES ***Use the rule of 78 to find the part of the interest owed on a one-year loan for each of the following. The total amount of interest is \$72. Round amounts to the nearest cent.***

1. first two months

2. the ninth month

3. first eight months

4. last six months

Solve. Round amounts to the nearest cent.

5. The total amount of interest on a one-year loan is \$96. Find the interest owed for the first month.

6. The amount of interest owed on a one-year loan is \$195. Find the interest owed for the first four months.

7. Gail Knisely owes \$132 interest for the first three months of a one-year loan. Find the total amount of interest for the entire one-year loan.

8. Jud Harris owes \$12 interest for the last three months of a one-year loan. Find the total amount of interest for the entire one-year loan.

Chapter 4 Review

VOCABULARY reciprocal (104) complex fraction (107)

***EXERCISES* Add or subtract. Write each sum or difference in simplest form. (87-95)**

1. $\frac{1}{9} + \frac{5}{9}$
2. $\frac{4}{7} + \frac{5}{7}$
3. $\frac{1}{3} + \frac{1}{9}$
4. $\frac{1}{8} + \frac{2}{3}$
5. $\frac{2}{5} + \frac{2}{3}$
6. $\frac{7}{10} + \frac{5}{6}$
7. $4\frac{4}{9} + 3\frac{3}{9}$
8. $2\frac{1}{8} + 1\frac{7}{8}$
9. $7\frac{1}{3} + 10\frac{1}{6}$
10. $11\frac{4}{5} + 15\frac{1}{4}$
11. $\frac{11}{12} - \frac{1}{12}$
12. $\frac{5}{16} - \frac{1}{4}$
13. $\frac{3}{5} - \frac{1}{3}$
14. $8\frac{7}{9} - 1\frac{4}{9}$
15. $12 - 3\frac{6}{7}$
16. $5\frac{5}{18} - 2\frac{5}{6}$

Multiply. Write each product in simplest form. (100-103)

17. $\frac{7}{8} \times \frac{3}{5}$
18. $\frac{5}{6} \times \frac{1}{4}$
19. $\frac{1}{4} \times \frac{4}{5}$
20. $\frac{9}{10} \times \frac{5}{6}$
21. $\frac{1}{2} \times 1\frac{1}{3}$
22. $10 \times \frac{4}{5}$
23. $3\frac{1}{7} \times 1\frac{5}{9}$
24. $3\frac{1}{8} \times 4\frac{4}{5}$

Divide. Write each quotient in simplest form. (104-107)

25. $\frac{9}{10} \div \frac{1}{3}$
26. $\frac{5}{8} \div \frac{15}{16}$
27. $5 \div \frac{3}{4}$
28. $3\frac{3}{7} \div \frac{3}{4}$
29. $\frac{5}{8} \div 2\frac{1}{4}$
30. $2\frac{1}{3} \div 1\frac{1}{2}$
31. $\dfrac{\frac{9}{16}}{\frac{2}{3}}$
32. $\dfrac{1\frac{5}{7}}{2}$

If the problem has enough facts, solve it. If not, state the missing facts. (96-97, 108-109)

33. A board has been cut into four lengths of $15\frac{1}{2}$ inches each. What was the original length of the board?
34. A recipe calls for $\frac{1}{4}$ cup of brown sugar. If the recipe is tripled, how many cups of brown sugar are needed?
35. Andy Rupp saves $\frac{1}{5}$ of his weekly income. In how many weeks will he save at least $100?
36. Jessica Heard's standing long jumps are 84 inches, $78\frac{1}{4}$ inches, and $80\frac{1}{2}$ inches. Find the average length of her long jumps.

Chapter 4 Test

Add or subtract. Write each sum or difference in simplest form.

1. $\frac{3}{5} + \frac{1}{5}$ **2.** $\frac{5}{12} + \frac{11}{12}$ **3.** $\frac{2}{5} + \frac{3}{10}$ **4.** $\frac{2}{3} + \frac{4}{5}$

5. $6\frac{2}{9} + 8\frac{4}{9}$ **6.** $9\frac{5}{6} + 8\frac{1}{6}$ **7.** $13\frac{3}{8} + 8\frac{7}{8}$ **8.** $9\frac{2}{3} + 8\frac{1}{6}$

9. $18\frac{3}{4} + 25\frac{7}{16}$ **10.** $\frac{6}{7} - \frac{4}{7}$ **11.** $\frac{11}{16} - \frac{3}{16}$ **12.** $\frac{7}{10} - \frac{2}{5}$

13. $\frac{2}{3} - \frac{3}{7}$ **14.** $\frac{11}{15} - \frac{3}{10}$ **15.** $7\frac{3}{5} - 3\frac{1}{5}$ **16.** $9 - 4\frac{4}{7}$

17. $12\frac{1}{8} - 5\frac{3}{8}$ **18.** $8\frac{3}{4} - 4\frac{5}{12}$ **19.** $19\frac{1}{6} - 7\frac{4}{9}$ **20.** $26\frac{2}{5} - 15\frac{11}{15}$

Multiply. Write each product in simplest form.

21. $\frac{2}{3} \times \frac{4}{5}$ **22.** $\frac{1}{2} \times \frac{1}{7}$ **23.** $\frac{2}{3} \times \frac{3}{7}$ **24.** $\frac{3}{16} \times \frac{8}{9}$

25. $\frac{5}{9} \times 21$ **26.** $\frac{6}{7} \times 3\frac{1}{9}$ **27.** $1\frac{7}{8} \times 20$ **28.** $2\frac{4}{9} \times 2\frac{2}{11}$

Name the reciprocal of each of the following.

29. $\frac{4}{5}$ **30.** 9 **31.** $\frac{1}{3}$ **32.** $\frac{10}{13}$ **33.** 10 **34.** $\frac{5}{2}$

Divide. Write each quotient in simplest form.

35. $\frac{1}{2} \div \frac{5}{6}$ **36.** $\frac{4}{5} \div \frac{3}{5}$ **37.** $3 \div \frac{9}{10}$ **38.** $2\frac{4}{5} \div 7$

39. $10 \div 1\frac{7}{8}$ **40.** $2\frac{4}{9} \div 1\frac{5}{6}$ **41.** $\frac{4}{9} \div \frac{2}{3}$ **42.** $4\frac{5}{8} \div 1\frac{1}{2}$

Solve if possible. Use the recipe card.

43. Kelly doubles the recipe. How much sugar is needed?

44. How much more flour than sugar does the recipe call for?

45. For a large group, 15 cups of sugar were used. How many times was the recipe increased?

46. Mark has 5 cups of flour. Does he have enough to triple the recipe?

Blueberry Muffins

$1\frac{1}{2}$ cups flour
$\frac{3}{4}$ cup sugar
$\frac{1}{2}$ cup milk
2 eggs
1 teaspoon baking powder
$\frac{1}{2}$ teaspoon salt
$\frac{1}{4}$ cup salad oil
1 cup blueberries

Enrichment

Logic deals with the formal principles of reasoning. Most discussions which use logic begin with a **statement.** Consider the following statements.

1. Columbus is the capital of Ohio.
2. Columbus is not the capital of Ohio.
3. He weighs 140 pounds.
4. $10 \div 5 = 2$.

Statements may be true, such as 1 and 4, or false, such as 2. Some statements, like 3, are neither true nor false. The truth or falsity of a statement is called its **truth value.**

We can form a new statement called a **conditional,** by connecting two statements with the words if . . . then. "If Charlie is a horse, then Charlie has four legs" is a conditional. New conditionals can be formed as follows.

Charlie is a horse. Charlie has four legs.	True
Charlie has four legs. Charlie is a horse.	No conclusion
If Charlie is not a horse, then Charlie does not have four legs.	No conclusion
If Charlie does not have four legs, then Charlie is not a horse.	True

EXERCISES ***State the truth value for each of the following.***

1. Washington, D.C. is the capital of the United States.

2. The Mississippi River flows through the state of Maine.

3. $17 \div 5 = p$

4. $\frac{1}{2} \times \frac{1}{4} = \frac{1}{6}$

5. The number 21 is prime.

6. Mars has two moons.

Determine the truth value for each of the following. Use the original true statement, "If Wolf is a beagle, then Wolf is a dog."

7. Wolf is a dog. Wolf is a beagle.

8. Wolf is a beagle. Wolf is a dog.

9. If Wolf is a dog, then Wolf is a beagle.

10. If Wolf is not a dog, then Wolf is not a beagle.

5 Geometry

Anne Ryan draws the design for a new building. The design provides a basis for constructing the building. Mrs. Ryan uses geometric ideas such as point, line, and plane in the design.

5-1 Basic Geometric Terms

The foundation of a building illustrates the basic ideas of geometry.

A **point** indicates an exact location. Find point A.

A **line** is all the points in a never ending straight path. Line DE is symbolized $\overleftrightarrow{DE}$. Find $\overleftrightarrow{DE}$.

A **line segment** consists of two endpoints and the straight path between them. Line segment BC is symbolized $\overline{BC}$. Find $\overline{BC}$.

A **ray** consists of one endpoint and a never ending straight path in one direction. Ray AB is symbolized $\overrightarrow{AB}$. Find $\overrightarrow{AB}$. The first letter names the endpoint.

A **plane** is a never ending flat surface with no boundaries. A plane is named by three points not on a line. Find plane BCE.

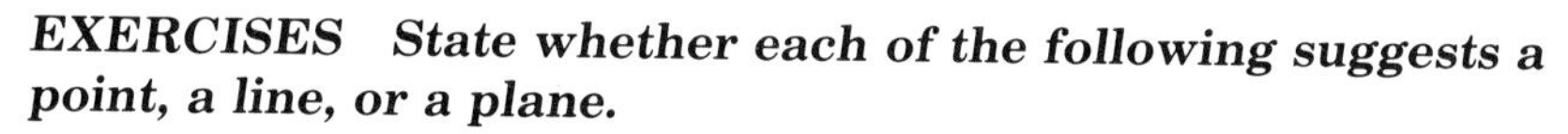

EXERCISES ***State whether each of the following suggests a point, a line, or a plane.***

1. pencil	**2.** pane of glass	**3.** light beam
4. star in the sky	**5.** grain of salt	**6.** record album

Use symbols to name each of the following.

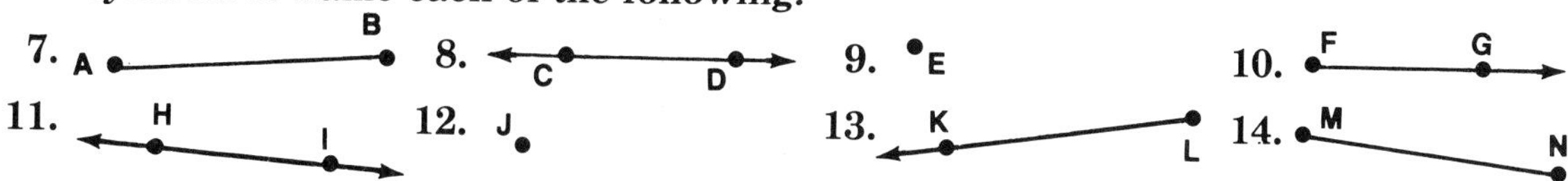

Draw representations of each of the following.

15. point P	**16.** ray QR	**17.** line segment ST	**18.** line VW
19. $\overrightarrow{XY}$	**20.** $\overline{ZA}$	**21.** $\overleftrightarrow{BC}$	**22.** point D

5-2 Angles

Builders construct the framework of a building. When pieces of lumber are nailed together, angles are formed.

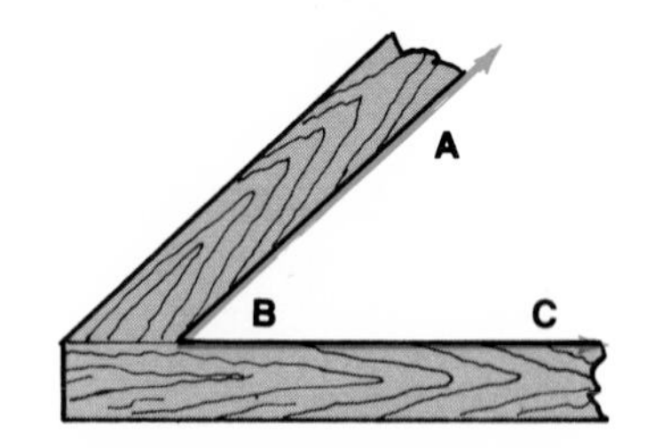

An **angle** is formed by two rays with a common endpoint called the **vertex.** The rays are called **sides** of the angle. Rays BA and BC form angle ABC. Point B is the vertex. Angle ABC is symbolized ∠ABC. The letter naming the vertex must be in the middle.

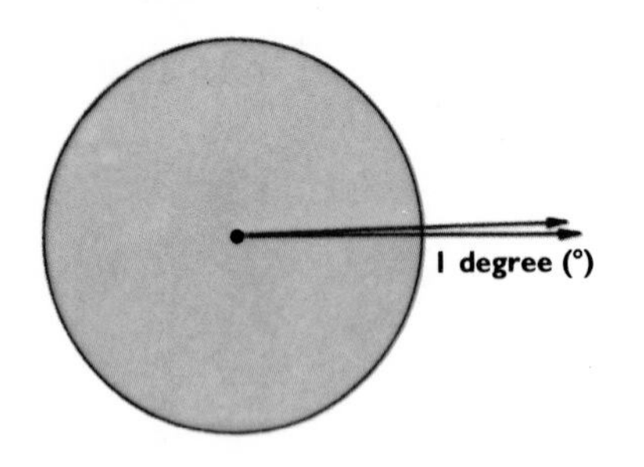

The most common unit used in measuring angles is the **degree.** Imagine a circle separated into 360 equal-sized parts. Each part would form a one-degree (1°) angle.

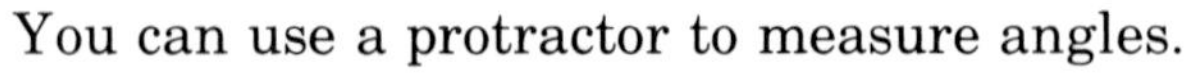

You can use a protractor to measure angles.

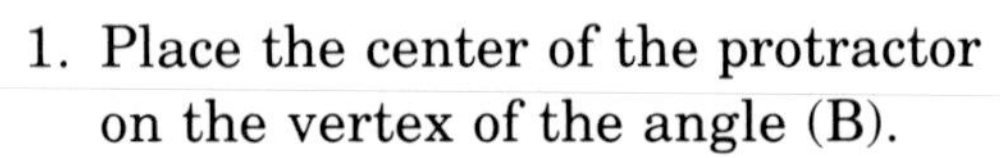

1. Place the center of the protractor on the vertex of the angle (B).

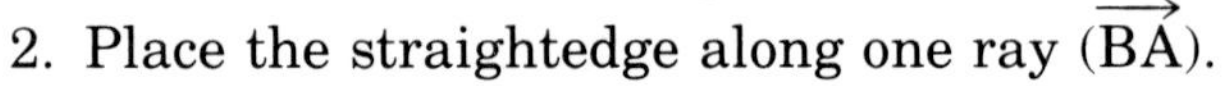

2. Place the straightedge along one ray ($\overrightarrow{BA}$).

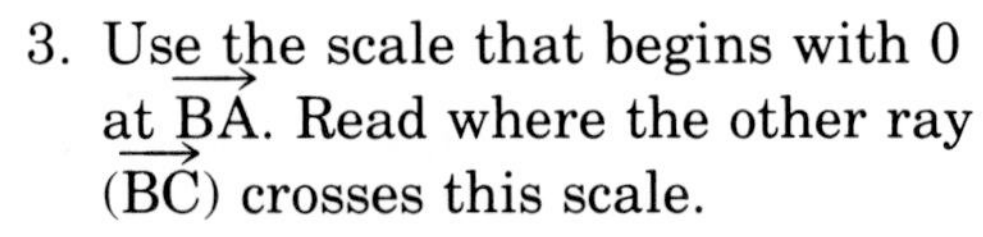

3. Use the scale that begins with 0 at $\overrightarrow{BA}$. Read where the other ray ($\overrightarrow{BC}$) crosses this scale.

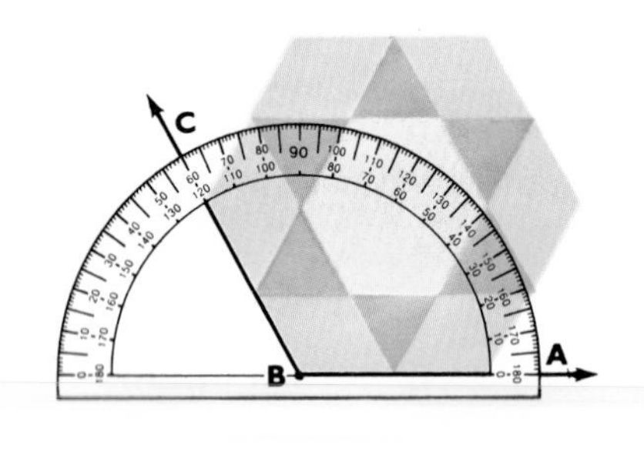

The degree measure of angle ABC is 120.

m ∠ABC = 120

EXERCISES ***Use symbols to name each of the following.***

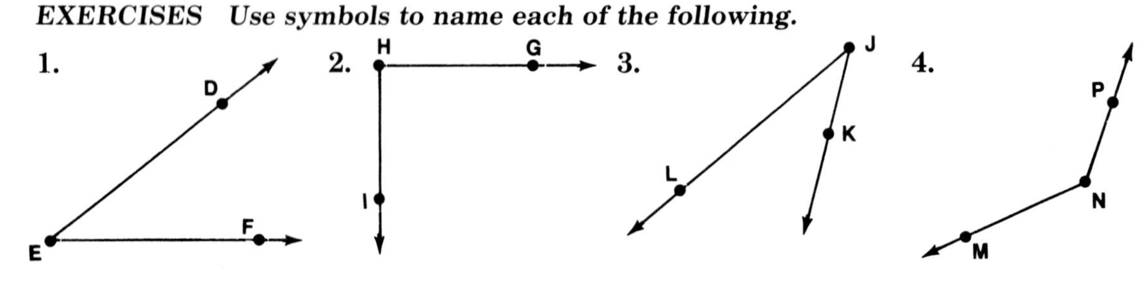

Use the protractor to find the measure of each of the following.

5. ∠LQM **6.** ∠LQN **7.** ∠LQP

8. ∠LQR **9.** ∠LQS **10.** ∠LQT

11. ∠WQT **12.** ∠WQS **13.** ∠WQR

14. ∠WQP **15.** ∠NQW **16.** ∠MQW

17. Use a protractor to measure each of the angles shown in exercises 1-4.

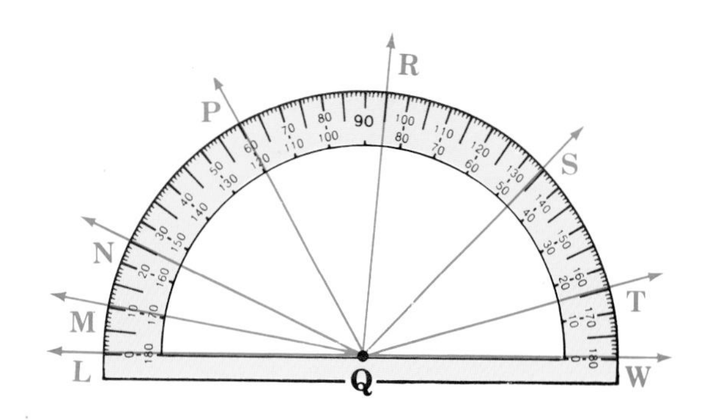

Draw angles having each of the following measurements.

18. 70° **19.** 150° **20.** 13° **21.** 97°

Angles can be named according to their degree measure.

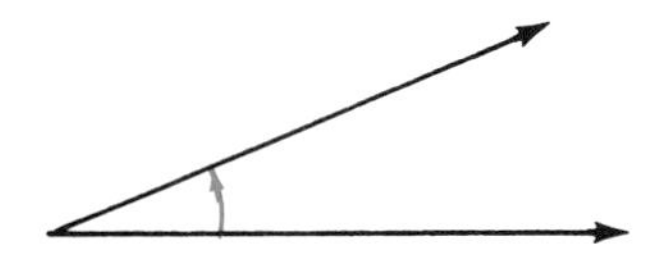

This mark indicates a right angle.

An **acute angle** measures between 0 and 90.

A **right angle** measures 90.

An **obtuse angle** measures between 90 and 180.

EXERCISES Classify angles having each of the following measurements as acute, right, or obtuse.

22. 120° **23.** 65° **24.** 13° **25.** 1°

26. 90° **27.** 179° **28.** 48.9° **29.** 90.5°

Use the figure shown below to answer each of the following.

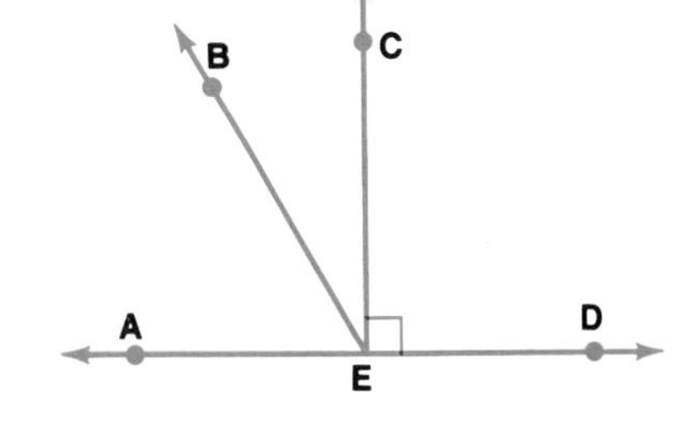

30. Name two right angles.

31. Name two acute angles.

32. Name one obtuse angle.

33. Find the measures of ∠AEB and ∠BEC.

34. Find the sum of the measures of ∠AEB and ∠BEC.

35. Find the measure of ∠AEC. How does this compare with your answer in exercise 34?

5-3 Angle Relationships

The framework of a high voltage tower contains many lines and angles. Two angles are **adjacent** when they have a common side, the same vertex, and do not overlap.

In the figure shown at the right, ∠ADB and ∠BDC are adjacent angles. Their common side is $\overrightarrow{DB}$ and their vertex is D.

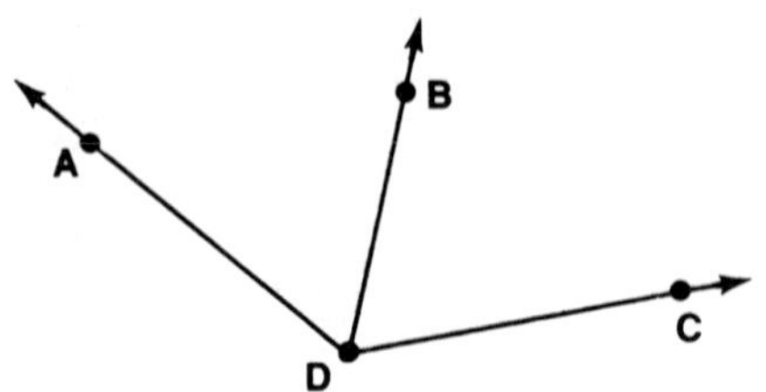

Two angles are **complementary** if the sum of their degree measures is 90.

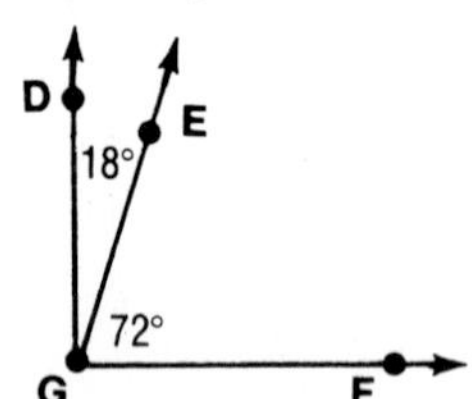

m∠DGE + m∠EGF = 18 + 72 = 90

∠DGE and ∠EGF are complementary.

Two angles are **supplementary** if the sum of their degree measures is 180.

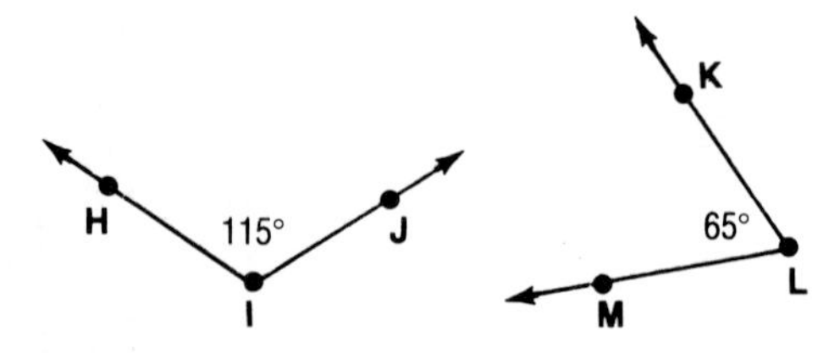

m∠I + m∠L = 115 + 65 = 180.

∠I and ∠L are supplementary.

EXERCISES ***State whether each of the following pairs of angles are adjacent. Use the figure shown at the right.***

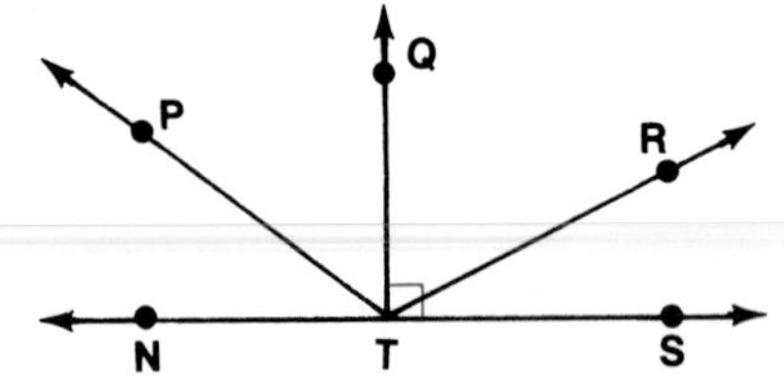

1. ∠NTP and ∠PTQ
2. ∠NTP and ∠QTR
3. ∠PTQ and ∠RTS
4. ∠PTQ and ∠QTR
5. ∠NTP and ∠NTQ
6. ∠QTR and ∠RTS
7. ∠NTR and ∠RTS
8. ∠NTQ and ∠PTR

Use the figure shown above to complete each of the following.

9. ∠QTS and ▒ are right angles.
10. ∠NTP and ▒ are complementary.
11. ∠QTR and ▒ are complementary.
12. ∠NTR and ▒ are supplementary.
13. ∠QTN and ▒ are supplementary.
14. ∠PTN and ▒ are supplementary.
15. If ∠NTR measures 148, then ∠RTS measures ▒.
16. If ∠PTQ measures 46, then ∠NTP measures ▒.

Intersecting lines form pairs of **vertical angles.**

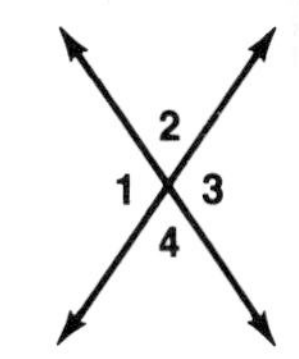

Angles can be named by numbers.

$\angle 1$ and $\angle 3$ are vertical angles.
$\angle 2$ and $\angle 4$ are vertical angles.

Can you explain why vertical angles have the same measure?

The measures of angles can be found using complementary, supplementary, and vertical angles. Study the figure shown at the right. Explain why the following are true.

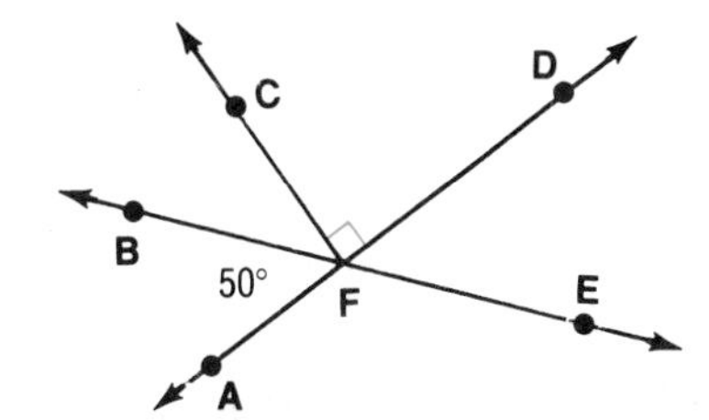

$m\angle DFE = 50$ $\quad$ $m\angle BFC = 40$ $\quad$ $m\angle AFE = 130$

EXERCISES ***Use the figure at the right to complete each of the following.***

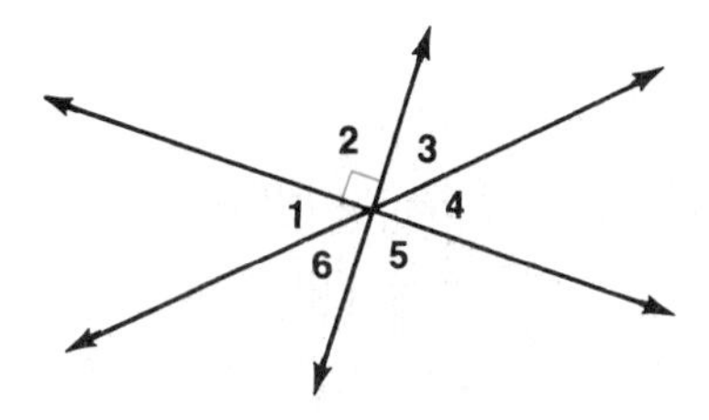

17. $\angle 1$ and ▒ are vertical angles.

18. $\angle 3$ and ▒ are vertical angles.

19. If $m\angle 1 = 40$, then $m\angle 4 =$ ▒.

20. If $m\angle 1 = 50$, then $m\angle 3 =$ ▒.

21. If $m\angle 5 + m\angle 4 = 140$, then $m\angle 6 =$ ▒.

22. If $m\angle 4 + m\angle 5 = 135$, then $m\angle 4 =$ ▒.

23. If $m\angle 4 = x$, then $m\angle 1 =$ ▒.

24. If $m\angle 1 = y$, its supplement measures ▒.

FOUR LINES

Trace the nine points at the right. Draw four straight, connected lines that pass through all nine points. Do *not* lift your pencil or retrace your path.

5-4 Perpendicular and Parallel Lines

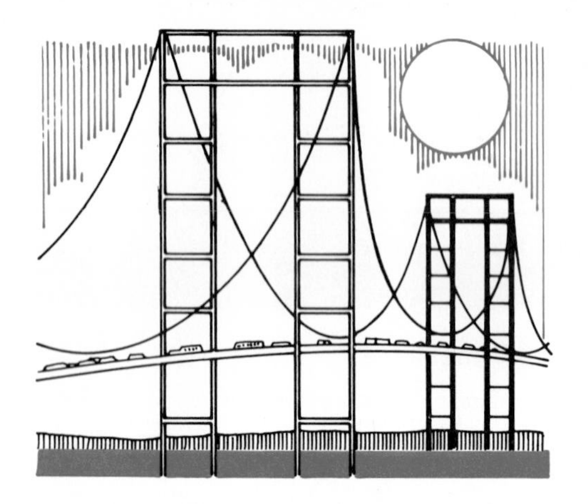

The supports of a bridge meet to form right angles. Two lines that intersect to form right angles are **perpendicular** to each other. Line AB is perpendicular to line CD. This is symbolized $\overleftrightarrow{AB} \perp \overleftrightarrow{CD}$.

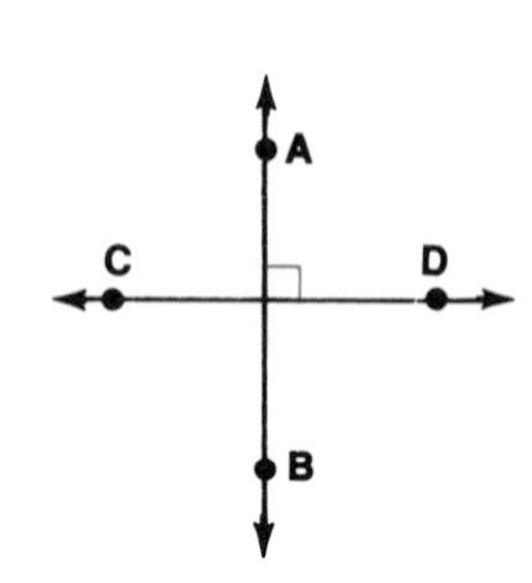

Lines in the same plane that do not intersect are **parallel.** Line EF is parallel to line CD. This is symbolized $\overleftrightarrow{EF} \parallel \overleftrightarrow{CD}$.

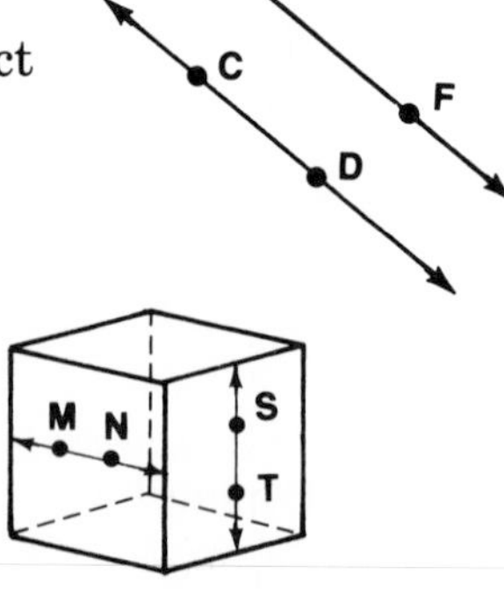

Lines in space that neither intersect nor are parallel are **skew** lines. Line MN is skew to line ST.

M N
S
T

Rays and segments may be perpendicular, parallel, or skew.

EXERCISES ***State whether each of the following suggests perpendicular, parallel, or skew lines.***

1. rungs on a ladder
2. rows of corn in a field
3. lines on a football field
4. airplane flight paths
5. airport runways
6. guitar strings
7. artist's T-square

Use the rectangular prism. State whether each of the following pairs are parallel, perpendicular, or skew.

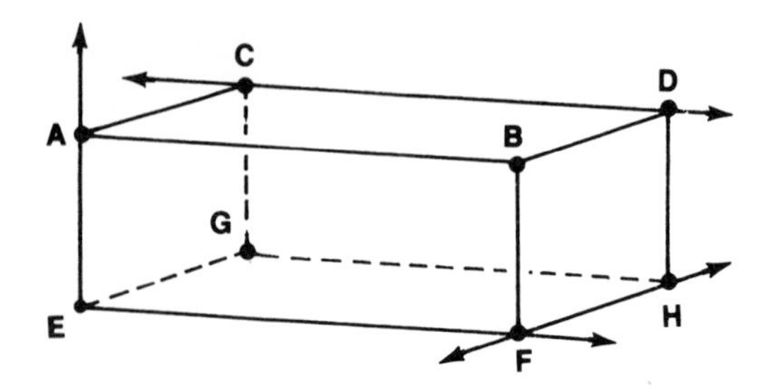

8. $\overline{AB}$, $\overrightarrow{EF}$
9. $\overrightarrow{EF}$, $\overline{BF}$
10. $\overline{BF}$, $\overline{EG}$
11. $\overrightarrow{EA}$, $\overline{AB}$
12. $\overleftrightarrow{CD}$, $\overleftrightarrow{FH}$
13. $\overline{BD}$, $\overleftrightarrow{FH}$
14. $\overline{CG}$, $\overline{GH}$
15. $\overrightarrow{EA}$, $\overline{BF}$
16. $\overline{AC}$, $\overleftrightarrow{FH}$

A **transversal** is a line that intersects two or more lines. Transversal JK intersects lines LM and NP. Eight angles are formed by the intersection of a transversal and two lines.

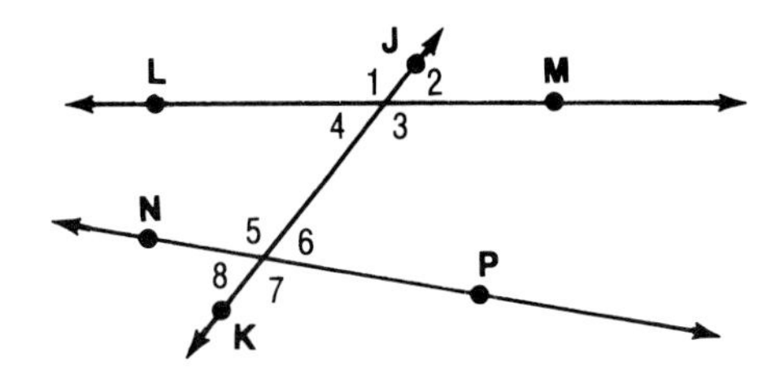

corresponding angles: $\angle 1$ and $\angle 5$, $\angle 2$ and $\angle 6$, $\angle 3$ and $\angle 7$, $\angle 4$ and $\angle 8$
alternate interior angles: $\angle 4$ and $\angle 6$, $\angle 3$ and $\angle 5$
alternate exterior angles: $\angle 1$ and $\angle 7$, $\angle 2$ and $\angle 8$

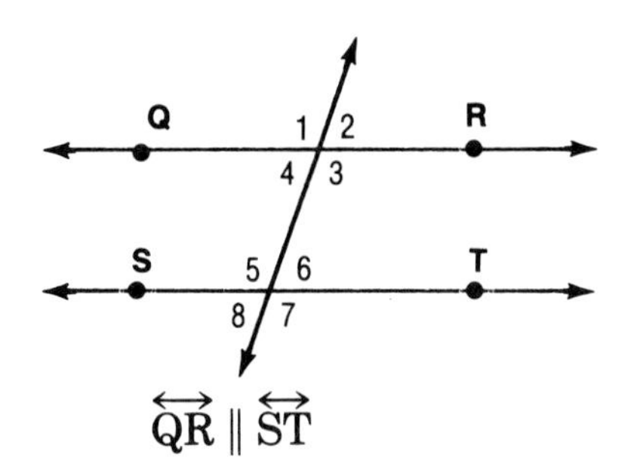

What happens if two parallel lines are cut by a transversal? Use the figure shown at the left to measure the pairs of angles listed above. You can conclude that corresponding angles have the same measure. This is also true for alternate interior angles and alternate exterior angles.

EXERCISES ***Use the figure shown below. State whether each of the following pairs are corresponding, alternate interior, or alternate exterior angles.***

17. $\angle 12$ and $\angle 14$ **18.** $\angle 9$ and $\angle 13$
19. $\angle 10$ and $\angle 16$ **20.** $\angle 11$ and $\angle 13$
21. $\angle 11$ and $\angle 15$ **22.** $\angle 9$ and $\angle 15$

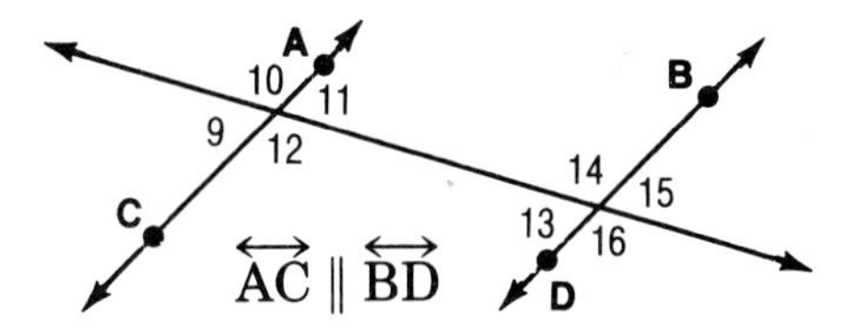

Use the figure shown above to name all the angles that have the same measure as each of the following.

23. $\angle 9$ **24.** $\angle 10$

Use the figure shown at the right to find the measure of each of the following.

25. $\angle 1$ **26.** $\angle 2$ **27.** $\angle 4$
28. $\angle 3$ **29.** $\angle 5$ **30.** $\angle 7$
31. $\angle 6$ **32.** $\angle 8$ **33.** $\angle 9$
34. $\angle 10$ **35.** $\angle 11$ **36.** $\angle 12$
37. $\angle 13$ **38.** $\angle 14$

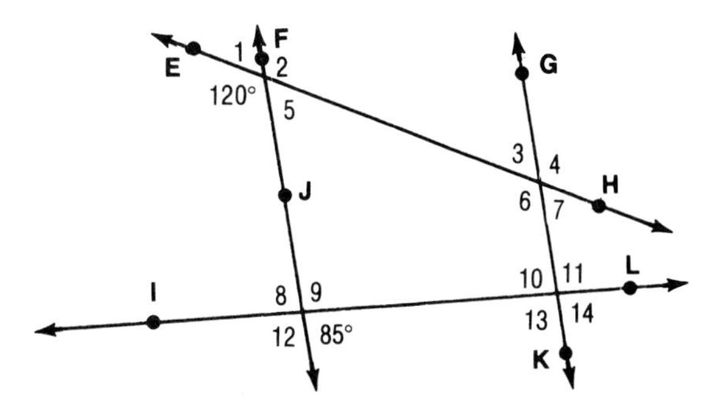

5-5 Congruent Figures

The roof supports of a building may have the same size and shape. Figures that have the same size and shape are **congruent.**

Two angles with the same measure are congruent. Angle ABC is congruent to angle DEF. This is symbolized $\angle ABC \cong \angle DEF$.

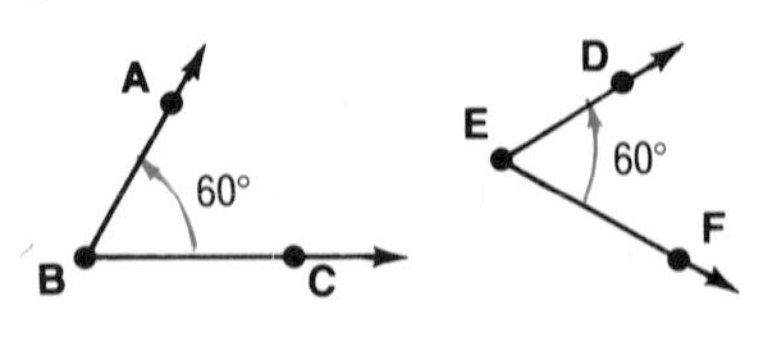

Two line segments with the same measure are congruent. Line segment GH is congruent to line segment JK. This is symbolized $\overline{GH} \cong \overline{JK}$.

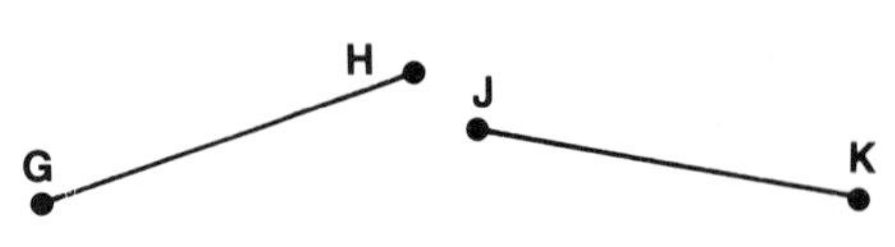

If the corresponding sides and angles of two triangles are congruent, the triangles are congruent. Triangle LMN is congruent to triangle PQR. This is symbolized $\triangle LMN \cong \triangle PQR$. Matching marks show congruent sides and angles.

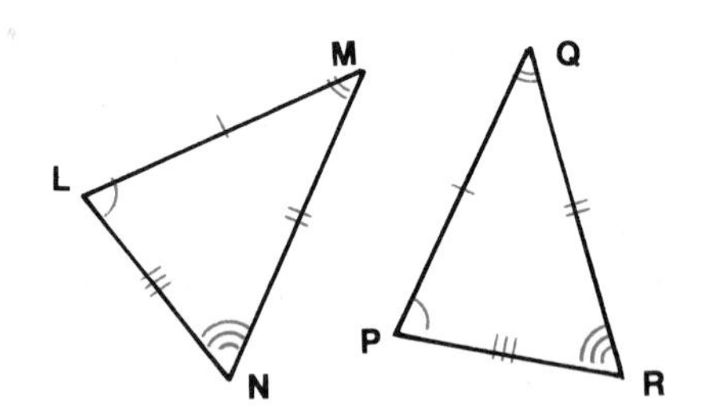

EXERCISES ***Use the congruent triangles shown to complete each of the following.***

1. $\overline{JK} \cong$ ▒
2. $\angle JKL \cong$ ▒
3. $\angle KJL \cong$ ▒

4. $\overline{MP} \cong$ ▒
5. $\overline{NP} \cong$ ▒
6. $\angle NPM \cong$ ▒

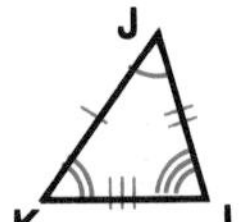

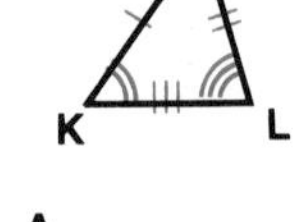

7. $\angle ABC \cong$ ▒

8. $\angle BAC \cong$ ▒
9. $\overline{AB} \cong$ ▒
10. $\overline{EF} \cong$ ▒
11. $\angle DFE \cong$ ▒
12. $\overline{DF} \cong$ ▒

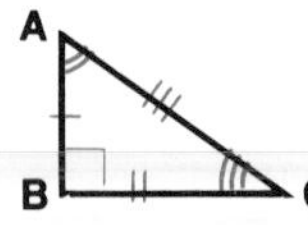

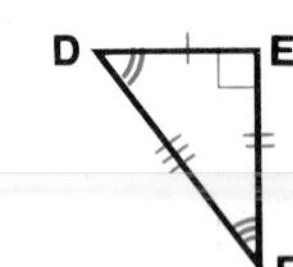

13. $\angle QRS \cong$ ▒
14. $\overline{QR} \cong$ ▒
15. $\overline{RS} \cong$ ▒
16. $\angle XZY \cong$ ▒
17. $\angle ZXY \cong$ ▒
18. $\overline{XZ} \cong$ ▒

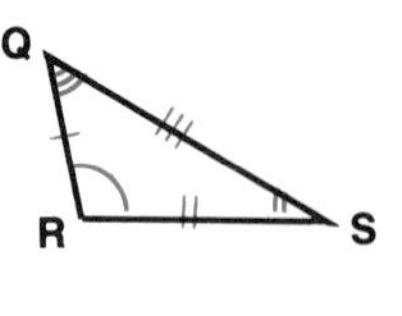

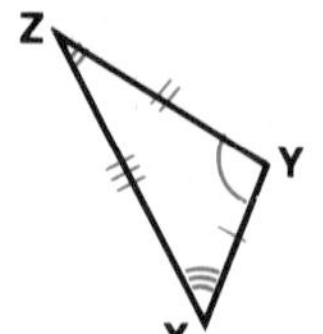

When the corresponding sides of two triangles are congruent, the triangles are congruent.

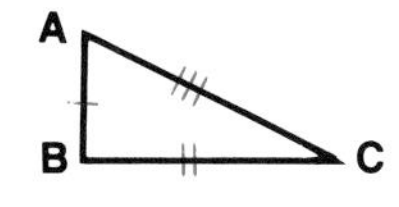

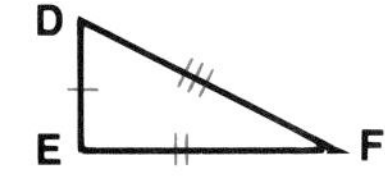

$\overline{AB} \cong \overline{DE}$, $\overline{BC} \cong \overline{EF}$, $\overline{AC} \cong \overline{DF}$

side – side – side **(SSS)**

When two corresponding sides and the included angle are congruent, the triangles are congruent.

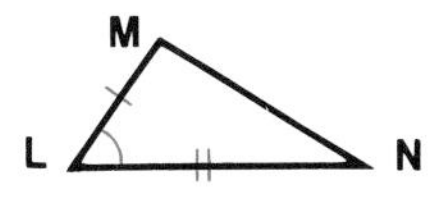

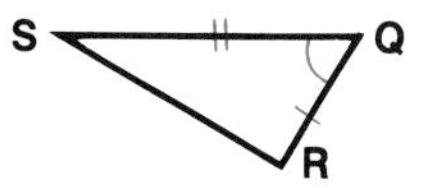

$\overline{LM} \cong \overline{QR}$, $\angle MLN \cong \angle RQS$, $\overline{LN} \cong \overline{QS}$

side – angle – side **(SAS)**

When two corresponding angles and the included side are congruent, the triangles are congruent.

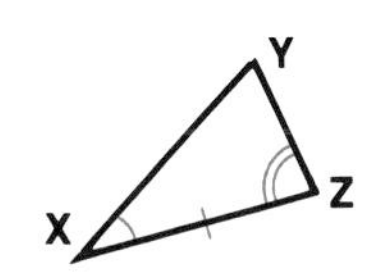

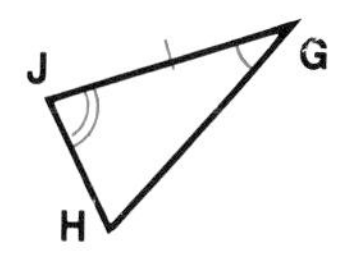

$\angle YXZ \cong \angle HGJ$, $\overline{XZ} \cong \overline{GJ}$, $\angle XZY \cong \angle GJH$

angle – side – angle **(ASA)**

EXERCISES ***Is each pair of triangles congruent by SSS, SAS, or ASA?***

19. 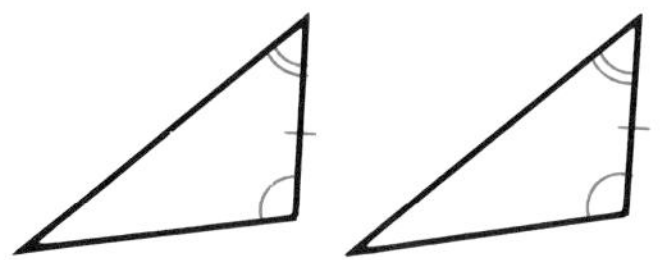

20. 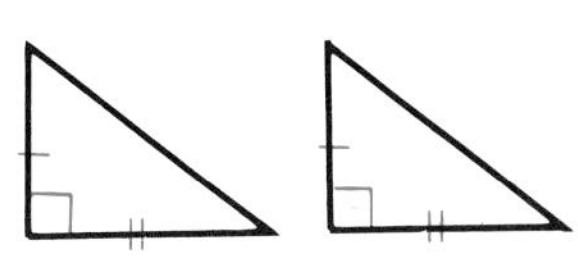

21. 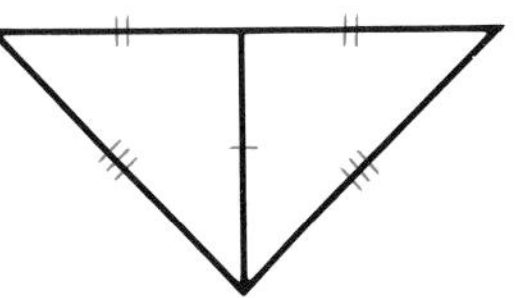

22. 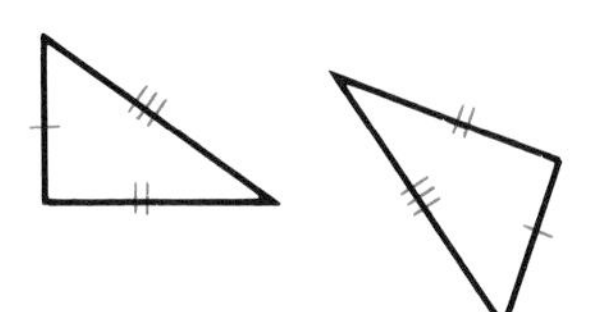

23. 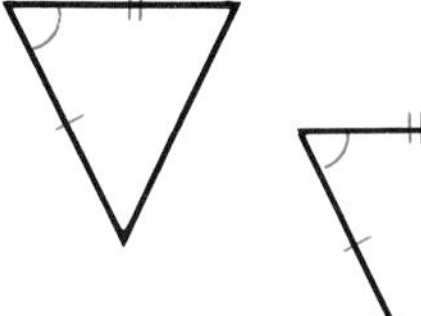

24. 

LINE OF SYMMETRY

A line can be drawn through some figures so that the figure on one side is a mirror image of the figure on the other side. This line is called a **line of symmetry.**

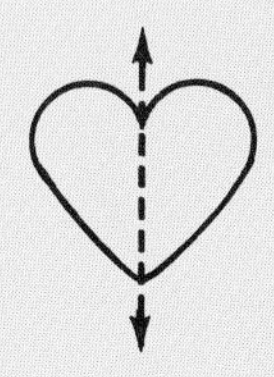

Copy each figure shown below. Draw all possible lines of symmetry.

1. 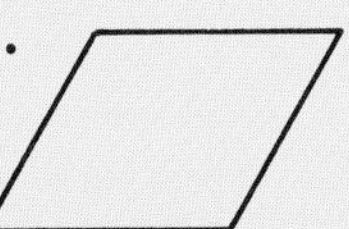

2. 

3. 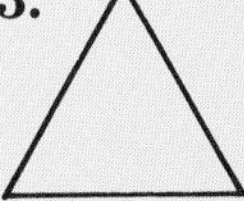

4. 

5-6 Polygons

Polygons are closed plane figures formed by line segments. When you trace a polygon, you can return to the starting point without tracing any point more than once.
Which of the following figures are polygons?

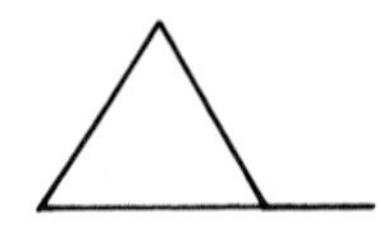

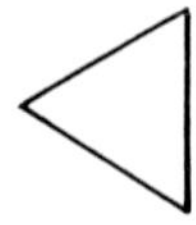

Polygons are named by the number of sides they have. Some common polygons are listed in the chart.

Sides	Name
3	triangle
4	quadrilateral
5	pentagon
6	hexagon
8	octagon
10	decagon

A polygon has the same number of vertices as sides.

A polygon in which all sides are congruent and all angles are congruent is called a **regular polygon.**

regular octagon

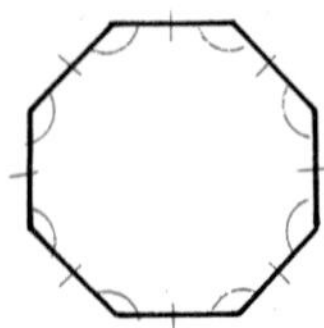

regular pentagon

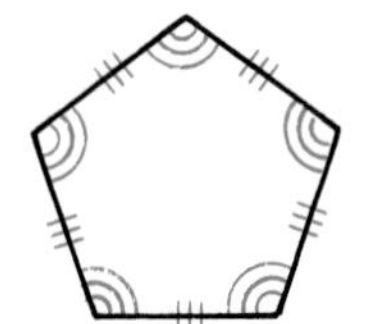

regular hexagon

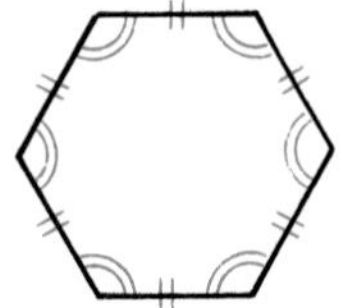

EXERCISES ***Name each of the following polygons by the number of sides. Then state whether it is regular or not regular.***

1. 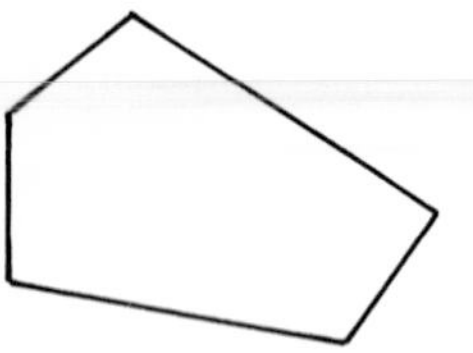

2. 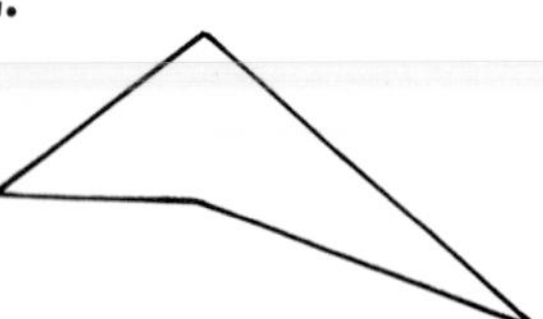

3. 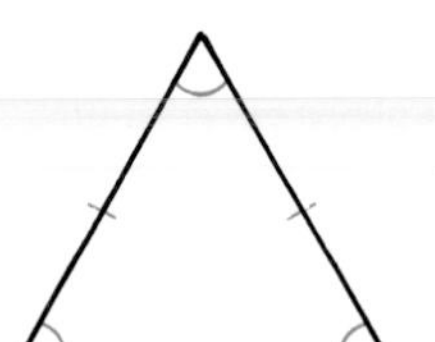

4. 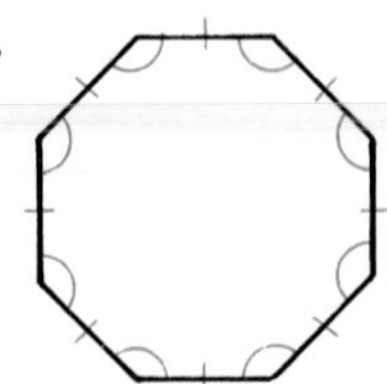

5. 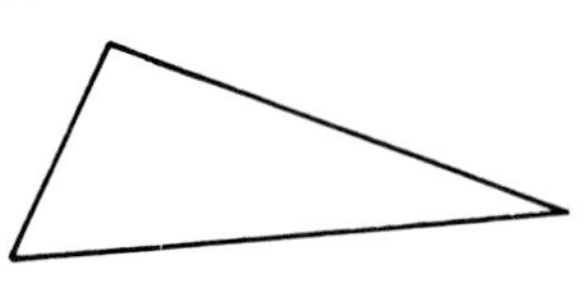

6. 

7. 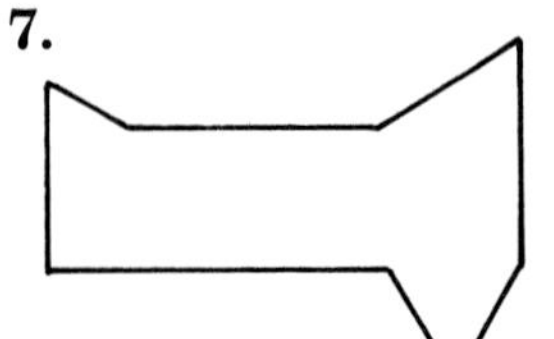

8. 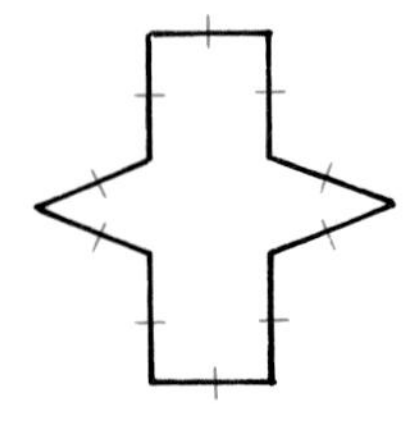

Suppose you fold a triangle three times as shown at the right. Each vertex then meets at the same point.

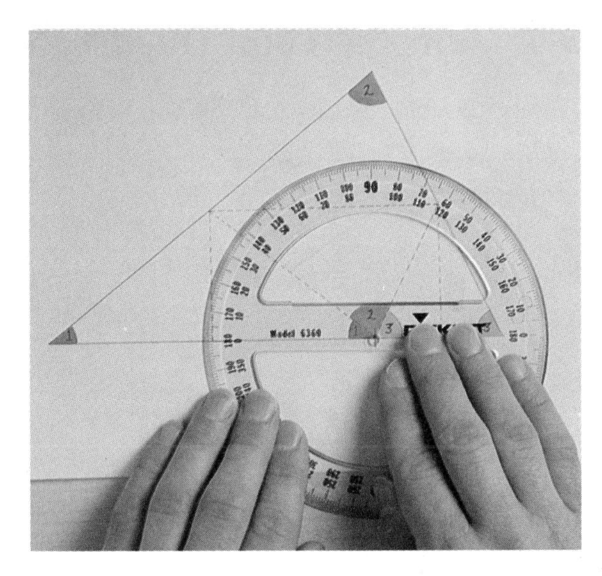

The protractor on the folded triangle suggests the following fact about the sum of the degree measures of any triangle.

$$\mathbf{m\angle 1 + m\angle 2 + m\angle 3 = 180}$$

> **The sum of the degree measures of the angles of a triangle is 180.**

Suppose $m\angle 1 = 50$ and $m\angle 2 = 80$. Find $m\angle 3$.

Subtract the total measure of $\angle 1$ and $\angle 2$ from 180 to find $m\angle 3$. Why?

$$\mathbf{m\angle 1 + m\angle 2 = 50 + 80 = 130}$$

$$\mathbf{m\angle 3 = 180 - 130 = 50}$$

EXERCISES ***Find the measure of the third angle of each triangle.***

9. 75° 55°

10.

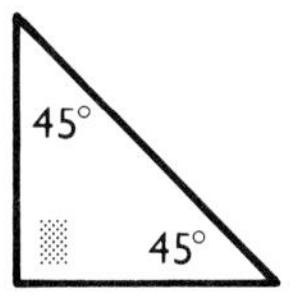

11.

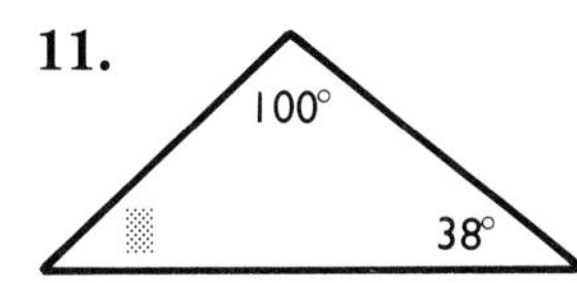

12.

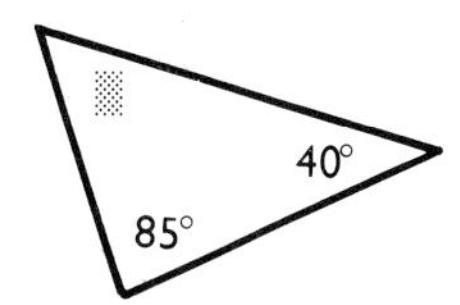

Use diagonals to find the sum of the measures of the angles of each polygon. Note that each diagonal separates the polygon into triangles.

13.

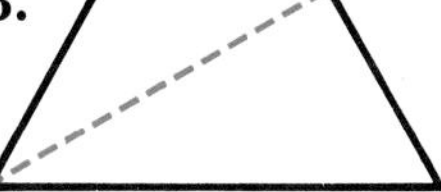

14.

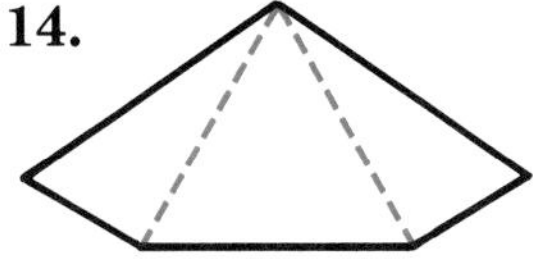

15.

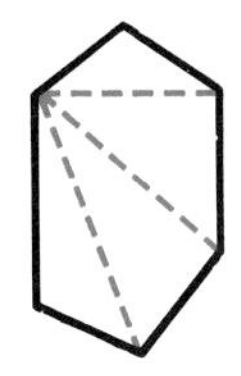

16.

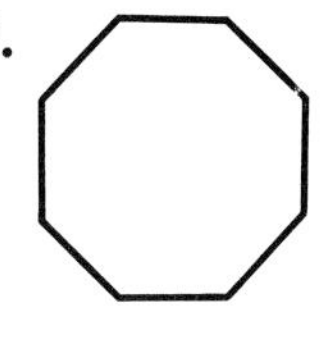

Find the measure of each angle in the following regular polygons.

17.

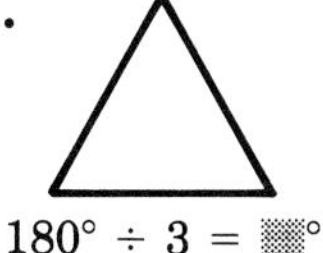

$180° \div 3 = ▒°$

18.

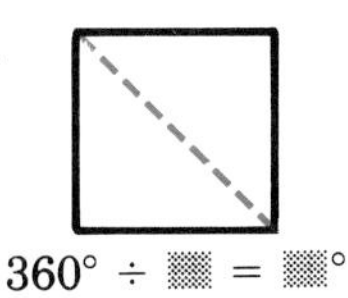

$360° \div ▒ = ▒°$

19.

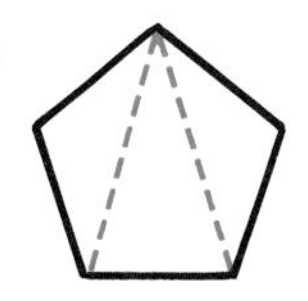

20.

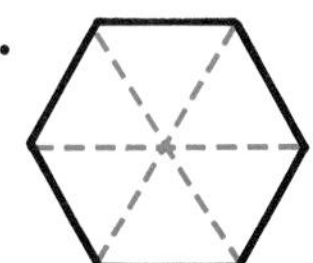

5-7 Triangles and Quadrilaterals

Triangular braces are used in the construction of roller coasters.

Triangles can be classified by the number of congruent sides.

3 congruent sides	at least 2 congruent sides	no congruent sides
equilateral triangle	**isosceles triangle**	**scalene triangle**

Triangles also can be classified by angles. All triangles have at least two acute angles. Use the third angle to classify the triangle.

third angle—right

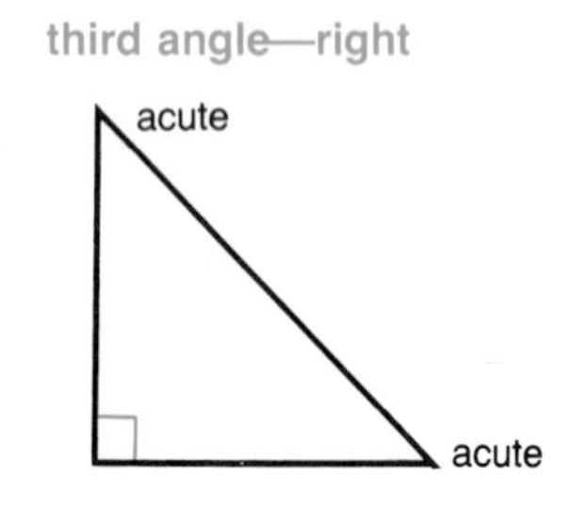

right triangle

third angle—obtuse

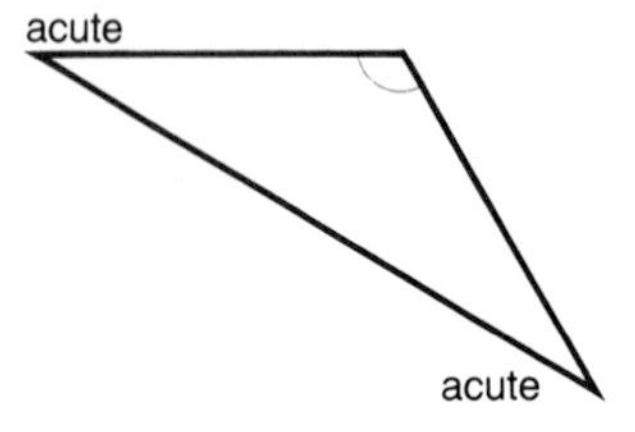

obtuse triangle

third angle—acute

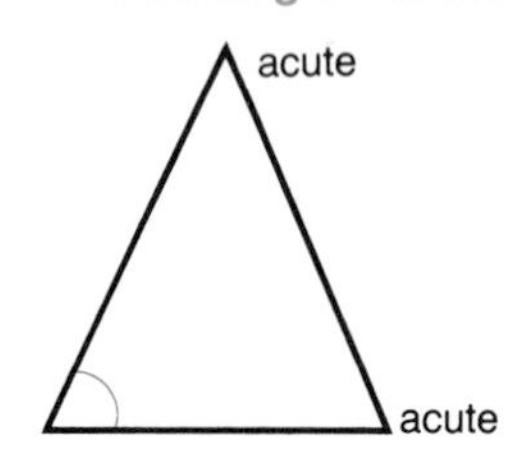

acute triangle

EXERCISES ***Classify each triangle by its sides and then by its angles.***

1.  **2.**  **3.** 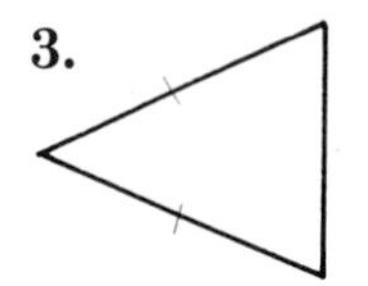 **4.** 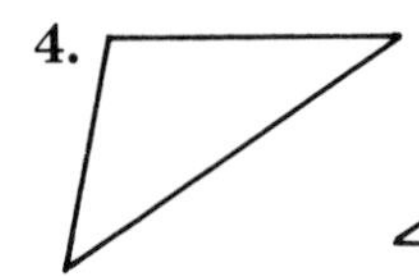 **5.** 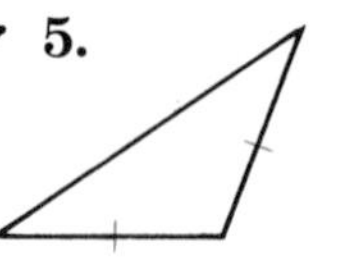 **6.** 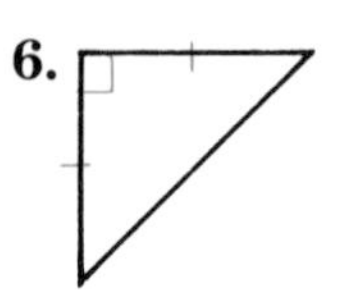

Draw a triangle that satisfies each of the following. If no such triangle exists, write none.

7. isosceles, right **8.** equilateral, obtuse **9.** scalene, acute

Quadrilaterals are classified as follows.

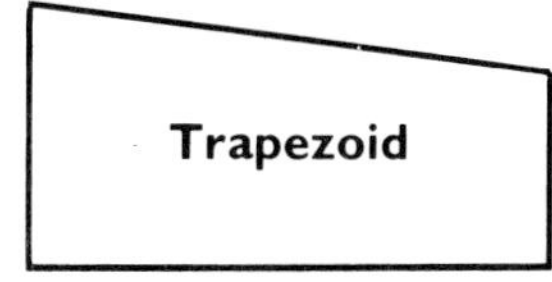

quadrilateral with exactly one pair of parallel sides

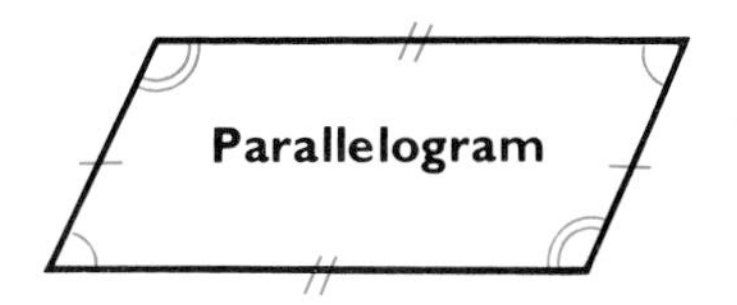

quadrilateral with two pairs of parallel sides

parallelogram with 4 congruent angles

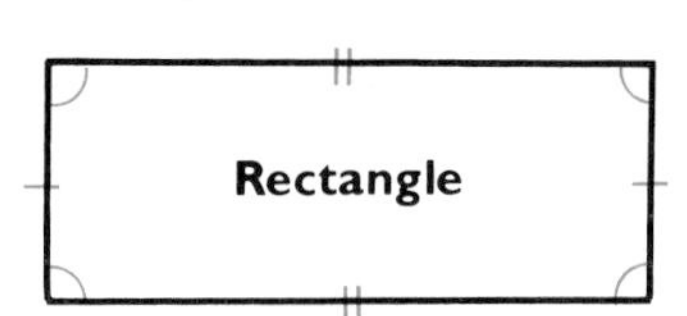

parallelogram with 4 congruent sides

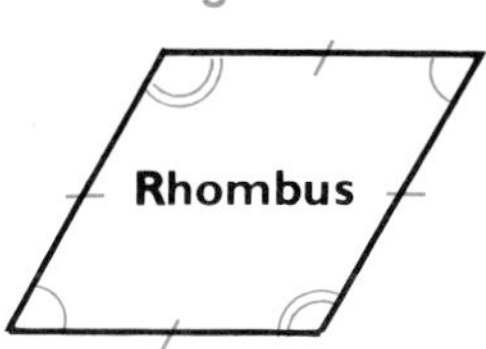

parallelogram with 4 congruent sides and 4 congruent angles

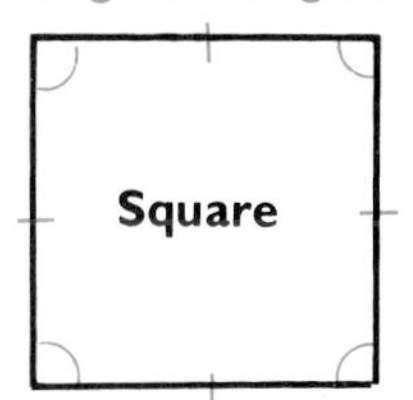

EXERCISES ***List all quadrilaterals with the following characteristics.***

10. two pairs of parallel sides

11. exactly one pair of parallel sides

12. all sides congruent

13. all angles congruent

State whether each of the following is always, sometimes, or never true.

14. A rectangle is a parallelogram.

15. A rectangle is a square.

16. A rhombus is a square.

17. A trapezoid is a parallelogram.

18. A square is a parallelogram.

19. A square is a rhombus.

Skills Review: Pages 115-127

Draw each of the following.

1. an angle with measure 60

2. an obtuse angle

3. two congruent triangles

4. a regular hexagon

5. an isosceles triangle

6. a rhombus

Use the figure below to complete each of the following.

7. If $m\angle 1 = 70$, then $m\angle 2 = $ ▒.

8. If $m\angle 5 = 160$, then $m\angle 4 = $ ▒.

9. If $m\angle 8 = 80$, then $m\angle 3 = $ ▒.

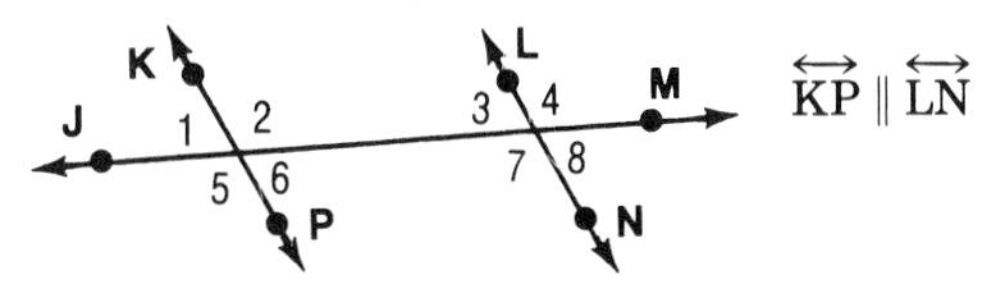

Cumulative Review

Estimate.

1. $\begin{array}{r} 3.21 \\ +\ 6.84 \\ \hline \end{array}$
2. $\begin{array}{r} 483 \\ -\ 78 \\ \hline \end{array}$
3. $\begin{array}{r} 72 \\ \times\ 39 \\ \hline \end{array}$
4. $73\overline{)296}$
5. $0.18\overline{)0.615}$

Add or subtract.

6. $\begin{array}{r} 83.6 \\ +\ 2.09 \\ \hline \end{array}$
7. $\begin{array}{r} \$6.74 \\ -\ 2.98 \\ \hline \end{array}$
8. $\begin{array}{r} 3,000 \\ -\ 127 \\ \hline \end{array}$
9. $\begin{array}{r} 58.2 \\ 172.39 \\ +\ 9.18 \\ \hline \end{array}$
10. $\begin{array}{r} \$4,69 \\ 29.08 \\ +\ 8.98 \\ \hline \end{array}$

11. $6.295 - 0.837$
12. $14.6 + 2.75 + 246.031$
13. $\$27.65 + \$0.89 + \$6.78$
14. $0.84 - 0.308$

Multiply or divide.

15. $\begin{array}{r} 924 \\ \times\ 36 \\ \hline \end{array}$
16. $\begin{array}{r} 0.186 \\ \times\ 7 \\ \hline \end{array}$
17. $\begin{array}{r} 2.9 \\ \times\ 0.2 \\ \hline \end{array}$
18. $\begin{array}{r} 57.9 \\ \times\ 0.81 \\ \hline \end{array}$
19. $\begin{array}{r} 6.728 \\ \times\ 0.104 \\ \hline \end{array}$

20. $6\overline{)5.4}$
21. $3\overline{)\$14.94}$
22. $15\overline{)10.5}$
23. $42\overline{)252}$
24. $8\overline{)4}$
25. $17\overline{)88.91}$
26. $0.26\overline{)48.1}$
27. $0.081\overline{)3.483}$
28. $8.2 \times 1,000$
29. 0.49×10
30. $39 \div 100$
31. $87 \div 1,000$

Find the greatest common factor (GCF) for each group of numbers.

32. 6, 27
33. 14, 35
34. 8, 12, 16

Find the least common multiple (LCM) for each group of numbers.

35. 4, 7
36. 12, 16
37. 3, 7, 9

Write each fraction in simplest form.

38. $\frac{3}{15}$
39. $\frac{6}{20}$
40. $\frac{14}{35}$
41. $\frac{16}{24}$
42. $\frac{30}{54}$

Add or subtract. Write each sum or difference in simplest form.

43. $\frac{1}{3} + \frac{1}{9}$
44. $\frac{3}{5} + \frac{4}{5}$
45. $3\frac{1}{3} + 2\frac{4}{5}$
46. $8\frac{6}{7} + 1\frac{2}{3}$
47. $\frac{1}{3} - \frac{1}{4}$
48. $6 - \frac{7}{9}$
49. $9\frac{7}{8} - 5\frac{1}{6}$
50. $4\frac{1}{4} - 3\frac{2}{3}$

Multiply or divide. Write each product or quotient in simplest form.

51. $\frac{3}{4} \times 20$ **52.** $\frac{4}{9} \times \frac{3}{8}$ **53.** $\frac{5}{7} \times 1\frac{2}{5}$ **54.** $1\frac{2}{3} \times 2\frac{1}{4}$

55. $3 \div \frac{1}{6}$ **56.** $\frac{4}{5} \div \frac{8}{9}$ **57.** $5\frac{1}{4} \div \frac{7}{8}$ **58.** $4\frac{1}{4} \div 2\frac{1}{8}$

Solve.

59. Andy skies down a slope in 72.3 seconds. This is 4.5 seconds slower than his best time. What is his best time?

60. The width of a gymnasium is $\frac{2}{3}$ of the length. It is 60 meters long. How wide is it?

61. The foundation of the Stinard home used 12 cubic yards of concrete. The bill was $498. Find the cost per cubic yard.

62. Chris Messer orders a truckload of sand. She uses $\frac{1}{2}$ in the patio, $\frac{1}{3}$ in the sidewalk, and $\frac{1}{6}$ in a sandbox. How much is left?

Mathematics Lab

You can use paper folding to bisect a line segment or an angle. To **bisect** means to separate a figure into two congruent parts.

Line Segment

1. Draw line segment AB on a piece of paper.
2. Fold the paper so that point A touches point B.
3. Label the line on the fold $\overleftrightarrow{PQ}$ and indicate point M.

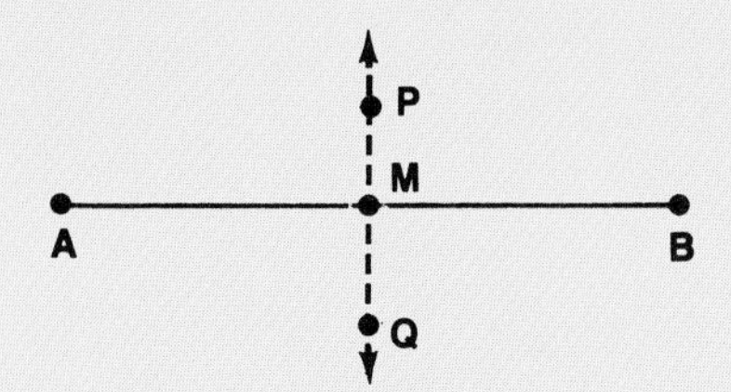

Complete the following.

1. Measure $\overline{AM}$ and $\overline{MB}$.

2. Does $\overleftrightarrow{PQ}$ bisect $\overline{AB}$?

Angle

1. Draw angle AOB on a piece of paper.
2. Fold the paper so that ray OA aligns with ray OB.
3. Label the line on the fold $\overleftrightarrow{OC}$.

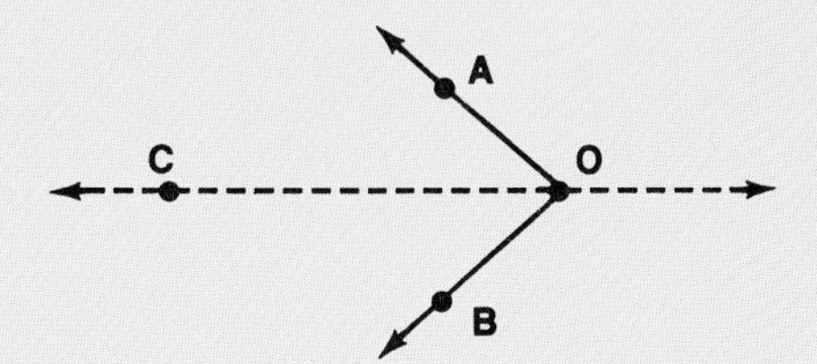

Complete the following.

3. Measure $\angle AOC$ and $\angle BOC$.

4. Does $\overleftrightarrow{OC}$ bisect $\angle AOB$?

5-8 Constructions: Line Segments and Angles

An architect uses a compass and straightedge to draw the design for a new building. You can use a compass and straightedge to construct congruent line segments and congruent angles.

Construct a line segment congruent to a given line segment.

Given:

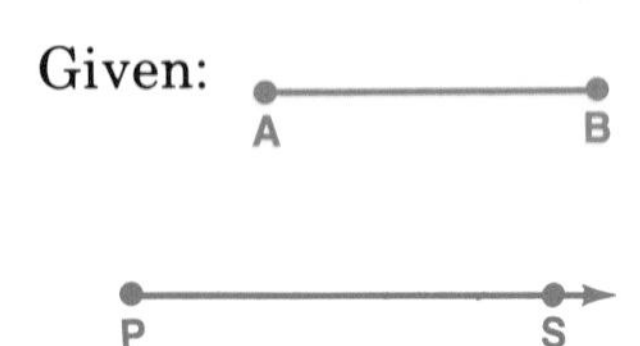

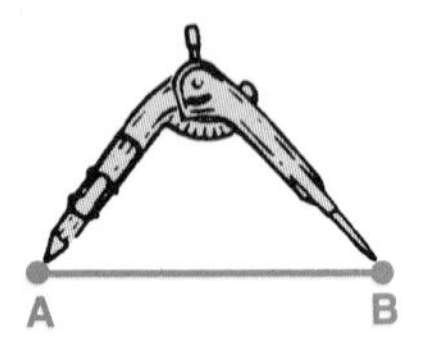

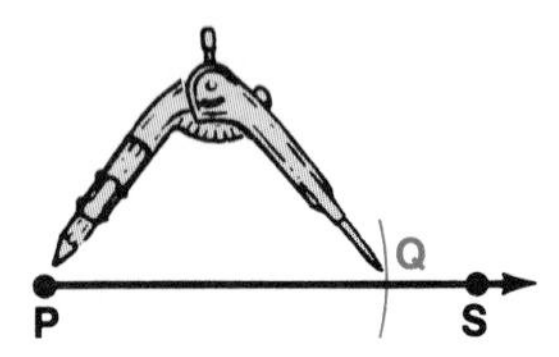

1. Use a straightedge to draw $\overrightarrow{PS}$.

2. Open compass to match $\overline{AB}$.

3. Keep the compass at the same setting and use P as the center. Draw an arc that intersects $\overrightarrow{PS}$ at Q.

$$\overline{PQ} \cong \overline{AB}$$

Construct an angle congruent to a given angle.

Given: $\angle ABC$

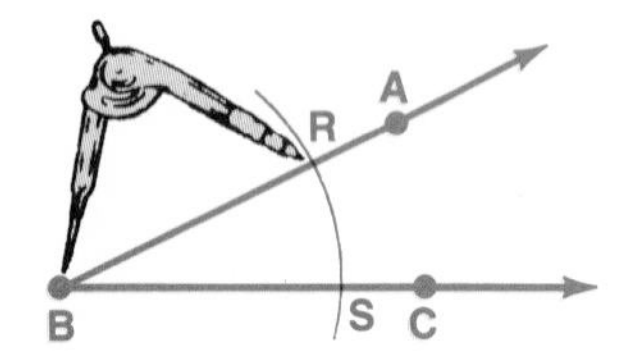

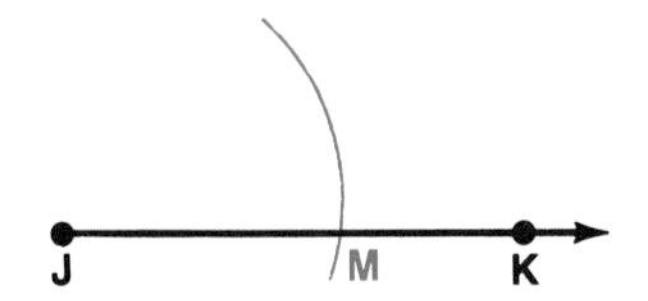

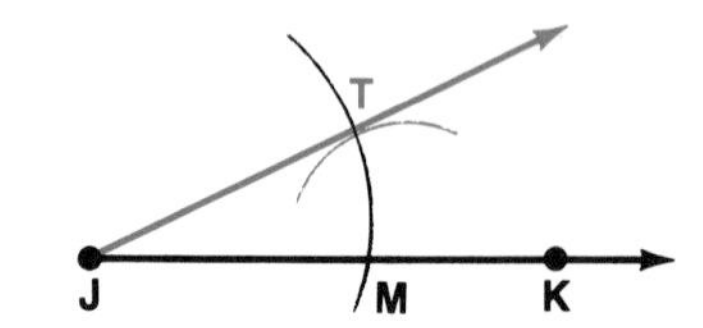

1. Use a straightedge to draw $\overrightarrow{JK}$.

2. Using B as the center, draw an arc that intersects $\angle ABC$ at R and S.

3. Keep the compass at the same setting and use J as the center. Draw an arc that intersects $\overrightarrow{JK}$ at M.

4. Open compass to match $\overline{RS}$. Draw an arc using M as the center. Label the intersection of the arcs T. Draw $\overrightarrow{JT}$.

$$\angle TJM \cong \angle ABC$$

EXERCISES ***Trace each of following from the figure shown below. Then construct a new figure that is congruent to each figure.***

1. $\overline{SQ}$	2. $\overline{SR}$	3. $\overline{TQ}$
4. $\angle STP$	5. $\angle TQR$	6. $\angle PTQ$
7. $\overline{RQ}$	8. $\overline{TN}$	9. $\overline{MP}$
10. $\angle RSP$	11. $\angle STM$	12. $\angle NTP$

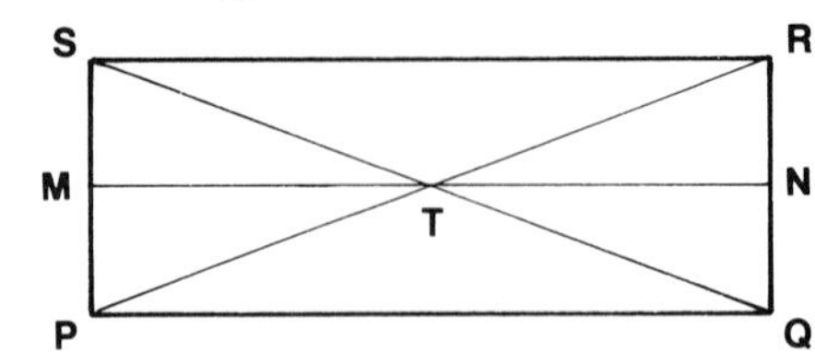

13. Draw a line segment. Then construct an equilateral triangle with the line segment as one side.

In construction, it may be necessary to cut lumber into congruent parts. You can use a compass and straightedge to bisect a figure.

Bisect a given line segment.

Given: $\overline{AB}$

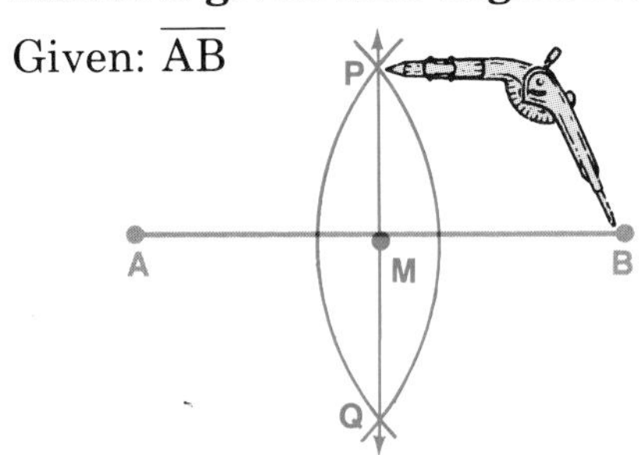

1. Open the compass to more than half the length of $\overline{AB}$. Draw two arcs using A and B as centers. Label the intersections of the arcs P and Q.
2. Draw $\overleftrightarrow{PQ}$. Then $\overline{AB}$ is bisected at the midpoint M.

$$\overline{AM} \cong \overline{MB}$$

Bisect a given angle.

Given: $\angle NAM$

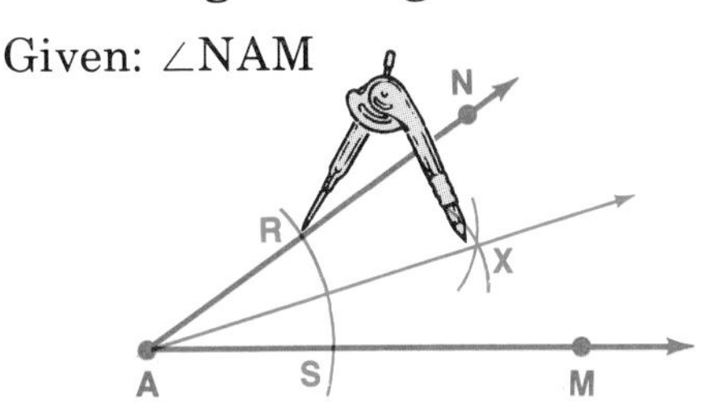

1. Using A as the center, draw an arc that intersects $\angle NAM$ at R and S.
2. Draw two arcs using R and S as centers. Label their intersection X.
3. Draw $\overrightarrow{AX}$. This ray bisects $\angle NAM$.

$$\angle NAX \cong \angle XAM$$

EXERCISES ***Trace each of the following from the figure shown. Then, construct the bisector of each figure.***

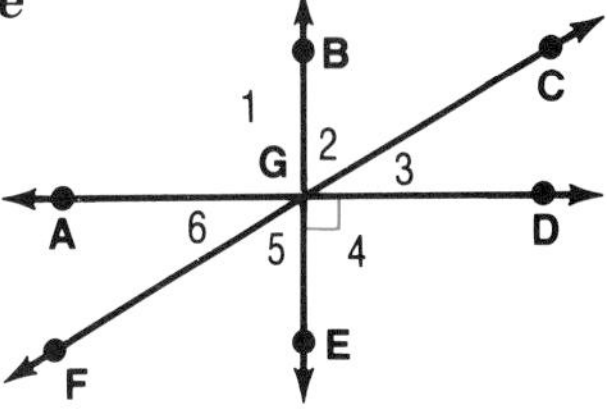

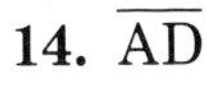

14. $\overline{AD}$ **15.** $\overline{GC}$ **16.** $\angle AGF$

17. $\angle BGC$ **18.** $\overline{BG}$ **19.** $\overline{BE}$

20. $\angle DGE$ **21.** $\angle FGB$ **22.** $\overline{AG}$

Trace each angle shown at the right. Then, construct angles that have each of the following measures.

23. $\frac{1}{2}x°$ **24.** $\frac{1}{2}y°$

25. $\frac{1}{4}x°$ **26.** $\frac{3}{4}y°$

***27.** $x° + y°$ ***28.** $\frac{1}{2}(x° + y°)$

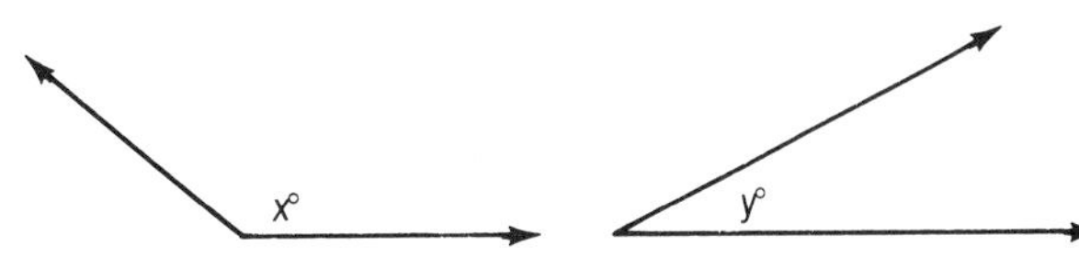

5-9 Constructions: Perpendicular and Parallel Lines

The steel beams of this building show both perpendicular and parallel line segments. You can use a compass and straightedge to construct perpendicular and parallel lines.

Construct a line perpendicular to a line at a given point on the line.

Given:

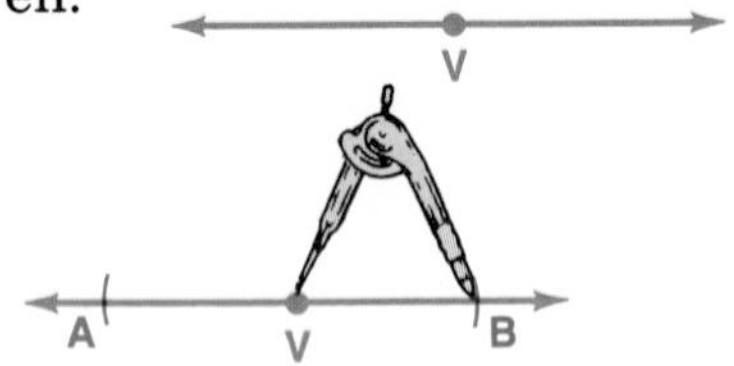

1. Using V as the center, draw two arcs to intersect the line. Label the intersections A and B.

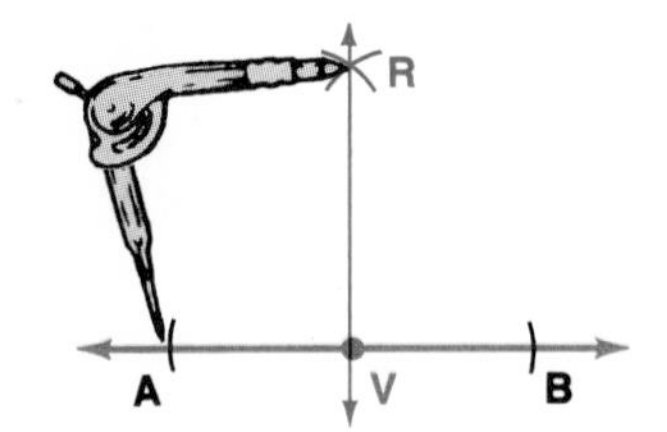

2. Draw two arcs using A and B as centers. Label their intersection R. Draw $\overleftrightarrow{RV}$.

$\overleftrightarrow{RV} \perp \overleftrightarrow{AB}$ at point V

Construct a line perpendicular to a line through a given point *not* on the line.

Given:

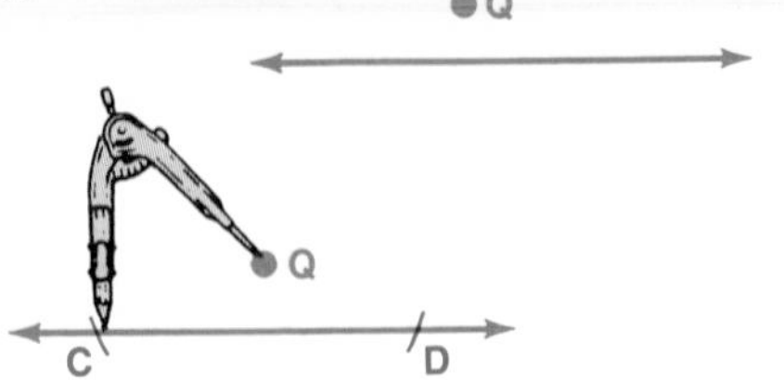

1. Using Q as the center, draw two arcs to intersect the line. Label the intersections C and D.

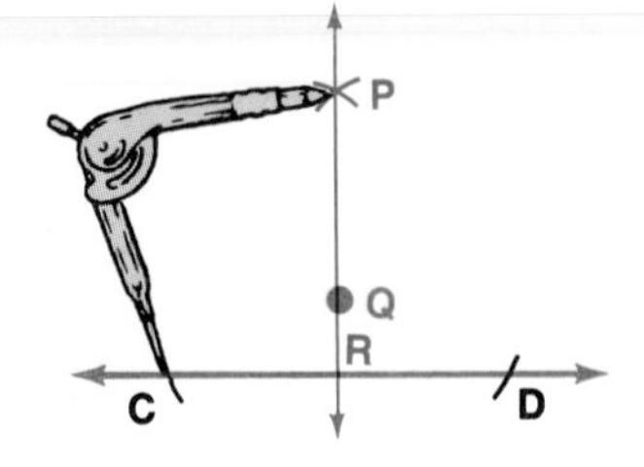

2. Draw two arcs using C and D as centers. Label their intersection P. Draw $\overleftrightarrow{PQ}$.

$\overleftrightarrow{PR} \perp \overleftrightarrow{CD}$ through point Q at point R

Construct a line parallel to a given line.

Given:

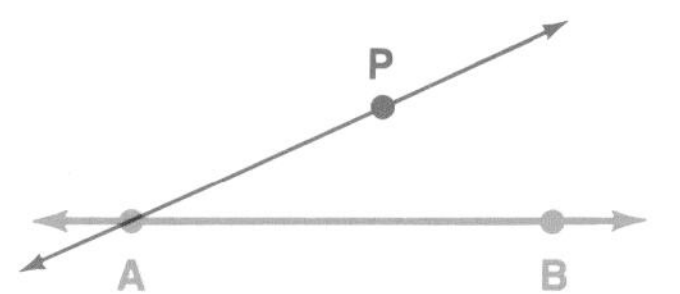

1. Place point P above the line. Draw a line through P to intersect $\overleftrightarrow{AB}$ at A.

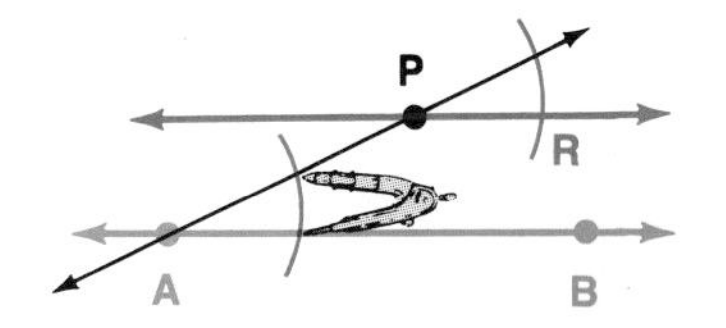

2. With P as a vertex, construct an angle congruent to ∠PAB. Draw $\overleftrightarrow{PR}$.

$$\overleftrightarrow{PR} \parallel \overleftrightarrow{AB}$$

EXERCISES ***Trace the given figure to complete each of the following.***

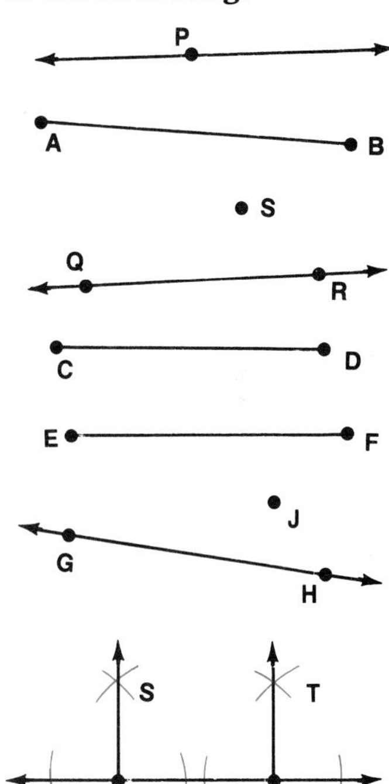

1. Given a line with P being a point on the line, construct a line perpendicular to the line at P.
2. Given $\overline{AB}$, construct the perpendicular bisector of $\overline{AB}$.
3. Given $\overleftrightarrow{QR}$ with S being a point *not* on $\overleftrightarrow{QR}$, construct a line through S perpendicular to $\overleftrightarrow{QR}$.
4. Given $\overline{CD}$, construct an isosceles right triangle with $\overline{CD}$ as one of the legs.
5. Given $\overline{EF}$, construct a square with $\overline{EF}$ as one of the sides.
6. Given $\overleftrightarrow{GH}$ with J being a point *not* on $\overleftrightarrow{GH}$, construct a line through J parallel to $\overleftrightarrow{GH}$.
7. Rays XS and YT are perpendicular to $\overleftrightarrow{XY}$. How do $\overrightarrow{XS}$ and $\overrightarrow{YT}$ relate to each other?

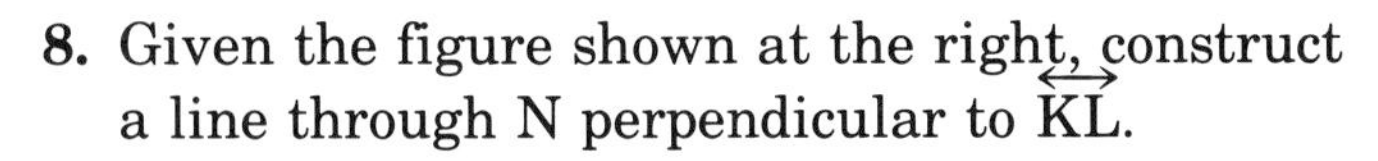

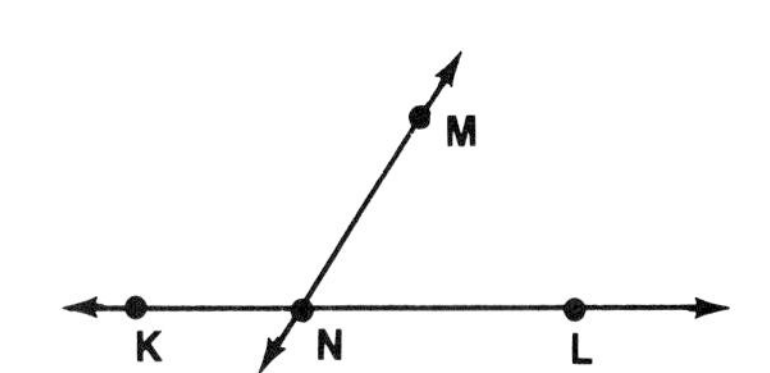

8. Given the figure shown at the right, construct a line through N perpendicular to $\overleftrightarrow{KL}$.
9. Given the figure shown at the right, construct a line through M parallel to $\overleftrightarrow{KL}$.
10. Given the figure shown at the right, construct a line through L parallel to $\overleftrightarrow{MN}$.

5–10 Constructions: Congruent Triangles

You can use a compass and straightedge to construct congruent triangles.

Construct a triangle congruent to a given triangle using the SSS rule.

Given:

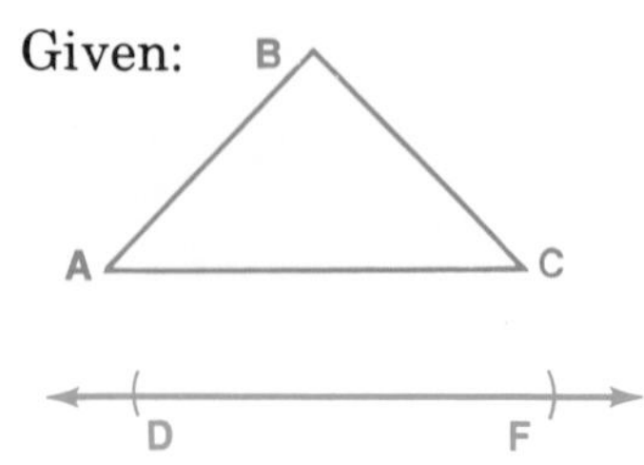

1. Draw a line. Construct a line segment congruent to $\overline{AC}$. Label it $\overline{DF}$.

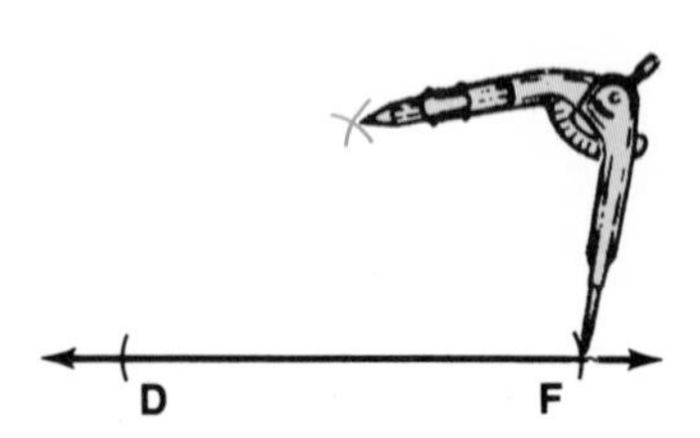

2. With compass open to the length of $\overline{AB}$, draw an arc from point D. With compass open to the length of $\overline{BC}$, draw an arc from point F.

$\triangle DEF \cong \triangle ABC$

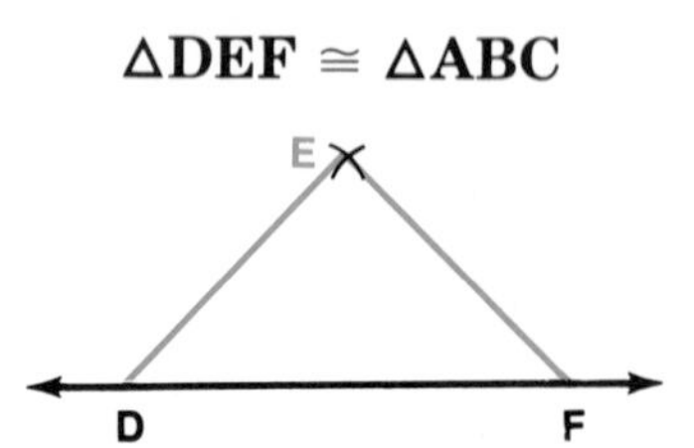

3. Label the intersection of the arcs E. Draw $\overline{DE}$ and $\overline{EF}$.

Construct a triangle congruent to a given triangle using the SAS rule.

Given:

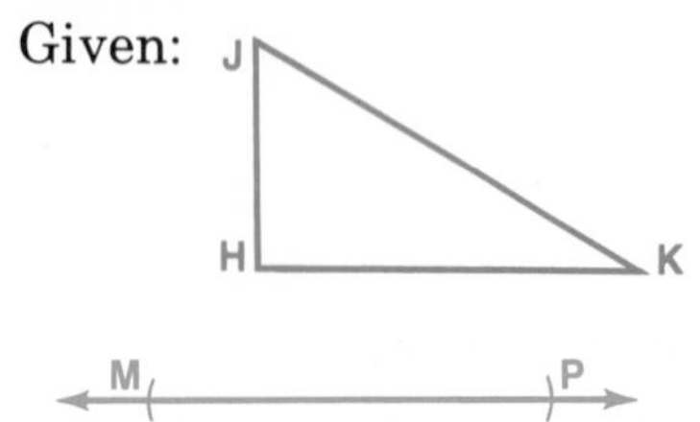

1. Draw a line. Construct a line segment congruent to $\overline{HK}$. Label it $\overline{MP}$.

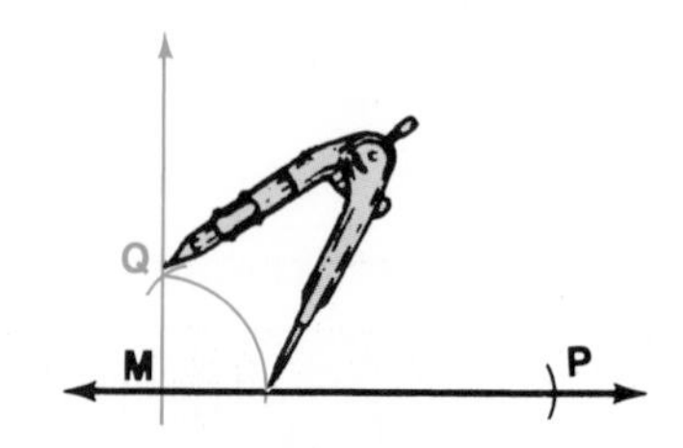

2. Construct an angle at M that is congruent to ∠H. Draw a ray from M through point Q.

$\triangle MNP \cong \triangle HJK$

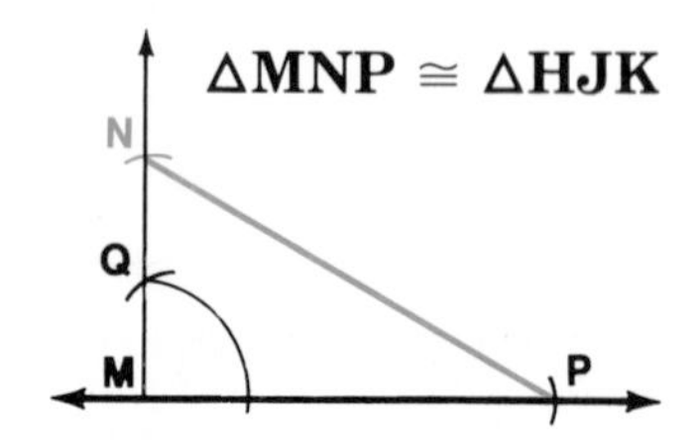

3. With compass open to the length of $\overline{HJ}$, draw an arc from point M across $\overrightarrow{MQ}$. Label it N. Draw $\overline{NP}$.

Construct a triangle congruent to a given triangle using the ASA rule.

Given:

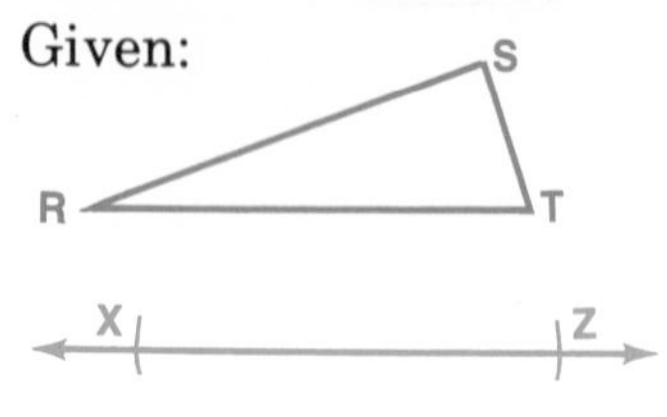

1. Draw a line. Construct a line segment congruent to $\overline{RT}$. Label it $\overline{XZ}$.

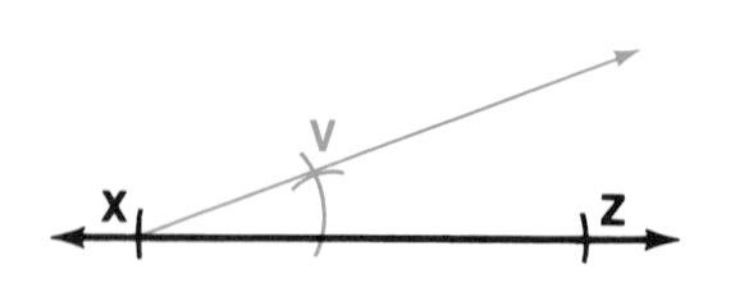

2. Construct an angle at X that is congruent to ∠R. Draw a ray from X through point V.

$\triangle XYZ \cong \triangle RST$

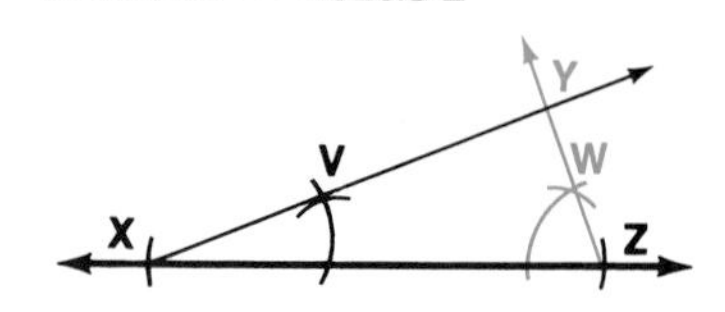

3. Construct an angle at Z that is congruent to ∠T. Draw a ray from Z through W and $\overrightarrow{XV}$. Label the intersection of the rays Y.

EXERCISES ***In △ABC, name the sides and angles required to construct a congruent triangle using the following rules.***

1. SSS **2.** SAS **3.** ASA

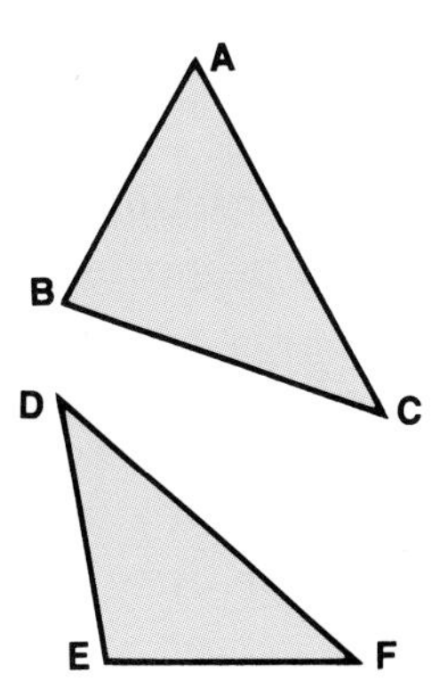

Trace △DEF. Construct congruent triangles using the following rules.

4. SSS **5.** SAS **6.** ASA

Trace △MNP. Construct congruent triangles using the following rules.

7. SSS **8.** SAS **9.** ASA

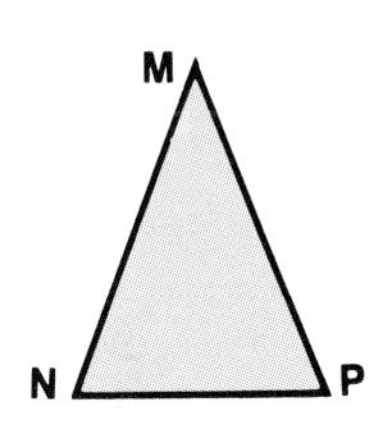

Trace each of the following. Construct a triangle using the SSS, SAS, or ASA rule.

10.

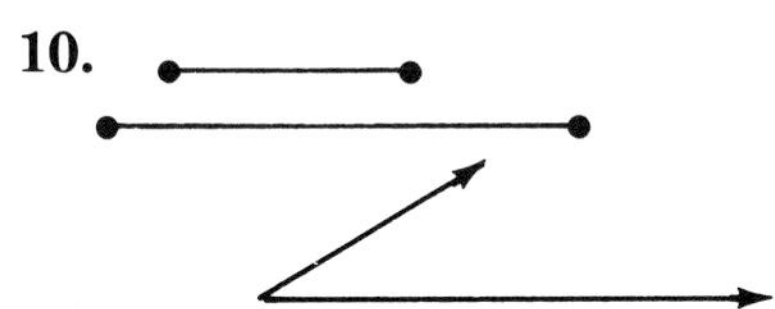

11.

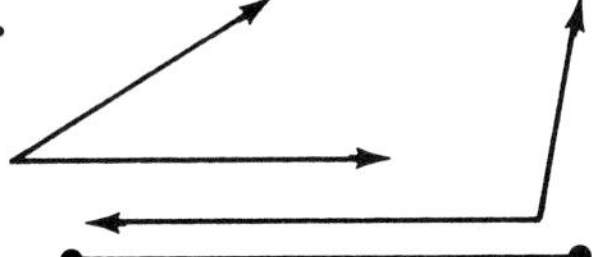

12.

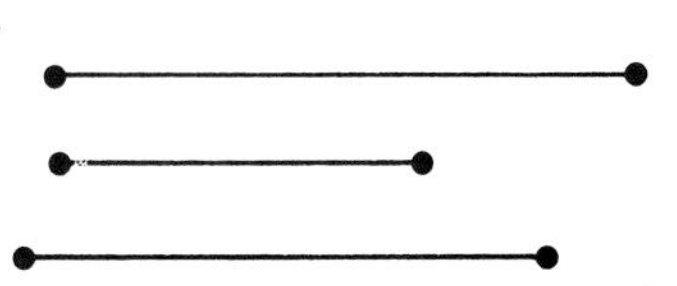

POINT OF SYMMETRY

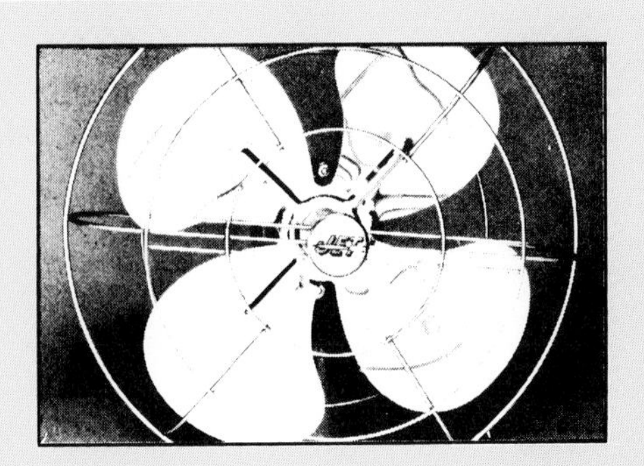

Suppose the blades of a fan make a half-turn (180°) about the center of the fan. The new position of the blades is the same as the old. The center of the fan is a **point of symmetry.**

State whether P is a point of symmetry in each of the following figures.

1.

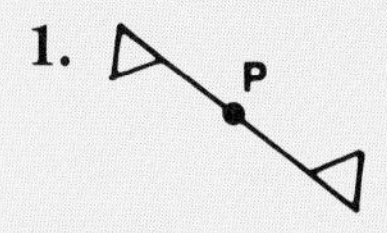

2.

3.

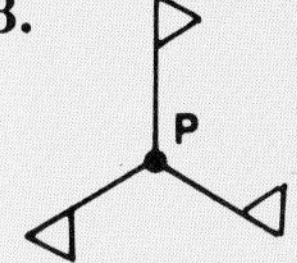

4.

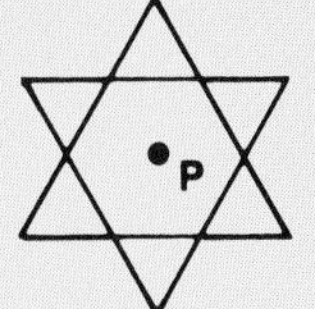

5.

5-11 Constructions: Regular Polygons

The construction of a ferris wheel involves properties of circles.

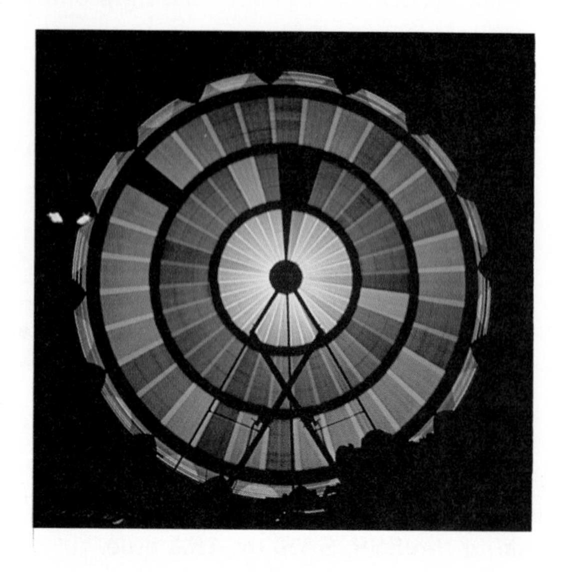

A **circle** is a closed path of points in a plane. All the points are the same distance from a fixed point called the **center.** Any segment whose endpoints are the center and a point of the circle is a **radius.** A segment whose endpoints are both points of the circle is a **chord.** A chord that contains the center of the circle is a **diameter.** An **arc** is part of a circle.

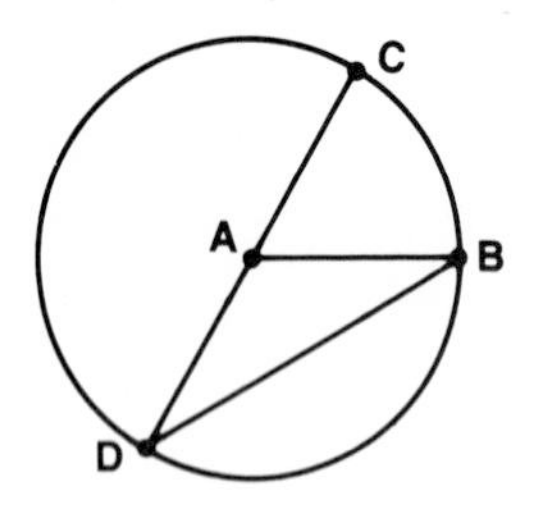

A is the center.

$\overline{AB}$ is a radius.

$\overline{CD}$ is a diameter.

$\overline{BD}$ is a chord.

$\overset{\frown}{BC}$ is an arc.

The plural of radius is radii.
Is a radius also a chord?

You can use a compass and straightedge to construct a regular polygon in a circle. A polygon is **inscribed** in a circle if each of its vertices lies on the circle.

Inscribe a hexagon in a circle.

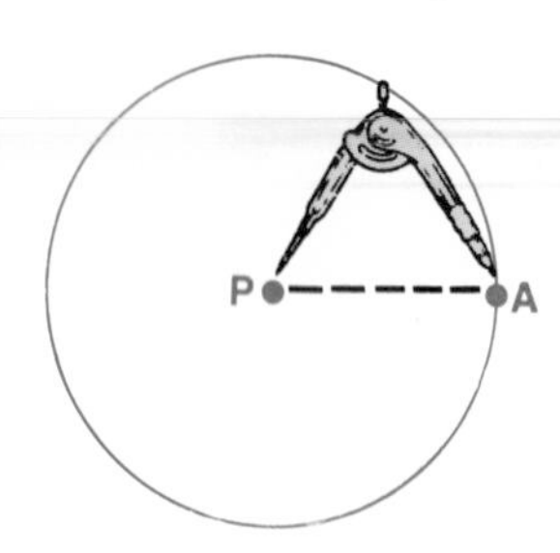

1. Draw a circle. The compass opening will match the radius $\overline{PA}$.

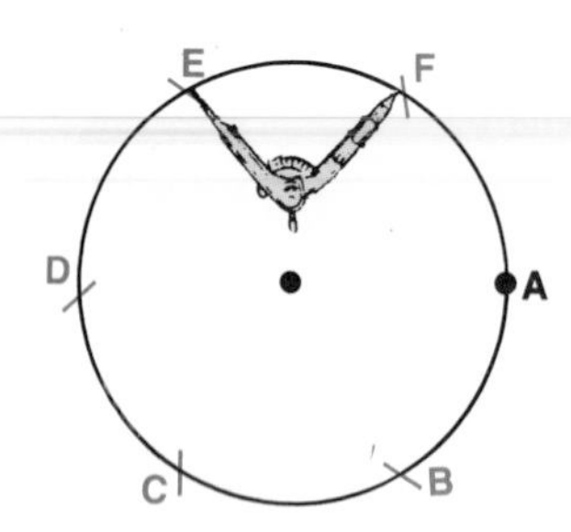

2. Keep this same compass setting. Start at point A. Draw arcs at B, C, D, E, and F. This separates the circle into six congruent arcs.

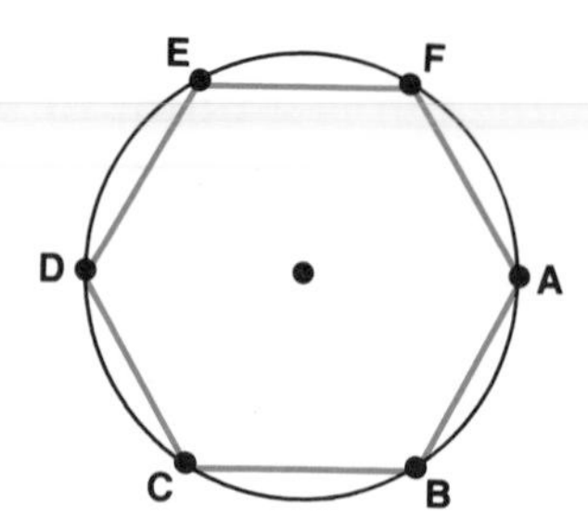

3. Draw chords $\overline{AB}$, $\overline{BC}$, $\overline{CD}$, $\overline{DE}$, $\overline{EF}$, and $\overline{FA}$.

The chords form a regular hexagon.

Inscribe a square in a circle.

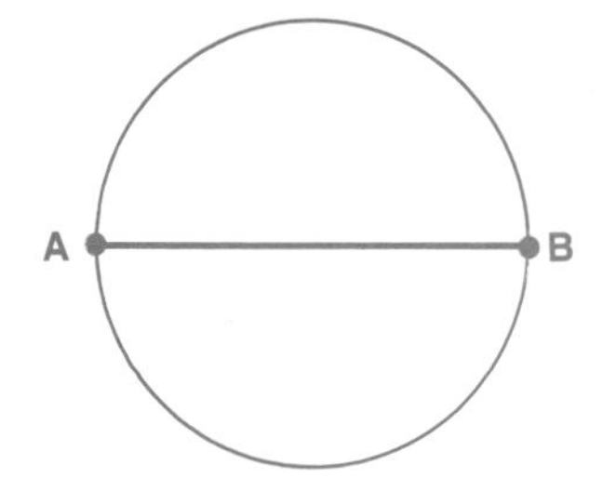

1. Draw a circle. Draw the diameter $\overline{AB}$.

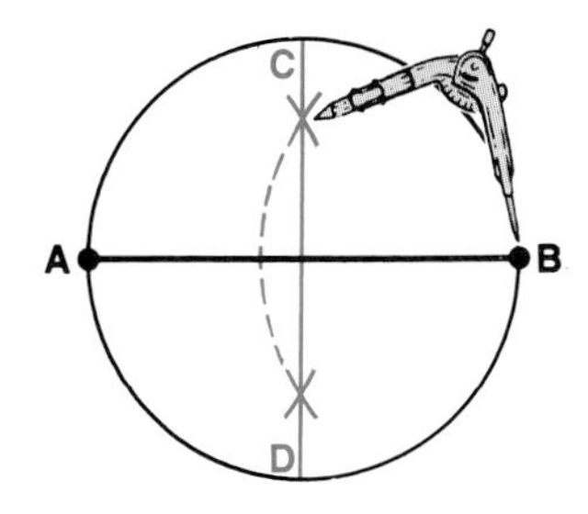

2. Construct the perpendicular bisector of $\overline{AB}$. Label the points where the bisector crosses the circle C and D.

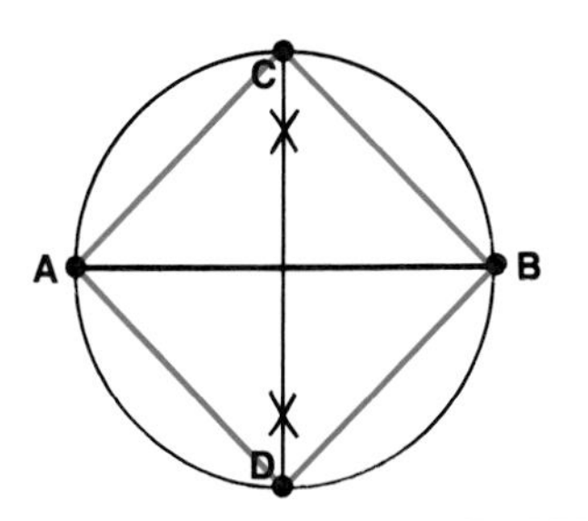

3. Draw chords $\overline{AC}$, $\overline{CB}$, $\overline{BD}$, and $\overline{DA}$.

The chords form a square.

EXERCISES ***Use the figure to name the following.***

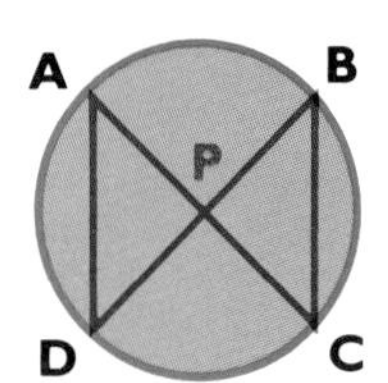

1. the center
2. four radii
3. two diameters
4. two chords

Complete each of the following.

5. Inscribe a regular hexagon in a circle.
6. Connect alternate vertices of any hexagon. What type of figure is formed?
7. Inscribe a square in a circle.
8. Inscribe a regular octagon in a circle by finding the perpendicular bisector of each side of an inscribed square.
9. Copy the design shown at the right.

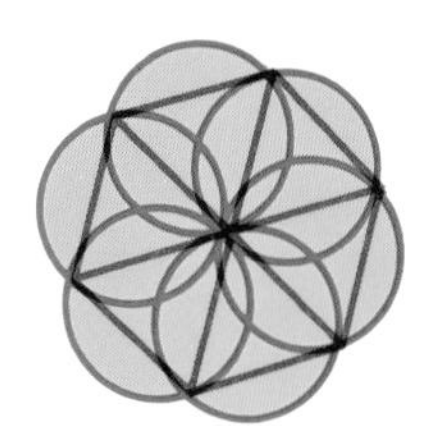

Skills Review: Pages 130-137

Trace the figure shown below. Construct each of the following.

1. a line segment congruent to $\overline{AB}$
2. the bisector of $\angle BCA$
3. a line perpendicular to $\overline{BC}$
4. a line through X parallel to $\overline{AB}$
5. a triangle congruent to $\triangle ABC$

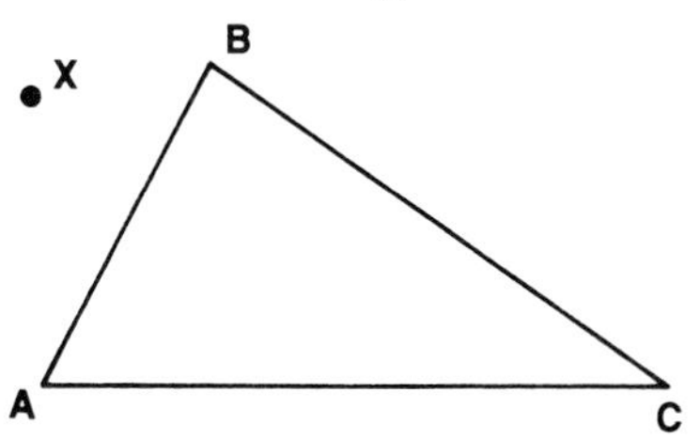

Mathematics and History

The ancient Greeks often used a certain kind of rectangle in their architecture and art. The **golden rectangle** has the special property that the length divided by the width is approximately 1.6. The front of the famous Parthenon has the shape of a golden rectangle.

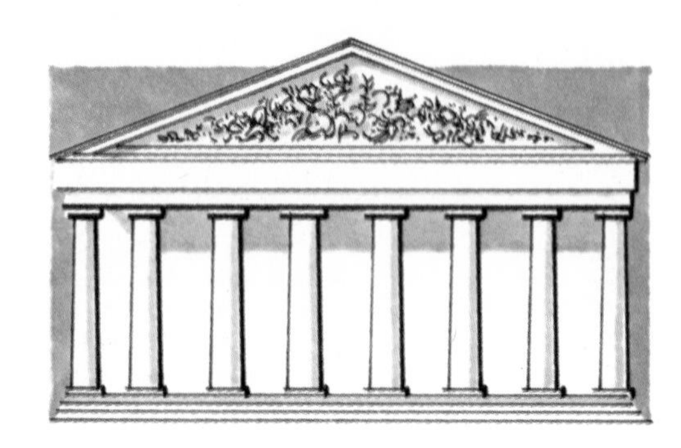

You can use a compass and straightedge to construct a golden rectangle.

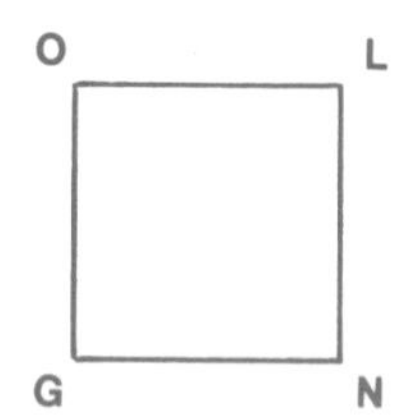

1. **Construct a square.**

2. **Bisect $\overline{GN}$. Label the midpoint C.**

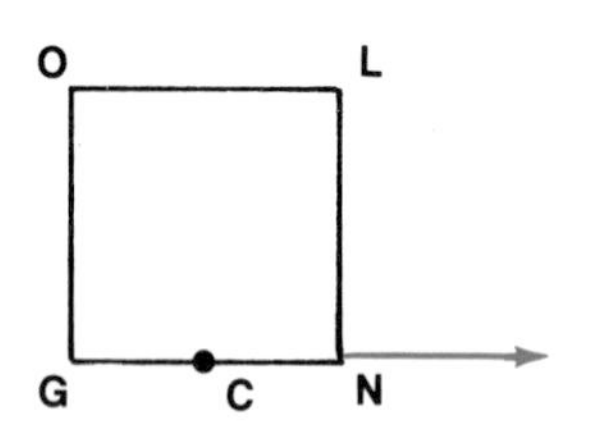

3. **Extend side GN as shown.**

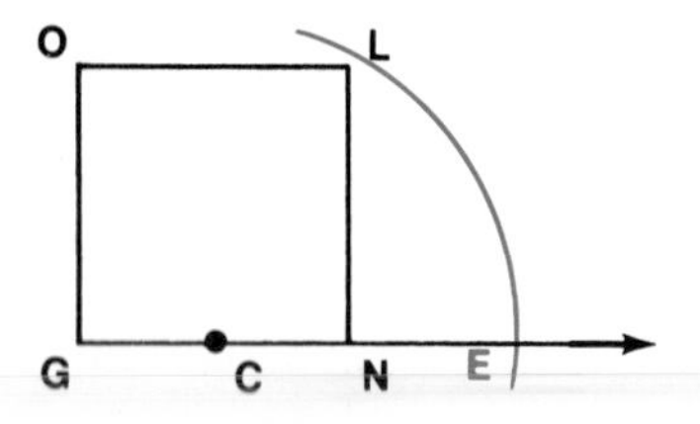

4. **Using C as the center, draw an arc through L that intersects $\overrightarrow{GN}$ at E.**

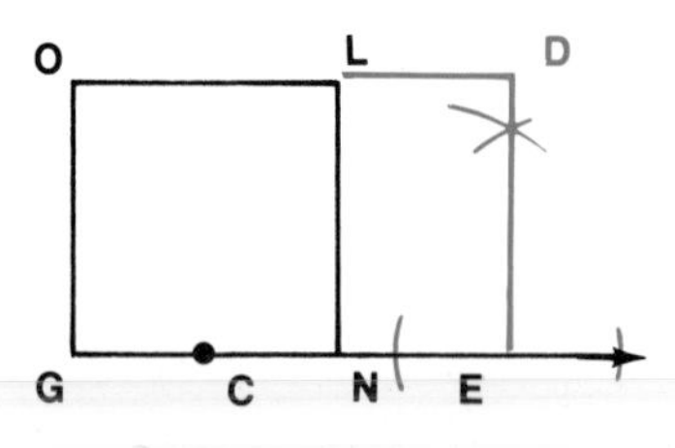

5. **Construct a perpendicular to $\overrightarrow{GN}$ at E. Extend side OL to intersect the perpendicular at D.**

The measure of $\overline{GE}$ divided by the measure of $\overline{OG}$ is about 1.6. This figure is a golden rectangle.

Complete the following.

1. Construct a square 4 cm on a side. Then construct a golden rectangle.
2. Is rectangle LDEN shown above a golden rectangle? Measure to find out.

Chapter 5 Review

VOCABULARY

skew (120)
transversal (121)
alternate interior angles (121)
alternate exterior angles (121)
SSS (123)
SAS (123)
ASA (123)
inscribed (136)

EXERCISES ***Use the figures shown below to complete each of the following.***

1. Name two rays that have endpoint D. (115)

2. Name two acute angles. (117)

3. $\angle 3$ and ___ are supplementary. (118)

4. Name two angles adjacent to $\angle 5$. (118)

5. $\angle 6$ and ___ are vertical angles. (119)

6. Name two perpendicular lines. (120)

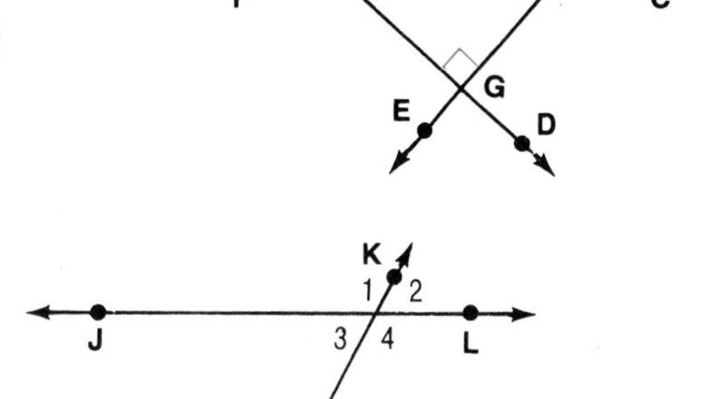

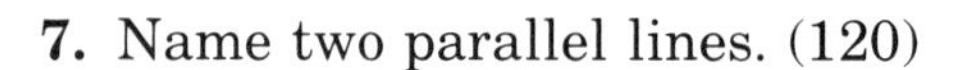

7. Name two parallel lines. (120)

8. Line ___ is a transversal. (121)

9. Name two pairs of alternate interior angles. (121)

10. If $m\angle 4 = 105$, then $m\angle 8 =$ ___. (121)

11. $\overline{RS} \cong$ ___

12. $\overline{QR} \cong$ ___

13. $\overline{TX} \cong$ ___

14. $\angle RQS \cong$ ___

15. $\angle XVT \cong$ ___

16. $\angle TXV \cong$ ___ (122)

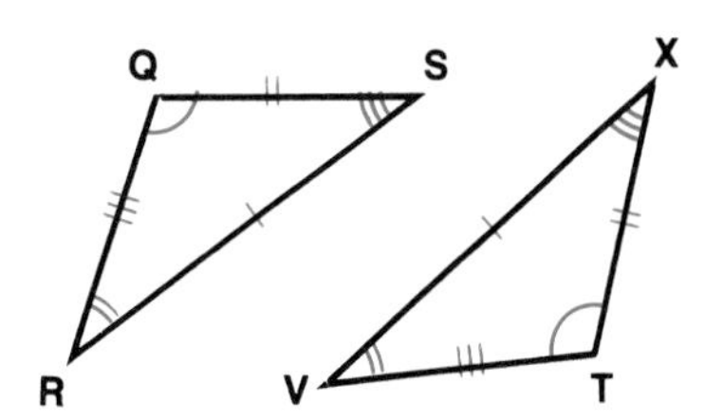

Complete each of the following.

17. In $\triangle ABC$, $m\angle A = 37$ and $m\angle B = 66$. Find $m\angle C$. (125)

18. Draw a scalene triangle. (126)

19. Draw a line DL and a point R not on the line. Construct a line through R perpendicular to $\overleftrightarrow{DL}$. (132)

20. Draw a triangle. Construct a congruent triangle using the ASA rule. (134)

21. Name the quadrilaterals that have two pairs of parallel sides. (127)

22. Inscribe an equilateral triangle in a circle. (136)

Chapter 5 Test

Match the letter of each figure to its most exact description.

1. line segment
2. ray
3. obtuse angle
4. vertical angles
5. supplementary angles
6. perpendicular lines
7. transversal
8. equilateral triangle
9. regular quadrilateral
10. rhombus

a.

b. 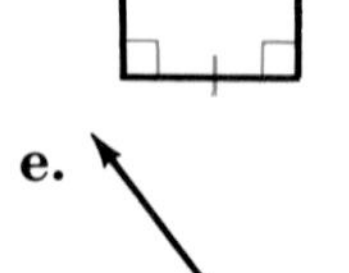

c. 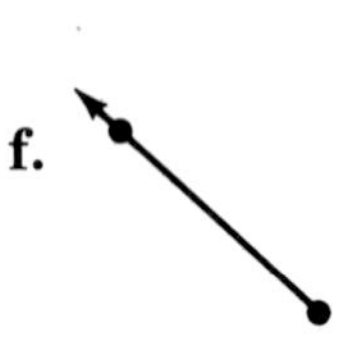

d.

e.

f.

g. 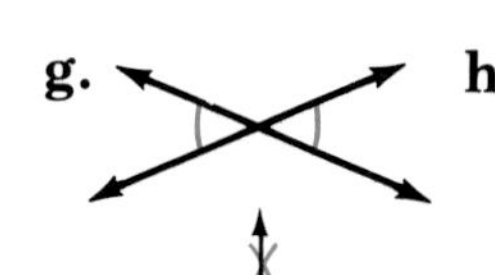

h. 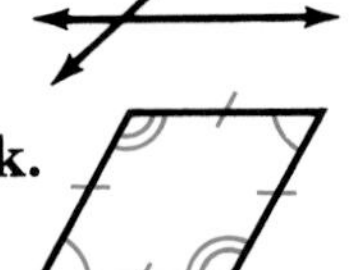

i. 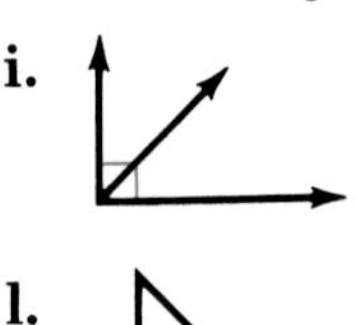

j.

k.

l. 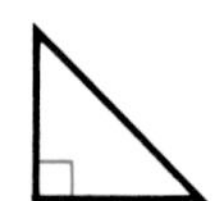

Use the figure shown at the right to name each of the following.

11. perpendicular lines
12. right angles
13. vertical angles
14. complementary angles

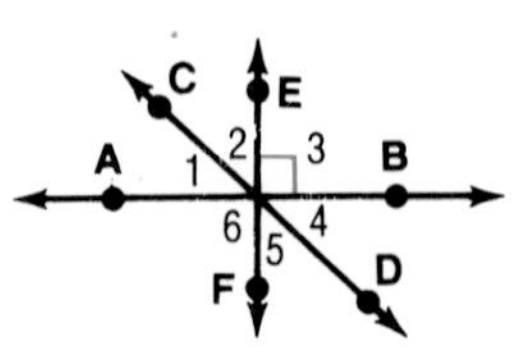

Use the figure shown at the right to name each of the following.

15. parallel lines
16. corresponding angles
17. alternate interior angles
18. alternate exterior angles

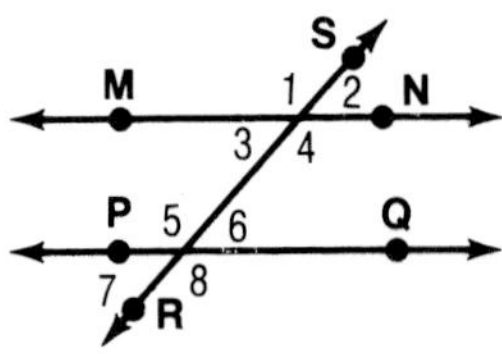

Use the congruent triangles shown at the right to complete each of the following.

19. $\overline{AB} \cong$ ▒ 20. $\overline{XZ} \cong$ ▒ 21. $\overline{BC} \cong$ ▒

22. $\angle ACB \cong$ ▒ 23. $\angle XYZ \cong$ ▒ 24. $\angle YXZ \cong$ ▒

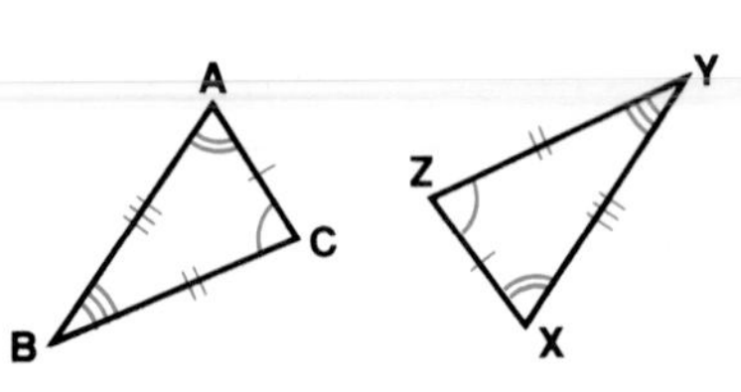

Complete each of the following.

25. Construct a triangle congruent to any triangle using the SAS rule.
26. Name the quadrilaterals that have four congruent sides.
27. Inscribe a square in a circle.

Enrichment

A circle can be drawn through any three points not in a straight line. So a circle can be circumscribed around (or inscribed within) any triangle.

Circumscribed Circle

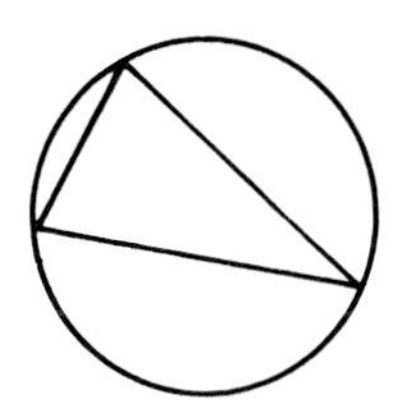

The circle is *outside* the triangle. The three *vertices* touch the circle.

Draw any triangle. Construct the perpendicular bisector of each side. The intersection of the bisectors locates the circumcenter. The circumcenter to any vertex is the radius. Draw the circle.

Inscribed Circles

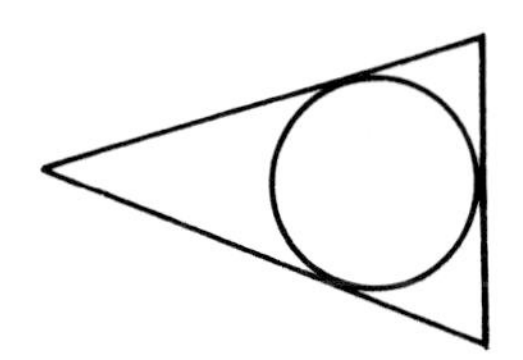

The circle is *inside* the triangle. The three *sides* touch the circle.

Draw any triangle. Construct the bisector of each angle. The intersection of the bisectors locates the incenter. The incenter to the intersection of a side and a bisector is the radius. Draw the circle.

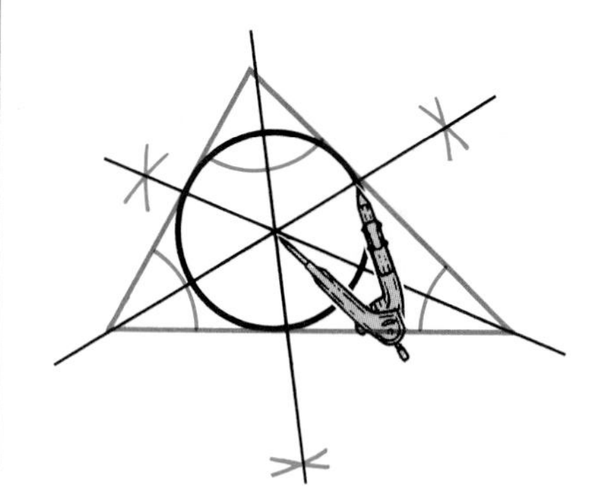

EXERCISES ***Construct a circumscribed circle and an inscribed circle for each of the following types of triangles.***

1. scalene **2.** obtuse **3.** equilateral **4.** isosceles

5. Is the circumcenter always inside the triangle?

6. What type of triangle has its incenter and circumcenter at the same point?

7. The **medians** of a triangle are segments connecting each vertex to the midpoint of the opposite side. Draw any triangle and construct its medians.

8. The **altitudes** of a triangle are segments from each vertex perpendicular to the opposite side. Draw any triangle and construct its altitudes.

6 Equations

When Mike Simons makes banana bread, he reads the recipe to see in what order to add the ingredients. Likewise, when finding the value of the expression $5 + 6 \times 4$, you must follow the rules for the order of operations.

6-1 Order of Operations

Unless order is specified, you could evaluate an expression such as $5 + 6 \times 4$ in more than one way.

$$5 + 6 \times 4 \rightarrow 5 + 24 \rightarrow 29 \qquad 5 + 6 \times 4 \rightarrow 11 \times 4 \rightarrow 44$$

Which value is correct, 29 or 44?

To make certain that an expression like $5 + 6 \times 4$ has only one value, there are rules for the order of operations.

1. **First, evaluate all powers.**
2. **Then, do all multiplication and/or division from left to right.**
3. **Then, do all addition and/or subtraction from left to right.**

The value of $5 + 6 \times 4$ is 29.

Evaluate $24 \div 2^2 \times 2 - 1$.

$24 \div 2^2 \times 2 - 1 = 24 \div 4 \times 2 - 1$	First, evaluate the power 2^2.
$= 6 \times 2 - 1$	Then, divide 24 by 4.
$= 12 - 1$	Then, multiply 6 and 2.
$= 11$	Then, subtract 1 from 12.

EXERCISES ***Evaluate each expression.***

1. $9 + 3 - 7$
2. $15 - 6 + 2$
3. $8 \times 4 \div 2$
4. $7 \div 3 \times 12$
5. $14 - 3 \times 4 \div 6$
6. $4 + 7 \times 3 - 18$
7. $36 \div 3^2$
8. $4^2 + 2^3 \times 5$
9. $7.2 + 8.1 \div 3 \times 0.2$
10. $9 \div 12 \times \frac{4}{5} - \frac{1}{3}$
11. $9 + 10 \div \frac{1}{2} - 7$
12. $20 \times \frac{5}{6} - \frac{1}{3} \div \frac{2}{9}$
13. Show that you can find at least three different values for $3 + 4 \times 7 - 1$ if you do not use the rules for the order of operations. Which value is correct?

6–2 Variables and Expressions

Sara makes pies for a restaurant. She makes different kinds of pies by using different kinds of fillings.

The value of an expression, such as $b - 7$, may be changed by replacing b with different numbers. The letter b is called a **variable.** A variable is used to stand for some number.

Evaluate $b - 7$ if $b = 16$.

$\mathbf{b - 7 = 16 - 7}$ Replace b with 16.

$\mathbf{= 9}$

Evaluate $b - 7$ if $b = 131.5$.

$\mathbf{b - 7 = 131.5 - 7}$ Replace b with 131.5.

$\mathbf{= 124.5}$

A product with a variable is usually expressed without the multiplication sign. For example, $5 \times n$ is usually expressed as $5n$.

An expression may contain more than one variable.

Evaluate $2r + 3t$ if $r = 2.5$ and $t = 6$.

$\mathbf{2r + 3t = 2 \times 2.5 + 3 \times 6}$ Replace r with 2.5 and t with 6.

$\mathbf{= 5 + 18}$ First, multiply.

$\mathbf{= 23}$ Then, add.

EXERCISES **Evaluate each expression if $a = 2$, $b = 5$, $n = \frac{1}{3}$, $x = 4$, and $y = 1.5$.**

1. $y + 3$ **2.** $94 + x$ **3.** $12 - b$ **4.** $a - 2$

5. $6x$ **6.** $9n$ **7.** $a \div 8$ **8.** $54 \div y$

9. $6a + 5$ **10.** $a^2 - 3$

11. $10 - 4n$ **12.** $6n \div 2$

13. $2 - n^2$ **14.** $4a + 5b$

15. $x - y$ **16.** $y + x$

17. $3a - x$ **18.** $4b + y$

19. $4x - y$ **20.** $a - 5n$

21. $7a - b - 7$ **22.** $ax + y$

23. $b - x^2 \div 8$ **24.** $2x + n^2 - b$

Parentheses ( ) and brackets [ ] are used when a different order of operations is desired. Always do the operations within the parentheses or brackets first.

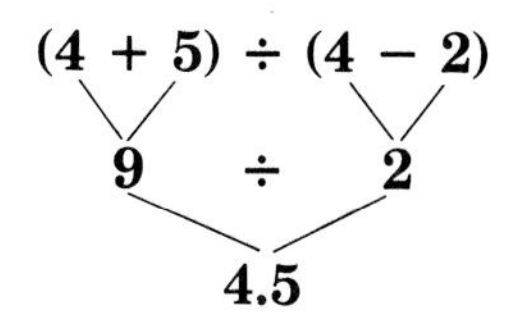

Do the operations within the parentheses first.

$[(21 + 7) + 4] \times 3$

$[28 + 4] \times 3$

32×3

96

Do the operation within the innermost parentheses or brackets first.

EXERCISES **Evaluate each expression.**

25. $(8 + 6) \div 2$ **26.** $3^2 - (4 + 5)$ **27.** $(3 + 6) \times 5$

28. $24 \div [6 \div (12 - 3)]$ **29.** $36 - [(6 \times 2) + 4]$ **30.** $[(36 - 6) \times 2] + 4$

Evaluate each expression if $r = 3$, $s = 7$, $t = \frac{1}{2}$, and $u = 0.3$.

31. $r + (s - u)$ **32.** $6 \times (r - t)$ **33.** $7t \times (s + r)$

34. $2u \div (3t - 1)$ **35.** $(s - r)^2$ **36.** $[(6r + 4t)] \div 15$

Copy. Insert parentheses to make a true sentence.

37. $19 - 5 + 4 = 10$ **38.** $8 \times 7 - 4 = 24$ **39.** $9 \div 2 + 1 = 3$

40. $7.5 \times 20 \div 10 = 15$ **41.** $15 - 12 \div 3 = 1$ **42.** $6 + 4 \times 7 = 70$

Evaluate each expression if $a = 4$, $b = 2$, and $c = 3$.

$$\frac{b + 10}{c - 2} = \frac{2 + 10}{3 - 2} = \frac{12}{1} \text{ or } 12$$

Evaluate the numerator and denominator separately. Then evaluate the fraction.

43. $\frac{7 + b}{c}$ **44.** $\frac{14 - a}{b + 7}$ **45.** $\frac{6c - 2}{a + 2b}$ **46.** $\frac{(3 + a) \times 5}{7b}$

NUMBER PUZZLE

Each whole number from 1 through 15 can be expressed using the numerals 1, 2, 3, and 4 exactly once and any of the operation signs. For example, $1 = (1 + 4) \div (2 + 3)$. Write an expression for each of the others.

6-3 Formulas

Martin Diller is preparing a turkey dinner. He uses the formula $t = 16w + 15$ to determine how long to roast the turkey. Suppose the turkey weighs 12 pounds. How long should the turkey roast?

$\mathbf{t = 16w + 15}$ *t* represents time (minutes). *w* represents weight (pounds).

$\mathbf{t = 16 \times 12 + 15}$ Replace *w* with 12.

$\mathbf{t = 192 + 15}$ First, multiply.

$\mathbf{t = 207}$ Then, add.

The turkey should roast for 207 minutes or 3 hours and 27 minutes.

$$\begin{array}{r} 3\ \text{R27} \\ 60\overline{)207} \\ -180 \\ \hline 27 \end{array}$$

A **formula** shows the relationship between certain quantities. For example, the formula $I = \frac{V}{R}$ shows the relationship between the current (I), voltage (V), and resistance (R) in an electrical circuit.

$$I \text{ (current in amperes)} = \frac{V\text{(voltage in volts)}}{R\text{(resistance in ohms)}}$$

Suppose V is 12 volts and R is 3 ohms. Find the current (I).

$\mathbf{I = \frac{V}{R}}$

$\mathbf{I = \frac{12}{3}}$ Replace *V* with 12 and *R* with 3.

$\mathbf{I = 4}$ The current is 4 amps.

EXERCISES ***Use the formula t = 16w + 15 to find the time needed to roast a turkey whose weight is given. Express the time in hours and minutes.***

1. 15 pounds
2. 18 pounds
3. 13 pounds
4. 9.7 pounds
5. 14.25 pounds
6. 16 pounds 8 ounces

Use the formula $I = \frac{V}{R}$ to find the current for each of the following.

7. V, 110 volts; R, 20 ohms

8. V, 120 volts; R, 5 ohms

9. V, 18 volts; R, 1.5 ohms

10. V, 37.5 volts; R, 3 ohms

11. V, 6 volts; R, 0.2 ohms

12. V, $37\frac{1}{2}$ volts; R, $1\frac{1}{2}$ ohms

The formula for the distance traveled by a moving object is $d = rt$. In the formula, d represents distance in kilometers (km), r the rate in kilometers per hour (km/h), and t the time in hours (h). Use the formula to find the distance traveled for each of the following.

13. r, 70 km/h; t, 6 h

14. r, 80 km/h; t, 4 h

15. r, 55 km/h; t, 4.5 h

16. r, 75 km/h; t, 2.25 h

17. r, 50 km/h; t, $2\frac{1}{2}$ h

18. r, 60 km/h; t, $3\frac{1}{3}$ h

The formula for horsepower rating is $H = \frac{D^2 \times n}{2.5}$. In the formula, H represents horsepower, D the piston diameter in inches (in.), and n the number of cylinders. Use the formula to find the horsepower rating for each of the following.

19. D, 3 in.; n, 6

20. D, 4 in.; n, 4

21. D, 3.5 in.; n, 8

22. D, 3.5 in.; n, 6

23. D, 2.5 in.; n, 4

24. D, 2.5 in.; n, 8

Solve. Use the correct formula.

25. Gary rides his bike at a rate of 14 miles per hour. How far does he ride in $1\frac{1}{2}$ hours?

26. What is the current in a 12-volt circuit that has a resistance of 3 ohms?

27. Dena is preparing a 22-pound turkey for dinner. How long should the turkey roast?

28. Mark Brauen has an 8-cylinder car that has a piston diameter of three inches. What is its horsepower rating?

29. The table at the right gives the cost of bowling at Suzi's Bowling Lanes. If g represents number of games and c represents cost, write a formula to show the relationship. How much does it cost to bowl five games?

Number of Games	Cost
1	$1.40
2	$2.80
3	$4.20

6-4 Using Variables

Juanita makes a cake for a bake sale. The icing takes 2 more cups of sugar than the cake.

If the cake takes 1 cup of sugar, then the icing takes $1 + 2$ cups of sugar.

If the cake takes x cups of sugar, then the icing takes $x + 2$ cups of sugar.

If the icing takes 4 cups of sugar, then the cake takes $4 - 2$ cups of sugar.

If the icing takes w cups of sugar, then the cake takes $w - 2$ cups of sugar.

You can translate words into mathematical expressions. Use variables to stand for unnamed numbers.

Words	Expressions
some number increased by 6	$h + 6$
the difference of b and 9	$b - 9$
5 multiplied by some number	$5z$
the quotient of 8 and n	$8 \div n$

EXERCISES ***Match.***

1. y increased by 11
2. 5 more than e
3. e less than 11
4. 5 decreased by y
5. the product of 11 and y
6. 5 multiplied by e
7. 11 divided by e
8. the quotient of e and y

a. $5e$
b. $5 - y$
c. $11y$
d. $11 - e$
e. $y + 11$
f. $e \div y$
g. $11 \div e$
h. $e + 5$

Translate each of the following into a mathematical expression.

9. 17 more than a

10. 10 less than p

11. 5 times k

12. the quotient of t and 29

13. the difference of a number and 16

14. a number increased by 4

15. a number divided by 6

16. the product of 215 and a number

An **equation** is a mathematical sentence with an equals sign. You can translate many sentences into equations.

Sentences	Equations
Five more than x is 17.	$x + 5 = 17$
A number decreased by 4 is 25.	$n - 4 = 25$
The product of 8 and a number is 60.	$8q = 60$
Eighteen divided by d is 3.	$18 \div d = 3$

EXERCISES Translate each of the following into an equation.

17. The sum of m and 15 is 45.

18. Five decreased by r is 2.

19. The quotient of d and 7 is 6.

20. The product of 5 and y is 30.

21. Six less than a number is 8.

22. Two more than a number is 6.

23. Seven times a number is 21.

24. A number divided by 4 is 5.

Translate each of the following into words.

25. $b + 6$

26. $8 - e$

27. $r \div 7$

28. $18a$

29. $14g = 7$

30. $26 + v = 9$

31. $d - 1 = 42$

32. $100 \div t = 5$

Translate each of the following into an equation.

$$\underbrace{\text{Two}}_{2}\ \underbrace{\text{times}}_{\times}\ \underbrace{\text{the sum of a number and 4}}_{(b+4)}\ \underbrace{\text{is}}_{=}\ \underbrace{14.}_{14} \quad \text{or} \quad 2(b + 4) = 14$$

33. Three more than four times y is equal to 27.

34. Six less than twice g is equal to 14.

35. Five times the difference of a number and 18 is 42.

36. The sum of 6 times a number and 3 is 48.

6-5 Solving Equations Using Subtraction

Kenny enjoys making wheat bread. He must use an exact amount of yeast. Otherwise, the bread will not rise properly.

Likewise, when solving an equation, you must find an exact replacement for the variable. Otherwise, the equation will not be satisfied.

Consider the equation $x + 9 = 13$. This equation may be solved by using subtraction. If you subtract the same number from each side of an equation, then the result is an equation that has the same solution. It is called an **equivalent equation.**

$$\mathbf{x + 9 = 13}$$

$$\mathbf{x + 9 - 9 = 13 - 9} \quad \text{Subtract 9 from each side.}$$

$$\mathbf{x = 4}$$

Why is 9 subtracted from each side instead of another number? To check the solution, replace x with 4 in the first equation.

$$\mathbf{x + 9 = 13}$$

$$\mathbf{4 + 9 \stackrel{?}{=} 13} \quad \text{Replace x with 4.}$$

$$\mathbf{13 = 13} \ \checkmark \quad \text{The solution is 4.}$$

EXERCISES ***Name the number you would subtract from each side to solve each of the following equations.***

1. $n + 3 = 5$ **2.** $x + 2 = 8$ **3.** $4 + t = 9$

4. $7 + k = 13$ **5.** $7 = n + 5$ **6.** $6 = x + 2$

7. $8 = 1 + a$ **8.** $5 = 4 + b$ **9.** $m + 15 = 21$

10. $10 + c = 13$ **11.** $13 + m = 22$ **12.** $24 + d = 30$

13. $19 = j + 16$ **14.** $45 = e + 15$ **15.** $41 = 32 + y$

State whether the given number is a solution of the equation.

16. $6;\ y + 3 = 8$ **17.** $3;\ 6 + a = 9$ **18.** $4;\ p + 5 = 8$

19. $7;\ r + 18 = 26$ **20.** $6;\ 15 = x + 9$ **21.** $14;\ 13 + b = 27$

Solve each equation. Check your solution.

22. $a + 6 = 8$ **23.** $k + 1 = 5$ **24.** $8 + f = 11$

25. $7 + g = 12$ **26.** $18 = b + 7$ **27.** $9 = m + 2$

28. $21 = 3 + n$ **29.** $24 = 10 + h$ **30.** $c + 0.7 = 1.6$

31. $0.3 + d = 1.3$ **32.** $1.4 = m + 0.9$ **33.** $2.3 = 1.6 + t$

34. $u + \frac{1}{3} = \frac{1}{2}$ **35.** $\frac{2}{3} + b = 1\frac{1}{4}$ **36.** $1\frac{3}{5} = q + \frac{3}{4}$

Translate each of the following into an equation. Then solve the equation and check your solution.

37. The sum of y and 3 is 14.

38. Seven increased by x is 31.

39. Five more than r is 6.

40. The sum of 12 and a is 29.

41. Nine increased by some number is 100.

42. Thirteen more than a number is 46.

CALCULATOR PALINDROMES

Palindrome numbers are numbers that read the same forward and backward. For example, 131, 22, and 916,619 are palindromes. You can use a calculator to form a palindrome.

Enter any whole number.

Reverse the digits and add the result to the original number.

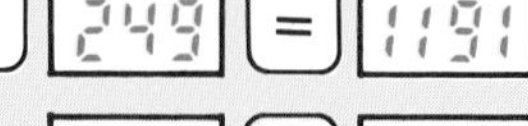

Repeat this process until the sum is a palindrome.

Form a palindrome starting with each of the following numbers.

1. 736 **2.** 183 **3.** 380 **4.** 985 **5.** 761

6-6 Solving Equations Using Addition

Bob Gaultney uses a scale to weigh vegetables at his market. Suppose the scale is balanced and he adds weight to one pan. Does the scale still balance? What happens if he adds the same weight to each pan? Does the scale still balance?

Equations are like scales in balance. If you add the same number to each side of an equation, an equivalent equation results.

$$m - 3 = 8$$

$$m - 3 + 3 = 8 + 3 \quad \text{Add 3 to each side.}$$

$$m = 11$$

Why is 3 added to each side instead of another number?

To check the solution, replace m with 11 in the first equation.

$$m - 3 = 8$$

$$11 - 3 \stackrel{?}{=} 8 \quad \text{Replace } m \text{ with 11.}$$

$$8 = 8 \ \checkmark \quad \text{The solution is 11.}$$

EXERCISES ***Name the number you would add to each side to solve each of the following equations.***

1. $m - 8 = 11$ **2.** $t - 6 = 11$ **3.** $n - 12 = 12$

4. $k - 3 = 9$ **5.** $16 = x - 12$ **6.** $21 = a - 10$

7. $18 = x - 13$ **8.** $30 = d - 7$ **9.** $m - 6 = 21$

10. $r - 8 = 23$ **11.** $b - \frac{1}{2} = 16\frac{1}{2}$ **12.** $c - 3 = 1\frac{3}{4}$

13. $9 = e - 36$ **14.** $0.4 = r - 1$ **15.** $7 = f - 6.6$

State whether the given number is a solution of the equation.

16. 25; $y - 13 = 12$ **17.** 23; $a - 6 = 29$ **18.** 5; $7 = b - 2$

19. 58; $22 = m - 36$ **20.** 24; $15 = f - 19$ **21.** 96; $y - 76 = 23$

Solve each equation. Check your solution.

22. $h - 7 = 24$ **23.** $t - 13 = 42$ **24.** $n - 13 = 17$

25. $p - 8 = 8$ **26.** $16 = x - 2$ **27.** $15 = u - 17$

28. $5 = v - 9$ **29.** $76 = q - 51$ **30.** $y - 1.7 = 3.4$

31. $k - 1.6 = 4.3$ **32.** $w - \frac{1}{3} = \frac{1}{2}$ **33.** $r - 1\frac{1}{2} = 2\frac{1}{3}$

34. $\frac{2}{3} = s - 1\frac{7}{8}$ **35.** $2\frac{4}{5} = m - 1\frac{2}{3}$ **36.** $3.14 = x - 1.73$

Translate each of the following into an equation. Then solve the equation and check your solution.

37. The difference of b and 6 is 5.

38. Eighteen less than g is 5.

39. r decreased by 3 is 49.

40. Six is twelve less than m.

41. The difference of some number and 23 is 19.

42. n decreased by 78 is 3.

Skills Review: Pages 143-153

Evaluate each expression.

1. $4 + 5 \times 2 - 3$ **2.** $(4 + 8) \times 2 \div 6$ **3.** $\frac{5 + 3}{4^2}$

Evaluate each expression if a = 5 and b = 0.4.

4. $3a - 13$ **5.** $a^2 + b^2$

Use the formula d = rt to find the distance traveled for the following.

6. r, 65 km/h; t, 6 h

Solve each equation. Check your solution.

7. $v + 8 = 20$

8. $m - 7 = 12$

Translate each of the following into a mathematical expression or equation.

9. 15 more than d

10. The quotient of 6 and a number is 3.

Cumulative Review

Estimate.

1. $\begin{array}{r} 7.093 \\ +\ 4.7 \\ \hline \end{array}$ **2.** $\begin{array}{r} 4{,}702 \\ -\ \ 945 \\ \hline \end{array}$ **3.** $\begin{array}{r} 51.8 \\ \times\ 0.64 \\ \hline \end{array}$ **4.** $77\overline{)5{,}578}$ **5.** $3.4\overline{)0.0597}$

Add, subtract, multiply, or divide.

6. $\begin{array}{r} 32.7 \\ +\ 19.5 \\ \hline \end{array}$ **7.** $\begin{array}{r} 4.83 \\ +\ 19.6 \\ \hline \end{array}$ **8.** $\begin{array}{r} \$79.36 \\ -\ \$24.57 \\ \hline \end{array}$ **9.** $\begin{array}{r} 66 \\ -\ 29.13 \\ \hline \end{array}$ **10.** $\begin{array}{r} 47 \\ \times\ 3.1 \\ \hline \end{array}$

11. $\begin{array}{r} 0.07 \\ \times\ 0.13 \\ \hline \end{array}$ **12.** $\begin{array}{r} 47.6 \\ \times\ 9.35 \\ \hline \end{array}$ **13.** $\begin{array}{r} 460 \\ \times\ 0.45 \\ \hline \end{array}$ **14.** $0.4\overline{)276}$ **15.** $24\overline{)60}$

16. $5.6\overline{)42}$ **17.** $47\overline{)88.36}$ **18.** $0.17\overline{)2.3885}$ **19.** $6.8\overline{)0.0374}$

20. $15.6 + 0.34 + 5.194$ **21.** $34.7 - 21.55$ **22.** $\$2.73 + \$17.95 + \$23$

23. 7.41×100 **24.** 3.47×10 **25.** $28 \div 1{,}000$ **26.** $1.7 \div 100$

Find the greatest common factor (GCF) for each group of numbers.

27. 20, 30 **28.** 24, 32 **29.** 10, 27, 32

Find the least common multiple (LCM) for each group of numbers.

30. 8, 12 **31.** 4, 7 **32.** 4, 6, 9

Add, subtract, multiply, or divide. Write each answer in simplest form.

33. $\frac{3}{8} + \frac{5}{12}$ **34.** $4\frac{1}{2} + 7\frac{5}{8}$ **35.** $4\frac{5}{8} + 6\frac{5}{12}$ **36.** $9\frac{8}{9} + 6\frac{2}{5}$

37. $\frac{7}{9} - \frac{1}{6}$ **38.** $7\frac{11}{12} - 2\frac{5}{12}$ **39.** $8\frac{2}{3} - 5\frac{1}{4}$ **40.** $4\frac{1}{4} - 1\frac{2}{3}$

41. $\frac{7}{12} \times \frac{6}{7}$ **42.** $3 \times \frac{5}{9}$ **43.** $2\frac{1}{2} \times 1\frac{3}{5}$ **44.** $4\frac{5}{6} \times 2\frac{1}{4}$

45. $\frac{5}{6} \div \frac{5}{9}$ **46.** $2\frac{5}{12} \div \frac{5}{6}$ **47.** $1\frac{2}{3} \div 5\frac{1}{2}$ **48.** $2\frac{1}{5} \div 3\frac{3}{10}$

Evaluate each expression if $x = 3$ and $y = 5$.

49. $6x$ **50.** $y - 4$ **51.** $32 \div y$ **52.** $x + 2\frac{1}{2}$

Solve each equation. Check your solution.

53. $a + 7 = 9$ **54.** $c + 2.7 = 8.1$ **55.** $b - 6 = 6$ **56.** $m - 9\frac{3}{4} = 1\frac{2}{5}$

Solve.

57. Mrs. Lopez buys a notebook for \$1.49, a pen for \$0.99, and a ruler for \$0.79. If she gives the clerk \$5, what is her change?

58. Ted needs 3 cups of peaches for a fruit salad. If each can of peaches contains $\frac{3}{4}$ cup, how many cans should he buy?

59. An empty book carton weighs 1 pound. Each book weighs 4.25 pounds. What is the total weight when the carton is filled with ten books?

Mathematics Lab

Suppose you want to make a calendar for the year 2025. To do this, find the day of the week for January 1, 2025. You can find the day of the week for any date after September 14, 1752, by following these steps.

1. Add the following numbers.

   last two digits of the year → 25
   $\frac{1}{4}$ of the previous number → 6
   (Neglect any remainder.)
   day of the month → 1
   month number from Table A → 1
   century number from Table B → + 6
   39

2. Divide the sum by 7. 39 ÷ 7 = 5 R4

3. Use Table C and the remainder to find the day of the week. January 1, 2025 is a Wednesday since the remainder is 4.

Table A — Month			
January	1	June	5
(leap year)	0	July	0
February	4	August	3
(leap year)	3	September	6
March	4	October	1
April	0	November	4
May	2	December	6

Table B — Century			
18th	4	20th	0
19th	2	21st	6

Table C — Day of Week			
1	Sunday	5	Thursday
2	Monday	6	Friday
3	Tuesday	0	Saturday
4	Wednesday		

Solve.

1. Make a calendar for April, 2000.
2. Determine the day of the week you were born.

6-7 Solving Equations Using Division

Robin has a recipe for apple salad that makes 8 servings. To make 4 servings, Robin divides the number of servings and the amount of each ingredient by 2.

$$\frac{\textbf{8 servings}}{\textbf{2}} \Rightarrow \textbf{4 servings}$$

$$\frac{\textbf{amount of each ingredient}}{\textbf{2}} \Rightarrow \textbf{half the original amount}$$

A similar process is used to solve equations such as $6n = 78$. If you divide each side of an equation by the same nonzero number, an equivalent equation results.

$$6n = 78$$

$$\frac{6n}{6} = \frac{78}{6} \quad \text{Divide each side by 6.}$$

$$n = 13$$

Why is each side divided by 6 instead of another number? To check the solution, replace n with 13 in the first equation.

$$6n = 78$$

$$6 \times 13 \stackrel{?}{=} 78 \quad \text{Replace } n \text{ with 13.}$$

$$78 = 78 \quad \checkmark \quad \text{The solution is 13.}$$

EXERCISES ***Name the number you would divide by to solve each of the following equations.***

1. $4x = 12$ **2.** $6n = 48$ **3.** $15a = 180$ **4.** $4t = 52$

5. $56 = 7y$ **6.** $87 = 3y$ **7.** $35 = 7b$ **8.** $63 = 9z$

9. $5c = 100$ **10.** $12w = 90$ **11.** $87 = 10r$ **12.** $38 = 4d$

State whether the given number is a solution of the equation.

13. 18; $3y = 21$ **14.** 5; $11z = 55$ **15.** 15; $75 = 5w$

16. 39; $392 = 8k$ **17.** 10; $27a = 297$ **18.** 21; $13z = 273$

Solve each equation. Check your solution.

19. $9k = 72$ **20.** $7m = 42$ **21.** $6y = 150$ **22.** $72y = 0$

23. $32 = 8a$ **24.** $192 = 12c$ **25.** $207 = 23t$ **26.** $160 = 32g$

27. $25x = 25$ **28.** $18u = 45$ **29.** $4r = 31$ **30.** $0.8k = 0.32$

31. $115 = 20a$ **32.** $3.52 = 3.2n$ **33.** $9.68 = 0.4c$ **34.** $1.2d = 54$

Translate each of the following into an equation. Then solve the equation and check your solution.

35. The product of 6 and x is 72.

36. Seven multiplied by m is 105.

37. Fourteen times d is 126.

38. Sixty times a number is 140.

39. Four multiplied by some number is fifty.

40. The product of a number and 9 is 72.

MAGIC SQUARES

A magic square is a number square whose rows, columns, and diagonals all have the same sum. Study the magic square at the right. The magic sum is 21.

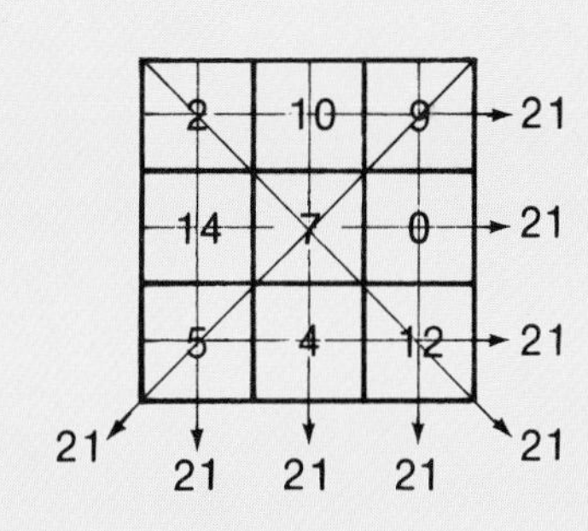

Find the value of each variable in each magic square. What is the magic sum?

1.

f	6	11
g	10	*h*
r	14	*t*

2.

a	*b*	1.8	5.8
c	5	4.6	3.8
d	3.4	3	*e*
2.2	6.2	*f*	*g*

3.

h	12	*u*	4	*w*
k	*m*	*n*	7	8
2	3	*p*	10	11
5	6	*q*	$10\frac{1}{2}$	*r*
$5\frac{1}{2}$	9	*s*	1	$4\frac{1}{2}$

4. Make your own magic square. What is the magic sum?

6-8 Solving Equations Using Multiplication

Bonnie has a recipe that makes 20 appetizers. To make 60 appetizers, Bonnie multiplies the number of servings and the amount of each ingredient by 3.

20 appetizers × 3 ➡ **60 appetizers**

amount of each ingredient × 3 ➡ **triple the original amount**

A similar process is used to solve equations such as $\frac{x}{7} = 9$. If you multiply each side of an equation by the same number, an equivalent equation results.

$$\frac{x}{7} = 9$$

$$\frac{x}{7} \times 7 = 9 \times 7 \quad \text{Multiply each side by 7.}$$

$$x = 63$$

Why is each side multiplied by 7 instead of another number? To check the solution, replace x with 63 in the first equation.

$$\frac{x}{7} = 9$$

$$\frac{63}{7} \stackrel{?}{=} 9 \quad \text{Replace x with 63.}$$

$$9 = 9 \quad \checkmark$$

The solution is 63.

EXERCISES ***Name the number by which you would multiply to solve each of the following equations.***

1. $\frac{x}{9} = 7$ **2.** $\frac{y}{4} = 10$ **3.** $\frac{a}{5} = 3$ **4.** $\frac{n}{10} = 11$

5. $6 = \frac{b}{5}$ **6.** $9 = \frac{k}{8}$ **7.** $6 = \frac{b}{3}$ **8.** $15 = \frac{g}{2}$

9. $\frac{y}{7} = 8$ **10.** $\frac{p}{9} = 12$ **11.** $21 = \frac{h}{6}$ **12.** $18 = \frac{u}{7}$

State whether the given number is a solution of the equation.

13. $15; \frac{a}{6} = 9$ **14.** $48; \frac{x}{7} = 8$ **15.** $66; 6 = \frac{m}{11}$

16. $32; 8 = \frac{z}{4}$ **17.** $30; \frac{y}{10} = 3$ **18.** $3; \frac{k}{21} = 7$

Solve each equation. Check your solution.

19. $\frac{x}{8} = 6$ **20.** $\frac{z}{4} = 5$ **21.** $\frac{b}{7} = 16$ **22.** $\frac{a}{15} = 4$

23. $9 = \frac{t}{6}$ **24.** $7 = \frac{y}{3}$ **25.** $9 = \frac{r}{16}$ **26.** $6 = \frac{k}{21}$

27. $\frac{w}{1.3} = 10$ **28.** $\frac{s}{1.4} = 28$ **29.** $9 = \frac{y}{2.25}$ **30.** $55 = \frac{c}{1.5}$

31. $\frac{v}{5} = 9.5$ **32.** $\frac{x}{7} = 2.5$ **33.** $\frac{x}{3.5} = 9.1$ **34.** $8.4 = \frac{b}{0.12}$

Name the operation shown in each equation. Then name the operation you would perform to solve the equation.

35. $x + 7 = 13$ **36.** $a - 3 = 16$ **37.** $7p = 63$ **38.** $81 = 9r$

39. $\frac{h}{6} = 31$ **40.** $9 + b = 14$ **41.** $y - 6 = 23$ **42.** $\frac{c}{10} = 1$

Solve each equation. Check your solution.

43. $a + 6 = 9$ **44.** $y - 4 = 8$ **45.** $14g = 42$ **46.** $6 = m - 24$

47. $\frac{d}{8} = 63$ **48.** $8 + k = 24$ **49.** $7 = \frac{t}{5}$ **50.** $0.8 = 2v$

Translate each of the following into an equation. Then solve the equation and check your solution.

51. The difference of n and 5 is 19.

52. q increased by 9 is 17.

53. Six multiplied by t is 45.

54. The quotient of y and 3 is 18.

55. The sum of 1.8 and a number is 2.9.

56. Seven less than a number is 5.1.

57. Some number divided by 5 is 1.2.

58. Nine times a number is 0.54.

6-9 Problem Solving: Using Equations

Maroa Hall cans 15 quarts of peaches. All together she cans 48 quarts of peaches and cherries. How many quarts of cherries does she can? You can use an equation to solve this problem.

Read the problem. Mrs. Hall cans 15 quarts of peaches. She cans 48 quarts of peaches and cherries. You need to find how many quarts of cherries she cans.

Decide what to do. Let c represent the number of quarts of cherries. Translate the words into an equation using the variable.

Solve the problem.

quarts of peaches	plus	quarts of cherries	equals	total quarts of peaches and cherries
15	+	c	=	48

Solve the equation.

$$15 + c = 48$$
$$15 - 15 + c = 48 - 15$$
$$c = 33$$

The solution is 33. Mrs. Hall cans 33 quarts of cherries.

Examine the solution. If Mrs. Hall cans 33 quarts of cherries, what is the total number of quarts of peaches and cherries she cans?

$$15 + 33 = 48 \ \checkmark$$

(15: quarts of peaches; 33: quarts of cherries; 48: total number of quarts)

The answer is reasonable and correct.

Translate each problem into an equation. Then solve each equation.

1. A pineapple cake takes $1\frac{1}{2}$ cups of nuts. All together the cake and its icing take 2 cups of nuts. How many cups of nuts does the icing take?

2. Adam Graber has 4 hamsters and some fish. The number of fish divided by 5 is equal to the number of hamsters. How many fish does Adam have?

3. Akiko has 3 less rows of tomatoes than rows of beans. She has 5 rows of tomatoes. How many rows of beans does Akiko have?

4. Roy's recipe for punch makes 20 more servings than Dixie's recipe. Roy's recipe makes 50 servings. How many servings does Dixie's recipe make?

5. John weighs 66 kilograms. This is three times Carlos' weight. What is Carlos' weight?

6. Mrs. Cassidy earns $7.50 per hour. How many hours does she need to work to earn $105.00?

7. One orange tree produces 157 oranges. This is 38 fewer than another tree. How many oranges does the other tree produce?

8. Vicki Riegle separates her goats evenly in 6 pens. There are 8 goats in each pen. How many goats does Vicki have?

9. Janet takes a 300-kilometer trip. She travels 246 kilometers by plane and the rest by car. How far does she travel by car?

10. Steve Herr was 14 years old five years ago. His birthday is September 16. How old is he now?

11. Dave makes $55.75 a week. He decides to save $3.75 a week. How many weeks does it take him to save $120.00?

12. There are 96 students signed up for soccer. They have 16 sponsors. How many teams of 8 players each can be formed?

Write a problem using the given information.

x = Erica's age **x − 5 = 8**	Since Erica's age is represented by x, then $x - 5$ must be her age 5 years ago. The following problem could be written: If Erica's age 5 years ago was 8, how old is she now?

13. x = Sam's age
    $x + 7 = 21$

14. n = number of novels on a shelf
    $13 + n = 32$

15. w = Noelle's weight in kilograms
    $w - 4 = 39$

16. a = number of albums Jorge has
    $4a = 56$

6–10 Solving Two-step Equations

A cake is made in stages. The ingredients are mixed, the cake is baked, and the icing is applied. If an equation contains more than one operation, the equation is solved in stages. In general, to solve equations, undo the addition or subtraction first. Then undo the multiplication or division. This is the reverse of the order of operations.

Solve the equation $7k + 5 = 33$.

$$7k + 5 = 33$$

$$7k + 5 - 5 = 33 - 5$$ First, undo the addition by subtracting 5 from each side.

$$7k = 28$$

$$\frac{7k}{7} = \frac{28}{7}$$ Then, undo the multiplication by dividing each side by 7.

$$k = 4$$

To check the solution, replace k with 4 in the first equation.

$$7k + 5 = 33$$

$$7 \times 4 + 5 \stackrel{?}{=} 33$$ Replace k with 4.

$$28 + 5 \stackrel{?}{=} 33$$ Why multiply first?

$$33 = 33 \quad \checkmark$$ The solution is 4.

Solve the equation $16 = \frac{x}{4} - 7$.

$$16 = \frac{x}{4} - 7$$

$$16 + 7 = \frac{x}{4} - 7 + 7$$ First undo the subtraction by adding 7 to each side.

$$23 = \frac{x}{4}$$

$$23 \times 4 = \frac{x}{4} \times 4$$ Then, undo the division by multiplying each side by 4.

$$92 = x$$

You can check the solution by replacing x with 92 in the first equation.

EXERCISES ***Solve each equation. Check your solution.***

1. $4y + 3 = 19$
2. $3x - 8 = 13$
3. $8k - 21 = 75$
4. $5r - 6 = 29$
5. $2 + 3m = 18$
6. $57 = 4z - 9$
7. $\frac{b}{8} - 17 = 13$
8. $\frac{g}{12} - 4 = 7$
9. $19 = \frac{h}{3} + 8$
10. $9 + \frac{j}{4} = 12$
11. $3 + \frac{p}{3} = 12$
12. $31 = 3 + \frac{c}{6}$
13. $0.3b + 0.8 = 1.4$
14. $1.6m - 0.2 = 3$
15. $2.1 = 0.5x + 0.6$
16. $\frac{t}{0.7} + 9 = 10$
17. $\frac{x}{0.9} - 0.7 = 1.3$
18. $6.2 = \frac{m}{9} - 6.2$

Translate each of the following into an equation. Then solve the equation and check your solution.

19. Nine less than the quotient of x and 2 is 12.
20. Five plus the quotient of n and 8 is 7.
21. The sum of 8 and the product of 2 and y is 24.
22. Four less than the product of 3 and x is 23.

USING FORMULAS

The Motter family plans their vacation to the beach. They will travel 825 miles. The average speed will be 50 miles per hour. They use the formula $d = rt$ to estimate their travel time. Solve $d = rt$ if $d = 825$ and $r = 50$.

$$\mathbf{d = rt}$$

$825 = 50t$ — Replace d with 825 and r with 50.

$\frac{825}{50} = \frac{50t}{50}$ — Divide each side by 50.

$16.5 = t$ — The travel time, t, is 16.5 hours.

Solve.

1. Carol travels 605 miles at a speed of 55 miles per hour. How many hours does Carol travel?
2. Roger travels 282 kilometers in 4 hours. At what speed does he travel?
3. Randy leaves home at 11:30 A.M. and arrives in Wichita at 1:00 P.M. He drives 50 miles per hour. How far is Wichita from his home?

6–11 Sequences

Chef Wang prepares a certain amount of fried rice each day.

Day	Sunday Monday	Tuesday	Wednesday Thursday	Friday Saturday
Number of Servings	20	35	50	65

A list of numbers in a certain order is a **sequence.** The numbers 20, 35, 50, and 65 are an example of an **arithmetic sequence.** Consecutive numbers in this sequence have the same difference.

20, 35, 50, 65 Each number in the pattern is 15 more than the number before it.

26, 22, 18, 14 Each number in the pattern is 4 less than the number before it.

$1\frac{1}{2}$, 3, $4\frac{1}{2}$, 6 How are the numbers in this pattern obtained?

EXERCISES ***Write the next three numbers of each arithmetic sequence.***

1. 2, 8, 14, 20, __, __, __
2. 4, 8, 12, 16, __, __, __
3. 36, 32, 28, 24, __, __, __
4. 44, 39, 34, 29, __, __, __
5. 147, 137, 127, 117, __, __, __
6. 3, 3, 3, 3, __, __, __
7. $\frac{1}{8}$, $\frac{1}{4}$, $\frac{3}{8}$, $\frac{1}{2}$, __, __, __
8. $2\frac{1}{4}$, 2, $1\frac{3}{4}$, $1\frac{1}{2}$, __, __, __
9. 2.2, 2, 1.8, 1.6, __, __, __
10. 2, 3.5, 5, 6.5, __, __, __

Copy and complete each arithmetic sequence.

11. 7, 13, __, 25, __, 37, __, __
12. 8, __, 26, __, 44, __, __, 71
13. 96, 93, __, __, 84, 81, __
14. __, 49, __, 35, __, 21, __

A **geometric sequence** is formed by multiplying the previous term by the same number.

2, 4, 8, 16, 32 Each number in the pattern is 2 times the number before it.

81, 27, 9, 3, 1 Each number in the pattern is $\frac{1}{3}$ of the number before it.

1, 4, 16, 64, 256 How are the numbers in this pattern obtained?

EXERCISES ***Write the next three numbers of each geometric sequence.***

15. 5, 15, 45, __, __, __

16. 2, 10, 50, __, __, __

17. 625, 125, 25, __, __, __

18. 96, 48, 24, __, __, __

19. 4, 4, 4, __, __, __

20. 256, 64, 16, __, __, __

21. $\frac{3}{2}$, 1, $\frac{2}{3}$, __, __, __

22. $\frac{1}{9}$, $\frac{1}{3}$, 1, __, __, __

23. 0.01, 0.1, 1, __, __, __

24. 270, 27, 2.7, __, __, __

Copy and complete each geometric sequence.

25. 2, 6, __, __, 162, __

26. __, 243, 81, __, 9, __

27. $\frac{1}{4}$, $\frac{1}{2}$, __, 2, __, __

28. 50, __, $12\frac{1}{2}$, __, $3\frac{1}{8}$, __

State whether each sequence is arithmetic or geometric.

29. 7, 14, 21, 28

30. 4, 20, 100, 500

31. 12, 10, 8, 6

32. 3.5, 4.6, 5.7, 6.8

33. 1, 7, 49, 343

34. 9, 6, 4, $2\frac{2}{3}$

Solve.

35. Diane opens a savings account. She deposits $2 the first week, $4 the second week, $6 the third week, and so on. How much does she save in ten weeks?

36. Mr. Blair has 130 fish in his pond. The number of fish in the pond triples every year. How many fish will Mr. Blair have in four years?

37. Becky cuts a piece of paper in half. She cuts each piece in half again. She repeats this process five more times. What is the size of each piece compared to the original?

Focus on Problem Solving

6-12 Look for a Pattern

Gomez has a triangular garden plot. In the first row he plants 1 corn seed. In the second row he plants 3 corn seeds. In the third row he plants 5 corn seeds and so on. In each successive row he plants 2 more corn seeds than in the row before. How many corn seeds does Gomez plant in the twelfth row? How many corn seeds does he plant in the first 12 rows?

Read the problem. You need to find the number of corn seeds in a certain row and the total number at that row. You know how many are in the first three rows.

Decide what to do. First make a list showing the information you are given. Then extend the list and look for a pattern.

Solve the problem.

Row Number	Number of Corn Seeds	Total Number of Corn Seeds
1	1	1
2	3	1 + 3 = 4
3	5	4 + 5 = 9
4	7	9 + 7 = 16
5	9	16 + 9 = 25
6	11	25 + 11 = 36

Notice that the number of corn seeds in each row is always 1 less than twice the row number. So in the twelfth row, Gomez plants $2 \times 12 - 1$ or 23 corn seeds.

Notice also that the total number of corn seeds planted is the row number squared. So Gomez plants 12^2 or 144 corn seeds in the first 12 rows.

Examine the solution. You can check the solutions by extending the list to row number 12. The solutions are correct.

Solve.

1. The Summit City Council has ten members. Suppose each member shakes hands with each other member. How many handshakes are there?

2. How many triangles are shown in the figure at the right?

3. A raft can hold 270 liters of water before sinking. It hits a rock and springs a leak. It gains 10 liters of water the first mile, 15 the second, 20 the third, and so on. How far does it go before sinking?

Write the next three terms of each sequence.

1, 2, 4, 7, 11, —, —, —

Notice the pattern in the differences of successive terms.
Then add to find the next terms.

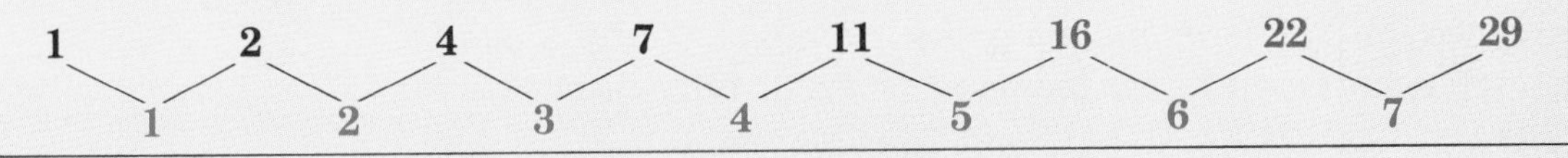

4. 1, 2, 5, 10, 17, —, —, —
5. 1, 2, 3, 5, 8, 13, 21, —, —, —
6. 101, 100, 98, 95, —, —, —
7. $\frac{1}{2}, \frac{3}{4}, \frac{6}{7}, \frac{10}{11}$, —, —, —
8. 1, 4, 3, 6, 5, 8, 7, —, —, —
9. 10, 11, 9, 12, 8, 13, —, —, —
10. *A*26, *B*25, *C*24, —, —, —
11. ZA, XB, VC, —, —, —

Skills Review: Pages 156-167

Solve each equation. Check your solution.

1. $7t = 84$
2. $11 = \frac{x}{5}$
3. $\frac{v}{3} + 7 = 12$
4. $6y - 7 = 41$

Translate the problem into an equation. Then solve the equation and check your solution.

5. Rena bowls a 162 game Monday. This is 27 pins above her average. What is her average?

Write the next numbers of each sequence. State whether the sequence is arithmetic, geometric, or neither.

6. 1, 5, 25, 125, —, —, —
7. 44, 38, 32, 26, —, —, —
8. 15, 17, 21, 27, —, —, —

Mathematics and Careers

Joyce Paxton is a loan officer at the Arlington branch of the First National Bank. She interviews persons who are applying for a loan. She also reviews their loan application and studies their credit rating.

One formula Ms. Paxton uses to see if an applicant is qualified to obtain a loan for a house is given below.

$$\mathbf{0.28 \times (T - P) = H}$$

T represents total monthly income before any deductions (gross).
P represents other monthly payments such as for cars or furniture.
H represents the greatest monthly house payment that can be approved.

Suppose the Madieras have a gross income of $3,150 a month. They have a monthly car payment of $268. What is the greatest monthly house payment that Ms. Paxton could approve for the Madieras?

$$0.28 \times (T - P) = H$$

$$0.28 \times (3{,}150 - 268) = H$$ Replace T with 3,150 and P with 268.

$$0.28 \times 2{,}882 = H$$

$$806.96 = H$$

The greatest monthly house payment Ms. Paxton could approve for the Madieras is about $800.

EXERCISES ***Find the greatest monthly house payment Ms. Paxton could approve for each of the following.***

1. T, $2,300; P, $240 **2.** T, $2,880; P, $410 **3.** T, $1,800; P, $108

Solve.

4. Charles and Laura Hill make $22,550 a year before deductions. They pay $146 a month for a boat. What is the greatest monthly house payment that Ms. Paxton can approve for the Hills?

Chapter 6 Review

VOCABULARY

equation (149)
variable (144)
sequence (164)
formula (146)

EXERCISES **Evaluate each expression. (143)**

1. $18 - 3 \times 4$
2. $28 \div (5 + 2) \times 8$
3. $\frac{21 - 9}{3 + 1}$

Evaluate each expression if a = 3, b = 5, and c = 0.2. (144–145)

4. $14 - a^2$
5. $\frac{b}{2} + 10c$
6. $ab - 5c$
7. $4 \times (b + a)$

Use the formula $I = \frac{V}{R}$ ***to find the current for each problem. (146–147)***

8. V, 136 volts; R, 40 ohms
9. V, 117.5 volts; R, 12.5 ohms

Translate each of the following into a mathematical expression or equation. (148–149)

10. the difference of a number and 17
11. 23 multiplied by some number
12. The quotient of w and 6 is 78.
13. Fifteen more than r is 61.

Solve each equation. Check your solution. (150–159, 162–163)

14. $m + 8 = 21$
15. $15 = p + 11$
16. $1.25 + a = 2.5$
17. $r - 5 = 12$
18. $36 = h - 12$
19. $18 = \frac{v}{8}$
20. $\frac{b}{4} = 20$
21. $\frac{c}{15} = 7$
22. $n - 1.7 = 3.9$
23. $4x = 72$
24. $56 = 8y$
25. $6g = 5.16$
26. $2a - 1 = 13$
27. $\frac{c}{4} + 8 = 16$
28. $32 = 4x + 7$
29. $\frac{n}{2} - 3 = 9$

Translate each problem into an equation. Then solve each equation. (160–161)

30. Alberto buys 2 dozen eggs. After making omelets he has 9 eggs left. How many eggs did he use in the omelets?
31. Sally earns \$5 for mowing the lawn and \$4 for weeding the garden. How many times must she mow the lawn to earn \$60?

Write the next three terms of each sequence. (164–167)

32. 3, 5, 7, __, __, __
33. 28, 21, 15, 10, __, __, __
34. 768, 192, 48, __, __, __
35. 66, 57, 48, __, __, __

Chapter 6 Test

Evaluate each expression.

1. $4 \times 3 + 2 \times 4$
2. $7 \times 6 - 12 \div 2$
3. $7^2 - (3 + 2)$

Evaluate each expression if x = 5, y = 4, and z = 0.5.

4. $6z + 1$
5. $\frac{x + y}{6}$
6. $x + y^2$
7. $(x + 4) \div (2 - z)$

The formula for typing speed is $S = \frac{w - 10e}{m}$. In the formula, S represents speed, w represents number of words, e represents number of errors, and m represents time in minutes. Use the formula to find the typing speed for each problem.

8. w, 450; e, 12; m, 10
9. w, 480; e, 6; m, 8

Solve each equation. Check your solution.

10. $a + 8 = 23$
11. $6 + x = 25$
12. $4.7 = t + 2.9$
13. $n - 12 = 42$
14. $r - 7 = 2$
15. $1.8 = g - 3.4$
16. $9z = 36$
17. $4w = 44$
18. $15.6 = 1.3c$
19. $\frac{k}{5} = 15$
20. $\frac{s}{3} = 12$
21. $1.3 = \frac{m}{7}$
22. $2t - 17 = 55$
23. $4.6 = \frac{d}{6} + 0.9$
24. $4x + 8 = 12$

Translate each of the following into an equation. Then solve each equation and check your solution.

25. The product of 8 and t is 20.
26. Six increased by a is 19.
27. Four less than twice a number is 78.
28. The difference of 5 times a number and 7 is 45.
29. Joy sells sweet corn for 25¢ less a dozen than Savers Mart. She charges $1.35 for a dozen. How much does Savers Mart charge?
30. Glen's car gets 34 miles per gallon of gasoline. How many gallons of gasoline does he need to travel 289 miles?

Copy and complete each sequence.

31. 95, —, 85, 80, —, —, 65
32. $\frac{1}{6}$, 1, —, 36, —, —
33. 729, 243, —, —, 9, —
34. 25, 31, —, 43, —, —, 61
35. 17, 13, 18, 14, 19, —, —, —
36. 0, 3, 9, 18, —, —, —

Enrichment

Every terminating decimal can be expressed as a fraction.

$$\mathbf{0.52 = \frac{52}{100}} \qquad \mathbf{0.483 = \frac{483}{1{,}000}}$$

Can a repeating decimal, such as $0.4\overline{5}$, be expressed as a fraction?

Let $n = 0.4\overline{5}$ or $0.4555 \ldots$.

Then, $10n = 4.5555 \ldots$. Multiply n by 10^1 or 10 since one digit repeats.

$$\begin{aligned} 10n &= 4.5555 \ldots \\ -\quad n &= 0.4555 \ldots \\ \hline 9n &= 4.1 \end{aligned}$$

Subtract $n = 0.4555 \ldots$ from $10n = 4.5555 \ldots$ to eliminate the repeating digits.

$$\frac{9n}{9} = \frac{4.1}{9}$$

Divide each side by 9.

$$n = \frac{4.1}{9} \text{ or } \frac{41}{90}$$

The decimal $0.4\overline{5}$ can be expressed as $\frac{41}{90}$.

Express $1.\overline{34}$ as a fraction.

Let $n = 1.\overline{34}$.

$$\begin{aligned} \text{Then, } 100n &= 134.\overline{34}. \\ -\quad n &= 1.\overline{34} \\ \hline 99n &= 133 \end{aligned}$$

Multiply n by 10^2 or 100 since two digits repeat.

Subtract. $n = \frac{133}{99}$ or $1\frac{34}{99}$

The decimal $1.\overline{34}$ can be expressed as $1\frac{34}{99}$.

You can use this technique to express *any* repeating decimal as a fraction.

***EXERCISES* Express each of the following as a fraction.**

1. $0.\overline{8}$ **2.** $0.\overline{6}$ **3.** $0.\overline{81}$ **4.** $0.\overline{21}$ **5.** $0.\overline{16}$

6. $0.\overline{27}$ **7.** $1.\overline{3}$ **8.** $2.\overline{5}$ **9.** $0.\overline{24}$ **10.** $3.\overline{60}$

11. Show that 4.6 and $4.5\overline{9}$ can be expressed as the same fraction.

7 Ratio, Proportion, and Percent

In the United States, there are about 68 telephones for every 100 persons. A **ratio** is a comparison of two numbers. The ratio that compares 68 to 100 can be written in the following ways.

$$68 \text{ out of } 100,\ 68 \text{ to } 100,\ 68 : 100, \text{ or } \frac{68}{100}$$

7-1 Ratios

In an apartment building, there are a total of 42 telephones. Of these telephones, 30 are dial models and the rest are pushbutton models. The ratio of dial models to the total number of telephones is 30 to 42, or $\frac{30}{42}$.

Write $\frac{30}{42}$ in simplest form.

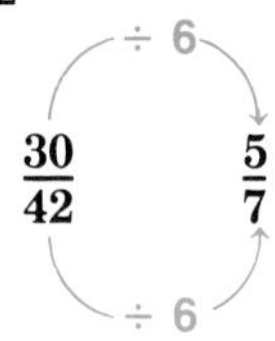

The GCF of 30 and 42 is 6.

The ratio 30 to 42 written as a fraction in simplest form is $\frac{5}{7}$.

EXERCISES ***Write each of the following ratios as a fraction in simplest form.***

1. 4 out of 9 **2.** 1 to 1 **3.** 10 : 1

4. 4 : 2 **5.** 9 out of 12 **6.** 3 to 6

7. 6 to 16 **8.** 28 : 7 **9.** 2 out of 16

10. 11 out of 11 **11.** 14 to 8 **12.** 72 : 18

13. 63 : 105 **14.** 112 out of 140 **15.** 462 to 770

16. $\frac{1}{4}$ to $\frac{1}{2}$ **17.** 0.2 : 5 **18.** $\frac{1}{3}$ to $\frac{1}{9}$

19. $\frac{3}{4}$ to 10 **20.** 0.03 : 0.005 **21.** 24 : 2.4

Solve.

22. In the apartment building described above, what is the ratio of pushbutton models to the total number of telephones?

23. There are 15 girls and 12 boys in a class. What is the ratio of the number of boys to the total number of students in the class?

24. The Senate passed a bill by a ratio of 8 to 1. If 90 senators voted in all, how many voted for and how many voted against?

25. A club has 15 members. The ratio of men to women in the club is 2:1. How many men and how many women are in the club?

7-2 Proportions

A survey shows that 30 out of 50 people surveyed watch Channel 6 News. Another survey shows that 24 out of 40 people surveyed watch Channel 6 News. These two ratios, $\frac{30}{50}$ and $\frac{24}{40}$, name the same number, $\frac{3}{5}$. So, $\frac{30}{50}$ and $\frac{24}{40}$ are equivalent ratios. An equation that states two ratios are equivalent is called a **proportion.**

$$\frac{30}{50} = \frac{24}{40} \quad \textbf{proportion}$$

In a proportion, the **cross products** are equal. For example, in $\frac{30}{50} = \frac{24}{40}$, the cross products are 30×40 and 50×24. Both equal 1,200.

Two ratios form a proportion only if their cross products are equal.

$$\frac{30}{50} = \frac{24}{40}$$

$$30 \times 40 = 50 \times 24$$

$$1{,}200 = 1{,}200$$

EXERCISES ***Match.***

1. $\frac{3}{8} = \frac{9}{24}$ — **a.** 33.6
2. $\frac{50}{25} = \frac{250}{125}$ — **b.** 276.632
3. $\frac{36}{20} = \frac{9}{5}$ — **c.** 180
4. $\frac{7}{16} = \frac{2.1}{4.8}$ — **d.** 72
5. $\frac{9}{2} = \frac{0.09}{0.02}$ — **e.** 6,250
6. $\frac{9.16}{12.08} = \frac{22.9}{30.2}$ — **f.** 0.18

Use cross products to see if each pair of ratios forms a proportion. Replace each ▒ with = (is equal to) or ≠ (is not equal to) to make a true sentence.

7. $\frac{1}{2}$ ▒ $\frac{3}{7}$ **8.** $\frac{4}{6}$ ▒ $\frac{2}{3}$ **9.** $\frac{4}{5}$ ▒ $\frac{13}{15}$ **10.** $\frac{8}{3}$ ▒ $\frac{24}{8}$

11. $\frac{24}{4}$ ▒ $\frac{12}{2}$ **12.** $\frac{4}{9}$ ▒ $\frac{8}{18}$ **13.** $\frac{7}{5}$ ▒ $\frac{15}{10}$ **14.** $\frac{9}{1.35}$ ▒ $\frac{7}{1}$

15. $\frac{4}{6}$ ▒ $\frac{0.8}{1.2}$ **16.** $\frac{6}{8}$ ▒ $\frac{15}{20}$ **17.** $\frac{4}{5}$ ▒ $\frac{0.8}{1}$ **18.** $\frac{0.07}{0.14}$ ▒ $\frac{1.5}{0.3}$

You can solve a proportion like $\frac{1}{2} = \frac{z}{50}$ using cross products.

$$\frac{1}{2} = \frac{z}{50}$$

$$1 \times 50 = 2 \times z$$ Cross products are equal.

$$50 = 2z$$ Solve for z.

$$\frac{50}{2} = \frac{2z}{2}$$ Divide each side by 2.

$$25 = z$$ The solution is 25.

EXERCISES ***Solve each proportion.***

19. $\frac{1}{4} = \frac{n}{24}$
20. $\frac{1}{2} = \frac{a}{14}$
21. $\frac{1}{5} = \frac{w}{25}$
22. $\frac{1}{3} = \frac{f}{15}$
23. $\frac{3}{4} = \frac{s}{12}$
24. $\frac{r}{7} = \frac{8}{56}$
25. $\frac{5}{4} = \frac{25}{g}$
26. $\frac{g}{20} = \frac{25}{100}$
27. $\frac{6}{m} = \frac{48}{40}$
28. $\frac{4}{7} = \frac{20}{d}$
29. $\frac{6}{c} = \frac{12}{15}$
30. $\frac{3}{4} = \frac{27}{x}$
31. $\frac{12}{16} = \frac{p}{32}$
32. $\frac{h}{9.6} = \frac{5}{16}$
33. $\frac{2}{3} = \frac{1.2}{k}$
34. $\frac{r}{3} = \frac{8}{15}$
35. $\frac{t}{7} = \frac{1}{2}$
36. $\frac{9}{n} = \frac{36}{50}$
37. $\frac{12}{18} = \frac{y}{24}$
38. $\frac{0.2}{s} = \frac{1}{12}$
39. $\frac{15}{v} = \frac{6}{8}$
40. $\frac{5}{8} = \frac{b}{100}$
41. $\frac{v}{4.8} = \frac{5}{16}$
42. $\frac{2.25}{1} = \frac{u}{6}$
43. $\frac{2.4}{3.6} = \frac{q}{1.8}$
44. $\frac{6}{2.56} = \frac{9}{m}$
45. $\frac{s}{9.6} = \frac{7}{16}$
46. $\frac{19.2}{d} = \frac{7}{29.4}$

Solve. Use the proportion given.

47. The ratio of radios to persons is about 1.7 to 1. How many radios are there for 1,000 people?

$$\frac{1.7}{1} = \frac{r}{1{,}000}$$

48. About 41 out of 50 homes have color television. How many would you expect in 550 homes?

$$\frac{41}{50} = \frac{t}{550}$$

49. A recipe uses 3 cups of flour for 48 cookies. How much flour is needed for 72 cookies?

$$\frac{3}{48} = \frac{c}{72}$$

50. A 5-acre field has a yield of 280 bushels of wheat. What yield can be expected for a 42-acre field?

$$\frac{280}{5} = \frac{b}{42}$$

7-3 Using Proportions

Ralph Mendoz is building a base for a television antenna. He needs 9 cubic feet of concrete. It takes 200 pounds of sand to make 4 cubic feet of concrete. How much sand does he need?

Let s represent the amount of sand needed.

The ratios of the sand to the concrete must be the same. So, set up a proportion and solve for s.

sand → 200, concrete → 4; s ← sand, 9 ← concrete

$$\frac{200}{4} = \frac{s}{9}$$

$200 \times 9 = 4 \times s$ Cross products are equal.

$1,800 = 4s$

$\frac{1,800}{4} = \frac{4s}{4}$ Divide each side by 4.

$450 = s$ Mr. Mendoz needs 450 pounds of sand.

***EXERCISES* Set up a proportion for each of the following. Then solve each proportion.**

1. It takes 260 pounds of gravel to make 4 cubic feet of concrete. It takes g pounds of gravel to make 9 cubic feet of concrete.
2. It takes 94 pounds of cement to make 4 cubic feet of concrete. It takes c pounds of cement to make 9 cubic feet of concrete.
3. 2 pounds yield 5 servings. n pounds yield 7 servings.
4. 9 gallons cost $12.15. n gallons cost $20.25.
5. 2 boxes cost $0.98. 5 boxes cost n dollars.
6. 3 acres yield n bushels. 7 acres yield 875 bushels.

Solve. Use a proportion.

7. Erma buys four packages of paper for $6. How many packages can she buy for $9?
8. Six tomato plants yield 108 tomatoes. How many tomato plants yield 162 tomatoes?
9. Wai Lui works 5 hours and earns $23.25. If he works 8 hours, how much does he earn?
10. Mr. Fisher plows a 10-acre field in $2\frac{1}{2}$ hours. How many acres can he plow in 14 hours?

A dozen ears of sweet corn sell for $1.30. Michelle buys five ears of corn. How much do they cost?

Let c represent the cost of five ears of corn. Set up a proportion.

number of ears → $\frac{12}{1.30} = \frac{5}{c}$ ← number of ears
cost → ← cost

$$12 \times c = 1.30 \times 5$$ Cross products are equal.

$$\frac{12c}{12} = \frac{6.5}{12}$$ Divide each side by 12.

$$c \approx 0.54$$ To the nearest cent, five ears of corn cost $0.54.

Solve.

11. A 5-pound bag of potatoes costs $1.79. Abe buys 2 pounds of potatoes. How much do they cost?

12. A piece of material $2\frac{1}{2}$ yards long costs $3.65. How much material can Joan buy for $2.19?

13. A recipe uses 3 cups of sugar for 5 dozen cookies. How many cookies can be made with $1\frac{1}{4}$ cups of sugar?

14. A 165-mile trip takes 6 gallons of gas. How many gallons does a 240-mile trip take?

15. Three loaves of bread cost $1.19. How much do two loaves cost?

16. A stew recipe uses 2 pounds of meat for 12 servings. How much is needed to make 9 servings?

A FAMOUS RACE

This is the story of a race between a turtle and a rabbit. They had the following conversation.

Rabbit I can run 10 times as fast as you. I'll give you a 1 km head start and still win.

Turtle But, while you run the 1 km, I'll run another 0.1 km. Then, while you run the 0.1 km, I'll run another 0.01 km, and so on. You will never catch me!

Did the rabbit ever catch the turtle? If so, how far did the turtle run before the rabbit caught up?

7-4 Rates

A record makes 135 revolutions every 3 minutes. The ratio 135 : 3 compares the number of revolutions to the number of minutes. A **rate** is a ratio of two measurements having different units.

$$\left.\frac{\textbf{135 revolutions}}{\textbf{3 minutes}}\right\} \quad \textbf{rate}$$

A rate with a denominator of 1 is called a **unit rate.**

$$\left.\frac{\overset{45}{\cancel{135}}\ \textbf{revolutions}}{\underset{1}{\cancel{3}}\ \textbf{minutes}} = \frac{\textbf{45 revolutions}}{\textbf{1 minute}}\right\} \quad \textbf{unit rate}$$

The unit rate is 45 revolutions per minute (45 rpm).

EXERCISES ***Write each of the following as a rate.***

1. 100 miles in 4 hours
2. 24 pounds lost in 3 weeks
3. $320 saved in 8 months
4. 225 kilometers in 5 hours
5. 12 revolutions in 0.5 seconds
6. 87.6 miles on 2.5 gallons

Write each of the following as a unit rate.

7. $\frac{\$430}{5\text{ weeks}}$
8. $\frac{505\text{ words}}{10\text{ minutes}}$
9. $\frac{18\text{ pounds}}{15\text{ days}}$
10. 88 calculators in 8 days
11. 342 meters in 9 seconds
12. $3.84 for 3 gallons
13. 6 pounds gained in 8 weeks
14. 250 grams in 2.5 liters
15. 9.6 meters in 0.4 hours
16. 9 meters in 0.75 seconds
17. $6 in 0.4 hours

A drive shaft makes 36,000 revolutions in 6 minutes. How many revolutions does it make in 15 minutes?

rate ➧ $\frac{\overset{6{,}000}{\cancel{36{,}000}}\text{ revolutions}}{\underset{1}{\cancel{6}}\text{ minutes}} = \frac{6{,}000\text{ revolutions}}{1\text{ minute}}$ ➧ **unit rate**

Let n represent the number of revolutions in 15 minutes and set up a proportion.

revolutions → $\frac{6{,}000}{1} = \frac{n}{15}$ ← revolutions
minutes → ← minutes

$$6{,}000 \times 15 = 1 \times n$$

$$90{,}000 = n$$

The drive shaft makes 90,000 revolutions in 15 minutes.

Solve.

18. Connie Vance travels 301 km in 3.5 hours. At that rate, how far can she travel in 10.5 hours?

19. Harry travels 27.5 miles in 0.5 hours. At that rate, how long does it take him to travel 770 miles?

20. Gabriela saves $45 in four months. At that rate, how long will it take her to save $180?

21. A 10-ounce jar of jelly is 99¢. A 16-ounce jar of jelly is $1.29. Which is the better buy?

22. At Saver's, two quarts of strawberries cost $2.30. At Carson's, five quarts are on sale for $6. Which is the better buy?

23. A computer performs 43,000 additions per second. At that rate, how many additions can it perform in three minutes?

Solve. Use the chart.

24. What is the rate for a 1-minute call from Columbus to Boston at 7:45 A.M. on Tuesday?

25. What is the unit rate for each additional minute for the call described in problem 24?

26. Lester calls his friend in Houston at 8:30 P.M. on Sunday. They talk for 9 minutes. What is the unit rate for the last 8 minutes?

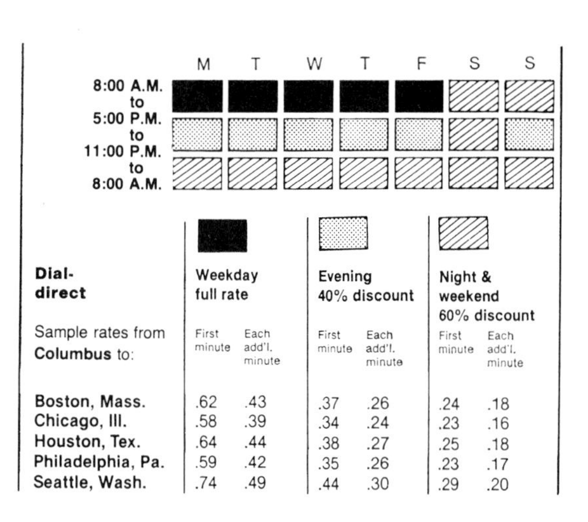

Dial-direct	Weekday full rate		Evening 40% discount		Night & weekend 60% discount	
Sample rates from Columbus to:	First minute	Each add'l. minute	First minute	Each add'l. minute	First minute	Each add'l. minute
Boston, Mass.	.62	.43	.37	.26	.24	.18
Chicago, Ill.	.58	.39	.34	.24	.23	.16
Houston, Tex.	.64	.44	.38	.27	.25	.18
Philadelphia, Pa.	.59	.42	.35	.26	.23	.17
Seattle, Wash.	.74	.49	.44	.30	.29	.20

7-5 Problem Solving: Using Rates and Proportions

Kenton Audio Shop sells and installs car stereo systems. Out of every 100 cars in Kenton, 23 have stereo systems. There are 5,372 cars in Kenton. Ann Colston, the manager of Kenton Audio, wants to find out how many cars in Kenton do not have stereo systems.

Read the problem. You need to find the number of cars in Kenton that do not have stereo systems. You know the total number of cars in Kenton. You also are given the rate of cars with stereo systems for every 100 cars.

Decide what to do. Set up a proportion to find the number of cars in Kenton that do have stereo systems. Then subtract this number from the total number of cars in Kenton.

Solve the problem. Let n represent the number of cars in Kenton that have stereo systems.

cars with stereo systems → 23, cars → 100; n ← cars with stereo systems, 5,372 ← cars

$$\frac{23}{100} = \frac{n}{5{,}372}$$

$$23 \times 5{,}372 = 100 \times n$$ Cross products are equal.

$$123{,}556 = 100n$$

$$1{,}235.56 = n$$

About 1,236 cars in Kenton have stereo systems. Subtract 1,236 from 5,372 to find out how many cars do not have stereo systems.

$$\begin{array}{r} \overset{6\,12}{5{,}3\cancel{7}\cancel{2}} \\ -\ 1{,}236 \\ \hline 4{,}136 \end{array}$$

About 4,136 cars in Kenton do not have stereo systems.

Examine the solution. Almost 25 out of 100 cars or $\frac{1}{4}$ of the cars in Kenton have stereo systems. This means about $\frac{3}{4}$ of the cars do not have stereo systems. 4,136 is close to $\frac{3}{4}$ of 5,372. The answer is reasonable.

Replace n with 1,235.56 in the original proportion and check the cross products. The answer is correct.

Solve.

1. Three out of five people in Bayview listen to the radio in the morning. There are 10,055 people in Bayview. How many listen to the radio in the morning?

2. About four out of every ten radio stations are connected with a national network. In Central City there are twenty radio stations. About how many are connected with a national network?

3. Shevon hit 13 home runs in 200 times at bat. At that rate, how many home runs can she expect to hit in 520 times at bat?

4. A recipe uses $1\frac{3}{4}$ cups of uncooked rice for an 8-serving casserole. How much uncooked rice is needed to make 14 servings?

5. There are 560 calories in a 16-ounce carton of cottage cheese. How many calories are in a 24-ounce carton of cottage cheese?

6. Your eyes blink about 25 times each minute. If you are awake for 15 hours, about how many times do you blink?

7. A commercial claims that 3 out of 5 dentists recommend Smile Toothpaste. At this rate, out of 350 dentists, how many would not recommend Smile Toothpaste?

8. From 9:00 A.M. to 3:00 P.M. Joe Ryan drives 280 kilometers. He begins driving the next day at 8:00 A.M. At the same rate, how far can he travel in 18 hours?

The ratio of weight on Earth to weight on the moon is 6 : 1. Find the equivalent weight for each of the following.

9. 120 pounds on Earth

10. 155 kilograms on Earth

11. 56 kilograms on the moon

12. 2,000 pounds on the moon

13. Find your equivalent weight on the moon.

7-6 Scale Drawings

A **scale drawing** is used to represent something that is too large or too small to be conveniently drawn actual size. A map is a scale drawing.

Mrs. Dorris lives in Terre Haute, Indiana. She wants to drive to Indianapolis. She can use the map to find the actual distance from Terre Haute to Indianapolis.

On the map, 1 centimeter represents 50 kilometers. The map distance between the two cities is about 2.3 centimeters.

Set up a proportion to find the actual distance, d.

$$\begin{matrix}\text{map} \rightarrow \\ \text{actual} \rightarrow\end{matrix} \frac{1}{50} = \frac{2.3}{d} \begin{matrix}\leftarrow \text{map} \\ \leftarrow \text{actual}\end{matrix}$$

$$1 \times d = 50 \times 2.3$$

$$d = 115$$

The actual distance from Terre Haute to Indianapolis is about 115 kilometers.

EXERCISES ***Find the actual distance between the cities. The map distance is given. Use the Indiana map.***

1. Gary, New Albany, 8.0 cm

2. Anderson, Muncie, 0.6 cm

3. Kokomo, Lafayette, 1.3 cm

4. Ft. Wayne, Richmond, 2.8 cm

5. South Bend, Ft. Wayne, 2.3 cm

6. Bloomington, Indianapolis, 1.5 cm

7. New Albany, Richmond, 3.9 cm

8. Kokomo, Anderson, 1.2 cm

9. Richmond, South Bend, 4.8 cm

10. South Bend, Evansville, 8.7 cm

Estimate the actual length of each trip. Use the map on page 182.

11. Terre Haute to Indianapolis to Bloomington

12. Ft. Wayne to Richmond to New Albany

13. Lafayette to Kokomo to Anderson to Muncie

14. New Albany to Richmond to South Bend

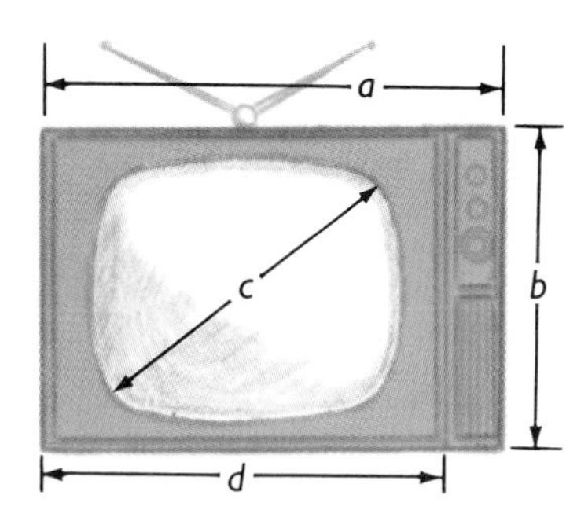

On the scale drawing at the right, 1 millimeter represents 0.015 meter. Find each of the following actual measurements.

15. a, 40 mm

16. b, 27 mm

17. c, 29 mm

18. d, 35 mm

Solve.

19. On a scale drawing of a building, 1 inch represents 5 feet. The actual width of a window is $3\frac{1}{2}$ feet. How wide should the window be on the scale drawing?

Skills Review: Pages 173-183

Write each of the following ratios as a fraction in simplest form.

1. 8 out of 9

2. 25 : 100

3. 20 to 12

Solve each proportion.

4. $\frac{1}{3} = \frac{x}{12}$

5. $\frac{21}{3} = \frac{63}{r}$

6. $\frac{2}{2.5} = \frac{n}{2.25}$

Solve.

7. A recipe uses $\frac{3}{4}$ cup of butter to make five servings. How much butter is needed to make twelve servings?

8. A record makes 100 revolutions every three minutes. What is the unit rate?

On a scale drawing of a car, 1 millimeter represents 8 centimeters. Scale drawing measurements are given below. Find the actual measurement of each.

9. wheelbase, 74 mm

10. rear leg room, 26 mm

Cumulative Review

Estimate.

1. $\begin{array}{r} 685 \\ +\ 93 \\ \hline \end{array}$ **2.** $\begin{array}{r} 4.06 \\ -\ 0.487 \\ \hline \end{array}$ **3.** $\begin{array}{r} 188 \\ \times\ 18 \\ \hline \end{array}$ **4.** $21\overline{)406}$ **5.** $0.077\overline{)6.33}$

Add, subtract, multiply, or divide.

6. $\begin{array}{r} 47{,}218 \\ -\ 9{,}809 \\ \hline \end{array}$ **7.** $\begin{array}{r} \$24.16 \\ -\ 2.98 \\ \hline \end{array}$ **8.** $\begin{array}{r} 16.4 \\ +\ 2.96 \\ \hline \end{array}$ **9.** $\begin{array}{r} 3.98 \\ +\ 40.7 \\ \hline \end{array}$ **10.** $\begin{array}{r} 10.41 \\ -\ 2.068 \\ \hline \end{array}$

11. $\begin{array}{r} 27 \\ \times\ 14 \\ \hline \end{array}$ **12.** $\begin{array}{r} 8.6 \\ \times\ 5 \\ \hline \end{array}$ **13.** $\begin{array}{r} 0.632 \\ \times\ 15 \\ \hline \end{array}$ **14.** $\begin{array}{r} 27.6 \\ \times\ 1.4 \\ \hline \end{array}$ **15.** $\begin{array}{r} 2.064 \\ \times\ 7.5 \\ \hline \end{array}$

16. $28\overline{)1{,}876}$ **17.** $3\overline{)8.1}$ **18.** $33\overline{)18.81}$ **19.** $15\overline{)93}$

20. $0.9\overline{)20.79}$ **21.** $0.26\overline{)0.8008}$ **22.** $0.05\overline{)3{,}925}$ **23.** $0.261\overline{)5.2983}$

24. $2.65 + 1.82$ **25.** $1.016 - 0.84$ **26.** $\$23.64 + \$9.92 + \$14$

27. 0.86×10 **28.** 23.1×100 **29.** $4 \div 1{,}000$ **30.** $7.2 \div 10$

Find the greatest common factor (GCF) for each group of numbers.

31. 6, 10 **32.** 24, 15 **33.** 16, 24, 32

Find the least common multiple (LCM) for each group of numbers.

34. 2, 3 **35.** 8, 6 **36.** 15, 18, 6

Add, subtract, multiply, or divide. Write each answer in simplest form.

37. $\frac{4}{9} + \frac{7}{9}$ **38.** $\frac{2}{5} + \frac{2}{3}$ **39.** $6\frac{9}{10} + 2\frac{3}{10}$ **40.** $16\frac{3}{5} + 28\frac{1}{3}$

41. $\frac{5}{6} - \frac{1}{4}$ **42.** $\frac{5}{6} - \frac{2}{9}$ **43.** $2\frac{3}{4} - 1\frac{9}{10}$ **44.** $10\frac{3}{8} - 4\frac{2}{3}$

45. $27 \times \frac{4}{9}$ **46.** $\frac{1}{4} \times \frac{3}{5}$ **47.** $1\frac{2}{5} \times \frac{15}{22}$ **48.** $5\frac{1}{5} \times 4\frac{3}{8}$

49. $\frac{4}{7} \div 8$ **50.** $\frac{7}{8} \div \frac{7}{4}$ **51.** $2\frac{1}{2} \div 2\frac{3}{4}$ **52.** $2\frac{6}{7} \div 1\frac{11}{21}$

Evaluate each expression if a = 2, b = 3, and c = $\frac{1}{2}$.

53. $a - 2$ **54.** $b + c$ **55.** $a^2 + b$

Solve each equation. Check your solution.

56. $a + 5 = 7$

57. $2 + b = 5.62$

58. $c - 13 = 4$

59. $5e = 48$

60. $3\frac{1}{10} = d - 6\frac{3}{5}$

61. $\frac{g}{7} = 2.3$

62. $1\frac{1}{4} = \frac{h}{2}$

63. $2m - 5 = 23$

Solve each proportion.

64. $\frac{6}{5} = \frac{a}{35}$

65. $\frac{2.5}{r} = \frac{4}{8}$

66. $\frac{10}{7} = \frac{6}{s}$

67. $\frac{0.3}{b} = \frac{1.8}{9.6}$

Solve.

68. A color television costs $328. What is the price of a set that costs $1\frac{1}{2}$ times as much?

69. Mr. Sutherland paid $493.20 for a stereo in 24 equal payments. How much was each payment?

70. Tracy's Bakery sells a $2\frac{1}{4}$-pound coffee cake for $3.60. A $\frac{3}{4}$-pound coffee cake costs $1.50. Which is the better buy?

71. One dozen oranges cost $1.89. Roderico has $3.25. Does he have enough money to buy 21 oranges?

Mathematics Lab

Grid paper may be used to make scale drawings. The scale drawing of a living room is shown at the right.

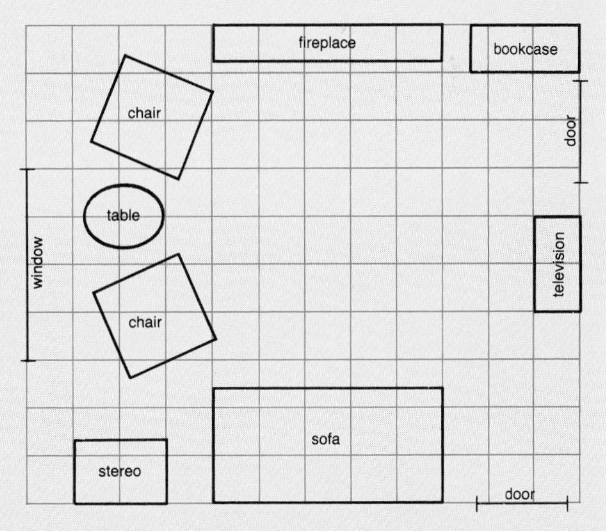

Solve. Use the scale drawing.

1. What is the scale?
2. What are the actual dimensions of the room?
3. What are the actual dimensions of the sofa?
4. What are the actual dimensions of each chair?
5. Measure your classroom and the objects in the classroom. Then, set up a scale and make a scale drawing of your classroom.

7-7 Percents and Decimals

Shaun writes an article about the library for the school newspaper. He asks 100 students if they have a library card. He fills in a square for each person that has a library card. He finds that 53 out of 100 students, or 53% (53 percent), have library cards.

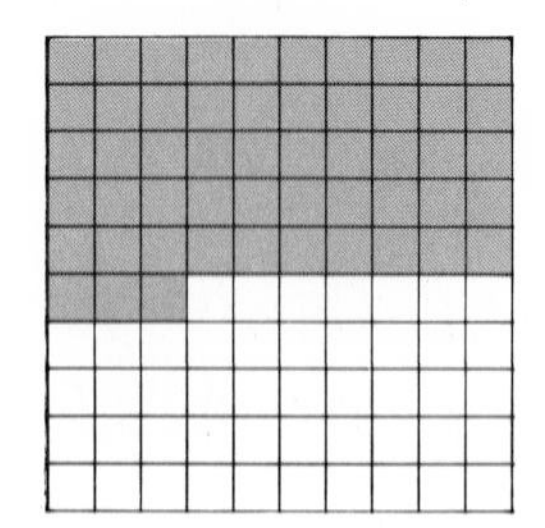

Percent means hundredths.

53 out of 100 ➧ **53 hundredths** ➧ **0.53** ➧ **53%**

To change a decimal to a percent, multiply by 100 (move the decimal point two places to the *right*). Then write the percent sign.

0.53 ➧ **0.53** ➧ **53%**

0.259 ➧ **0.259** ➧ **25.9%**

1.62 ➧ **1.62** ➧ **162%**

0.005 ➧ **0.005** ➧ **0.5%**

EXERCISES ***Write a percent for each diagram.***

1. **2.** **3.** **4.**

Change each decimal to a percent.

5. 0.24	**6.** 0.17	**7.** 0.63	**8.** 0.44	**9.** 0.98
10. 0.07	**11.** 0.02	**12.** 0.05	**13.** 0.418	**14.** 0.236
15. 0.567	**16.** 0.692	**17.** 0.303	**18.** 0.602	**19.** 0.003
20. 0.006	**21.** 0.008	**22.** 0.102	**23.** 0.205	**24.** 0.709
25. 1.24	**26.** 1.07	**27.** 1.43	**28.** 1.79	**29.** 2.15

To change a percent to a decimal, divide by 100 (move the decimal point two places to the *left*). Then omit the percent sign.

80% ➡	**80%** ➡	**0.80**
125% ➡	**125%** ➡	**1.25**
61.6% ➡	**61.6%** ➡	**0.616**
4% ➡	**04%** ➡	**0.04**
$66\frac{2}{3}$% ➡	**$66\frac{2}{3}$%** ➡	**$0.66\frac{2}{3}$**

EXERCISES ***Change each percent to a decimal.***

30. 70%	**31.** 36%	**32.** 55%	**33.** 29%	**34.** 64%
35. 95%	**36.** 3%	**37.** 6%	**38.** 9%	**39.** 10%
40. 41.5%	**41.** 32.7%	**42.** 70.6%	**43.** 20.3%	**44.** 123%
45. 137%	**46.** 245%	**47.** 0.9%	**48.** 0.6%	**49.** 0.2%
50. 100%	**51.** 400%	**52.** 8.5%	**53.** 7.2%	**54.** $33\frac{1}{3}$%
55. $133\frac{1}{3}$%	**56.** $12\frac{1}{2}$%	**57.** $81\frac{2}{3}$%	**58.** $1\frac{1}{6}$%	**59.** $6\frac{5}{6}$%

Replace each ▒ with <, >, or = to make a true sentence.

60. 1.5 ▒ 100%	**61.** 0.15 ▒ 15%	**62.** 0.04 ▒ 10%
63. 0.007 ▒ 7%	**64.** 0.495 ▒ 1%	**65.** 1.75 ▒ 175%
66. 6.1 ▒ 610%	**67.** 0.029 ▒ 29%	**68.** 0.35 ▒ 3.6%

Solve.

69. In a 100-member orchestra, 19 people play the violin. What percent play the violin?

70. A ham radio club has 100 members. This year 18% are new members. How many are new members?

71. Out of 100 students in the eighth grade, 48 are boys. What percent of the students are girls?

72. There are 74 people in the gym and 26 in the cafeteria. What percent of the total are in the cafeteria?

7-8 Percents and Fractions

In the United States, $\frac{9}{10}$ of foreign news stories come from wire services. What percent is equivalent to $\frac{9}{10}$?

Remember that percent means *hundredths*.

Let x represent the percent that is equivalent to $\frac{9}{10}$. Set up a proportion to find the percent.

$$\frac{9}{10} = \frac{x}{100}$$

Solve the proportion.

$$9 \times 100 = 10 \times x$$

$$900 = 10x$$

$$90 = x$$

Wire services provide $\frac{9}{10}$ or 90% of the foreign news stories.

Change the mixed numeral $1\frac{1}{2}$ to a percent.

$$1\frac{1}{2} = \frac{x}{100}$$

$$\frac{3}{2} = \frac{x}{100} \qquad 1\frac{1}{2} = \frac{3}{2}$$

$$300 = 2x$$

$$150 = x$$

So, $1\frac{1}{2} = 150\%$.

Change the fraction $\frac{1}{6}$ to a percent.

$$\frac{1}{6} = \frac{x}{100}$$

$$100 = 6x$$

$$16\frac{2}{3} = x$$

$100 \div 6 = 16\frac{4}{6}$ or $16\frac{2}{3}$: $100 - 6 = 40$, $40 - 36 = 4$

So, $\frac{1}{6} = 16\frac{2}{3}\%$.

EXERCISES ***Change each fraction or mixed numeral to a percent.***

1. $\frac{21}{100}$	**2.** $\frac{9}{100}$	**3.** $\frac{53}{100}$	**4.** $\frac{37}{100}$	**5.** $\frac{89}{100}$	**6.** $\frac{1}{10}$
7. $\frac{1}{5}$	**8.** $\frac{7}{10}$	**9.** $\frac{3}{5}$	**10.** $\frac{1}{2}$	**11.** $\frac{1}{4}$	**12.** $\frac{3}{4}$
13. $\frac{9}{20}$	**14.** $\frac{11}{25}$	**15.** $\frac{7}{50}$	**16.** $1\frac{3}{10}$	**17.** $1\frac{1}{4}$	**18.** $1\frac{1}{2}$
19. $2\frac{3}{4}$	**20.** $2\frac{7}{20}$	**21.** $\frac{1}{8}$	**22.** $\frac{7}{16}$	**23.** $\frac{5}{6}$	**24.** $\frac{7}{8}$
25. $\frac{4}{7}$	**26.** $1\frac{3}{8}$	**27.** $1\frac{2}{9}$	**28.** $1\frac{9}{16}$	**29.** $2\frac{3}{7}$	**30.** $2\frac{7}{12}$

Change 75% to a fraction in simplest form.

Since percent means hundredths, 75% is equivalent to $\frac{75}{100}$.

$$\mathbf{75\%} \Rightarrow \frac{75}{100} = \frac{\overset{3}{\cancel{75}}}{\underset{4}{\cancel{100}}} = \frac{3}{4}$$

So, $75\% = \frac{3}{4}$.

Change $83\frac{1}{3}\%$ to a fraction in simplest form.

Since percent means hundredths, $83\frac{1}{3}\%$ is equivalent to $\frac{83\frac{1}{3}}{100}$.

$$\mathbf{83\tfrac{1}{3}\%} \Rightarrow \frac{83\frac{1}{3}}{100} = 83\tfrac{1}{3} \div 100$$

$$= \frac{250}{3} \times \frac{1}{100} \quad 83\tfrac{1}{3} = \frac{250}{3}$$

$$= \frac{\overset{5}{\cancel{250}}}{3} \times \frac{1}{\underset{2}{\cancel{100}}}$$

$$= \frac{5}{6}$$

So, $83\frac{1}{3}\% = \frac{5}{6}$.

EXERCISES* *Change each percent to a fraction or mixed numeral in simplest form.

31. 19%	**32.** 31%	**33.** 25%	**34.** 50%	**35.** 27%
36. 40%	**37.** 45%	**38.** 30%	**39.** 75%	**40.** 90%
41. 8%	**42.** 5%	**43.** 7%	**44.** 4%	**45.** 117%
46. 120%	**47.** 125%	**48.** 160%	**49.** 139%	**50.** 184%
51. $33\frac{1}{3}\%$	**52.** $87\frac{1}{2}\%$	**53.** $16\frac{2}{3}\%$	**54.** $12\frac{1}{2}\%$	**55.** $66\frac{2}{3}\%$
56. $37\frac{1}{2}\%$	**57.** $11\frac{1}{9}\%$	**58.** $144\frac{4}{9}\%$	**59.** $143\frac{3}{4}\%$	**60.** $173\frac{1}{3}\%$

Solve.

61. On a city block, $\frac{4}{5}$ of the people subscribe to the newspaper. What percent subscribe to the paper?

62. One third of the students at Allen Junior High attend a game. What percent attend the game?

63. If $\frac{2}{5}$ is equivalent to 40%, what percent is equivalent to $\frac{4}{5}$?

64. If $\frac{1}{3}$ is equivalent to $33\frac{1}{3}\%$, what percent is equivalent to $\frac{2}{3}$?

7-9 Percents, Decimals, and Fractions

Ramblebrook Developers offer either a home computer system or \$2,000 to each new home buyer. About 65% of the buyers choose a home computer system.

Change 65% to a decimal.

65% ➧ **65%** ➧ **0.65**

Change 65% to a fraction.

$$65\% \Rightarrow \frac{65}{100} = \frac{\overset{13}{\cancel{65}}}{\underset{20}{\cancel{100}}} = \frac{13}{20}$$

$65\% = \frac{13}{20}$

Change 1.35 to a mixed numeral and to a percent.

mixed numeral

$$1.35 \Rightarrow 1\frac{\overset{7}{\cancel{35}}}{\underset{20}{\cancel{100}}} \Rightarrow 1\frac{7}{20}$$

percent

1.35 ➧ **1.35** ➧ **135%**

Change $\frac{1}{8}$ to a decimal and to a percent.

decimal

$$\frac{1}{8} \Rightarrow \begin{array}{r} 0.125 \\ 8\overline{)1.000} \\ -\ 8 \\ \hline 20 \\ -\ 16 \\ \hline 40 \\ -\ 40 \\ \hline \end{array}$$

$\frac{1}{8} = 0.125$

percent

$$\frac{1}{8} = \frac{x}{100}$$

$$100 = 8x$$

$$12.5 = x$$

$\frac{1}{8} = 12.5\%$

EXERCISES ***Change each of the following to a decimal.***

1. 50%
2. 85%
3. 29%
4. 110%
5. $\frac{1}{4}$
6. $\frac{3}{5}$
7. $1\frac{1}{10}$
8. $\frac{2}{3}$
9. 76.7%
10. 1.5%
11. $\frac{9}{2}$
12. $2\frac{1}{2}$

Change each of the following to a percent.

13. 0.45
14. 0.345
15. 0.625
16. 0.90
17. $\frac{4}{5}$
18. $\frac{3}{10}$
19. $\frac{6}{5}$
20. $\frac{7}{8}$
21. 0.09
22. 1.25
23. $1\frac{2}{5}$
24. $5\frac{3}{4}$

Change each of the following to a fraction or a mixed numeral.

25. 0.8
26. 0.96
27. 0.258
28. 0.75
29. 60%
30. 62.5%
31. 144%
32. 4%
33. 0.004
34. 3.5
35. $6\frac{3}{4}\%$
36. $12\frac{1}{2}\%$

Skills Review: Pages 186-191

Change each decimal to a percent.

1. 0.25
2. 0.87
3. 1.51
4. 2.1
5. 0.005

Change each percent to a decimal.

6. 28%
7. 39%
8. 64.4%
9. 1%
10. 129%

Change each fraction or mixed numeral to a percent.

11. $\frac{1}{5}$
12. $\frac{3}{8}$
13. $\frac{5}{4}$
14. $1\frac{1}{2}$
15. $2\frac{2}{5}$

Change each percent to a fraction or mixed numeral.

16. 50%
17. 18%
18. 150%
19. 8%
20. $66\frac{2}{3}\%$

Solve.

21. Out of 100 students, 12 are on the student council. What percent are *not* on the student council?

Mathematics and Consumers

Utility bills provide various types of information. For example, the rate and the amount used for a certain time period are given. The chart lists the unit and rate (cost per unit) of electricity, natural gas, and water.

Utility	Unit	Rate
Electricity	kilowatt–hours (kWh)	about 8¢ per kWh
Natural gas	100 cubic feet (CCF)	about 82¢ per CCF
Water	cubic meters (m^3)	about 32¢ per m^3

Kim Ramirez estimates her utility bills each month. She reads the meters for each utility at the end of each month. On May 31, the electric meter reading was 23,208 kWh. On June 30, the meter reading was 23,791 kWh. Ms. Ramirez estimates her electric bill for the month of June as follows.

23,800 kWh	She used about	**600 kWh**
− 23,200 kWh	600 kWh of	**× 8¢ per kWh**
600 kWh	electricity.	**4,800¢** ← Change 4,800¢ to $48.

Ms. Ramirez estimates the bill as $48.

EXERCISES ***Estimate the amount of each utility bill. Use the rates given in the chart.***

	Previous Reading	Present Reading
1.	3,021 kWh	3,729 kWh
2.	4,965 CCF	4,989 CCF
3.	1,023 m^3	1,133 m^3
4.	16,325 kWh	17,615 kWh
5.	5,478 CCF	5,607 CCF
6.	7,697 m^3	7,851 m^3

7. What was the average amount of electricity used by Ms. Ramirez each day in June?

8. Mr. Scott's water bill is $24.36 for 84 m^3. At that rate, how much would it cost to use 67 m^3?

Chapter 7 Review

VOCABULARY ratio (172) proportion (174) rate (178) unit rate (178) scale drawing (182) percent (186)

EXERCISES ***Write each of the following ratios as a fraction in simplest form. (173)***

1. 5 out of 6 **2.** 3 to 6 **3.** 15 : 10

Solve each proportion. (175)

4. $\frac{1}{3} = \frac{n}{12}$ **5.** $\frac{18}{48} = \frac{6}{y}$ **6.** $\frac{2}{3} = \frac{x}{0.6}$ **7.** $\frac{8}{2.5} = \frac{10.4}{c}$

Set up a proportion for each of the following. Then solve each proportion. (176)

8. 4 pounds cost \$89.
9 pounds cost n dollars.

9. Al earns \$160.95 in 37 hours.
Al earns \$26.10 in n hours.

Write each of the following as a unit rate. (178)

10. 450 miles in 9 hours **11.** \$12 in 1.5 hours

Solve. (180–183)

12. A recipe calls for $2\frac{1}{2}$ cups of flour to make 3 dozen cookies. How much flour is needed to make 90 cookies?

13. Luis saves \$29 the first four months of the year. At that rate, how long will it take him to save \$116?

Change each of the following to a decimal. (187)

14. 29% **15.** 1.2% **16.** $137\frac{1}{2}\%$ **17.** $\frac{7}{8}$ **18.** $\frac{9}{5}$

Change each of the following to a percent. (186, 188)

19. 0.76 **20.** 0.004 **21.** $\frac{2}{5}$ **22.** $\frac{3}{8}$ **23.** $1\frac{3}{50}$

Change each of the following to a fraction or mixed numeral. (189)

24. 25% **25.** $33\frac{1}{3}\%$ **26.** 8% **27.** 0.012 **28.** 1.05

Chapter 7 Test

Write each of the following ratios as a fraction in simplest form.

1. 14 to 28
2. 21 : 9
3. 8 out of 18

Solve each proportion.

4. $\frac{1}{a} = \frac{11}{22}$
5. $\frac{3}{8} = \frac{y}{12}$
6. $\frac{4}{3} = \frac{10}{w}$
7. $\frac{6}{5} = \frac{f}{17.5}$

Set up a proportion for each of the following. Then solve each proportion.

8. 2 gallons cost \$2.38.
   n gallons cost \$10.71.
9. 6 packages cost 57¢.
   4 packages cost n cents.

Write each of the following as a unit rate.

10. 172 kilometers in 2 hours
11. \$119.85 for 3 tape players

Solve.

12. Mr. Thomas wins an election by a ratio of 6 to 2. His opponent receives 2,300 votes. How many votes does Mr. Thomas receive?
13. Shirley drives 484 kilometers in $5\frac{1}{2}$ hours. At the same rate, how far can she travel in 12 hours?

On a scale drawing of a calculator, 1 centimeter represents 4.5 centimeters. Scale drawing measurements are given below. Find the actual measurement of each.

14. width, 1.8 cm
15. length, 3.1 cm

Change each of the following to a decimal.

16. 46%
17. 7%
18. 40.7%
19. $\frac{23}{40}$
20. $1\frac{7}{8}$

Change each of the following to a percent.

21. 0.37
22. 0.061
23. $\frac{31}{100}$
24. $2\frac{3}{10}$
25. $\frac{19}{25}$

Change each of the following to a fraction or a mixed numeral.

26. 60%
27. 43%
28. 175%
29. 0.06
30. 0.275

Enrichment

In 1202, Leonardo de Pisa (also known as Fibonacci) published an interesting number pattern. This pattern, or sequence, has become known as the **Fibonacci sequence,** or Fibonacci numbers.

1, 1, 2, 3, 5, 8, . . . Fibonacci Sequence

How is each term related to the two terms before it? What is the next term of the sequence?

Fibonacci numbers often are found in nature. For example, the spirals of a pineapple run in three distinct directions. Usually five rows run up the pineapple. Eight rows run more steeply down and thirteen spirals run very steeply up the pineapple.

The Fibonacci sequence is the basis of other sequences as well. One of these is the sequence formed by dividing each term of the Fibonacci sequence by the term before it.

$\frac{1}{1}, \frac{2}{1}, \frac{3}{2}, \frac{5}{3}, \frac{8}{5}, \ldots$ What is the next term of this sequence?

EXERCISES Complete each of the following.

1. Find the first twenty terms of the Fibonacci sequence.

2. Find the first fifteen terms of the sequence $\frac{1}{1}, \frac{2}{1}, \frac{3}{2}, \frac{5}{3}, \frac{8}{5}, \ldots$.

3.
$1 + 1 = \blacksquare$
$1 + 1 + 2 = \blacksquare$
$1 + 1 + 2 + 3 = \blacksquare$
$1 + 1 + 2 + 3 + 5 = \blacksquare$

How do these sums compare to the Fibonacci sequence?

4.
$1^2 + 1^2 = \blacksquare$
$1^2 + 2^2 = \blacksquare$
$2^2 + 3^2 = \blacksquare$
$3^2 + 5^2 = \blacksquare$

How do these sums compare to the Fibonacci sequence?

5.
$1^2 + 1^2 = 1 \times 2$
$1^2 + 1^2 + 2^2 = 2 \times 3$
$1^2 + 1^2 + 2^2 + 3^2 = \blacksquare$
$\underline{\quad ? \quad} = \blacksquare$

6. Use a calculator to change the first ten terms of the sequence in exercise 2 to decimals rounded to the nearest thousandth. What do you discover?

Skills Test, Chapters 1-7

Standardized Format

Directions Work each problem on your own paper. Choose the letter of the correct answer. If the correct answer is not given, choose the letter for *none of the above.* Make no marks in this book.

1. Which group of numbers is arranged in order from least to greatest?

a 0.18, 0.081, 0.81, 1.08

b 0.081, 0.18, 0.81, 1.08

c 0.18, 0.81, 0.081, 1.08

d *none of the above*

2. Add. $\begin{array}{r} 8.6 \\ +\ 32.7 \\ \hline \end{array}$

e 41.3

f 40.13

g 40.3

h *none of the above*

3. Subtract. $\begin{array}{r} 11.1 \\ -\ 8.63 \\ \hline \end{array}$

a 2.53

b 3.53

c 2.47

d *none of the above*

4. Multiply. $\begin{array}{r} 3.6 \\ \times\ 0.2 \\ \hline \end{array}$

e 7.2

f 6.12

g 6.2

h *none of the above*

5. Divide.

$0.7\overline{)9.31}$

a 0.133

b 13.3

c 1.33

d *none of the above*

6. What is the least common multiple of 6 and 14?

e 42

f 84

g 20

h *none of the above*

7. Which two numbers have 4 as their greatest common factor?

a 16, 24

b 12, 32

c 1, 4

d *none of the above*

8. Which of the following is $\frac{28}{6}$ in simplest form?

e $\frac{14}{2}$

f $4\frac{4}{6}$

g $4\frac{2}{3}$

h *none of the above*

9. Add. $2\frac{3}{4} + 5\frac{1}{3}$

a $7\frac{1}{3}$

b $7\frac{4}{7}$

c $7\frac{1}{12}$

d *none of the above*

10. Subtract. $6\frac{5}{8} - 5\frac{3}{4}$

e $1\frac{1}{2}$

f $1\frac{7}{8}$

g $\frac{7}{8}$

h *none of the above*

11. Multiply. $6\frac{4}{5} \times \frac{3}{4}$

a $5\frac{1}{10}$

b $6\frac{3}{5}$

c $7\frac{1}{15}$

d *none of the above*

12. Divide. $\frac{3}{4} \div \frac{3}{8}$

e 2

f $\frac{1}{2}$

g $\frac{9}{32}$

h *none of the above*

GO ON TO THE NEXT PAGE

13. What is the value of $14 - 2 \times 3 + 4^2$?

a 52

b 24

c 228

d *none of the above*

14. Solve.

$$6y = 39$$

e 45

f 6.5

g 33

h *none of the above*

15. Solve.

$$2b + 1 = 7$$

a 4

b 5

c 8

d *none of the above*

16. Complete the sequence.

1, 2, 4, 8, ▒, ▒, ▒

e 12, 16, 20

f 4, 2, 1

g 13, 19, 26

h *none of the above*

17. Solve.

$$\frac{4}{5} = \frac{x}{2}$$

a 1.3

b 1

c 2.5

d *none of the above*

18. 43% is equivalent to which of the following?

e 43

f 4.3

g 0.43

h *none of the above*

19. $\frac{1}{6}$ is equivalent to which of the following?

a $\frac{1}{6}\%$

b 1.6%

c $16\frac{2}{3}\%$

d *none of the above*

20. Triangle ABC can be classified as which of the following?

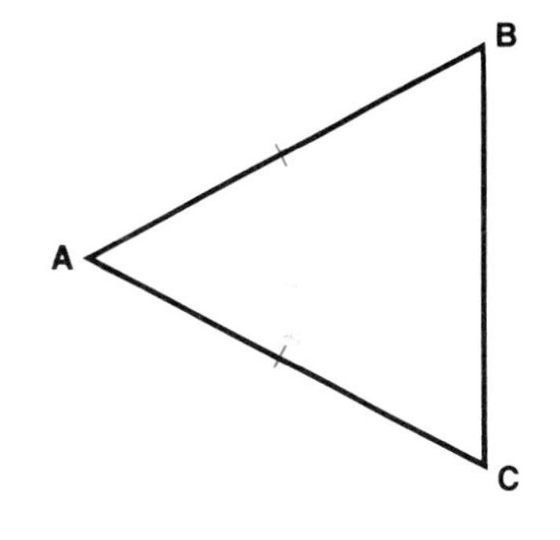

e equilateral, acute

f scalene, obtuse

g isosceles, acute

h *none of the above*

21. The repair bill for Jean Salazar's car is $25 more than the mechanic's estimate. The total bill is $350. How can you find the amount of the mechanic's estimate?

a multiply $350 by $25

b add $25 and $350

c subtract $25 from $350

d *none of the above*

22. Larry Weaver's heating bills have increased each month. In December, the bill was $85.63. It increased by $9.85 in January and another $5.52 in February. What was the total amount for December, January, and February?

e $282.11

f $101.00

g $272.26

h *none of the above*

STOP

Using Percents

A tire store sold 250 tires in a recent week. Out of the 250 tires, 84% were radial tires. You can use a proportion to find how many radial tires were sold.

8-1 Percents and Proportions

The proportion given below is used to solve problems involving percent.

$$\frac{\textbf{Percentage}}{\textbf{Base}} = \textbf{Rate} \quad \text{or} \quad \frac{P}{B} = \frac{r}{100}$$

The **percentage** (P) is a number that is compared to another number called the **base** (B). The **rate** is a percent. Always compare r to 100.

Use the proportion $\frac{P}{B} = \frac{r}{100}$ to find how many radial tires were sold.

$$\text{percentage} \rightarrow \frac{P}{250} = \frac{84}{100} \text{ rate}$$
base →

$$P \times 100 = 250 \times 84$$ Cross products are equal.

$$100P = 21{,}000$$ Divide each side by 100.

$$P = 210$$

The tire store sold 210 radial tires.

***EXERCISES* Solve. Use a proportion.**

1. Find 40% of 60.
2. Find 80% of 25.
3. What number is 30% of 30?
4. What number is 50% of 126?
5. 16% of 12.5 is what number?
6. 75% of 48 is what number?
7. Alice plays basketball. In one game she shoots 15 free throws and makes 80% of them. How many free throws does she make?
8. Tonio earns $63 each week. He gives 5% of his earnings to charity. How much money does he give to charity each week?
9. In a survey of 550 people, 62% liked Tasty Pizza. How many people liked Tasty Pizza?
10. 35% of the books in the Englewood Library are novels. There are 12,520 books in the library. How many are novels?

8-2 Finding the Percent of a Number

Penny Miller is a salesperson at a furniture store. She earns a commission of 10% of any sale she makes. If she sells a sofa for $739, how much commission does she earn?

Set up a proportion.

percentage → base → $\frac{P}{739} = \frac{10}{100}$ } rate

Solve the proportion.

$$P \times 100 = 739 \times 10$$

$$100P = 7{,}390$$

$$P = 73.9$$

Mrs. Miller earns a commission of $73.90.

You can also use an equation to solve this problem. Use a decimal or a fraction for the percent. Let c represent the commission.

10% of 739 is the commission.

$0.10 \times 739 = c$ 10% ➡ 0.10

$73.9 = c$

or

$\frac{1}{10} \times 739 = c$ 10% ➡ $\frac{10}{100}$ ➡ $\frac{1}{10}$

$\frac{739}{10} = c$

$73.9 = c$

Use the easiest method to solve percent problems. For example, if you recognize 10% as $\frac{1}{10}$, use the fraction method.

Find 2.5% of 720.

2.5% ➡ **0.025**

$\mathbf{0.025 \times 720 = x}$

$\mathbf{18 = x}$

2.5% of 720 is 18.

Find $33\frac{1}{3}\%$ of 96.

$\mathbf{33\frac{1}{3}\%}$ ➡ $\mathbf{\frac{1}{3}}$

$\mathbf{\frac{1}{3} \times 96 = x}$

$\mathbf{32 = x}$

$33\frac{1}{3}\%$ of 96 is 32.

EXERCISES ***Find each of the following. Use a proportion.***

1. 7% of 860
2. 16% of 1,920
3. 96% of 940
4. 15% of 20
5. 87% of 100
6. $6\frac{1}{2}\%$ of 900
7. 8% of 24.5
8. 120% of 650
9. 500% of 10

Find each of the following. Use a decimal for the percent.

10. 6% of 400
11. 85% of 65.4
12. 40% of 425
13. 1.5% of 600
14. 5.5% of 12
15. 4.2% of 68
16. 0.2% of 45
17. 0.05% of 48
18. 127% of 250

Find each of the following. Use a fraction for the percent.

19. 50% of 120
20. 25% of 200
21. 30% of 4.2
22. $33\frac{1}{3}\%$ of 390
23. $66\frac{2}{3}\%$ of 324
24. 60% of 15
25. 75% of 16
26. 150% of 418
27. 20% of 430

Solve.

28. Mrs. Miller sells a table for $279. If she earns a commission of 9%, how much money does she earn?

29. It rained on 40% of the days in April. How many days did it rain in April?

30. Of 84 sofas on display at a furniture store, about 12% have matching pillows. How many sofas have matching pillows?

31. James bought a stereo for $249. He made a down payment of $33\frac{1}{3}\%$. What is the amount he still must pay?

32. Donna Gonzalez earns $150 per week plus a 3.5% commission on all sales. One week she sells $4,950 worth of merchandise. How much money does she earn that week?

8-3 Finding the Percent One Number Is of Another

Juan Caprico earns $354 each week. After payroll deductions, his income is $261.96. What percent of his earnings does he actually receive?

Set up a proportion. percentage → base → $\frac{261.96}{354} = \frac{r}{100}$ } rate

Solve the proportion.

$$261.96 \times 100 = 354 \times r$$
$$26{,}196 = 354r$$
$$74 = r$$

Mr. Caprico actually receives 74% of his income.

You can also use an equation to solve this problem. Let r represent the percent.

$$\underbrace{r\%}\ \underbrace{\text{of}}\ \underbrace{354}\ \underbrace{\text{is}}\ \underbrace{261.96}$$
$$r \times 354 = 261.96$$
$$r = \frac{261.96}{354} \quad \text{Divide each side by 354.}$$
$$r = 0.74 \rightarrow 74\%$$

EXERCISES ***Solve. Use a proportion.***

1. What percent of 12 is 3?
2. What percent of 5 is 2?
3. 29 is what percent of 58?
4. 16 is what percent of 20?
5. What percent of 60 is 48?
6. What percent of 750 is 120?
7. 27 is what percent of 162?
8. 50 is what percent of 800?
9. What percent of 1.2 is 0.336?
10. 88 is what percent of 55?

Solve. Use an equation.

11. What percent of 90 is 9?
12. What percent of 90 is 54?
13. 24 is what percent of 48?
14. 26 is what percent of 39?
15. What percent of 100 is 59?
16. What percent of 50 is 12.5?
17. 170 is what percent of 85?
18. 1.8 is what percent of 24?
19. What percent of 1,000 is 5?
20. $\frac{4}{5}$ is what percent of $\frac{5}{4}$?

Solve.

21. Dan receives $196.84 out of total earnings of $259. What percent of his earnings does he actually receive?
22. Out of 48 cars at U-Rent-It, 6 are silver. What percent of the cars are silver?
23. On a 40-question test, Peggy answers 34 correctly. What percent of the questions does she answer correctly?
24. The Harrod Wildcats won 10 out of 16 games this year. What percent of games did they lose?
25. A jacket that regularly sells for $90 is on sale for $72. What percent of the regular price is the sale price?

Use the circle graph to find the percent of Stacy's monthly income ($230) budgeted for each of the following.

26. recreation
27. savings
28. food
29. clothing
30. transportation
31. miscellaneous

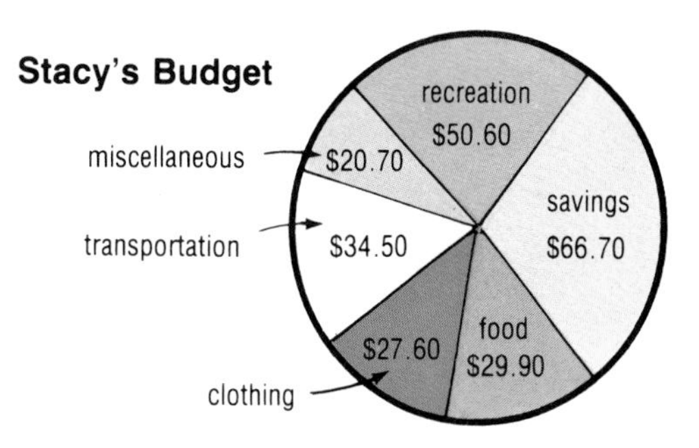

INFLATION

Inflation occurs when a rise in total spending is more than the rise in production and service.

Inflation Rate	Buying Power of $100 in 5 years	Buying Power of $100 in 10 years
4%	$81.54	$66.48
6%	$73.39	$53.86
9%	$62.40	$38.94

1. At 9% inflation, what is the buying power of $1,000 in 10 years?
2. At 4% inflation, what is the buying power of $1 in 5 years?

8-4 Finding a Number When a Percent of It Is Known

Quality Footwear sold 17 pairs of running shoes last week. This was $12\frac{1}{2}\%$ of the total shoe sales for the week. How many pairs of shoes were sold that week?

Set up a proportion.

percentage → base → $\frac{17}{B} = \frac{12\frac{1}{2}}{100}$ } rate

Solve the proportion.

$$17 \times 100 = 12\tfrac{1}{2} \times B$$

$$1{,}700 = 12\tfrac{1}{2}B$$ Divide each side by $12\frac{1}{2}$.

$$136 = B$$ 136 pairs of shoes were sold that week.

You can also use an equation to solve this problem. Let s represent the number of pairs of shoes sold.

$12\frac{1}{2}\%$ of shoes sold is 17.

$12\frac{1}{2}\%$ ➡ $\frac{1}{8}$ $\qquad \frac{1}{8} \times s = 17$

$$s = 136$$ Multiply each side by 8.

EXERCISES ***Solve. Use a proportion.***

1. 540 is 60% of what number?
2. 231 is 7% of what number?
3. 45% of what number is 135?
4. 27% of what number is 108?
5. 72 is 6% of what number?
6. 74.8 is 68% of what number?
7. 19.5% of what number is 117?
8. 8% of what number is 64?
9. 0.3% of what number is 9?
10. 120% of what number is 540?
11. 360 is 225% of what number?
12. 50 is 6.25% of what number?

Solve. Use an equation.

13. 820 is 20% of what number?

14. 21 is $33\frac{1}{3}$% of what number?

15. 50% of what number is 200?

16. 75% of what number is 27?

17. 25 is $62\frac{1}{2}$% of what number?

18. 22 is 80% of what number?

19. 225% of what number is 900?

20. 0.5% of what number is 16?

21. 68 is 2% of what number?

22. 42 is 175% of what number?

Solve.

23. A store receives a shipment of radios. Eight, or 2.5%, of the radios are defective. How many radios are in the shipment?

24. Mr. Jameson buys a suit for 80% of the regular price. He pays $180 for the suit. What is its regular price?

25. Kimiko's mother buys a new car and pays 15% down. If the down payment is $1,452.75, what is the price of the car?

26. Wayne plays basketball. In one game he makes 9 field goals, or 60% of his shots. How many shots did he take?

27. Beth answers 90%, or 27, of the questions on a test correctly. How many questions does she answer incorrectly?

28. Cassie's salary is $125 per week plus an 8% commission on all sales. How much must she sell to earn $200 per week?

Use the information in the chart to make a circle graph of the Davis family budget.

Davis Family Budget	
Housing	30%
Taxes	25%
Food	20%
Transportation	11%
Miscellaneous	9%
Savings	5%

29. Draw a circle using a compass.

Find the number of degrees for each item.

Housing ↓ — A circle has 360°. ↓

30% of 360 = 0.3 × 360

= 108

The sector for housing is 108°.

30. taxes

31. food

32. transportation

33. miscellaneous

34. savings

35. Use a protractor to draw angles in the circle having the degree measures found in exercises 30–34.

36. Make a circle graph of your classmates' hair colors.

8-5 Percents of Increase or Decrease

Andrea Evans had a paper route with 35 customers. A new apartment building was added to the route. She now has 49 customers. Find the **percent of increase.**

Subtract to find the amount of increase.

$$49 - 35 = 14$$

The route increased by 14 customers.

Set up a proportion. Compare the amount of increase to the original amount.

$$\begin{matrix}\text{percentage} \rightarrow \\ \text{base} \rightarrow\end{matrix} \frac{14}{35} = \frac{r}{100} \Big\} \text{ rate}$$

$$14 \times 100 = 35 \times r$$

$$1{,}400 = 35r$$

$$40 = r$$

The percent of increase is 40%.

A stereo system is reduced from \$380 to \$323. Find the **percent of decrease.**

Subtract to find the amount of decrease.

$$380 - 323 = 57$$

The price decreased by \$57.

Set up a proportion. Compare the amount of decrease to the original amount.

$$\begin{matrix}\text{percentage} \rightarrow \\ \text{base} \rightarrow\end{matrix} \frac{57}{380} = \frac{r}{100} \Big\} \text{ rate}$$

$$57 \times 100 = 380 \times r$$

$$5{,}700 = 380r$$

$$15 = r$$

The percent of decrease is 15%.

EXERCISES ***Find the percent of increase or decrease for each of the following.***

1. a \$40 radio increased to \$44

2. a \$450 oven decreased to \$396

3. 30 customers to 24 customers

4. 120 pounds to 126 pounds

5. a \$110 watch decreased to \$99

6. a \$325 antique increased to \$390

7. 40 books to 45 books

8. 170 pounds to 136 pounds

9. a \$60 lamp decreased to \$43.20

10. a \$1,300 sofa decreased to \$650

Solve.

11. A calculator usually sells for \$49. It is on sale for \$43.12. What is the percent of decrease?

12. One year a store sold 120 stereos. The next year, they sold 150. What is the percent of increase?

13. One time Felicia mows the yard in $2\frac{1}{2}$ hours. The next time she mows it in 2 hours and 5 minutes. What is the percent of decrease?

14. The price of lettuce increases from 69¢ to 92¢. What is the percent of increase?

15. The value of an antique table increases from \$320 to \$360 in three years. What is the percent of increase?

16. Joey went on a diet. He lost 13 pounds. Now he weighs 117 pounds. What was the percent of decrease in his weight?

17. A refrigerator usually sells for \$595. It is marked 20% off. What is the sale price?

18. A ring is on sale for \$105. It is 25% off its original price. What was its original price?

A SHORTCUT

You can use a shortcut to find amounts such as a sale price.

Suppose a coat that costs \$75 is on sale at 15% off. To find the sale price, you can use the equation shown at the right.

0.85 × \$75 = sale price

Why does this method work?

8-6 Problem Solving: Using Percent

Bob McCallister owns stock in an electronics company. The value of the stock increases by 13%. The stock was originally valued at $350. What is the current value of the stock?

Read the problem. You need to find the current value of the stock. You know the original value. You also know the percent of increase.

Decide what to do. Add 13% to 100% to find what percent the current value is of the original value. Then use an equation to find the current value (c).

Solve the problem. $100\% + 13\% = 113\%$

113% of $350 is the current value.

$$1.13 \times 350 = c$$

$$395.5 = c$$

The current value of the stock is $395.50.

Examine the solution. An estimate shows that the value of the stock increases slightly more than 10%. This is about a $40 increase. The answer is reasonable.

Solve.

1. Daryl earns $155.80 in regular pay and $34.20 in overtime pay. What percent of his earnings are overtime pay?

2. Normal rainfall for Dallas is 34.5 inches per year. The rainfall is 12% more this year. What is the rainfall this year?

3. Six co-op farmers share equally 90% of the profits. What share does each get from a profit of $56,000?

4. A tank is 85% full. If it holds 800 liters of water, how many more liters of water can it hold?

5. A solution is $2\frac{1}{2}$% distilled water. How many gallons of distilled water are there in 250 gallons of the solution?

6. Jovita saves $2.75 by buying a skirt that was reduced 10%. What was the original price of the skirt?

7. A camera costs $169.95. Ty can buy it for 20% down and 9 monthly payments of $16.50. How much does he save by paying in cash?

8. France is about 80% of the size of Texas. If Texas is 262,134 square miles, estimate the size of France.

Solve. Use the chart.

9. The full rate of a call is $4.20. If the call is made at 5:30 P.M., what is the cost of the call?

10. The full rate of a call is $6.70. What is the difference in cost if it is made at 7:00 P.M. and 11:15 P.M.?

11. Helen makes a call at 10:15 P.M. She is charged $9.36. What is the full rate?

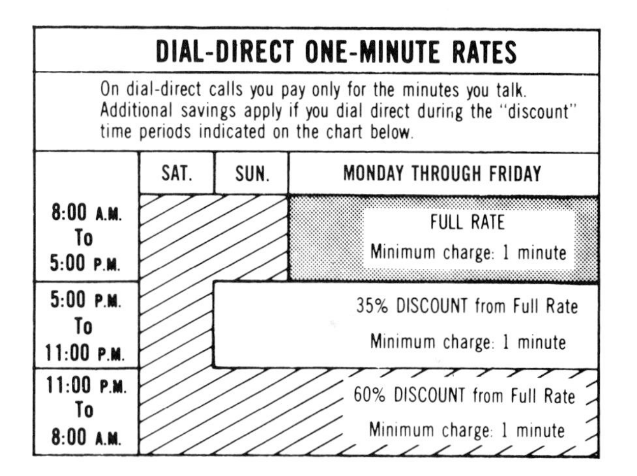

Skills Review: Pages 199-209

Solve.

1. What number is 20% of 45?
2. 95% of 135 is what number?
3. What percent of 8 is 6?
4. 21 is what percent of 56?
5. 57.6 is 48% of what number?
6. 15% of what number is 90?
7. How much does a $59 radio cost if it is marked down 20%?
8. The price of a dozen eggs is reduced from $0.90 to $0.81. Find the percent of decrease.

Cumulative Review

Estimate.

1. $\begin{array}{r} 6{,}283 \\ +\ 3{,}771 \\ \hline \end{array}$
2. $\begin{array}{r} 6.21 \\ -\ 1.887 \\ \hline \end{array}$
3. $\begin{array}{r} 423 \\ \times\ 1.8 \\ \hline \end{array}$
4. $32\overline{)276}$
5. $0.72\overline{)6.25}$

Add, subtract, multiply, or divide.

6. $\begin{array}{r} 16.99 \\ +\ 23.13 \\ \hline \end{array}$
7. $\begin{array}{r} 2{,}391.3 \\ +\ \ \ 49.7 \\ \hline \end{array}$
8. $\begin{array}{r} 2.111 \\ -\ 0.87 \\ \hline \end{array}$
9. $\begin{array}{r} 33.44 \\ -\ 17.5 \\ \hline \end{array}$
10. $\begin{array}{r} 23 \\ \times\ 0.4 \\ \hline \end{array}$
11. $\begin{array}{r} 0.4 \\ \times\ 0.9 \\ \hline \end{array}$
12. $\begin{array}{r} 0.217 \\ \times\ \ \ 4.9 \\ \hline \end{array}$
13. $\begin{array}{r} 8.32 \\ \times\ 0.053 \\ \hline \end{array}$
14. $7\overline{)3.15}$
15. $23\overline{)9.2}$
16. $0.31\overline{)16.74}$
17. $0.008\overline{)0.176}$
18. $0.24\overline{)1.248}$
19. $5.03\overline{)120.72}$
20. $0.586 \times 1{,}000$
21. $0.5 \div 10$
22. $21 \div 100$
23. 62×10
24. $312 \div 1{,}000$
25. 8.3×100
26. 0.107×10
27. $0.916 \div 10$

Find the greatest common factor (GCF) for each group of numbers.

28. 6, 32
29. 14, 56
30. 12, 18, 32

Find the least common multiple (LCM) for each group of numbers.

31. 4, 7
32. 9, 15
33. 8, 12, 16

Add, subtract, multiply, or divide. Write each answer in simplest form.

34. $\frac{2}{9} + \frac{8}{9}$
35. $\frac{3}{4} + \frac{1}{6}$
36. $3\frac{2}{3} + 1\frac{1}{9}$
37. $\frac{9}{10} - \frac{3}{10}$
38. $\frac{7}{12} - \frac{3}{8}$
39. $5\frac{2}{9} - \frac{2}{3}$
40. $6 \times \frac{3}{5}$
41. $\frac{3}{8} \times \frac{4}{9}$
42. $3\frac{1}{6} \times 3$
43. $\frac{5}{6} \div 2$
44. $\frac{3}{5} \div \frac{9}{10}$
45. $1\frac{2}{9} \div 1\frac{1}{12}$

Solve each equation. Check your solution.

46. $2 + g = 7$
47. $h + 1.8 = 8.4$
48. $p - 47 = 22$
49. $88.9 = s - 6.21$
50. $7g = 49$
51. $7c = 4.2$
52. $\frac{w}{17} = 24$
53. $2.84 = \frac{d}{2}$
54. $2x - 5 = 3$
55. $4t + 5 = 37$
56. $\frac{e}{5} + 6 = 12$
57. $\frac{d}{4} - 8 = 5$

Solve.

58. What number is 47% of 32?

59. 11 is what percent of 44?

60. What percent of 66 is 49.5?

61. 70% of what number is 4.2?

62. 135 is 27% of what number?

63. 1.7% of 52 is what number?

64. It costs $272 per month to feed a bear. The City Zoo has five bears. How much does it cost to feed the bears for one year?

65. Six students in Mrs. Moyer's class are absent. This is 24% of the class. How many students are in Mrs. Moyer's class?

66. Angles 1 and 2 are complementary angles. If $m\angle 1$ is 79, what is $m\angle 2$?

67. In 7 hours, Patty drove 364 kilometers. If she drives at the same rate, what distance will she drive in 12 hours?

Mathematics Lab

A 100% bar graph can be used to show parts of a whole. For example, you can make a 100% bar graph to show the time spent in various activities for one day.

a. Draw a bar 10 centimeters long. How many millimeters is this?
b. Find the length of each part.

Susan sleeps 8 hours each day. What percent of 24 is 8?

$$\frac{8}{24} = \frac{r}{100}$$

$$33\frac{1}{3} = r$$

$33\frac{1}{3}$% of 100 mm is about 33 mm.

Use a ruler to measure the length.
Label this part "sleep, $33\frac{1}{3}$%."

How Susan Spends a Typical Day

sleep $33\frac{1}{3}$%	

Find the length of the part that represents each of the following activities.

1. school, $6\frac{1}{2}$ hours

2. meals, $2\frac{1}{2}$ hours

3. study, 2 hours

4. recreation, $1\frac{1}{2}$ hours

5. other, $3\frac{1}{2}$ hours

6. Make a 100% bar graph showing how you spend a typical Wednesday.

8–7 Percent and Tax

Jennifer Hall buys a car that costs \$8,950. The sales tax rate is 4%. This means that 4¢ tax is charged for each \$1 of the purchase price. How much sales tax does Mrs. Hall pay?

$$\underbrace{4\%}\ \underbrace{\text{of}}\ \underbrace{\$8{,}950}\ \underbrace{\text{is}}\ \underbrace{\text{the sales tax.}}$$

$$0.04 \times 8{,}950 = t$$

$$358 = t$$

Mrs. Hall pays \$358 in sales tax.

EXERCISES ***Find the sales tax to the nearest cent for each of the following items.***

1. blouse, \$20
   tax rate, 3%
2. bookcase, \$58
   tax rate, 4%
3. lawnmower, \$265
   tax rate, 6%
4. car, \$11,079
   tax rate, 5%
5. hair dryer, \$33
   tax rate, 3%
6. jeans, \$18.50
   tax rate, 4.5%
7. album, \$8.99
   tax rate, $5\frac{1}{2}\%$
8. dishes, \$83.95
   tax rate, 5.25%
9. sofa, \$659.60
   tax rate, $4\frac{3}{4}\%$

Solve.

10. The price of an exercise bike is \$166. The sales tax is \$9.13. What is the sales tax rate?
11. The price of a shirt is \$14.95. The sales tax rate is $5\frac{1}{2}\%$. What is the total cost of the shirt?
12. The price of a calculator is \$15.95. The sales tax rate is 4.6%. What is the total cost of the calculator?
13. The sales tax on a digital clock is \$1.25. The sales tax rate is 5%. What is the price of the clock?
14. Larry buys a \$13 book and an \$8 calendar. Each item is on sale for 20% off. If the tax rate is 5%, what is the total cost of the items?
15. Marcia buys a \$6 T-shirt for 20% off and a \$35 warm-up suit for 30% off. If the tax rate is $4\frac{1}{2}\%$, what is the total cost of the items?

The federal government places a tax on each person's income so that it can provide services. The amount of federal withholding tax can be determined using a tax table.

TABLE 4. MONTHLY Payroll Period

(a) SINGLE person—including head of household:

If the amount of wages is:		*The amount of income tax to be withheld shall be:*	
Not over $118		0	
Over—	*But not over—*		*of excess over—*
$118	—$275	15%	—$118
$275	—$567	$23.55 plus 18%	—$275
$567	—$850	$76.11 plus 21%	—$567
$850	—$1,183	$135.54 plus 26%	—$850
$1,183	—$1,433	$222.12 plus 30%	—$1,183
$1,433	—$1,875	$297.12 plus 34%	—$1,433
$1,875		$447.40 plus 39%	—$1,875

(b) MARRIED person—

If the amount of wages is:		*The amount of income tax to be withheld shall be:*	
Not over $200		0	
Over—	*But not over—*		*of excess over—*
$200	—$550	15%	—$200
$550	—$908	$52.50 plus 18%	—$550
$908	—$1,250	$116.94 plus 21%	—$908
$1,250	—$1,600	$188.76 plus 24%	—$1,250
$1,600	—$1,967	$272.76 plus 28%	—$1,600
$1,967	—$2,408	$375.52 plus 32%	—$1,967
$2,408		$516.64 plus 37%	—$2,408

Mark Johnston is single and earns $680 each month. Find Mr. Johnston's monthly federal withholding tax.

Mr. Johnston's withholding tax is $76.11 plus 21% of everything over $567.

$$\begin{array}{r} \$680 \\ -\ \$567 \\ \hline \$113 \end{array} \text{ excess}$$

21% of $113 is $23.73

$$\begin{array}{rl} \$76.11 & \leftarrow \text{base tax} \\ +\ \$23.73 & \leftarrow \text{percent tax} \\ \hline \$99.84 & \leftarrow \text{total tax} \end{array}$$

Mr. Johnston's monthly federal withholding tax is $99.84.

EXERCISES ***Find the monthly federal withholding tax for each of the following.***

16. married, $1,100 monthly

17. single, $950 monthly

18. single, $215 monthly

19. married, $2,166 monthly

20. married, $1,533 monthly

21. single, $1,259 monthly

Solve.

22. Maria Alvarez is single and works 80 hours each month. She makes $5.10 per hour. What is her monthly withholding tax?

23. Neil Hunt is married and earns $1,350 each month. What is the amount of Mr. Hunt's federal withholding tax for one year?

24. Gerald Casper is married and earned $24,562 last year. What was the amount of Mr. Casper's federal withholding tax for the year?

8-8 Percent and Business

John Clark marks up merchandise in his sporting goods store 60% in order to cover his expenses and make a profit. **Markup** is a percent of increase.

Mr. Clark's cost for a pair of roller skates is $20. What is the selling price of the roller skates?

Set up a proportion. $\frac{P}{20} = \frac{160}{100}$ (selling price → P; his cost → 20; 160 ← 100% + 60%)

Solve the proportion. $20 \times 160 = P \times 100$

$32 = P$

The selling price of the roller skates is $32.

EXERCISES ***Find the selling price to the nearest cent for each of the following.***

1. weight set, $48.65
   50% markup
2. running shoes, $20
   80% markup
3. swimsuit, $14.25
   40% markup
4. tent, $174.37
   60% markup
5. tennis racket, $11.15
   70% markup
6. sleeping bag, $12.50
   100% markup
7. baseball bat, $6.30
   90% markup
8. fishing reel, $12.50
   75% markup
9. ping pong table, $103
   85% markup

Solve.

10. Mr. Clark's cost for a basketball is $15. The markup is 50%. What is the selling price?
11. A table costs $432. The markup is 90%. What is the selling price of the table?
12. A lamp that costs $35 is sold for $57.75. What is the percent of markup?
13. A diamond that costs $950 is sold for $1,995. What is the percent of markup?
14. The selling price of a baseball glove at Pedro's Sporting Goods is $27.90. The percent of markup is 80%. How much did the store pay for the glove?
15. The Record Shoppe sells an album for $10.98. The percent of markup is 100%. How much did the store pay for the album?

During October the expenses at Clark's Sporting Goods Store were $4,353. The amount of sales was $7,560. Find the amount and percent of their profit or loss based on sales.

Since the sales were greater than the expenses, Mr. Clark made a profit.

Subtract to find the amount of profit.

sales →	**$7,560**
expenses →	**− $4,353**
profit →	**$3,207**

Set up a proportion to find the percent of profit based on sales.

$$\begin{matrix}\text{profit} \rightarrow \\ \text{sales} \rightarrow\end{matrix} \frac{3{,}207}{7{,}560} = \frac{r}{100}$$

$$3{,}270 \times 100 = 7{,}560 \times r$$

$$42.4 = r \quad \text{(to the nearest tenth)}$$

The amount of profit was $3,207. The percent of profit based on sales was about 42.4%

EXERCISES Find the percent of profit or loss based on sales for each of the following. Label each as profit or loss.

16. sales, $956; expenses, $450

17. sales, $10,486; expenses, $4,515

18. sales, $1,560; expenses, $1,960

19. sales, $4,486; expenses, $4,569

Find the percent of profit or loss based on sales for each of the following months. Use the chart.

20. January
21. February
22. March
23. April
24. May
25. June

Acme Paint Company		
Month	**Sales**	**Expenses**
January	$45,904	$20,743
February	$30,505	$30,964
March	$49,846	$20,836
April	$50,895	$25,965
May	$51,965	$34,300
June	$52,213	$39,436

26. Find the total profit or loss for January through June.

27. Find the percent of profit or loss based on sales for January through June.

8-9 Percent and Interest

Sang Ko has $700 in his savings account. The bank pays $5\frac{3}{4}\%$ interest each year. How much interest does his account earn in two years?

$$\text{interest} = \text{principal} \times \text{rate} \times \text{time}$$

$$I = p \times r \times t$$

Principal (p) is the amount in the account. The rate (r) is a percent, and time (t) is given in years.

$$\begin{aligned} I &= p \times r \times t \\ &= 700 \times 0.0575 \times 2 \\ &= 80.5 \end{aligned}$$

His account earns $80.50 in interest in two years.

EXERCISES Find the interest to the nearest cent.

1. $20 at 5% for 1 year
2. $200 at 12% for 6 years
3. $800 at 8% for 2 years
4. $50 at 5.5% for 3 years
5. $1,590 at 10% for 5 years
6. $600 at $6\frac{1}{4}\%$ for 4 years
7. $10,000 at 13% for 6 months
8. $2,500 at 12% for $2\frac{1}{2}$ years
9. $100 at 6% for 9 months
10. $1,860 at $7\frac{1}{2}\%$ for 15 months
11. $2,200 at 9% for 91 days

Solve.

12. Martha opens a savings account with $62. It earns $6\frac{7}{8}\%$ interest. How much is in her account after one year?
13. Jim's savings account earned $30.72 in 6 months. The interest rate is $5\frac{3}{4}\%$. How much did he have before interest?

The monthly interest rates for the use of a certain credit card are 1.6% for the first $500 and 1.1% of the amount over $500. What is the interest charged on an unpaid balance of $732.60?

$732.60 − $500 = $232.60 ← amount over $500

1.6% of $500	**1.1% of $232.60**
0.016 × 500 = 8	**0.011 × 232.6 ≈ 2.56** (to the nearest hundredth)

$8.00 + $2.56 = $10.56

The interest charged is $10.56.

EXERCISES* *Find the interest charged on each unpaid balance. The interest rate is 1.6% for the first $500 and 1.1% on the amount over $500.

14. $132 **15.** $97 **16.** $203 **17.** $328

18. $783 **19.** $492 **20.** $189.40 **21.** $351.90

22. $671.70 **23.** $853.72 **24.** $74.91 **25.** $526.63

COMPOUND INTEREST

Compound interest means that the interest on an account is added to the account after certain intervals. In this way, interest earns interest.

Find the principal plus interest on $1,000 compounded semiannually for one year at 6%.

		principal + interest = new principal
First 6 months	**$1,000 × 0.06 × 0.5 = $30**	**$1,000 + $30 = $1,030**
Second 6 months	**$1,030 × 0.06 × 0.5 = $30.90**	

The principal plus interest is **$1,000 + $30 + $30.90** or **$1,060.90.**

Find the principal plus interest after one year for each savings account.

1. $2,000 at 8% compounded quarterly

2. $500 at $6\frac{1}{2}$% compounded semiannually

8-10 Focus on Problem Solving

Guess and Check

Emily decides to buy a computer with a loan. She budgets $125 per month for the loan payment. The loan is for one year at 15%. How much can Emily afford to pay for the computer?

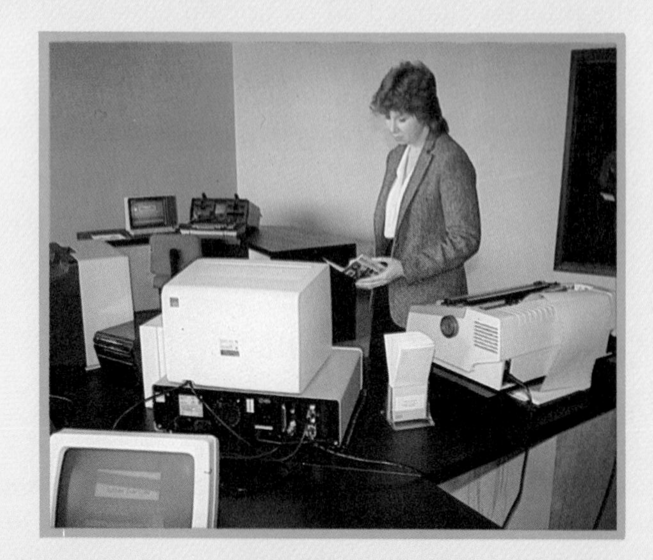

Read the problem. You need to find how much money Emily can spend for a computer. You know the interest rate and length of the loan. You also know how much she can afford each month for the loan payment.

Decide what to do. Multiply the budgeted monthly payment by 12 months. Then, guess and check amounts close to this including the 15% interest.

Solve the problem. **$125 × 12 months = $1,500**

Emily can spend a total of $1,500 for the computer and interest on the loan. Now, guess and check to see what the total cost is for several prices of computers.

Guess: **$1,400**	Check: **$1,400 × 115% = $1,610**	too high
Guess: **$1,200**	Check: **$1,200 × 115% = $1,380**	too low
Guess: **$1,300**	Check: **$1,300 × 115% = $1,495**	

Emily can afford a computer that costs about $1,300.

Examine the solution. The solution is reasonable since $1,300 at 15% interest is nearly $1,500.

Solve. Use the guess and check strategy.

1. Hugh wants to buy a coat. He can afford $10 monthly payments for one year. The interest rate is 18%. How much can Hugh afford to pay for the coat?
2. Cheryl has 6 coins in her pocket. The total value of the coins is $1.30. How many quarters, dimes, nickels, and pennies does she have?
3. Kevin is twice as old as his sister Kari. Four years ago he was three times as old. What are their ages now?
4. Mr. Cox is four times as old as his son. In 18 years he will be twice as old as his son. What are their ages now?

Solve. Use any strategy.

5. Ms. West gets a 7% discount by paying her rent before the third day of each month. She pays $288.30 on May 1. How much does she save by paying early?
6. Paper cups can be purchased in packages of 40 or 75. Akiko buys 7 packages and gets 350 cups. How many packages of 75 does she buy?
7. Find a digit for each letter so the problem is correct. Each letter represents a different digit.

$$\begin{array}{r} \text{ABCDE} \\ \times \quad 4 \\ \hline \text{EDCBA} \end{array}$$

8. Rich Kindle noticed on his birthday one year that if he multiplied his age by itself the answer was the year at that time. How old was he on his birthday in 1983?
9. Mr. Ortego earns a 3% commission on the first $1,000 in sales, $4\frac{1}{2}$% on the next $3,000, and $6\frac{1}{2}$% on all other sales. He sells $5,153 worth of merchandise. What is his commission rounded to the nearest cent?

Skills Review: Pages 212-219

Solve.

1. A table costs $458. The sales tax rate is 5.5%. What is the sales tax?
2. A store buyer buys an item for $11.65. The markup is 80%. What is the item's selling price?
3. Mel's Market had sales of $10,300 with expenses of $7,725. What was the percent of profit based on sales?
4. What is the amount of interest earned on $2,400 at 8.6% for 2 years?

Mathematics and Consumers

Katie Curtis receives a weekly earnings statement with her paycheck. It lists the hours that she worked, the rate of pay, and deductions. **Gross pay** is the amount earned before deductions. **Net pay** is the amount earned after deductions.

The Department Store — Weekly Earnings Statement

Katie Curtis — Period Ending Jan 31 — DETACH AND RETAIN FOR YOUR RECORDS

Gross Pay				Deductions		
Type	Time	Rate	Amount	Description	Amount	
Reg	H 40.00	6.00	240.00	FICA	16.08	
OT	H			FED W/H TAX	44.00	
				STATE TAX	2.40	
				CITY TAX	3.60	
				INSURANCES	5.25	
						Net Pay
Gross Pay			240.00	Total Deductions	71.33	168.67

What percent of Mrs. Curtis's gross pay is deducted for city tax?

$$c\% \text{ of } \$240.00 \text{ is } \$3.60$$

$$c \times 240 = 3.6$$

$$c = 0.015 \rightarrow 1.5\%$$

1.5% of Mrs. Curtis's gross pay is deducted for city tax.

EXERCISES ***Find the percent of gross pay for each of the following. Use Katie Curtis's weekly earnings statement.***

1. federal withholding tax

2. state tax

3. FICA (social security)

4. insurances

5. What percent of the gross pay is the net pay?

Solve.

6. Wes Hefner works 37.5 hours each week at $9.44 per hour. 27.5% of his gross pay is deducted for taxes and insurance. What is his net pay?

Chapter 8 Review

VOCABULARY percentage (199) base (199) rate (199) percent of increase (206) percent of decrease (206) markup (214)

EXERCISES ***Solve. (199–205)***

1. What number is 25% of 500?
2. 20% of 65 is what number?
3. What percent of 12 is 6?
4. 17 is what percent of 51?
5. 120 is 60% of what number?
6. 50% of what number is 46?
7. $83\frac{1}{3}\%$ of 48 is what number?
8. What is 0.6% of 59?
9. 250 is what percent of 100?
10. What percent of 400 is 2?
11. 1.2% of what number is 0.06?
12. 450% of what number is 49.5?

Find the percent of increase or decrease for each of the following. (206–207)

13. a $50 vase decreased to $37.50
14. 15 minutes to 25 minutes

Find the sales tax for each of the following items. Then, find the total cost of the item. (212–213)

15. coat, $70
    tax rate, 5%
16. bicycle, $129
    tax rate, $4\frac{1}{2}\%$
17. book, $4.95
    tax rate, 6%

Find the selling price for each of the following items. (214–215)

18. picture, $45
    70% markup
19. shoes, $20
    45% markup
20. swing set, $58
    110% markup

Find the interest to the nearest cent. (216–217)

21. $650 at 12% for 2 years
22. $1,250 at 10% for 3 months

Solve. (208, 218)

23. The Express Coffee Company had expenses of $273,509 and sales of $300,527 last year. What was the percent of profit based on sales?
24. Leroy has some dogs and birds. He counts all the heads and gets 10. He counts all the feet and gets 34. How many dogs and how many birds does he have?

Chapter 8 Test

Solve.

1. What number is 35% of 120?
2. 28% of 70 is what number?
3. 30 is what percent of 250?
4. What percent of 32 is 16?
5. 2.25 is 50% of what number?
6. 40% of what number is 35.8?
7. 5% of 50 is what number?
8. What number is $66\frac{2}{3}$% of 276?
9. What percent of 2.6 is 26?
10. 50.4 is what percent of 16,800?
11. 105% of what number is 37.8?
12. 1.08 is 9% of what number?
13. What number is 250% of 48?
14. What percent of 39 is 40?

Find the percent of increase or decrease for each of the following.

15. 40 tickets to 64 tickets
16. a $440 canoe decreased to $396

Find the sales tax for each of the following items. Then find the total cost of the item.

17. necktie, $9.50
tax rate, 6%
18. rug, $49
tax rate, $4\frac{1}{2}$%
19. car, $9,578
tax rate, $5\frac{1}{2}$%

Find the selling price for each of the following items.

20. blanket, $21
75% markup
21. album, $4.70
90% markup
22. mirror, $86
50% markup

Find the principal plus interest to the nearest cent.

23. $560 at 8% for 1 year
24. $4,000 at $9\frac{1}{4}$% for 6 months

Solve.

25. Yoakam's Music Store sells 24 pianos. This is 60% of the pianos in stock. How many are in stock?
26. Abby's mother lends her $600 for 4 years at 6% annual interest. How much does Abby owe her mother at the end of 4 years?
27. Tickets for the play are $2.50 for adults and $1.50 for students. Dario buys 8 tickets for $15.00. How many adult tickets does he buy?

Enrichment

Bargain House sells greeting cards at 20% off their list price. During a sale, there is another discount of 10%. What is the cost of a card that has a list price of $1.00? Is a single discount of 30% equal to successive discounts of 20% and 10%?

successive discounts

80% of list price = discount price

$$0.8 \times 1.00 = d$$

$$0.80 = d$$

90% of discount price = sale price

$$0.9 \times 0.80 = s$$

$$0.72 = s$$

single discount

70% of list price $\stackrel{?}{=}$ sale price

$$0.7 \times 1.00 \stackrel{?}{=} s$$

$$0.70 \stackrel{?}{=} s$$

The cost of the card is $0.72. A single discount of 30% is *not* equal to successive discounts of 20% and 10%.

Use the following method for changing successive discounts to a single discount.

1. Subtract the decimal equivalent of each discount from one. **1 − 0.2 = 0.8**, **1 − 0.1 = 0.9**
2. Multiply the results of step 1. **0.8 × 0.9 = 0.72**
3. Subtract the result of step 2 from one and change it to a percent. **1 − 0.72 = 0.28**, **0.28 ➔ 28%**

EXERCISES ***Change each set of successive discounts to a single discount.***

1. 20%, 15% **2.** 10%, 50% **3.** 15%, 25%

4. 10%, 30% **5.** 30%, 50%, 20% **6.** 25%, 40%, 40%

Solve.

7. Rosaria buys a $56 dress for $37. Tina buys the same dress with successive discounts of 10% and 25%. Who paid more for the dress? What is the difference in cost?

Rational Numbers

The average low temperature in International Falls, Minnesota for January is 8 degrees *below* zero Fahrenheit. You can express this temperature using a negative number.

9–1 Integers and Rational Numbers

Negative numbers are to the left of zero on a number line. **Positive** numbers are to the right of zero. The numbers named on the number line are called **integers.**

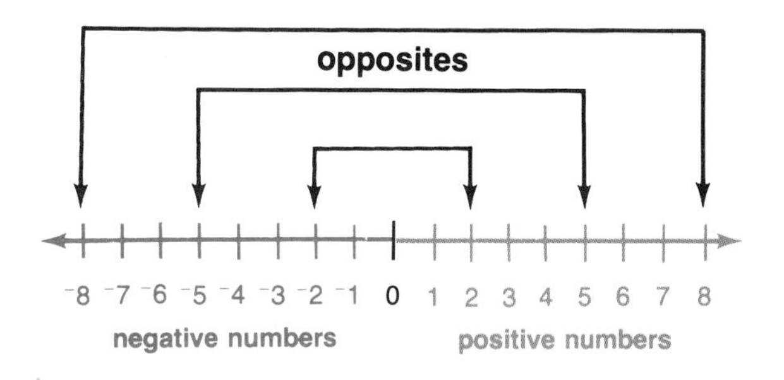

A raised minus sign is used to denote a negative number. A raised plus sign can be used to denote a postive number. If no sign is used, it is understood that the number is not negative.

⁻8 is read *negative 8.* ⁺8 or 8 is read *positive 8.* Zero is neither positive nor negative.

Integers: . . ., **⁻5, ⁻4, ⁻3, ⁻2, ⁻1, 0, 1, 2, 3, 4, 5, . . .** . . . means "and so on"

Any number that can be expressed as a quotient of two integers, when the divisor is not 0, is called a **rational number.** The following numbers are rational.

$$4 = \frac{4}{1} \qquad 1\frac{1}{2} = \frac{3}{2} \qquad \frac{^-3}{4} \qquad 1.6 = \frac{16}{10} \qquad 0 = \frac{0}{8}$$

Each rational number has an **opposite.** A rational number and its opposite are the same distance from zero. For example, the opposite of ⁻14 is 14. What is the opposite of 2.3?

EXERCISES ***Write an integer to describe each of the following.***

1. 5° above zero **2.** 14° below zero **3.** $500 loss

4. $600 profit **5.** 280 feet above sea level **6.** 540 feet below sea level

State the opposite of each of the following.

7. ⁺4 **8.** ⁻9 **9.** 42 **10.** ⁻11 **11.** 0 **12.** 4.1

13. ⁻5.7 **14.** ⁻12.6 **15.** $^-2\frac{1}{3}$ **16.** $12\frac{1}{8}$ **17.** $\frac{7}{13}$ **18.** ⁻(⁻5)

9-2 Comparing Rational Numbers

The average high temperature in Anchorage, Alaska for January is $^-7$ degrees Celsius. The average high temperature for February is $^-3$ degrees Celsius. Which temperature is greater?

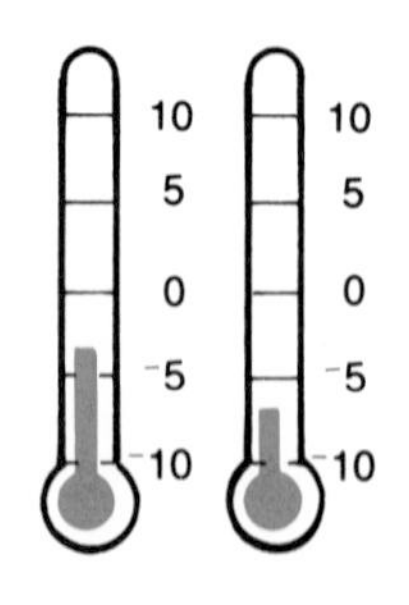

The thermometers show that $^-3$ is greater than $^-7$. Negative 3 is *above* $^-7$. Notice that $^-3$ is to the *right* of $^-7$ on the number line.

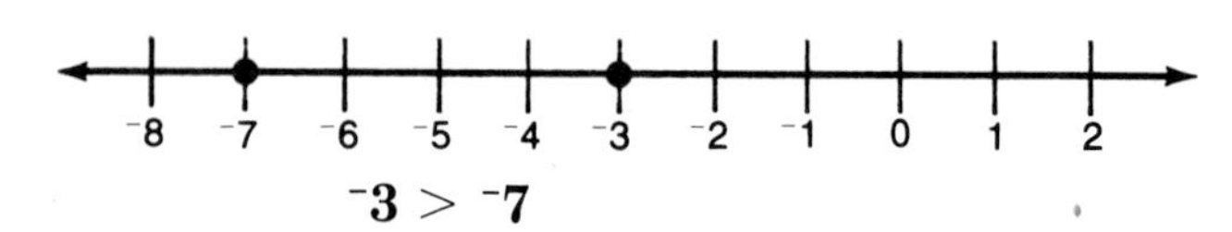

$^-3 > {}^-7$

On the number line an integer is greater than any integer to its left.

You can also use the number line to compare rational numbers.

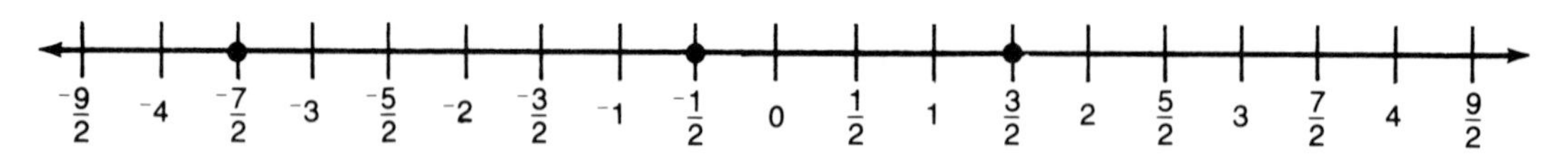

$\frac{3}{2}$ is to the right of $\frac{-7}{2}$ so $\frac{3}{2} > \frac{-7}{2}$.

$\frac{-7}{2}$ is to the left of $\frac{-1}{2}$ so $\frac{-7}{2} < \frac{-1}{2}$.

EXERCISES ***Replace each ▒ with <, >, or = to make a true sentence.***

1. 3 ▒ 5
2. $^-5$ ▒ 0
3. $^-7$ ▒ $^-3$
4. 0 ▒ 6
5. 0 ▒ $^-2$
6. 6 ▒ $^-2$
7. 4 ▒ $^+4$
8. $^-5$ ▒ $^-8$
9. 2 ▒ $^-3$
10. $^-4$ ▒ $^-1$
11. $\frac{4}{5}$ ▒ $\frac{3}{5}$
12. $\frac{1}{3}$ ▒ $\frac{3}{8}$
13. $\frac{1}{2}$ ▒ $^-1$
14. $^-1\frac{1}{4}$ ▒ $^-3\frac{3}{4}$
15. $\frac{3}{5}$ ▒ $\frac{6}{10}$
16. $^-4.6$ ▒ 4.6
17. $^-0.8$ ▒ $^-0.7$
18. $^-3.2$ ▒ $^-3.4$
19. $^-0.6$ ▒ $^-0.62$
20. $^-2.14$ ▒ $^-2.1$
21. $^-0.1$ ▒ $^-0.01$
22. $\frac{-3}{4}$ ▒ $\frac{-4}{5}$
23. $\frac{2}{5}$ ▒ 0.4
24. 1.75 ▒ $^-1\frac{3}{4}$

Order the numbers in each list from least to greatest.

25. $^{-}3, 5, ^{-}1$

26. $13, ^{-}12, ^{-}6, 5$

27. $^{-}1.5, ^{-}1.8, ^{-}1.4, ^{-}1.1$

28. $\frac{2}{3}, \frac{^{-}2}{3}, \frac{3}{4}, \frac{^{-}3}{4}, \frac{1}{2}, \frac{^{-}1}{2}$

29. $^{-}1\frac{5}{8}, ^{-}1\frac{5}{6}, ^{-}2\frac{1}{8}, \frac{1}{16}, \frac{^{-}1}{32}$

30. $^{-}3.1427, ^{-}3.1518, ^{-}3.2112$

31. $0, 5, ^{-}6, \frac{1}{5}, \frac{^{-}1}{6}, ^{-}5, \frac{1}{6}$

On the number line you can see that 4 and $^{-}4$ are different numbers. However, they are each 4 units from 0. The number of units a number is from 0 on the number line is called its **absolute value.** The symbol for absolute value is two vertical lines.

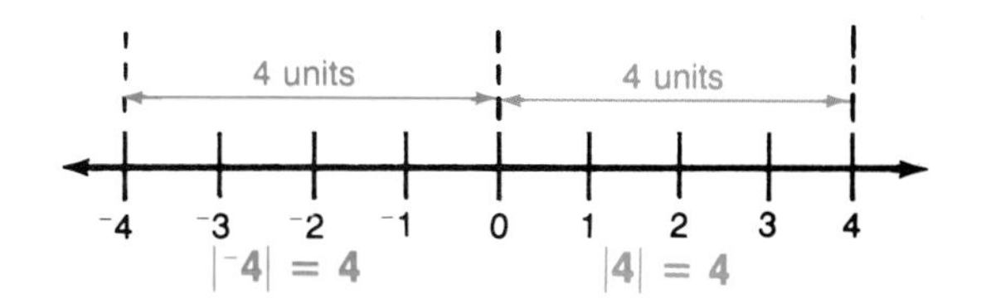

$|^{-}4|$ is read *the absolute value of negative four.*
$|4|$ is read *the absolute value of four.*

EXERCISES ***Find the value of each of the following.***

32. $|6|$

33. $|^{-}9|$

34. $|^{-}5|$

35. $|12|$

36. $|0|$

37. $|^{-}21|$

38. $|^{-}236|$

39. $|^{+}1.5|$

40. $|\frac{1}{10}|$

41. $|\frac{^{-}5}{6}|$

42. $|^{-}9| - |6|$

43. $|^{-}4| + |^{-}7|$

44. $|3| + |^{-}8|$

45. $|7 + 12|$

WINDCHILL FACTOR

The chart gives the combined effect of wind and temperature as an equivalent temperature in still air. This is known as the **windchill factor**.

Find the windchill factor for each of the following.

1. wind, 10 mph; temperature, 30°F
2. wind, 30 mph; temperature, 20°F
3. wind, 20 mph; temperature, 0°F
4. wind, 40 mph; temperature, 10°F

Windchill Factor

Wind Speed (mph)	Temperature (°F) 30	20	10	0	$^{-}10$
10	16	2	$^{-}9$	$^{-}22$	$^{-}31$
20	3	$^{-}9$	$^{-}24$	$^{-}40$	$^{-}52$
30	$^{-}2$	$^{-}18$	$^{-}33$	$^{-}49$	$^{-}63$
40	$^{-}4$	$^{-}22$	$^{-}36$	$^{-}54$	$^{-}69$
50	$^{-}7$	$^{-}24$	$^{-}38$	$^{-}56$	$^{-}70$

9-3 Adding Rational Numbers

The temperature at 7:00 A.M. is $^-4$ degrees Celsius. The temperature rises 7 degrees by noon. What is the temperature at noon? To find the noon temperature, find $^-4 + 7$. This addition can be shown on a number line. Move right when the sign is postive. Move left when the sign is negative.

Start at zero.
Move 4 units to the left.
From there move 7 units to the right.

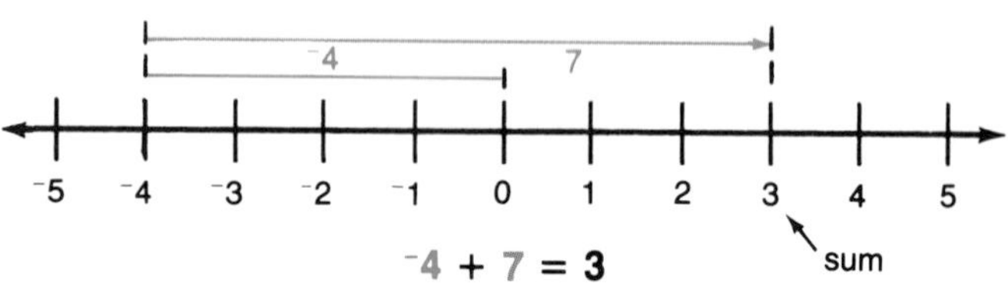

$^-4 + 7 = 3$

The temperature at noon is 3 degrees Celsius.

Find $2 + {}^-6$.

Start at zero.
Move 2 units to the right.
From there move 6 units to the left.

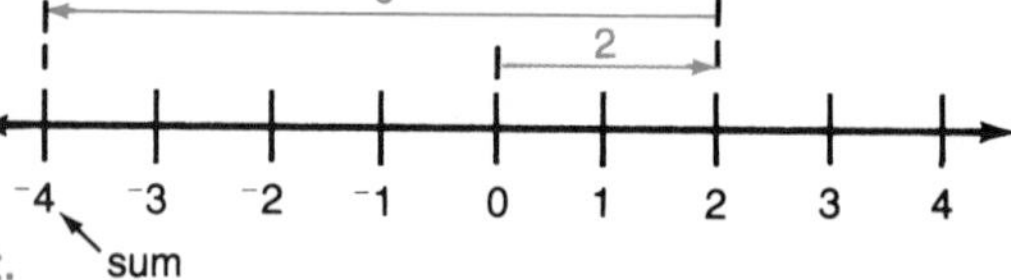

$2 + {}^-6 = {}^-4$

$|^-6| = 6 \qquad |2| = 2$

$6 - 2 = 4$

Which number being added has the greater absolute value? The sum has the same sign as this number.

These examples suggest the following rule.

To add rational numbers with different signs, find the difference of their absolute values. The sum has the same sign as the addend with the greater absolute value.

Find $^-3 + {}^-2$.

Start at zero.
Move 3 units to the left.
From there move 2 more units to the left.

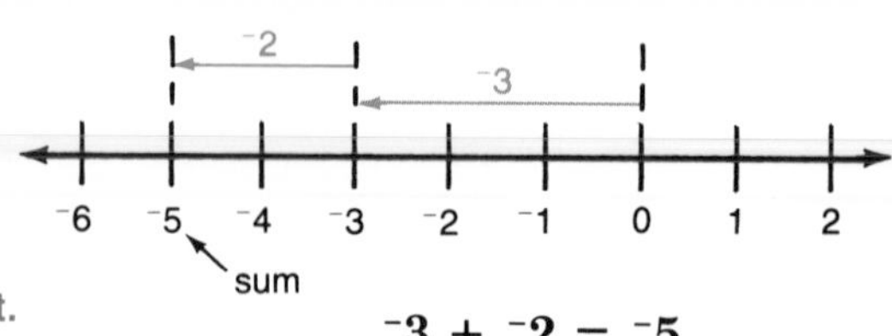

$^-3 + {}^-2 = {}^-5$

The sum of two negative rational numbers is negative. You already know that the sum of two positive rational numbers is positive. This suggests the following rule.

To add rational numbers with the same sign, add their absolute values. The sum has the same sign as the addends.

EXERCISES ***Write an addition sentence for each diagram.***

1.

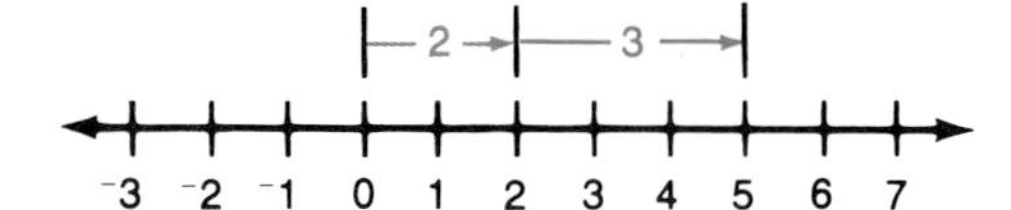

2.

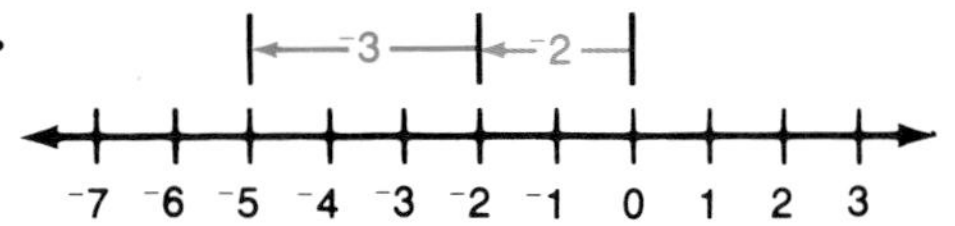

3.

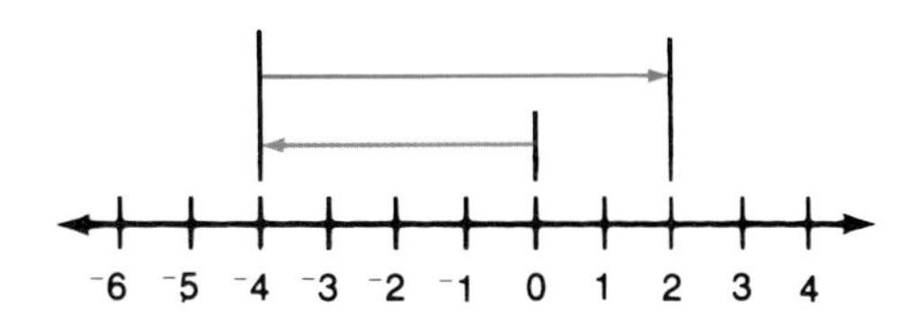

4.

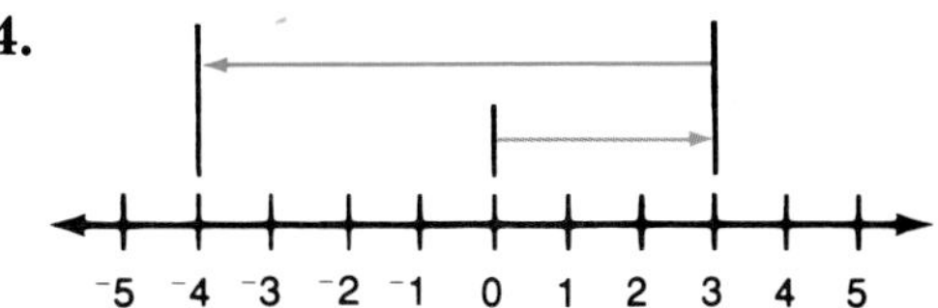

Add. Use a number line.

5. $6 + 8$ **6.** $^-6 + 8$ **7.** $6 + {}^-8$ **8.** $^-6 + {}^-8$

9. $^-9 + 7$ **10.** $9 + {}^-7$ **11.** $^-9 + {}^-7$ **12.** $9 + 7$

Add.

13. $^-4 + 0$ **14.** $3 + {}^-3$ **15.** $5 + 1$ **16.** $^-9 + {}^-3$

17. $7 + {}^-6$ **18.** $4 + 8$ **19.** $^-6 + {}^-6$ **20.** $^-2 + 8$

21. $5 + {}^-6$ **22.** $^-17 + 8$ **23.** $^-10 + {}^-3$ **24.** $26 + {}^-23$

25. $^-1.3 + 5.6$ **26.** $^-7.4 + 2.2$ **27.** $6.8 + {}^-2.5$ **28.** $^-13.12 + {}^-1.04$

29. $5\frac{7}{10} + {}^-3\frac{3}{10}$ **30.** $^-7\frac{3}{4} + 2\frac{1}{4}$ **31.** $\frac{5}{7} + \frac{^-4}{7}$ **32.** $\frac{^-2}{3} + \frac{^-2}{3}$

33. $54 + {}^-78$ **34.** $^-343 + {}^-241$ **35.** $^-0.05 + 0.018$ **36.** $87.3 + {}^-90.1$

37. $\frac{^-1}{2} + \frac{1}{3}$ **38.** $\frac{5}{6} + \frac{^-7}{8}$ **39.** $^-1\frac{3}{8} + \frac{^-2}{3}$ **40.** $^-1\frac{1}{4} + 4\frac{3}{20}$

Evaluate each expression if x = ⁻2 and y = 5.

41. $x + 4$ **42.** $^-6 + y$ **43.** $x + y$ **44.** $|x| + |y|$

Write an addition sentence for each of the following.

45. The temperature drops 7 degrees and then rises 11 degrees.

46. Lindy deposits \$15 on Thursday and withdraws \$12 on Friday.

47. Ricardo loses 15 pounds, gains 6 pounds, and loses 10 pounds.

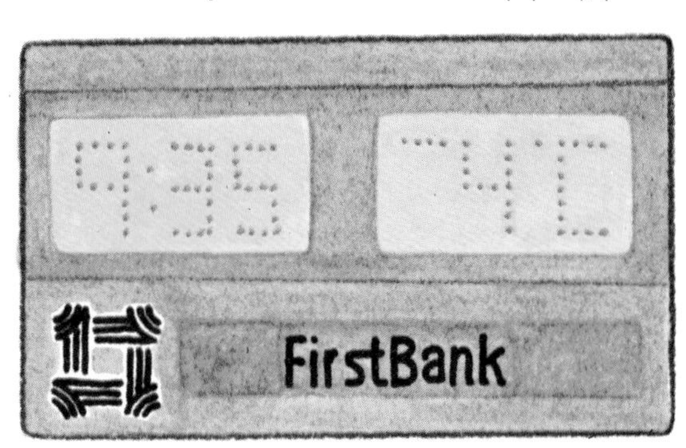

9-4 Subtracting Rational Numbers

Denver is 5,280 feet *above* sea level. New Orleans is 5 feet *below* sea level. What is the difference in their elevations? You can find the difference by subtracting $^-5$ from 5,280.

For every subtraction sentence, there is a corresponding addition sentence. Study the following examples.

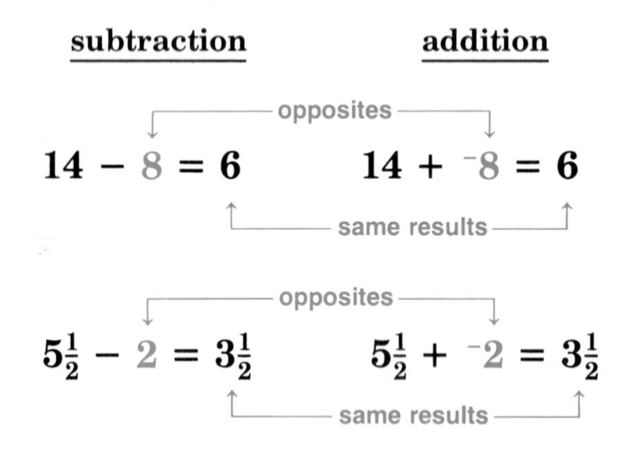

These examples suggest the following rule.

To subtract a rational number, add its opposite.

$$5{,}280 - {}^-5 = 5{,}280 + 5$$ To subtract $^-5$, add $^+5$.

$$= 5{,}285$$ The difference in the elevations is 5,285 feet.

EXERCISES ***Complete each of the following.***

1. $5 - 6 = 5 + {}^-6 = ▒$

2. $^-9 - 8 = {}^-9 + {}^-8 = ▒$

3. $^-2 - {}^-4 = {}^-2 + 4 = ▒$

4. $7 - {}^-1 = 7 + 1 = ▒$

5. $4 - 11 = 4 + ▒ = ▒$

6. $^-3 - {}^-10 = {}^-3 + ▒ = ▒$

Write an addition expression for each of the following.

7. $6 - 10$

8. $7 - {}^-6$

9. $^-8 - {}^-8$

10. $^-9 - 5$

11. $18 - {}^-18$

12. $25 - 25$

13. $^-2.6 - {}^-1.9$

14. $0.5 - 0.8$

15. $^-6.26 - 4.17$

16. $^-1\frac{3}{4} - \frac{1}{4}$

17. $5\frac{2}{3} - {}^-2\frac{1}{3}$

18. $\frac{^-2}{5} - \frac{^-2}{5}$

Subtract.

19. $7 - 9$ **20.** $9 - {}^{-}13$ **21.** ${}^{-}8 - 5$ **22.** ${}^{-}5 - {}^{-}4$

23. $28 - {}^{-}48$ **24.** ${}^{-}8 - 17$ **25.** ${}^{-}8 - {}^{-}14$ **26.** $26 - 42$

27. ${}^{-}8.2 - 5.7$ **28.** ${}^{-}6.4 - {}^{-}5.8$ **29.** $3.7 - 1.9$ **30.** $1.2 - {}^{-}1.5$

31. $6\frac{3}{7} - {}^{-}2\frac{1}{7}$ **32.** $\frac{{}^{-}3}{5} - \frac{4}{5}$ **33.** ${}^{-}9\frac{1}{4} - {}^{-}1\frac{3}{4}$ **34.** $\frac{2}{3} - 1\frac{1}{3}$

35. $0 - 0.8$ **36.** $0.18 - {}^{-}0.7$ **37.** ${}^{-}0.1 - 0.03$ **38.** ${}^{-}4.9 - {}^{-}7.01$

39. $\frac{{}^{-}1}{2} - \frac{1}{4}$ **40.** $\frac{{}^{-}3}{8} - \frac{{}^{-}1}{4}$ **41.** $2\frac{1}{2} - 3\frac{1}{4}$ **42.** $5\frac{3}{5} - {}^{-}2\frac{3}{4}$

Evaluate each expression if $a = {}^{-}4$ and $b = 6$.

43. $a - 5$ **44.** $2 - b$ **45.** $a - b$ **46.** $|a| - b$

Solve. Use the chart.

47. Mt. Everest is the highest point in the world. The Dead Sea is the lowest point on land. What is the difference in their elevations?

48. Mt. McKinley is the highest point in the United States. Death Valley is the lowest point. What is the difference in their elevations?

Geographic Extremes Elevation in Meters	
Mt. Everest	8,848
Mt. McKinley	6,193
Dead Sea	${}^{-}400$
Death Valley	${}^{-}86$
Pacific Ocean floor	${}^{-}11,034$

49. What is the difference in elevations of the highest point in the world and the Pacific Ocean floor?

50. How much deeper is the Pacific Ocean than the Dead Sea?

Skills Review: Pages 225–231

State the opposite of each of the following.

1. 14 **2.** ${}^{-}3.2$

Find the value of each of following.

5. $|{}^{-}7|$ **6.** $|{}^{-}10| - |4|$

Replace each ▒ with $<$, $>$, or $=$ to make a true sentence.

3. 4 ▒ ${}^{-}5$ **4.** ${}^{-}9.8$ ▒ ${}^{-}9.7$

Add or subtract.

7. ${}^{-}8 + {}^{-}6$ **8.** $3.2 + {}^{-}4.5$

9. ${}^{-}18 - {}^{-}33$ **10.** $\frac{{}^{-}2}{7} - \frac{4}{21}$

Cumulative Review

Estimate.

1. $\begin{array}{r} 0.092 \\ +\ 0.431 \\ \hline \end{array}$
2. $\begin{array}{r} 7,245 \\ -\ 2,866 \\ \hline \end{array}$
3. $\begin{array}{r} 2.77 \\ \times\ 0.68 \\ \hline \end{array}$
4. $46\overline{)247}$
5. $0.77\overline{)0.0719}$

Add, subtract, multiply, or divide.

6. $\begin{array}{r} 27.28 \\ +\ 5.8 \\ \hline \end{array}$
7. $\begin{array}{r} 52.9 \\ +\ 5.29 \\ \hline \end{array}$
8. $\begin{array}{r} 23,478 \\ -\ 6,592 \\ \hline \end{array}$
9. $\begin{array}{r} 31.3 \\ -\ 5.17 \\ \hline \end{array}$
10. $\begin{array}{r} 408 \\ \times\ 62 \\ \hline \end{array}$
11. $\begin{array}{r} 0.7 \\ \times\ 7 \\ \hline \end{array}$
12. $\begin{array}{r} 10.64 \\ \times\ 0.3 \\ \hline \end{array}$
13. $\begin{array}{r} 2.83 \\ \times\ 0.035 \\ \hline \end{array}$
14. $58\overline{)11,948}$
15. $4\overline{)3}$
16. $1.2\overline{)9}$
17. $0.3\overline{)9.6}$
18. $0.42\overline{)1.344}$
19. $2.04\overline{)71.4}$
20. $7.05 + 16.22 + 0.87$
21. 3.1×10
22. $44.8 \div 1,000$
23. $2 - {}^{-}12$
24. ${}^{-}41 + 3$
25. ${}^{-}6.4 - 8.13$

Find the greatest common factor (GCF) for each group of numbers.

26. 12, 15
27. 6, 18
28. 4, 9, 15

Find the least common multiple (LCM) for each group of numbers.

29. 4, 5
30. 6, 12
31. 6, 8, 12

Add, subtract, multiply, or divide. Write each answer in simplest form.

32. $\frac{1}{8} + \frac{1}{2}$
33. $2\frac{4}{5} + \frac{1}{2}$
34. $2\frac{3}{4} + 4\frac{5}{6}$
35. $\frac{4}{9} - \frac{1}{3}$
36. $5 - 2\frac{1}{5}$
37. $7\frac{1}{9} - 4\frac{5}{6}$
38. $6 \times \frac{3}{4}$
39. $2\frac{1}{3} \times \frac{2}{5}$
40. $3\frac{1}{2} \times 3\frac{1}{3}$
41. $9 \div \frac{3}{8}$
42. $2\frac{3}{5} \div \frac{2}{5}$
43. $2\frac{2}{3} \div 2\frac{5}{6}$

Solve.

44. What number is 55% of 34?
45. What percent of 60 is 15?
46. 28 is 70% of what number?
47. 6.3% of 34 is what number?

Solve each equation. Check your solution.

48. $x + 3 = 8$

49. $3b = 16$

50. $2y - 5 = 27$

51. $\frac{c}{9} + 1 = 2.3$

Solve.

52. Jack O'Day buys a record marked \$8.95 with 20% off. What is the purchase price after $5\frac{1}{2}$% sales tax is added?

53. One day the temperature reading changed from 11 degrees Celsius to a reading 14 degrees lower. What was the new reading?

54. Ruth's car gets 23 miles per gallon. It has a 27-gallon fuel tank. How many miles can it go on one tank of gasoline?

Mathematics Lab

A partial listing of the New York Stock Exchange for a recent day is shown at the right. Suppose you have one share of Lenox stock. The closing price is $38\frac{5}{8}$ or 38.63. A net change of $^{+}\frac{3}{8}$ means that your stock went up $\frac{3}{8}$ of a dollar from yesterday. What was the price of yesterday's stock?

52 Weeks High	52 Weeks Low	Stock	High	Low	Close	Net Chg.
15⅛	11½	Lehmn	11⅞	11¾	11¾	.....
16⅜	9¾	Lennar	12¼	12	12	.....
39⅞	30½	Lenox	38⅝	38¼	38⅝	+ ⅜
14¼	7⅝	Leucad	10½	10⅜	10⅜	.....
10⅝	9⅛	Leucd	11⅜	10⅝	11⅛	+ ⅝
39⅞	19⅜	LeviSt	24	23⅝	23⅞	− ⅜
41½	20⅝	LevitzF	27¼	26¾	27	+ ½
29¼	20¼	LOF	21	20⅞	20⅞	.....
15¼	10¾	LibtyCp	11½	11¼	11½	.....
33⅝	21⅝	Lifemk	26½	25⅝	25⅝	− ⅝
65¼	45¼	LillyEli	55¼	53¼	53¼	− 2¼
23⅜	19⅜	Limitd	23¼	22⅞	23	+ ¼
45	34	LincNt	38⅜	37¼	37⅜	− ⅝
17⅜	14¼	LincPi	16⅝	16½	16⅝	+ ¼
68¾	38¼	Litton	41½	39¾	39¾	− 1½

$$38\frac{5}{8} - {}^{+}\frac{3}{8} = 38\frac{2}{8} \text{ or } 38\frac{1}{4}$$

Suppose the net changes for the next three days are $^{+}\frac{1}{2}$, $^{-}\frac{1}{4}$, and $\frac{3}{8}$. You can make a line graph of the daily closing price of your stock.

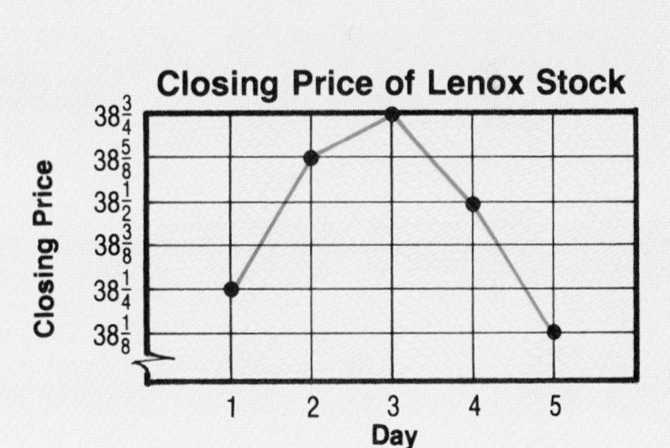

Solve. Use the stock listing.

1. What is the highest price paid for a share of Lenox stock this year?

2. Which stock decreased the most in price from the previous day?

3. What was the closing price for a share of Limited stock on the previous day?

4. Carmen Sanchez has 10 shares of Lincoln National. How much did her stock gain or lose on this day?

5. Choose a company listed in the stock report in the newspaper. Make a line graph showing the daily closing price of this stock for the next five days.

9-5 Multiplying Rational Numbers

Wave erosion may cause a coastline to recede. Suppose a certain beach loses 1.5 centimeters each year. How much does the beach lose in 3 years?

You can use a negative number to represent the loss of the coastline. So $^-1.5$ represents the loss of 1.5 centimeters.

Use addition or multiplication to solve the problem.

$$\underbrace{^-1.5 + {}^-1.5 + {}^-1.5}_{} = {}^-4.5 \qquad \underbrace{3 \times {}^-1.5}_{} = {}^-4.5$$

three addends of $^-1.5$

The beach loses 4.5 centimeters in 3 years.

The order of the factors does not change the product.

If $3 \times {}^-1.5 = {}^-4.5$, then $^-1.5 \times 3 = {}^-4.5$.

Notice that in each multiplication sentence the factors have different signs. What is the sign of each product?
These examples suggest the following rule.

The product of two rational numbers with different signs is negative.

EXERCISES ***Multiply.***

1. $^-9 \times 6$	**2.** $^-5 \times 7$	**3.** $48 \times {}^-7$	**4.** $16 \times {}^-4$
5. $^-19 \times 27$	**6.** $26 \times {}^-11$	**7.** $5 \times 14 \times {}^-7$	**8.** $31 \times {}^-2 \times 3$
9. $^-0.5 \times 9.7$	**10.** $^-8.1 \times 0.75$	**11.** $0.8 \times {}^-0.5$	**12.** $4.5 \times {}^-0.7$
13. $\frac{^-1}{2} \times \frac{3}{4}$	**14.** $\frac{5}{6} \times \frac{^-1}{4}$	**15.** $^-18 \times \frac{1}{3}$	**16.** $\frac{5}{6} \times {}^-3\frac{1}{2}$

You already know that the product of two positive rational numbers is positive.

Both factors are positive. $3 \times 4 = 12$ The product is also positive.

What is the sign of the product of two negative rational numbers? Study the following pattern.

Look at the first factor in each multiplication sentence. As you go down the list, each of these factors is 1 less than the one before it.

$$3 \times {}^{-}4 = {}^{-}12$$
$$2 \times {}^{-}4 = {}^{-}8$$
$$1 \times {}^{-}4 = {}^{-}4$$
$$0 \times {}^{-}4 = 0$$
$${}^{-}1 \times {}^{-}4 = ▒$$

Look at the product in each multiplication sentence. As you go down the list, each product is 4 more than the one before it.

What number is 4 more than 0? What numeral should replace ▒ ?

$^{-}1 \times {}^{-}4 = 4$ By the same reasoning, $^{-}2 \times {}^{-}4 = 8$.

These examples suggest the following rule.

The product of two rational numbers with the same sign is positive.

EXERCISES Multiply.

17. $^{-}9 \times {}^{-}3$ **18.** $^{-}3 \times {}^{-}12$ **19.** 5×27 **20.** $^{-}3 \times 31$

21. $^{-}14 \times {}^{-}5$ **22.** 13×17 **23.** $^{-}12 \times 11$ **24.** $^{-}24 \times {}^{-}4$

25. $^{-}3.1 \times 1.7$ **26.** $^{-}7 \times 1.4$ **27.** $^{-}2.05 \times {}^{-}10$ **28.** 0.04×5.6

29. $\frac{5}{8} \times \frac{2}{3}$ **30.** $\frac{4}{9} \times \frac{-3}{8}$ **31.** $\frac{-4}{5} \times \frac{-25}{36}$ **32.** $^{-}3\frac{1}{2} \times {}^{-}2\frac{1}{2}$

Evaluate each expression if m = ⁻4 and n = ⁻6.

33. $3m$ **34.** $4n$ **35.** mn **36.** m^2

Solve.

37. Several cliffs of Cap Cod recede 3.3 feet each year. How much do the cliffs recede in 5 years?

38. At 9:00 A.M. the temperature is 7 degrees Celsius. It drops 2 degrees each hour. What is the temperature at 1:00 P.M.?

9–6 Dividing Rational Numbers

The process of thawing undoes the process of freezing. In mathematics, multiplication undoes division. Study the following examples.

$8 \times 4 = 32$	➡	$32 \div 4 = 8$ (same sign)
$7 \times {}^{-}10 = {}^{-}70$	➡	${}^{-}70 \div {}^{-}10 = 7$ (same sign)

positive quotients

In each division sentence, the signs of the dividend and divisor are the same. What is the sign of each quotient? These examples suggest the following rule.

The quotient of two rational numbers with the same sign is positive.

${}^{-}8 \times 10 = {}^{-}80$	➡	${}^{-}80 \div 10 = {}^{-}8$ (different signs)
${}^{-}7 \times {}^{-}9 = 63$	➡	$63 \div {}^{-}9 = {}^{-}7$ (different signs)

negative quotients

In each division sentence, the signs of the dividend and divisor are different. What is the sign of each quotient? These examples suggest the following rule.

The quotient of two rational numbers with different signs is negative.

How are these rules for division of rational numbers similar to those for multiplication of rational numbers?

EXERCISES ***State the sign of each quotient.***

1. $20 \div 2$ **2.** $24 \div {}^{-}8$ **3.** ${}^{-}27 \div {}^{-}3$ **4.** ${}^{-}81 \div 9$

5. ${}^{-}40 \div 4$ **6.** $42 \div 6$ **7.** $45 \div {}^{-}9$ **8.** ${}^{-}18 \div {}^{-}3$

Divide.

9. $^{-}54 \div {}^{-}9$
10. $20 \div {}^{-}5$
11. $32 \div {}^{-}2$
12. $^{-}96 \div 12$
13. $^{-}120 \div {}^{-}5$
14. $^{-}48 \div {}^{-}3$
15. $80 \div {}^{-}6$
16. $^{-}91 \div 13$
17. $52 \div {}^{-}4$
18. $^{-}343 \div {}^{-}7$
19. $0.72 \div {}^{-}0.8$
20. $^{-}18.2 \div {}^{-}0.2$
21. $^{-}4.53 \div 0.03$
22. $^{-}7.82 \div 3.4$
23. $^{-}6.09 \div {}^{-}2.9$
24. $17.16 \div 5.2$
25. $^{-}1.56 \div 0.2$
26. $1.26 \div {}^{-}0.7$
27. $\frac{5}{6} \div \frac{2}{3}$
28. $\frac{3}{8} \div \frac{^{-}1}{2}$
29. $\frac{^{-}5}{6} \div \frac{1}{3}$
30. $\frac{^{-}4}{3} \div \frac{^{-}16}{9}$
31. $\frac{^{-}17}{9} \div \frac{^{-}7}{18}$
32. $\frac{^{-}3}{5} \div \frac{13}{60}$
33. $1\frac{7}{9} \div 4\frac{2}{9}$
34. $2\frac{4}{5} \div {}^{-}3\frac{1}{3}$

Evaluate each expression.

35. $8 - 54 \div {}^{-}6$
36. $^{-}6 + 4 \times {}^{-}2$
37. $^{-}4 \times (8 - 10)$
38. $^{-}4 \times (2 + 6)$
39. $^{-}12 \div 3 + 6 - 9$
40. $^{-}12 \times 6 \div 3 \times {}^{-}2$
41. $24 - 3 + 9 \div 3$
42. $({}^{-}6 - 12) \div 3^2$
43. $2 \times ({}^{-}3 + {}^{-}6 \div {}^{-}3)$

Solve.

44. Toledo receives a snowfall of 8.7 inches. It melts in three days. What is the average number of inches of snow that melts each day?

45. The population of Buffalo decreased from 462,768 to 357,870 in ten years. What was the average annual change in population?

AN INTEGER PUZZLE

Copy the figure at the right. Place the integers $^{-}4$ through 3 in the squares so that touching squares do *not* contain consecutive integers. For example, $^{-}4$ and $^{-}3$ are consecutive integers. The square marked $^{-}4$ cannot touch the square marked $^{-}3$. Use each integer exactly once.

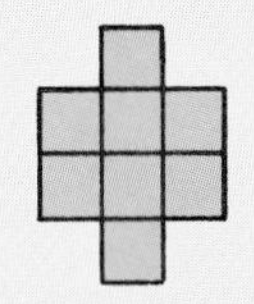

9-7 Solving Equations

Lyle Schick uses equations to predict his crop yield. These equations may involve rational numbers. The same rules used to solve equations with whole numbers are used to solve equations with other rational numbers.

Solve each equation. Check the solution.

$$x + {}^-5 = 3$$
$$x + {}^-5 - {}^-5 = 3 - {}^-5$$ Subtract $^-5$ from each side.
$$x = 8$$

$$x + {}^-5 = 3$$ Check.
$$8 + {}^-5 \stackrel{?}{=} 3$$
$$3 = 3 \ \checkmark$$

The solution is 8.

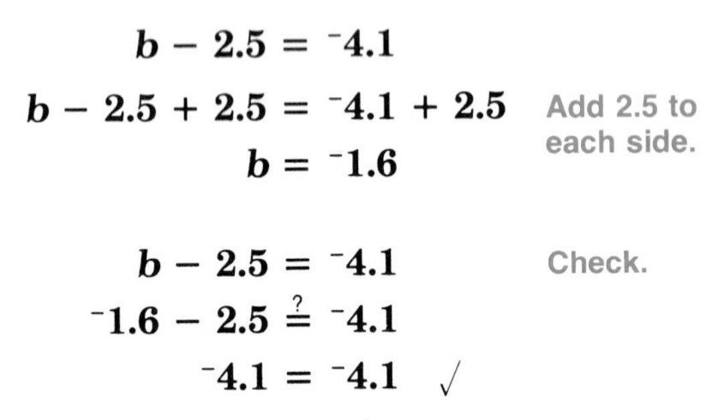

$$b - 2.5 = {}^-4.1$$
$$b - 2.5 + 2.5 = {}^-4.1 + 2.5$$ Add 2.5 to each side.
$$b = {}^-1.6$$

$$b - 2.5 = {}^-4.1$$ Check.
$${}^-1.6 - 2.5 \stackrel{?}{=} {}^-4.1$$
$${}^-4.1 = {}^-4.1 \ \checkmark$$

The solution is $^-1.6$.

EXERCISES ***Solve each equation. Check your solution.***

1. $y + {}^-2 = 5$
2. $x + 3 = {}^-2$
3. $b - 7 = {}^-3$
4. $c - 4 = {}^-12$
5. $q + 4 = {}^-7$
6. $m + {}^-1 = {}^-5$
7. $y - 8 = {}^-4$
8. $b - 6 = {}^-9$
9. $m + {}^-7 = 6$
10. $d + 5 = {}^-33$
11. ${}^-1.5 + q = {}^-2.3$
12. $t + 1.09 = {}^-2$
13. $w + 3.2 = 1.5$
14. $y + 8.7 = {}^-9.3$
15. $e - 2.9 = {}^-1.7$
16. $n - 2.3 = 3.5$
17. $x + 0.5 = 0.5$
18. $y + \frac{1}{5} = \frac{2}{5}$
19. $p - 1 = \frac{{}^-1}{3}$
20. $f - 11 = 4\frac{1}{2}$
21. $5\frac{2}{3} = m + 1\frac{1}{3}$
22. $a + 2\frac{1}{4} = {}^-1\frac{3}{4}$
23. $\frac{{}^-3}{5} + r = \frac{1}{20}$
24. $g - \frac{7}{8} = \frac{19}{6}$
25. $q - \frac{2}{3} = {}^-2\frac{4}{9}$
26. $v - 3\frac{2}{9} = {}^-3\frac{1}{6}$

If the product of two numbers is 1, each number is the **multiplicative inverse** or reciprocal of the other. For example, since $7 \times \frac{1}{7} = 1$, 7 and $\frac{1}{7}$ are multiplicative inverses of each other.

You can use multiplicative inverses to solve multiplication and division equations.

Solve $^-4b = 36$.

$$^-4b = 36$$

$$\frac{^-1}{4} \times {}^-4b = \frac{^-1}{4} \times 36$$

Multiply each side by $\frac{^-1}{4}$, the multiplicative inverse of $^-4$.

$$1 \times b = {}^-9$$

$$b = {}^-9$$

Check the solution.

$$^-4b = 36$$

$$^-4 \times {}^-9 \stackrel{?}{=} 36$$

$$36 = 36 \quad \checkmark$$

The solution is $^-9$.

EXERCISES ***State the multiplicative inverse of each of the following.***

27. 3 **28.** $^-9$ **29.** $^-1$ **30.** $\frac{3}{5}$ **31.** $\frac{^-2}{3}$

32. What rational number has no multiplicative inverse?

Solve each equation. Check your solution.

33. $2a = {}^-30$ **34.** $3t = {}^-48$ **35.** $^-11x = {}^-77$ **36.** $^-15u = {}^-45$

37. $3t = {}^-4$ **38.** $5r = {}^-4$ **39.** $4w = 2$ **40.** $9y = {}^-3$

41. $^-16m = 4$ **42.** $^-18v = {}^-9$ **43.** $1.5x = 0.45$ **44.** $^-4b = 0.8$

45. $^-0.3y = {}^-12$ **46.** $^-0.92 = 0.04y$ **47.** $8y = {}^-1.28$ **48.** $^-0.6b = {}^-8.4$

49. $\frac{x}{3} = 8$ **50.** $\frac{t}{2} = {}^-4$ **51.** $\frac{m}{6} = {}^-7$ **52.** $\frac{1}{8}w = {}^-9$

53. $^-10 = \frac{1}{4}v$ **54.** $\frac{3}{4}y = {}^-9$ **55.** $\frac{2}{3}z = \frac{4}{9}$ **56.** $\frac{^-3}{2}x = {}^-2\frac{1}{2}$

Translate each of the following into an equation. Then solve each equation and check your solution.

57. The sum of $^-15$ and y is 41.

58. The product of $\frac{2}{3}$ and x is $^-18$.

59. A number divided by 2.4 is 0.08.

60. Some number decreased by $^-3$ is 25.

9–8 Solving Two-Step Equations

The population of Lafayette is 4,800. Each year the population decreases by 35. In how many years will the population be 4,520?

The problem can be solved by using the equation $4{,}800 + {}^{-}35y = 4{,}520$. This equation contains more than one operation. Undo the addition first.

$$4{,}800 + {}^{-}35y = 4{,}520$$

$$4{,}800 - 4{,}800 + {}^{-}35y = 4{,}520 - 4{,}800$$ Subtract 4,800 from each side.

$$^{-}35y = {}^{-}280$$

Now undo the multiplication.

$$\frac{^{-}1}{35} \times {}^{-}35y = \frac{^{-}1}{35} \times {}^{-}280$$ Multiply each side by $\frac{^{-}1}{35}$, the multiplicative inverse of $^{-}35$.

$$y = 8$$

Check the solution.

$$4{,}800 + {}^{-}35y = 4{,}520$$

$$4{,}800 + {}^{-}35 \times 8 \stackrel{?}{=} 4{,}520$$

$$4{,}800 + {}^{-}280 \stackrel{?}{=} 4{,}520$$

$$4{,}520 = 4{,}520 \quad \checkmark$$

The population will be 4,520 in 8 years.

EXERCISES* *Copy. Complete each step of solving the equation.

1.

$2r - 7 = 1$

$2r - 7 + ▒ = 1 + ▒$

$2r = ▒$

$▒ \times 2r = ▒ \times 8$

$r = ▒$

2.

$\frac{y}{5} + 8 = 7$

$\frac{y}{5} + 8 - ▒ = 7 - ▒$

$\frac{y}{5} = ▒$

$▒ \times \frac{y}{5} = ▒ \times ▒$

$y = ▒$

3.

$4 - 2b = {}^{-}8$

$4 + ▒ - 2b = {}^{-}8 + ▒$

$^{-}2b = ▒$

$▒ \times {}^{-}2b = ▒ \times ▒$

$b = ▒$

Solve each equation. Check your solution.

4. $2y - 1 = 9$

5. $3m - 2 = 16$

6. $2y + 1 = {}^-31$

7. $2m + 5 = {}^-29$

8. ${}^-32 = {}^-2 + 5y$

9. ${}^-11 = 3d - 2$

10. $4t - 8 = 0$

11. $0 = 11y + 33$

12. ${}^-8 + 6m = {}^-50$

13. $13 = {}^-7 + 2y$

14. $1 - 3x = 7$

15. $10 - 2x = {}^-2$

16. $\frac{x}{4} + 6 = 10$

17. $\frac{y}{3} + 4 = 7$

18. $5 + \frac{t}{2} = 3$

19. $6 + \frac{z}{5} = 0$

20. $\frac{1}{4}t - 2 = 1$

21. $\frac{3}{2}x - 12 = 18$

22. $\frac{2}{3}y + 11 = 33$

23. ${}^-6 = 4 + \frac{5}{2}y$

24. $\frac{2y + 7}{9} = {}^-7$

Translate each of the following into an equation. Then solve each equation and check your solution.

25. Seven plus the quotient of g and 4 is 9.

26. The sum of 6 and the product of 4 and w is ${}^-42$.

27. Three less than the product of ${}^-4$ and r is ${}^-14$.

28. Eight less than the quotient of n and 3 is ${}^-16$.

DENSITY OF RATIONAL NUMBERS

Between any two rational numbers, there are an unlimited number of rational numbers. Consider 0 and 1.

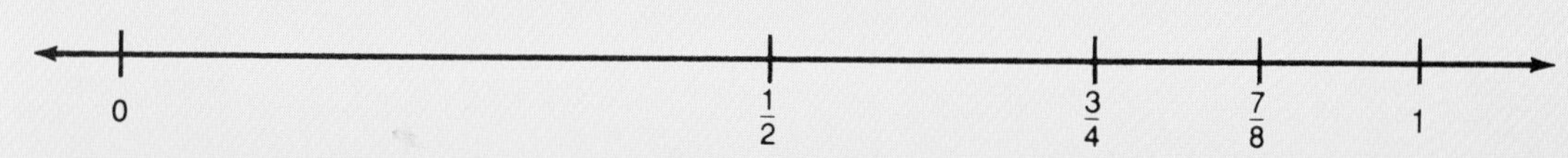

One way to find a rational number between 0 and 1 is to take the average of 0 and 1. You obtain $\frac{1}{2}$. If you take the average of $\frac{1}{2}$ and 1, you obtain $\frac{3}{4}$. The average of $\frac{3}{4}$ and 1 is $\frac{7}{8}$, and so on. You can continue doing this forever. So there are an unlimited number of rational numbers between any two rational numbers. This property is called the **density property** of rational numbers.

Find the rational number that is the average of the two given numbers.

1. 0 and 7

2. ${}^-4$ and ${}^-4.2$

3. $\frac{1}{2}$ and $\frac{2}{3}$

4. ${}^-3$ and $1\frac{1}{2}$

5. Is the density property true for integers?

9-9 Problem Solving: Using Rationals

The Nile River is about 1.8 times longer than the Missouri River. The Nile River is about 6,696 kilometers long.

About how long is the Missouri River?

Read the problem. You know how long the Nile River is. You also know that it is 1.8 times longer than the Missouri River. You need to find the length of the Missouri River.

Decide what to do. Let m represent the length of the Missouri River. Translate the words into an equation using the variable.

Solve the problem.

length of Missouri River	times	1.8	equals	length of Nile River
m	$\times$	1.8	=	6,696

Now solve the equation.

$$m \times 1.8 = 6{,}696$$

$$m \times 1.8 \times \frac{1}{1.8} = 6{,}696 \times \frac{1}{1.8}$$

Multiply each side by $\frac{1}{1.8}$.

$$m = 3{,}720$$

```
        372 0.
1.8)6,696.0
     5 4
     1 29
     1 26
        36
        36
         0
```

The solution is 3,720. The Missouri River is about 3,720 kilometers long.

Examine the solution. The Nile River is 1.8 times longer than the Missouri River.

length of Nile River $\rightarrow 6{,}696 \stackrel{?}{=} 1.8 \times 3{,}720 \leftarrow$ length of Missouri River

$$6{,}696 = 6{,}696 \quad \checkmark$$

Solve.

1. The temperature rises 5 degrees. It is now 2 degrees Celsius. What was the temperature before it rose?

2. A helicopter descends 160 meters to observe traffic. It levels off at 225 meters. What was its original altitude?

3. The record low temperature in Ohio is $^{-}39$ degrees Celsius. The record high temperature is 45 degrees Celsius. What is the difference in the temperatures?

4. Two kilometers above ground the temperature is 0 degrees Celsius. For each kilometer of altitude, the temperature drops 7 degrees. What is the temperature 3 kilometers above ground?

5. Jay Hawkins sells his stereo for \$235. This is \$6.50 more than half what he paid for it. How much did he pay for his stereo?

6. An airplane drops 750 feet. This is $\frac{1}{6}$ of its previous altitude. How high was the airplane before the drop?

7. Jane scores a total of 19.14 in two gymnastic events. Her score in one event is 9.59. What is her score in the other event?

8. Ernesto loses $14\frac{1}{2}$ pounds in 7 months. Now he weighs $156\frac{1}{2}$ pounds. How much did he weigh before?

9. Thi Lu is on a diet. She lost $1\frac{1}{2}$ pounds the first week and then $\frac{3}{4}$ pound each week. After 5 weeks she weighs 128 pounds. How much did she weigh before?

10. Fran borrows money from Clint. Fran pays Clint \$15. Fran still owes Clint \$4.75. How much money did Fran borrow if she does not pay interest?

11. A jet takes off and climbs to a height of 8,500 feet. This is $\frac{3}{5}$ of the height of the cloud cover. What is the height of the cloud cover?

12. Shannon Steiner opens a savings account with \$50. Each week after that she deposits \$8. How many weeks does it take her to save \$450?

Solve. Use the table.

13. Which city's population increased by the greatest percentage?

14. Which city's population decreased by the greatest percentage?

15. What was the population of Miami in 1970?

16. What was the population of New York in 1970?

City	1980 Population	Change from 1970
Baltimore	786,775	$^{-}13.1\%$
Honolulu	365,048	$^{+}12.4\%$
Miami	346,931	$^{+}3.6\%$
New York	7,071,031	$^{-}10.4\%$
Phoenix	764,911	$^{+}30.9\%$
Seattle	493,846	$^{-}7.0\%$

9-10 Integers as Exponents

The intensity of an earthquake is measured on the Richter Scale. Each increase of one on the Richter Scale means a ten-times increase in intensity. For example, an earthquake that measures 7 is ten times as intense as one that measures 6.

Richter Number	Intensity	Effect
1	10 or 10^1	not noticed by humans
2	100 or 10^2	hanging lamps sway
3	1,000 or 10^3	can be felt
4	10,000 or 10^4	glass breaks, buildings shake
5	100,000 or 10^5	furniture collapses
6	1,000,000 or 10^6	wooden houses damaged
7	10,000,000 or 10^7	buildings collapse
8	100,000,000 or 10^8	causes great damage

A positive exponent in a power, such as 10^5, tells how many times the base is used as a factor.

$$10^5 = \underbrace{10 \times 10 \times 10 \times 10 \times 10}_{\text{5 factors}} = 100{,}000$$

Negative integers can also be used as exponents. Study the following pattern.

$10^3 = 10 \times 10 \times 10 = 1{,}000$

$10^2 = 10 \times 10 \qquad = 100$

$10^1 = 10 \qquad = 10$

$10^0 = 1 \qquad = 1$

Remember that any number, except 0, to the zero power is 1.

$10^{-1} = \frac{1}{10^1} \qquad = 0.1$

$10^{-2} = \frac{1}{10^2} \qquad = 0.01$

$10^{-3} = ▒ \qquad = ▒$

What numerals should replace each ▒ ?

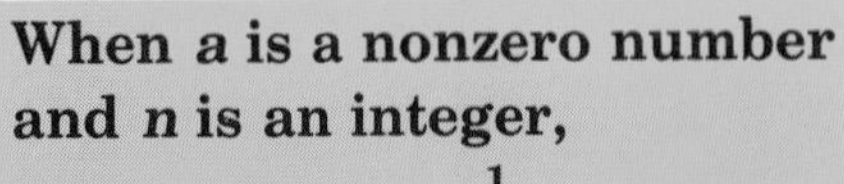

When a is a nonzero number and n is an integer,

$$a^{-n} = \frac{1}{a^n}.$$

Study the following examples.

$$2^{-4} = \frac{1}{2^4} = \frac{1}{2 \times 2 \times 2 \times 2} \text{ or } \frac{1}{16}$$

$$({}^-5)^2 = {}^-5 \times {}^-5 = 25$$

$$8^{-1} = \frac{1}{8^1} = \frac{1}{8}$$

***EXERCISES* Express each of the following as a product of factors.**

1. 3^5 **2.** $({}^-9)^2$ **3.** $({}^-1.2)^4$ **4.** 2^{-5} **5.** 3^{-2} **6.** $({}^-8)^{-2}$

Express each of the following using integers as exponents.

7. $2 \times 2 \times 2 \times 2 \times 2$ **8.** ${}^-6 \times {}^-6 \times {}^-6 \times {}^-6$ **9.** $2.7 \times 2.7 \times 2.7$

10. $\frac{1}{4 \times 4}$ **11.** $\frac{1}{{}^-9 \times {}^-9 \times {}^-9}$ **12.** $\frac{1}{2} \times \frac{1}{2}$

Copy and complete.

13. $64 = 4^{\square}$ **14.** $9 = ({}^-3)^{\square}$ **15.** $81 = ({}^-9)^{\square}$ **16.** ${}^-8 = \square^3$

17. ${}^-1 = \square^5$ **18.** $\frac{1}{2} = 2^{\square}$ **19.** $\frac{1}{9} = 3^{\square}$ **20.** $\frac{1}{36} = \square^{-2}$

Evaluate.

21. 2^3 **22.** 7^2 **23.** 2^{-3} **24.** 3^{-2} **25.** 6^0 **26.** 14^{-1}

27. 5^{-3} **28.** 8^{-2} **29.** $({}^-2)^5$ **30.** $({}^-4)^2$ **31.** $({}^-3)^{-4}$ **32.** $({}^-5)^{-2}$

Solve. Use the chart on page 244.

33. An earthquate in San Francisco in 1906 measured 8.3. An earthquake in Yugoslavia in 1979 measured 7.2. About how many times more intense was the San Francisco earthquake than the Yugoslavia earthquake?

DECIMALS IN EXPANDED FORM

You can write decimals in expanded form using negative exponents.

$$634.75 = (6 \times 10^2) + (3 \times 10^1) + (4 \times 10^0) + (7 \times 10^{-1}) + (5 \times 10^{-2})$$

Express each of the following in expanded form using exponents.

1. 147 **2.** 30.8 **3.** 11,423.96 **4.** 0.00256 **5.** 9.3606

9–11 Scientific Notation

The Pacific Ocean covers 64,000,000 square miles. This number can be expressed in **scientific notation.** Express it as the product of a number greater than or equal to 1 and less than 10, and a power of ten.

$$64{,}000{,}000 = 6.4000000 \times 10{,}000{,}000$$
$$= 6.4 \times 10^7$$

Move the decimal point 7 places left and multiply by 10,000,000 or 10^7.

Express 84,320 in scientific notation.

$$84{,}320 = 8.4320 \times 10{,}000$$
$$= 8.4320 \times 10^4$$

Move the decimal point 4 places left.

The diameter of a grain of sand is between 0.0006 meters and 0.0021 meters. Numbers such as 0.0006 and 0.0021 can also be expressed in scientific notation.

$$0.0006 = 00006. \times 0.0001$$
$$= 6 \times \frac{1}{10{,}000}$$
$$= 6 \times \frac{1}{10^4}$$
$$= 6 \times 10^{-4}$$

Move the decimal point 4 places right and multiply by 0.0001 or 10^{-4}.

$$0.0021 = 0002.1 \times 0.001$$
$$= 2.1 \times \frac{1}{1{,}000}$$
$$= 2.1 \times \frac{1}{10^3}$$
$$= 2.1 \times 10^{-3}$$

Move the decimal point 3 places right.

The exponent is positive if the decimal point is moved left. It is negative if the decimal point is moved right.

EXERCISES ***Express each of the following in scientific notation.***

1. 460
2. 3,200
3. 266,000
4. 49,000
5. 0.0015
6. 0.000083
7. 0.000261
8. 0.051
9. 50,370
10. 68,040,000
11. 8,201,000
12. 131,000
13. 0.0000000714
14. 0.00000916
15. 0.00432
16. 0.000001002

Express each of the following in standard form.

$6.1 \times 10^5 = 6.1 \times 100{,}000$
$= 610{,}000$

17. 3.25×10^2
18. 4.67×10^5
19. 4.39×10^{-3}
20. 6.8×10^{-4}
21. 7.05×10^7
22. 5.75×10^9
23. 8.6×10^{-5}
24. 2.17×10^{-8}
25. 1.28×10^6
26. 7.67×10^{-2}

Solve.

27. The area of the Atlantic Ocean is 31,830,000 square miles. Write this number in scientific notation.
28. The area of Greenland is 840,000 square miles. Write this number in scientific notation.
29. In a recent year the population of California was about 2.37×10^7. Its area is about 4.05×10^5 km^2. What is the average number of people per square kilometer?
30. In a recent year the world production of wheat was about 4.5×10^8 metric tons. Canada produced 4.7% of this. About how much wheat did Canada produce?

Skills Review: Pages 234–247

Multiply or divide.

1. $^-2 \times 3$
2. $^-5 \times {}^-7$
3. $^-132 \div 1.6$
4. $^-52 \div {}^-4$

Solve each equation. Check your solution.

5. $x + 15 = {}^-28$
6. $5y = {}^-45$
7. $\frac{p}{4} = {}^-6$
8. $3x + {}^-9 = 54$

Solve.

9. The temperature is 5 degrees Celsius. It drops 2 degrees each hour. In how many hours will it be $^-1$ degrees Celsius?

Evaluate.

10. 7^3
11. 2^{-4}
12. $({}^-6)^{-2}$

Express in scientific notation.

13. 1,740,000
14. 0.000059

Mathematics and Science

Temperature is commonly measured in degrees Celsius (°C) or degrees Fahrenheit (°F). A Celsius thermometer and a Fahrenheit thermometer are shown at the right.

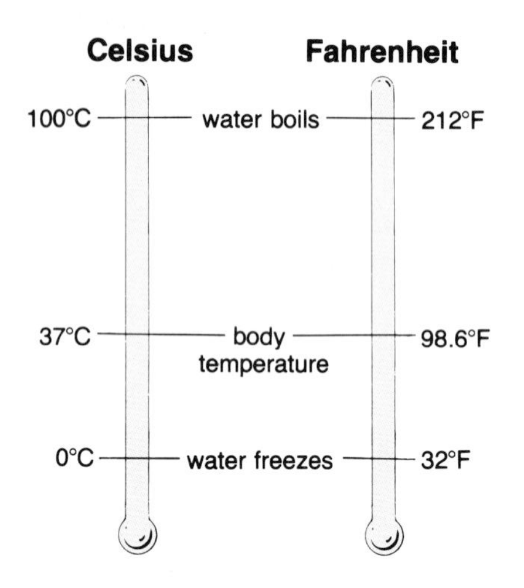

You may need to change from one temperature unit to another. You can use the following formulas.

Celsius to Fahrenheit: $F = \frac{9}{5}C + 32$

Change 45°C to degrees Fahrenheit.

$$F = \frac{9}{5}C + 32$$
$$= \frac{9}{5} \times 45 + 32 \quad \text{Replace } C \text{ with 45.}$$
$$= 81 + 32$$
$$= 113$$

45°C is the same as 113°F.

Fahrenheit to Celsius: $C = \frac{5}{9}(F - 32)$

Change ⁻4°F to degrees Celsius.

$$C = \frac{5}{9}(F - 32)$$
$$= \frac{5}{9}({}^{-}4 - 32) \quad \text{Replace } F \text{ with } {}^{-}4.$$
$$= \frac{5}{9}({}^{-}36)$$
$$= {}^{-}20$$

⁻4°F is the same as ⁻20°C.

EXERCISES ***Change each of the following to degrees Fahrenheit.***

1. 25°C **2.** ⁻15°C **3.** 0°C **4.** 33.6°C **5.** ⁻22.5°C

Change each of the following to degrees Celsius.

6. 41°F **7.** 59°F **8.** ⁻13°F **9.** ⁻44°F **10.** ⁻70°F

Solve.

11. At night the average surface temperature on the planet Saturn is ⁻150°C. What is the temperature in degrees Fahrenheit?

Chapter 9 Review

VOCABULARY	negative (225)	positive (225)
integer (225)	rational number (225)	opposite (225)
absolute value (227)	multiplicative inverse (239)	scientific notation (246)

EXERCISES ***State the opposite of each of the following. (225)***

1. $^{-}2$ **2.** 5 **3.** $^{+}30$ **4.** $^{-}6.7$

Replace each ▒ with <, >, or = to make a true sentence. (226)

5. $^{-}4$ ▒ 2 **6.** 3.5 ▒ $^{-}5.3$ **7.** $^{-}1$ ▒ $\frac{^{-}1}{2}$ **8.** $\frac{^{-}2}{3}$ ▒ $\frac{^{-}3}{4}$

Add, subtract, multiply, or divide. (228–231, 234–237)

9. $72 - {}^{-}25$ **10.** $^{-}27 - 8$ **11.** $37 + 13$ **12.** $40 + {}^{-}11$ **13.** $^{-}9 \times 14$

14. $^{-}15 \times {}^{-}6$ **15.** $^{-}66 \div {}^{-}3$ **16.** $34 \div 4$ **17.** $^{-}31 + 30$ **18.** $^{-}6 - {}^{-}24$

19. $2.13 \div {}^{-}0.3$ **20.** $^{-}1.4 \div 7$ **21.** 9.6×2.02 **22.** $10.8 \times {}^{-}11$

23. $\frac{3}{4} + \frac{^{-}1}{4}$ **24.** $\frac{^{-}2}{3} - \frac{5}{6}$ **25.** $\frac{^{-}5}{7} \times \frac{^{-}4}{5}$ **26.** $\frac{3}{10} \div \frac{6}{11}$

27. $^{-}1\frac{1}{2} - {}^{-}2\frac{1}{2}$ **28.** $^{-}3\frac{1}{3} + 2\frac{1}{6}$ **39.** $\frac{5}{6} \div {}^{-}6\frac{2}{3}$ **30.** $\frac{3}{4} \times 1\frac{5}{9}$

Solve each equation. Check your solution. (238–241)

31. $y + {}^{-}2 = 18$ **32.** $x - 3 = {}^{-}4$ **33.** $^{-}3x = 24$ **34.** $^{-}2.4 + r = 4$

35. $b - \frac{1}{2} = {}^{-}6$ **36.** $\frac{p}{5} = {}^{-}2$ **37.** $\frac{1}{4}d = 1.7$ **38.** $7a = \frac{14}{15}$

39. $2t + 11 = {}^{-}41$ **40.** $8 - 5b = {}^{-}17$ **41.** $^{-}6p + 1.4 = {}^{-}21.4$

Solve. (242)

42. Vernon Jones removes 33.5 gallons of water from a swimming pool. Then it contains 450 gallons of water. How many gallons did it contain before?

Copy and complete. (244)

43. $16 = 2^{■}$ **44.** $16 = ({}^{-}4)^{■}$ **45.** $\frac{1}{27} = 3^{■}$ **46.** $\frac{1}{25} = {■}^{-2}$

Express each of the following in scientific notation. (246)

47. 65,000 **48.** 198,000,000 **49.** 0.0021 **50.** 0.00000743

Chapter 9 Test

Order the numbers in each list from least to greatest.

1. $^{-}5, 14, 0, ^{-}10, 1.5$ **2.** $10, ^{-}1.5, ^{-}7.2, 3.1, ^{-}0.6$ **3.** $1, ^{-}2, \frac{-1}{2}, \frac{3}{4}, 0$

Add, subtract, multiply, or divide.

4. $^{-}16 + ^{-}11$ **5.** $^{-}25 + 17$ **6.** $^{-}5 - 18$ **7.** $23 - ^{-}16$

8. $14 \times ^{-}6$ **9.** 13×27 **10.** $312 \div 24$ **11.** $^{-}72 \div ^{-}9$

12. $^{-}8 \times ^{-}11$ **13.** $^{-}42 \div 3$ **14.** $3.1 + ^{-}1.4$ **15.** $0.33 + 2.2$

16. $1.4 - 2.1$ **17.** $^{-}31.4 - ^{-}4.2$ **18.** $2.6 \div 0.2$ **19.** $^{-}6 \times 2.3$

20. $\frac{-1}{2} + \frac{3}{4}$ **21.** $1\frac{5}{6} - ^{-}2\frac{1}{6}$ **22.** $\frac{4}{9} \times \frac{3}{5}$ **23.** $\frac{-7}{8} \div \frac{-3}{4}$

24. $\frac{5}{6} - \frac{2}{3}$ **25.** $^{-}3\frac{1}{3} \times \frac{-6}{7}$ **26.** $^{-}1\frac{1}{4} \div \frac{3}{10}$ **27.** $\frac{1}{3} + ^{-}2\frac{3}{4}$

Evaluate each expression if b = $^{-}4$ and r = $^{-}1.5$.

28. $b + r$ **29.** $r - b$ **30.** $|b|$ **31.** $|r| + 1$

Solve each equation. Check your solution.

32. $y - 4 = ^{-}9$ **33.** $^{-}7 + c = 43$ **34.** $^{-}4.2 = a + ^{-}2.5$ **35.** $5x = ^{-}165$

36. $\frac{n}{3} = ^{-}19$ **37.** $6\frac{1}{2} = b - \frac{3}{4}$ **38.** $^{-}7y = \frac{2}{3}$ **39.** $\frac{m}{7} = ^{-}9.19$

40. $3k + ^{-}1 = ^{-}10$ **41.** $\frac{t}{2} - 5 = 7$ **42.** $^{-}4n - 3 = -19$ **43.** $\frac{2}{3}k - 1 = 13$

Solve.

44. At 6:00 A.M. the temperature is $^{-}2$ degrees Celsius. At noon it is 7 degrees Celsius. What is the average change each hour?

Evaluate.

45. 3^3 **46.** 3^{-2} **47.** $(^{-}2)^3$ **48.** $(^{-}4)^{-2}$

Express each of the following in scientific notation.

49. 13,490,000 **50.** 0.00000674 **51.** 0.00032 **52.** 5,810

Express each of the following in standard form.

53. 1.4×10^{-5} **54.** 3.15×10^{7} **55.** 9.6×10^{3} **56.** 1.08×10^{-2}

Enrichment

Rich Clark earns \$5.50 an hour. He works 4 hours on Monday and 5 hours on Tuesday. What does he earn on these two days?

There are two ways to find his pay.

1. Multiply the total number of hours he works by \$5.50.

   $\mathbf{5.50 \times (4 + 5) = 5.50 \times 9}$ **or** $\mathbf{49.50}$

2. Find his Monday earnings and his Tuesday earnings and add.

   $\mathbf{(5.50 \times 4) + (5.50 \times 5) = 22 + 27.50}$ **or** $\mathbf{49.50}$

Both ways give the same answer.

$$\mathbf{5.50 \times (4 + 5) = (5.50 \times 4) + (5.50 \times 5)}$$

This example illustrates the distributive property of multiplication over addition. For the set of rational numbers, the distributive property may be stated as follows.

> **For any three rational numbers represented by the letters *a, b,* and *c,***
>
> $$a(b + c) = ab + ac.$$

EXERCISES ***Copy and complete.***

1. $8 \times 43 = 8 \times (\square + 3)$

$= 8 \times \square + 8 \times \square$

$= 320 + \square$

$= \square$

2. $12 \times 20.5 = 12 \times (20 + \square)$

$= \square \times 20 + \square \times \square$

$= \square + 6$

$= \square$

3. $8t + 5t = (\square + 5)t$

$= \square\, t$

4. $^-9y + 4y = (^-9 + \square)\square$

$= {}^-5\,\square$

5. $1.5b + {}^-6b = (\square + \square)b$

$= \square$

6. Is there a distributive property for multiplication over subtraction?

10 Measurement

Many people have at least one hobby. Most hobbies involve some form of measurement. For example, the model plane shown can fly as high as 100 meters.

10–1 Metric Units of Length

The wingspan of the model plane is about 1 meter. The **meter** is the basic unit of length in the metric system. Prefixes relate all other metric units to the basic unit by multiples of ten. The chart shows how these prefixes are related to decimal place values.

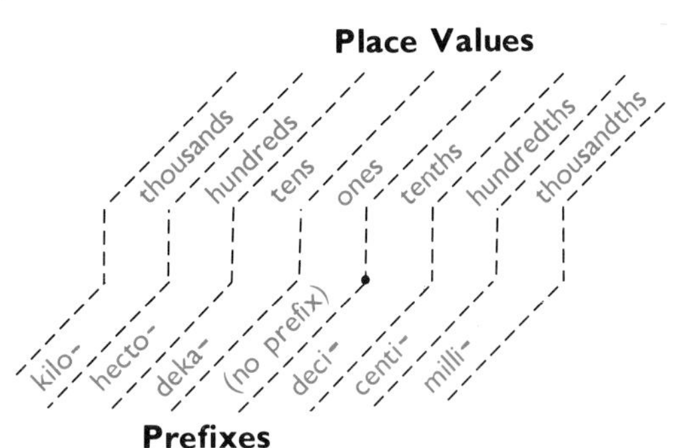

The most frequently used metric units of length are the following.

meter (m)	about the width of a door
centimeter (cm)	about the width of the little finger
millimeter (mm)	about the thickness of a paper match
kilometer (km)	about the length of five city blocks

EXERCISES ***Name the longer unit.***

1. meter or centimeter

2. kilometer or millimeter

3. millimeter or meter

4. centimeter or millimeter

5. kilometer or centimeter

6. meter or kilometer

Choose the most reasonable unit of measure for each of the following. Use millimeter, centimeter, meter, or kilometer.

7. width of picture frame

8. length of bike trail

9. width of staple

10. length of river

11. thickness of rope

12. width of book

Choose the most reasonable answer for each of the following.

13. width of a kite	85 mm	85 cm	85 m
14. thickness of a button	6 mm	6 cm	6 km
15. length of a quilt	2.5 cm	2.5 m	2.5 km
16. highest altitude of a glider	14.102 km	14.102 m	14.102 cm

10-2 Measuring Length

Sue collects coins. She measures a coin to find a place for it in her coin album.

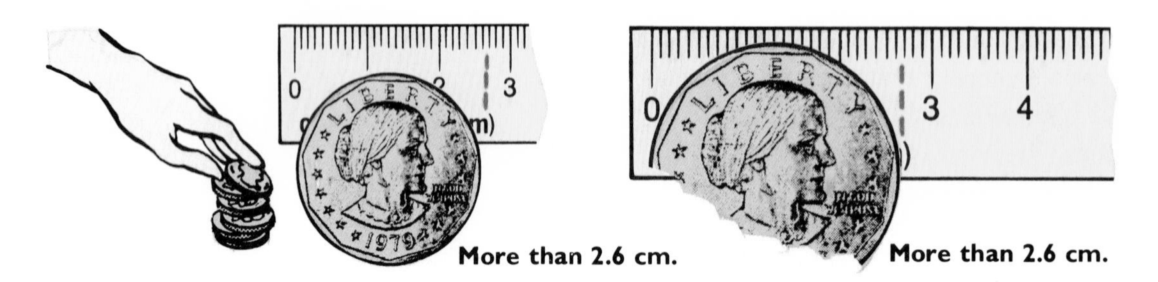

A measurement may come close but it never aligns with the measuring scale exactly. No measurement is exact.

All measurements are approximate.

The ruler below can be used to measure $\overline{AB}$ and $\overline{AC}$ in both centimeters and millimeters.

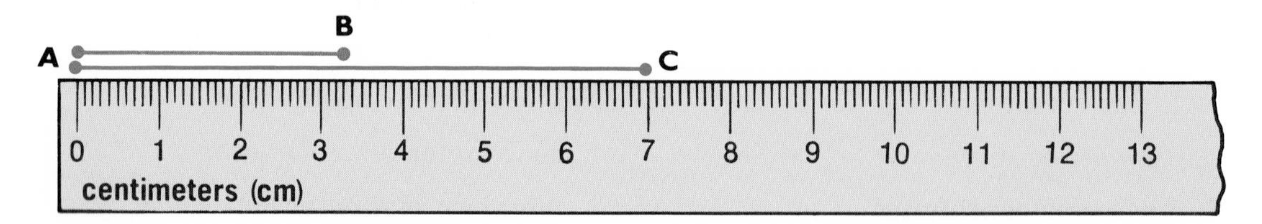

centimeters	millimeters
Each space between two numbered marks is a centimeter. Each centimeter is separated into tenths.	Each space between two marks is a millimeter. One millimeter is one-tenth of a centimeter.
The measure of $\overline{AC}$ is close to 7. The length of $\overline{AC}$ is 7 cm.	The measure of $\overline{AC}$ is close to 70. The length of $\overline{AC}$ is 70 mm.
The measure of $\overline{AB}$ is close to 3.3. The length of $\overline{AB}$ is 3.3 cm.	The measure of $\overline{AB}$ is close to 33. The length of $\overline{AB}$ is 33 mm.

EXERCISES ***Find the length of each line segment below. Give your answers in centimeters and then in millimeters.***

1. $\overline{AB}$ 2. $\overline{AC}$ 3. $\overline{AD}$ 4. $\overline{AE}$ 5. $\overline{AF}$

6. $\overline{AG}$ 7. $\overline{AH}$ 8. $\overline{AJ}$ 9. $\overline{AK}$ 10. $\overline{EK}$

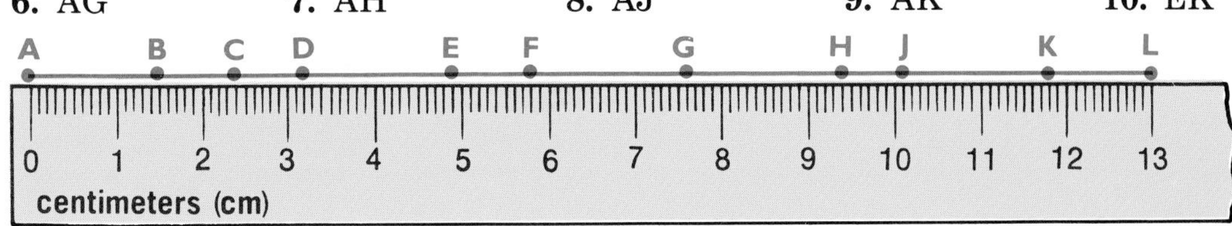

With a ruler, measure the length of each line segment below. Give your answer in centimeters and then in millimeters.

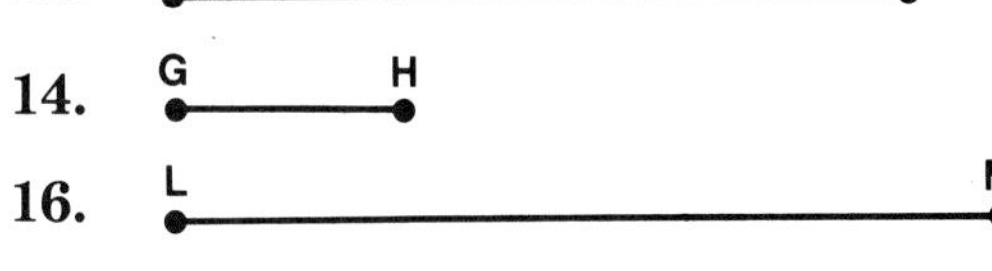

11. A—B 12. C—D

13. E—F 14. G—H

15. J—K 16. L—M

17. N—P 18. Q—R

19. S—T 20. X—Y

Draw line segments having the following lengths.

21. 12 cm **22.** 9.5 cm **23.** 0.8 cm **24.** 49 mm **25.** 90 mm

HISTORY OF MEASUREMENT

In early times, measurements were made by comparing distances or weights with available units. These units often were related to parts of the body, such as the foot, arm, and finger.

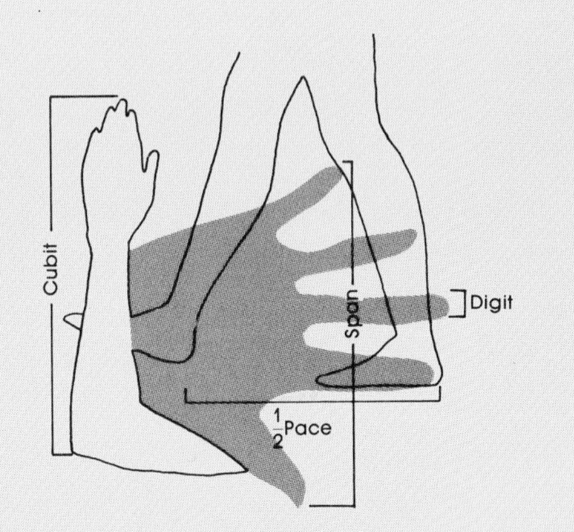

Measure each of the following using your own cubit, pace, span, or digit. Use a reasonable unit for each.

1. thickness of this book
2. width of your desk
3. height of a door
4. length of your bedroom

10-3 Changing Metric Units

Tim Elliott restores antique cars. The wheelbase of a certain car measures 290 centimeters. How many meters is 290 centimeters?

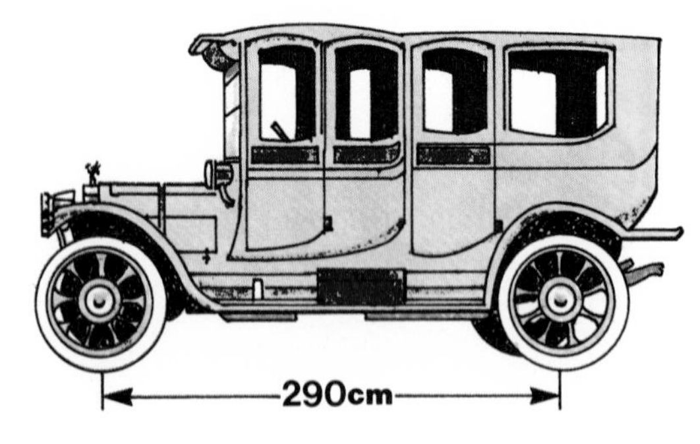

Changing metric units is like moving from one place-value position to another.

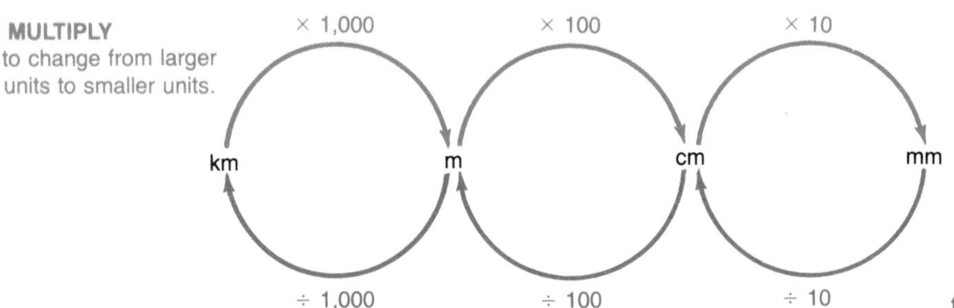

Change 290 centimeters to meters. **290 cm = ▒ m**

You are changing from a smaller unit to a larger unit. So, DIVIDE. Since there are 100 centimeters in 1 meter, divide by 100.

290 ÷ 100 = 290

Move the decimal point two places to the left.

290 cm = 2.9 m

EXERCISES ***Complete each of the following.***

1. To change millimeters to centimeters, divide by ______.

2. To change meters to millimeters, multiply by ______.

3. To change meters to centimeters, ______ by 100.

4. To change meters to kilometers, ______ by 1,000.

5. To change centimeters to meters, divide by ______.

6. To change centimeters to millimeters, multiply by ______.

7. To change kilometers to centimeters, ______ by 100,000.

8. To change millimeters to meters, ______ by 1,000.

State whether you should multiply or divide to complete each of the following. Then state whether you should use 10, 100, or 1,000.

9. 6,050 m = ▒ km **10.** 300 cm = ▒ m

11. 8 mm = ▒ cm **12.** 34 m = ▒ cm

13. 8.1 km = ▒ m **14.** 3.2 cm = ▒ mm

15. 0.96 m = ▒ mm **16.** 17 mm = ▒ m

Complete each of the following.

17. 1,000 m = ▒ km **18.** 1 cm = ▒ mm **19.** 2,000 mm = ▒ m

20. 2 m = ▒ cm **21.** 200 cm = ▒ m **22.** 300 mm = ▒ cm

23. 7 cm = ▒ mm **24.** 1,600 mm = ▒ cm **25.** 20 km = ▒ m

26. 30 m = ▒ cm **27.** 8,700 cm = ▒ m **28.** 24,000 mm = ▒ m

29. 2,000 m = ▒ km **30.** 42,000 m = ▒ km **31.** 42 cm = ▒ mm

32. 0.6 m = ▒ cm **33.** 4.1 km = ▒ m **34.** 16.3 mm = ▒ cm

35. 185.3 km = ▒ m **36.** 2.05 m = ▒ mm **37.** 120.5 mm = ▒ cm

38. 4,100 cm = ▒ m **39.** 40.7 cm = ▒ mm **40.** 41.9 m = ▒ mm

Solve.

41. Line segment DL is 4 centimeters long. Line segment GM is 15 millimeters long. How many millimeters longer is $\overline{DL}$ than $\overline{GM}$?

42. A tan napkin is 107 centimeters long. A blue napkin is 0.28 meters long. How many centimeters longer is the tan napkin than the blue napkin?

TASTY RECIPES

Four volumes of International Recipes are on a shelf. The total pages of each volume are 5 cm thick. Each cover is 5 mm thick. A bookworm started eating at page 1 of Volume I and ate through to the last page of Volume IV. What distance did the bookworm cover?

10-4 Precision and Error

Bill mounts his butterfly collection in a display box. He measures the wingspan of a Red Admiral to find a place for it.

Measure the wingspan to the nearest centimeter and millimeter. Which is the more precise measurement?

To the nearest centimeter, it measures 4 cm

To the nearest millimeter, it measures 42 mm.

The more precise measurement is 42 mm.

Precision depends upon the unit of measure used. The smaller the unit of measure, the greater the precision of the measurement.

The table below lists several measurements and their precision.

Measurement	Precision
4 mm	nearest millimeter
19 m	nearest meter
920 m	nearest 10 meters
8.1 cm	nearest 0.1 centimeter

EXERCISES ***Name the more precise measurement in each of the following.***

1. 2,300 m, 2 km
2. 457 mm, 46 cm
3. 6.8 m, 68.3 cm
4. 8 m, 790 cm
5. 2.8 km, 2,790 m
6. 355 mm, 35 cm
7. 5 cm, 49 mm
8. 2 m, 1,960 mm
9. 370 m, 0.4 km

Give the precision of each of the following measurements.

10. 6 m
11. 17 cm
12. 495 km
13. 1,294 mm
14. 6.7 cm
15. 160 cm
16. 8.3 m
17. 3.06 km
18. 15,000 cm
19. 1,850 km
20. 1,300 mm
21. 9.04 m

Bill orders a moth from a collector's catalog. The catalog states that the wingspan of the moth is 7 cm rounded to the nearest centimeter.

Bill knows the moth will be at least 6.5 cm, but less than 7.5 cm long. The length of the moth can vary no more than 0.5 cm either way.

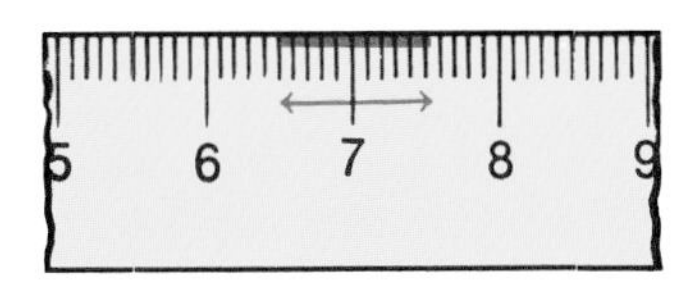

The difference between the true length and the measured length is called the **error of measurement.**

The *greatest possible error* is 0.5 or one-half the unit of measure.

Bill measures the wingspan of a Checkerspot. To the nearest millimeter, it is 43 mm. This means the wingspan is at least 42.5 mm, but less than 43.5 mm. The greatest possible error is 0.5 mm.

EXERCISES ***Give the lengths that the following measurements can vary.***

22. 146 cm **23.** 63 mm **24.** 36 cm **25.** 182 m **26.** 43 km

27. 259 cm **28.** 3 m **29.** 490 m **30.** 10 mm **31.** 360 km

Give the greatest possible error for each measurement.

32. 15 mm **33.** 85 km **34.** 362 m **35.** 49 mm **36.** 1 km

37. 31 m **38.** 197 cm **39.** 78 mm **40.** 1,278 km **41.** 8 cm

SIGNIFICANT DIGITS

The significant digits of an approximate number are those digits which indicate the results of a measurement. For example, the width of a field, measured to the nearest 100 meters, is 800 m. The measurement 800 m has one significant digit, 8. The width of the field, measured to the nearest meter, is 817 m. The measurement 817 m has three significant digits, 8, 1, and 7. Significant digits can be used to find the precision of a given measurement.

10–5 Mass and Capacity

Kelly's hobby is having an aquarium. The aquarium is too heavy to move when it is full. The mass of the water in the aquarium is about 76 kilograms.

She uses a pitcher to fill the aquarium after cleaning it. The pitcher has a capacity of 750 milliliters.

The **gram** is the basic unit of mass in the metric system. The most frequently used metric units of mass are the following.

gram (g)	about the mass of a guppy
milligram (mg)	about the mass of a few grains of sand
kilogram (kg)	about the mass of an aquarium air pump

The **liter** is the basic unit of capacity in the metric system. The most frequently used metric units of capacity are the following.

liter (L)	about the capacity of a pitcher
milliliter (mL)	about the capacity of an eyedropper
kiloliter (kL)	about the capacity of a child's swimming pool

EXERCISES ***Choose the most reasonable answer for each of the following.***

1. sack of potatoes	5 g	5 mg	5 kg
2. a piece of thread	25 mg	25 g	25 kg
3. tennis shoes	800 kg	800 g	800 mg
4. pencil	10 mg	10 g	10 kg
5. a staple	50 kg	50 mg	50 g
6. bicycle	10 kg	10 g	10 mg
7. glass of milk	250 L	250 mL	250 kL
8. tank of gasoline	30 mL	30 kL	30 L
9. hot air balloon	2.5 mL	2.5 L	2.5 kL
10. aquarium water	38 L	38 mL	38 kL
11. large tank ship	10 kL	10 L	10 mL
12. bottle of ketchup	500 L	500 kL	500 mL

The procedure for changing metric units of mass and capacity is similar to the procedure for changing metric units of length.

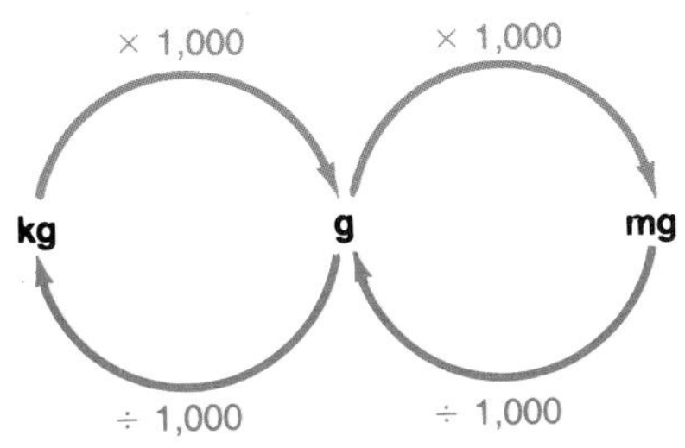

1,325 milligrams = ▒ grams

You are changing from a smaller unit to a larger unit. So, DIVIDE. Since there are 1,000 milligrams in 1 gram, divide by 1,000.

1,325 ÷ 1,000 = 1.325

1,325 milligrams = 1.325 grams

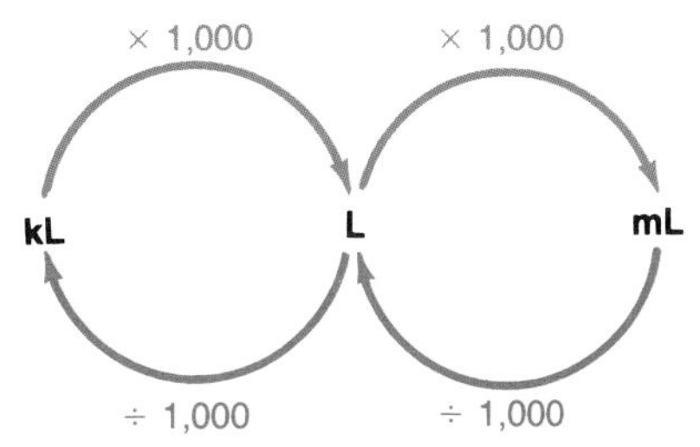

820 liters = ▒ milliliters

You are changing from a larger unit to a smaller unit. So, MULTIPLY. Since there are 1,000 milliliters in 1 liter, multiply by 1,000.

820 × 1,000 = 820,000

820 liters = 820,000 milliliters

EXERCISES ***Complete each of the following.***

13. 5 kg = ▒ g
14. 2,000 g = ▒ kg
15. 4 g = ▒ mg
16. 1,400 g = ▒ kg
17. 3,250 mg = ▒ g
18. 3.4 kg = ▒ g
19. 0.4 kg = ▒ g
20. 750 g = ▒ kg
21. 940 mg = ▒ g
22. 0.06 kg = ▒ g
23. 850 g = ▒ kg
24. 50 g = ▒ kg
25. 2.4 g = ▒ mg
26. 0.3 kg = ▒ g
27. 89 mg = ▒ g
28. 6 L = ▒ mL
29. 4,000 mL = ▒ L
30. 3.2 kL = ▒ L
31. 12 L = ▒ mL
32. 2,000 L = ▒ kL
33. 3,400 mL = ▒ L
34. 3.8 kL = ▒ L
35. 0.4 L = ▒ mL
36. 250 mL = ▒ L
37. 5.35 L = ▒ mL
38. 4 mL = ▒ L
39. 10.6 kL = ▒ L
40. 8.03 L = ▒ mL
41. 2,350 L = ▒ kL
42. 750 mL = ▒ L

Solve.

43. Which is the greatest mass, 2,500 g, 250 mg, or 0.0025 kg?

44. Which is the greatest capacity, 3,100 mL, 31 L, or 0.31 kL?

45. A water tank has a mass of 3.6 kg when empty. It has a mass of 51.8 kg when filled. What is the mass of the water?

46. A tank contains 35 L of water. It drains at the rate of 0.7 L per minute. How long does it take the tank to drain?

10-6 Problem Solving: Using Metric Measurements

Dan Hausman takes pictures and develops his own film. He mixes 60 mL of stop bath with 4 L of water in a tray. How many milliliters of liquid are in the tray?

Read the problem. You need to find the total number of milliliters of liquid in the tray. You know each amount of stop bath and water that are mixed in the tray.

Decide what to do. To find the total number of milliliters of liquid, add.
To add or subtract measurements, they must have the same unit of measure.

Solve the problem. First change 4 liters to milliliters

4 L = 4,000 mL Multiply by 1,000.

Then add.

$$\begin{array}{r} 4{,}000 \\ +\quad 60 \\ \hline 4{,}060 \end{array}$$

There are 4,060 mL of liquid in the tray.

Examine the solution. Since 60 mL is a small part of a liter, the total should be slightly more than 4 L. The answer is reasonable. To check the accuracy, change 60 mL to liters and find the actual total in liters. This total is equivalent to 4,060 mL. The answer is accurate.

EXERCISES ***Add or subtract.***

1. 39.4 km + 14.1 km = ▒ km
2. 7.2 cm + 4.3 mm = ▒ mm
3. 190 m − 230 cm = ▒ cm
4. 49.23 kg − 180 g = ▒ kg
5. 9,205 mg + 14 g = ▒ g
6. 12,000 mg − 3.2 g = ▒ mg
7. 34.4 kL − 2,200 L = ▒ kL
8. 26.3 L + 93 mL = ▒ mL

Solve.

9. Aaron is 1.8 meters tall. Bethany is 191 centimeters tall. How much taller is Bethany than Aaron?
10. Lynn has 2 meters of ribbon. She cuts the ribbon into pieces that measure 8 cm in length. How many pieces does she have?
11. A dime has a mass of 2.3 grams. Luisa has a roll of dimes worth $5. What is the total mass of the dimes?
12. Kyle has three 750-mL cans of juice. Will a 2-liter container hold all the juice?
13. Mr. Schulz drives 156 km and uses 6 L of gasoline. At that rate, how many liters of gasoline does he need to drive 286 km?
14. A 25-L tank fills at the rate of 500 milliliters per minute. How long does it take the tank to fill?

Skills Review: Pages 253-263

Choose the most reasonable answer for each of the following.

1. width of a record album	30 cm	30 m	30 mm
2. mass of a football player	100 g	100 kg	100 mg
3. ear drops	0.5 mL	0.5 L	0.5 kL

Complete each of the following.

4. 60 mm = ▒ cm
5. 3.6 km = ▒ m
6. 0.20 kg = ▒ g
7. 3,400 mg = ▒ g
8. 825 mL = ▒ L
9. 3.047 kL = ▒ L

Solve.

10. Which measurement is the most precise, 239 mm, 24 cm, or 0.2 m?
11. A shelf is 83.2 cm wide. How many books can fit on the shelf if each book is 32 mm wide?

Cumulative Review

Estimate.

1. $\begin{array}{r} 4{,}329 \\ +\ 8{,}837 \\ \hline \end{array}$
2. $\begin{array}{r} 72.9 \\ -\ 28.3 \\ \hline \end{array}$
3. $\begin{array}{r} 5.48 \\ \times\ \ 6.1 \\ \hline \end{array}$
4. $27\overline{)5{,}942}$
5. $6.2\overline{)1.79}$

Add, subtract, multiply, or divide.

6. $\begin{array}{r} 62.05 \\ +\ 84.26 \\ \hline \end{array}$
7. $\begin{array}{r} 37.33 \\ -\ 15.3 \\ \hline \end{array}$
8. $\begin{array}{r} 4.38 \\ \times\ 0.07 \\ \hline \end{array}$
9. $\begin{array}{r} 9.03 \\ \times\ 5.84 \\ \hline \end{array}$
10. $0.4\overline{)0.136}$
11. $0.96\overline{)13.152}$
12. 23.7×100
13. $68{,}746 \div 1{,}000$
14. $4 + {}^{-}7$
15. ${}^{-}6 + {}^{-}17.5$
16. ${}^{-}9 - 5$
17. ${}^{-}16 - {}^{-}1.2$
18. $15 \times {}^{-}5$
19. ${}^{-}21 \times {}^{-}0.1$
20. $18 \div {}^{-}6$
21. ${}^{-}72 \div 8$
22. ${}^{-}4.8 \div {}^{-}12$

Find the greatest common factor (GCF) for each group of numbers.

23. 10, 12
24. 9, 16
25. 18, 20, 30

Find the least common multiple (LCM) for each group of numbers.

26. 8, 6
27. 16, 24
28. 4, 7, 42

Add, subtract, multiply, or divide. Write each answer in simplest form.

29. $\frac{3}{8} + \frac{1}{4}$
30. $\frac{5}{8} + \frac{5}{6}$
31. $7\frac{4}{5} + 4\frac{7}{10}$
32. $\frac{9}{10} - \frac{3}{8}$
33. $2\frac{1}{4} - \frac{11}{12}$
34. $15\frac{1}{8} - 6\frac{2}{3}$
35. $\frac{7}{8} \times 12$
36. $1\frac{1}{9} \times \frac{3}{8}$
37. $4\frac{3}{4} \times 5\frac{2}{5}$
38. $\frac{4}{5} \div \frac{8}{12}$
39. $14 \div \frac{7}{10}$
40. $5\frac{3}{5} \div 2\frac{1}{10}$

Solve.

41. What number is 24% of 400?
42. What percent of 1,500 is 225?
43. 7 is 5% of what number?
44. 37.2% of 84 is what number?

Solve each equation.

45. $a + 9 = 14$
46. $3.2 + b = 7.75$
47. $c - 15 = 23$
48. $d - 6 = {}^{-}2$
49. $3e = {}^{-}48$
50. $\frac{1}{2}f = 49$
51. $\frac{g}{6} = 32$
52. $\frac{h}{4} = {}^{-}1.8$
53. $2k + 3 = 19$
54. $3m - 1 = {}^{-}4$
55. $\frac{n}{5} + 3 = {}^{-}2$
56. $\frac{p}{2} - 8.2 = 2.1$

Complete each of the following.

57. 82.5 cm = ▒ m

58. 0.67 km = ▒ m

59. 38.5 kg = ▒ g

60. 2,560 g = ▒ kg

61. 4.3 L = ▒ mL

62. 298 mL = ▒ L

Solve.

63. On a map, 1 cm represents 125 km. The map distance between two cities is 2.5 cm. Find the actual distance.

64. A dealer pays Bonnie Gardner $2,000 for her car. The dealer sells the car for $2,400. What is the percent of increase?

65. Ben Jackson buys a microwave oven for $90 more than half of its original price. He pays $329 for the oven. What was its original price?

Mathematics Lab

Mrs. Benitez wants her family to be aware of water usage. She makes a bar graph to compare how much water is used for various jobs. The chart lists the data. Use the following steps to display the data in a *bar graph.*

Job	Water Usage (in liters)
washing dishes	40
tub bath	140
5-minute shower	100
load of laundry	110
water the garden	250

A. *Look at the data.*

1. How many jobs are listed?
2. What is the range of the data (the difference between the greatest and least usage)?

B. *Label the graph.*

3. What is the title of the graph?
4. What is the label on each scale?

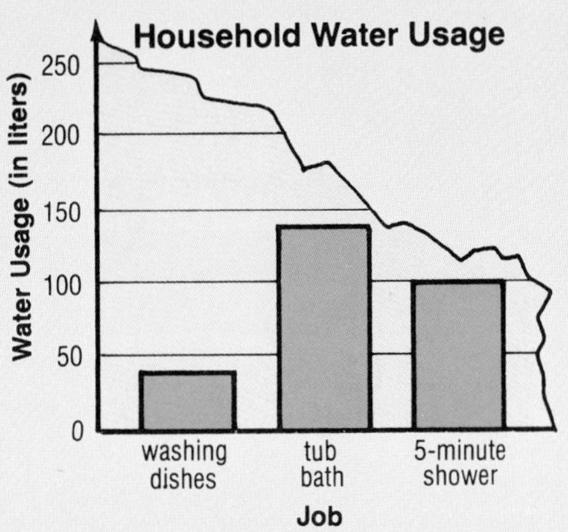

C. *Copy and complete the graph.*

5. How many bars does the completed graph have?
6. Which job takes the greatest amount of water?
7. Which job takes the least amount of water?

10–7 Time

Common units of time are shown in the chart.

1 day (d) = 24 hours (h)
1 hour (h) = 60 minutes (min)
1 minute (min) = 60 seconds (s)

Pat Rockhill fires a ceramic dish in a kiln for 2 hours and 45 minutes. How many minutes is that?

2 h 45 min = ▒ min

There are 60 minutes in an hour. Multiply 2 × 60. Then add 45.

2 × 60 = 120
120 + 45 = 165

2 h 45 min = 165 min

Measurements of time can be added or subtracted.

Add.

$$\begin{array}{r} \textbf{9 h 16 min} \\ \underline{+\ \textbf{15 h 55 min}} \\ \textbf{24 h 71 min} \end{array}$$

Rename 71 min as 1 h and 11 min and add to 24 h.

24 h 71 min = 25 h 11 min

Subtract.

$$\begin{array}{r} \textbf{5 min 26 s} \\ \underline{-\ \textbf{3 min 52 s}} \end{array}$$

Rename 5 min 26 s as 4 min 86 s.

$$\begin{array}{r} \overset{4}{\cancel{5}}\ \textbf{min}\ \overset{86}{\cancel{26}}\ \textbf{s} \\ \underline{-\ \textbf{3 min 52 s}} \\ \textbf{1 min 34 s} \end{array}$$

EXERCISES ***Complete each of the following.***

1. 3 min = ▒ s
2. 300 min = ▒ h
3. 360 s = ▒ min
4. 2 days = ▒ h
5. 3,120 s = ▒ min
6. 72 h = ▒ d
7. 45 min = ▒ h
8. 0.5 h = ▒ min
9. 253 min = ▒ h ▒ min
10. $\frac{1}{3}$ h = ▒ min
11. 3 d = ▒ min
12. 1 h 20 min = ▒ s
13. 45 h = ▒ d ▒ h
14. 5 min 5 s = ▒ s
15. 450 s = ▒ min ▒ s
16. 7 h 18 min = ▒ min
17. 6.25 d = ▒ h
18. 108,000 s = ▒ d

Add or subtract.

19. 1 h 25 min + 3 h 18 min

20. 29 min 16 s + 13 min 45 s

21. 18 h 29 min − 7 h 13 min

22. 17 min 12 s − 8 min 25 s

23. 4 d 10 h + 2 d 19 h

24. 54 min 16 s − 12 min 29 s

25. 14 h − 11 h 35 min

26. 21 h 22 min 54 s + 15 h 45 min 8 s

27. 17 h 6 min 11 s − 8 h 7 min 34 s

Solve.

28. Amy practices the piano 45 minutes each day. How many hours does she practice each week?

29. Juan works 3 h 45 min on Monday. He works twice that long on Tuesday. How long does he work on Tuesday?

30. Devon jogs 45 minutes three times a week. In one year, how many hours does Devon jog?

The time of day may be given in 24-hour notation. The A.M. times are 00:01 to 12:00. The P.M. times are 12:01 to 24:00.

The time 23:15 means 23 hours and 15 minutes after midnight or 11:15 P.M. What is 10:25 A.M. in 24-hour notation?

EXERCISES *Write each of the following in standard notation.*

31. 06:45 **32.** 11:20 **33.** 22:25 **34.** 10:20

35. 15:15 **36.** 23:10 **37.** 12:11 **38.** 18:19

Write each of the following in 24-hour notation.

39. 6:10 A.M. **40.** 4:30 P.M. **41.** 9:45 P.M. **42.** 5:20 A.M.

43. 1:00 A.M. **44.** 2:25 P.M. **45.** 11:42 P.M. **46.** 12:00 midnight

COMPUTER TIME

A human can add 15 four-digit numbers in 30 seconds. A human, working nonstop, could add 800,000,000 four-digit numbers in 51 years. A supercomputer can add 800,000,000 four-digit numbers in 1 second.

10-8 Customary Units

Megan enjoys riding her bicycle cross country. Last summer she rode her bicycle from her home to Atlanta, a distance of 645 miles.

The mile is a unit of length commonly used in the United States. Other customary units of length are inches, feet, and yards.

1 foot (ft)	=	12 inches (in.)
1 yard (yd)	=	3 feet (ft) or 36 inches (in.)
1 mile (mi)	=	5,280 feet (ft)

Megan's bicycle has 27-inch tires. Change 27 inches to feet.

27 in. = ▒ ft

You are changing from a smaller unit to a larger unit. So, DIVIDE.

Since there are 12 inches in 1 foot, divide by 12.

$27 \div 12 = 2\frac{3}{12}$ or $2\frac{1}{4}$

27 in. = $2\frac{1}{4}$ ft

EXERCISES ***Complete each of the following.***

1. 4 ft = ▒ in.
2. 3 yd = ▒ ft
3. 15,840 ft = ▒ mi
4. 18 ft = ▒ yd
5. 2 mi = ▒ ft
6. 3 yd = ▒ in.
7. 24 in. = ▒ ft
8. 48 in. = ▒ yd
9. 10 yd = ▒ ft
10. 10 ft = ▒ in.
11. $10\frac{1}{2}$ ft = ▒ yd
12. 1,760 ft = ▒ mi
13. $1\frac{1}{4}$ yd = ▒ in.
14. 5 mi = ▒ ft
15. 18 in. = ▒ yd
16. 102 in. = ▒ ft
17. $1\frac{1}{2}$ mi = ▒ yd
18. 4,400 yd = ▒ mi

Solve.

19. Megan rides her bicycle to school on sunny days. The distance from her house to school is $\frac{3}{4}$ mile. How many feet is that?

20. A football field is 100 yards long. How many feet is this?

The most weight that Megan carries in her backpack when bicycling is $10\frac{1}{2}$ pounds.

Customary units of weight are ounces, pounds, and tons.

1 pound (lb) = 16 ounces (oz)
1 ton = 2,000 pounds (lb)

Megan always carries a 1-quart canteen of water when bicycling.

In the customary system, liquids are measured using fluid ounces, cups, pints, quarts, and gallons.

1 cup (c) = 8 fluid ounces (oz)
1 pint (pt) = 2 cups (c)
1 quart (qt) = 2 pints (pt)
1 gallon (gal) = 4 quarts (qt)

Change $10\frac{1}{2}$ pounds to ounces. **$10\frac{1}{2}$ lb = ▒ oz**

You are changing from a larger unit to a smaller unit. So, MULTIPLY. **$10\frac{1}{2} \times 16 = 168$**

Since there are 16 ounces in 1 pound, multiply by 16. **$10\frac{1}{2}$ lb = 168 oz**

EXERCISES ***Complete each of the following.***

21. 256 oz = ▒ lb
22. 16 c = ▒ pt
23. 3 qt = ▒ pt
24. 7 tons = ▒ lb
25. 1,500 lb = ▒ ton
26. 28 oz = ▒ c
27. $3\frac{1}{2}$ gal = ▒ qt
28. $20\frac{3}{4}$ lb = ▒ oz
29. 8 oz = ▒ lb
30. 10 pt = ▒ qt
31. 12 c = ▒ oz
32. 40 lb 4 oz = ▒ oz
33. 14,500 lb = ▒ ton
34. 6 qt = ▒ gal
35. 4 pt 1 c = ▒ c
36. $\frac{1}{5}$ ton = ▒ lb
37. 17 c = ▒ pt
38. 1 ton = ▒ oz
39. 3 qt = ▒ c
40. 64 pt = ▒ gal
41. 24 oz = ▒ pt
42. 4 gal = ▒ c
43. 1 qt = ▒ oz
44. 96 oz = ▒ gal

Solve.

45. The maximum weight allowed in an elevator at University Hospital is 1.5 tons. How many pounds is that?

46. The gas tank on a certain lawn mower holds $1\frac{1}{4}$ gallons of gasoline. How many quarts is that?

10-9 Using the Customary System

Marshall's hobby is preparing gourmet foods. One recipe calls for 10 ounces of milk. Marshall triples the recipe. How many cups of milk does he need?

First multiply 10 oz by 3 to find how many ounces of milk are needed.

$$10 \text{ oz} \times 3 = 30 \text{ oz}$$

Then find how many cups are equivalent to 30 oz.

You are changing from a smaller unit to a larger unit. So, DIVIDE.

Since there are 8 ounces in 1 cup, divide by 8.

$30 \text{ oz} = \square \text{ c}$

$30 \div 8 = 3\frac{6}{8} \text{ or } 3\frac{3}{4}$

$30 \text{ oz} = 3\frac{3}{4} \text{ c}$

Marshall needs $3\frac{3}{4}$ cups of milk.

When you add, subtract, multiply, or divide measurements you may need to rename the measurements. Study the following examples.

$$\begin{array}{r} 5 \text{ ft } 8 \text{ in.} \\ +\ 2 \text{ ft } 6 \text{ in.} \\ \hline 7 \text{ ft } 14 \text{ in.} \end{array}$$

Add the units separately.

Rename the sum.

$7 \text{ ft } 14 \text{ in.} = 8 \text{ ft } 2 \text{ in.}$

$$\begin{array}{r} 6 \text{ gal } 1 \text{ qt} \\ -\ 3 \text{ gal } 3 \text{ qt} \\ \hline \end{array}$$

Rename

$$\begin{array}{r} \overset{5}{\cancel{6}} \text{ gal } \overset{5}{\cancel{1}} \text{ qt} \\ -\ 3 \text{ gal } 3 \text{ qt} \\ \hline 2 \text{ gal } 2 \text{ qt} \end{array}$$

$$\begin{array}{r} 3 \text{ lb} \quad 6 \text{ oz} \\ \times \qquad\quad 5 \\ \hline 15 \text{ lb } 30 \text{ oz} \end{array}$$

Multiply the units separately.

Rename the product.

$15 \text{ lb } 30 \text{ oz} = 16 \text{ lb } 14 \text{ oz}$

$2\overline{)3 \text{ yd } 1 \text{ ft}}$ — Rename → $\begin{array}{r} 1 \text{ yd } 2 \text{ ft} \\ 2\overline{)2 \text{ yd } 4 \text{ ft}} \end{array}$

EXERCISES ***Add, subtract, multiply, or divide.***

1.
```
  6 lb 12 oz
+ 4 lb  8 oz
```

2.
```
  2 gal 3 qt
+ 4 gal 1 qt
```

3.
```
  3 ft  8 in.
  2 ft  7 in.
+ 9 ft 10 in.
```

4.
```
  9 ft 4 in.
- 3 ft 7 in.
```

5.
```
  5 gal 3 qt
- 2 gal 2 qt
```

6.
```
  7 lb  8 oz
- 3 lb 13 oz
```

7.
```
  3 c 7 oz
×      5
```

8.
```
  3 yd 1 ft
×        9
```

9.
```
  9 lb 6 oz
×       4
```

10. $5\overline{)2 \text{ tons } 400 \text{ lb}}$

11. $4\overline{)13 \text{ ft } 8 \text{ in.}}$

12. $3\overline{)16 \text{ qt } 1 \text{ pt}}$

Solve.

13. Marcos buys 3.5 lb of ground beef for $4.48. What is the cost of the ground beef per ounce?

14. A pitcher holds 2 quarts of juice. Tina fills 8 glasses. How many ounces does each glass hold?

15. Marjorie is 5 ft 4 in. tall. Eric is 4 ft $10\frac{1}{2}$ in. tall. How much taller is Marjorie than Eric?

16. The Burchs' dog had three puppies. One weighed 1 lb 8 oz, another 1 lb 12 oz, and the other 1 lb 1 oz. What was the average weight of the puppies?

17. A 1-lb loaf of bread costs 34¢. A 20-oz loaf of bread costs 39¢. Which size loaf costs less per ounce?

BOXES OF CEREAL

Nineteen boxes of cereal are packaged each minute. If each box contains 10 ounces of cereal, how many pounds are packaged in eight hours?

Focus on Problem Solving

10-10 Working Backwards

Ron decides to give away some of his model cars. He gives one-fourth of his cars to Andy. Then he gives one-half of the remaining cars to Guido. If he is left with 9 cars, how many cars did he have in the beginning?

Read the problem. You need to find how many cars Ron started with. You know the end result and how Ron gave the cars away.

Decide what to do. The end result is 9. Work backwards step by step to find how many cars he had in the beginning.

Solve the problem. Ron ends up with 9 cars. This is one-half of the remaining cars since he gave the other half to Guido. So before this he had 9×2 or 18 cars left. This is three-fourths of the cars he had in the beginning since he gave one-fourth to Andy. Set up a proportion. Let c represent the number of cars he had in the beginning.

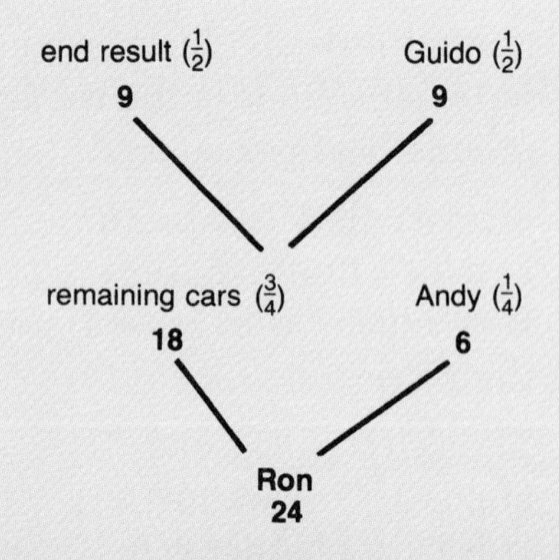

$$\frac{3}{4} = \frac{18}{c}$$

$$3 \times c = 4 \times 18$$

$$3c = 72$$

$$c = 24$$

Ron had 24 cars in the beginning.

Examine the solution. Start with 24 cars. Ron gives one-fourth of them, or 6, to Andy. There are 18 cars left. He gives one-half of these, or 9, to Guido. He is left with 9 cars.

Solve. Use the "working backwards" strategy.

1. Sol divides his coins equally among Mary, Doug, and Nathan. Mary shares her coins equally with five other people, who each receive 3 coins. How many coins does Sol have in the beginning?
2. Ned has a beaker filled with water. He uses half the water and gives half of the remaining amount to Jovita for her experiment. He has 225 mL left in the beaker. How much water was in the beaker originally?
3. Sue tries to sell an item at a garage sale. She reduces the price 25%. It does not sell, so she reduces the last price 50%. She finally sells the item for half of the last price, or 75¢. What was the original price of the item?

Solve. Use any strategy.

4. The sum of two numbers is 48. The first number is 3 times the second number. What are the numbers?
5. San-Wu works 3 h 15 min one day, 4 h 20 min the next day, and 3 h 30 min the third day. He earns $4.25 per hour. What does he earn for the three days?
6. A restaurant sold two million hamburgers, each 2 cm thick. If these hamburgers were stacked, how many kilometers high would the stack be?

Skills Review: Pages 266-273

Complete each of the following.

1. 225 min = ▒ h
2. 3.5 days = ▒ h
3. 3 yd 2 ft = ▒ ft
4. 11,880 ft = ▒ mi
5. 72 oz = ▒ lb
6. 5 c = ▒ oz

Add, subtract, multiply, or divide.

7. 3 gal 3 qt + 2 gal 3 qt
8. 9 h 6 min − 3 h 41 min
9. 3 ft 9 in. × 3
10. 3)7 lb 2 oz

Solve.

11. Half of the students in a class are boys. Four boys have blond hair. One-fourth of the boys have blond hair. How many students are in the class?

Mathematics and Computers

The **universal product code (UPC)** is a code of black and white bars that is printed on most products in a grocery store. It identifies the product and the manufacturer. This code is the key to computerized checkout systems.

A scanning device reads the UPC as an item passes over it. The code is sent to a computer. The computer reads the product code, finds the price of the product, and sends this data to the cash register. The cash register then displays the product name and price and prints a customer receipt.

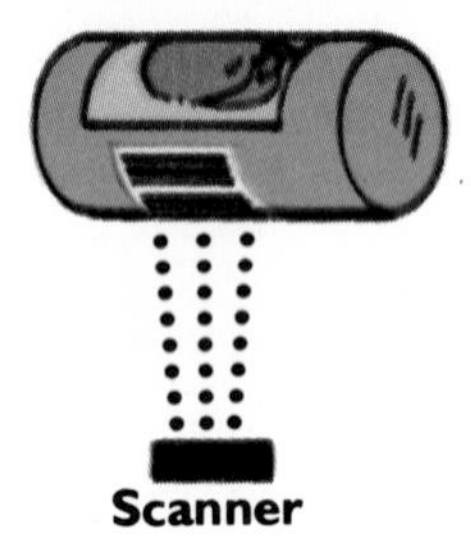

STORE #41	10/14/82
FLOUR	.49F
16 TEA BAGS	.67F
GROCRY	.85F
GREEN OLIVES	.55F
SAND SPREAD	.79F
2/.79	
GREEN BEANS	.40F
PROD	.25F
MARGARINE	79F
MEAT	3.47F
DELI	2.47F
PUDDING	.30F
DETERGENT	2.75T
SOFT DRINK	.99T
2/.79	
GREEN BEANS	.39F
CHILI SAUCE	.89F
TAX	.21
TOTAL	16.26

***EXERCISES* Answer each of the following. Use the customer receipt.**

1. What is the price of the pudding?
2. How many items are taxed?
3. What is the total cost of the cans of green beans?
4. Why does the receipt show two different prices for the green beans?
5. What information is found on the customer receipt other than product and price?
6. How can a computerized checkout system be used to control a store's inventory?

Chapter 10 Review

VOCABULARY meter (253) precision (258) error of measurement (259) greatest possible error (259) gram (260) liter (260)

EXERCISES ***With a ruler, measure the length of each line segment below. Give your answer in both centimeters and millimeters. (254-255)***

1. A———B **2.** C———D

Name the more precise measurement in each of the following. (258)

3. 7 m, 680 cm **4.** 460 m, 0.5 km **5.** 243 mm, 24 cm

Complete each of the following. (256-257, 260-261, 266-269)

6. 3 m = ▒ cm **7.** 5.4 km = ▒ m **8.** 1,400 mm = ▒ cm

9. 14,200 m = ▒ km **10.** 11 cm = ▒ mm **11.** 3,200 cm = ▒ m

12. 760 mg = ▒ g **13.** 6,000 g = ▒ kg **14.** 4 kg = ▒ g

15. 7.8 g = ▒ mg **16.** 43 mg = ▒ g **17.** 290 L = ▒ kL

18. 2 L = ▒ mL **19.** 3,000 mL = ▒ L **20.** 2.7 kL = ▒ L

21. 240 s = ▒ min **22.** 4.1 h = ▒ min **23.** $2\frac{1}{2}$ days = ▒ h

24. 4 yd = ▒ ft **25.** 7 ft = ▒ in. **26.** 8 lb 1 oz = ▒ oz

27. 4,500 lb = ▒ tons **28.** 10 qt = ▒ gal **29.** 3 pt = ▒ oz

Add, subtract, multiply, or divide. (266-271)

30. 4 h 30 min − 2 h 45 min

31. 11 min 19 s × 4

32. 4 ft 3 in. + 2 ft 11 in.

33. 8 yd 1 ft − 2 yd 2 ft

34. 6 lb 3 oz × 5

35. $3\overline{)13 \text{ c } 4 \text{ oz}}$

Solve. (262-263, 272-273)

36. A city block is 225 m long on each side. Eduardo jogs around the block four times. How many kilometers does he jog?

37. Grace's average score on three tests is 87. Her scores on two tests are 81 and 85. What is her score on the other test?

Chapter 10 Test

Find the length of each line segment shown below. Give each answer in centimeters and then in millimeters.

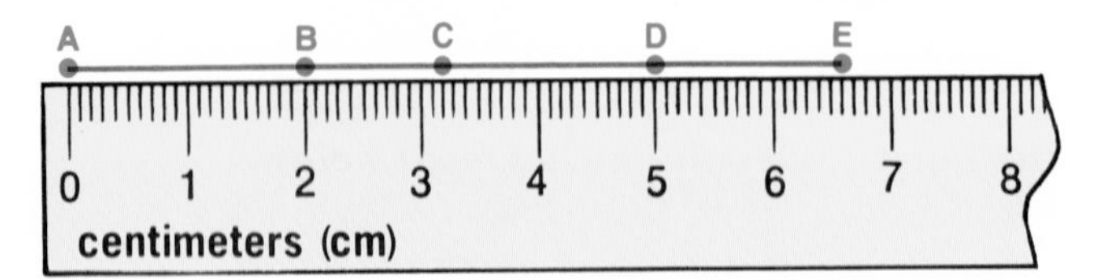

1. $\overline{AB}$ **2.** $\overline{AC}$

3. $\overline{AD}$ **4.** $\overline{AE}$

5. $\overline{BD}$ **6.** $\overline{DE}$

Name the more precise measurement in each of the following.

7. 1,435 m, 1.4 km **8.** 4 cm, 39 mm **9.** 2.9 m, 2,955 mm

Complete each of the following.

10. 2 m = ▒ cm **11.** 400 mm = ▒ cm **12.** 4.2 cm = ▒ mm

13. 4,120 m = ▒ km **14.** 310 cm = ▒ m **15.** 1,910 km = ▒ m

16. 2,180 g = ▒ kg **17.** 2.37 kg = ▒ g **18.** 0.8 g = ▒ mg

19. 500 mg = ▒ g **20.** 80 g = ▒ kg **21.** 3 L = ▒ kL

22. 9,050 mL = ▒ L **23.** 1.4 kL = ▒ L **24.** 8.5 L = ▒ mL

25. 9 h = ▒ min **26.** 3 min 20 s = ▒ s **27.** 558 min = ▒ h

28. 3 in. = ▒ ft **29.** 195 ft = ▒ yd **30.** 9.7 tons = ▒ lb

31. 0.75 lb = ▒ oz **32.** 3.2 gal = ▒ qt **33.** 5 pt = ▒ qt

Add, subtract, multiply, or divide.

34. 7 h 30 min + 10 h 45 min

35. 5 h 12 min × 8

36. 9 yd 6 ft − 5 yd 8 ft

37. 7 ft 3 in. + 2 ft 8 in.

38. 7 gal 2 qt × 3

39. $2\overline{)9 \text{ lb } 4 \text{ oz}}$

Solve.

40. Arlene buys 2 kg of clay. She uses 850 g. What is the mass of the remaining clay in grams?

41. A ship travels 16.8 miles in 2 hours. How many feet does it travel in 15 minutes?

42. Alex buys margarine for \$0.89 and two cans of tomato sauce for \$0.95 each. He receives change of \$2.21. How much money did he give the cashier?

Enrichment

All measurements are approximate. The accuracy of a measurement depends on the **relative error of measurement.** Relative error is the ratio of the greatest possible error to the measured length.

The smaller the relative error, the greater the accuracy.

Elena measures two photographs for an album. The measurement of one is 8 cm. The measurement of the other is 20 cm. Which measurement is more accurate?

The greatest possible error of each measurement is 0.5 cm. Why?

Find the relative error of 8 cm.

$$\frac{\text{greatest possible error}}{\text{measured length}} \rightarrow \frac{0.5}{8}$$

$$= 0.0625$$

Find the relative error of 20 cm.

$$\frac{\text{greatest possible error}}{\text{measured length}} \rightarrow \frac{0.5}{20}$$

$$= 0.025$$

The 20 cm measurement is more accurate since its relative error is less.

The **percent of error** is the relative error expressed as a percent. The percent of error of the 8-cm measurement is 6.25%. What is the percent of error of the 20-cm measurement?

EXERCISES ***Find the relative error, expressed as a ratio, for each of the following.***

1. 35 cm **2.** 21 mm **3.** 16 m **4.** 4 cm **5.** 148 m

Find the percent of error, to the nearest tenth, for each of the following.

6. 16 cm **7.** 9 km **8.** 3 mm **9.** 44 cm **10.** 680 m

Find which measurement is more accurate in each pair.

11. 7 m, 4 m **12.** 146 cm, 38 cm **13.** 40 mm, 12 cm

11 Perimeter, Area, and Volume

Dwight Bixel wants to put a new fence around a pasture. To determine how much fencing to buy, he needs to know the perimeter of the pasture.

11-1 Perimeter

The **perimeter** of any polygon is the distance around the polygon. It is found by adding the measures of the sides.

The diagram of Mr. Bixel's pasture is shown at the right.

330 + 330 + 460 + 460 = 1,580

The perimeter of the pasture is 1,580 meters.

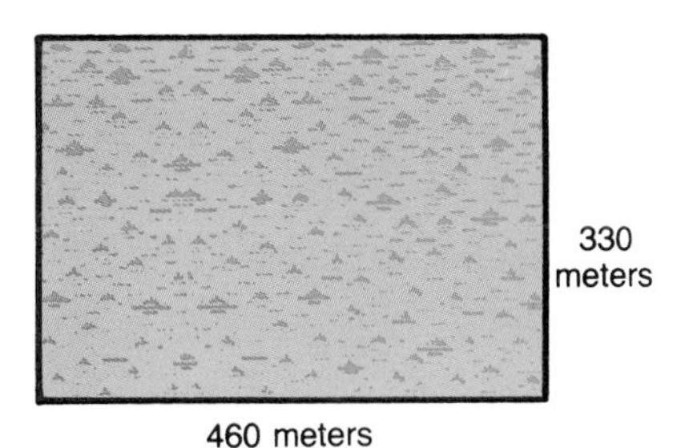

EXERCISES ***Find the perimeter of each of the following polygons.***

1.

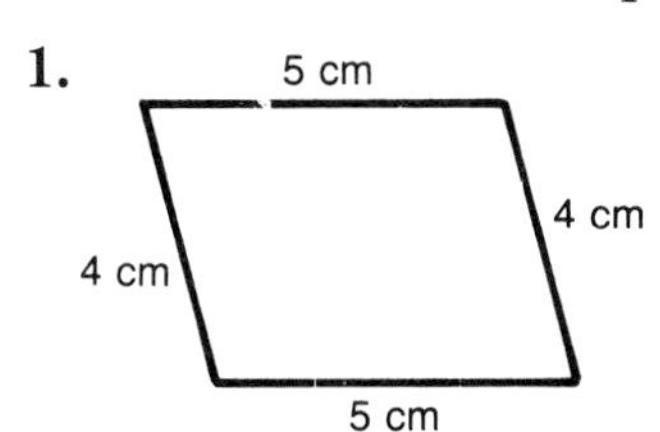

2.

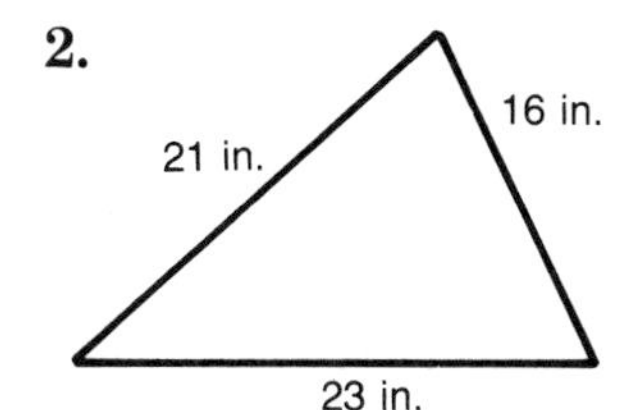

3.

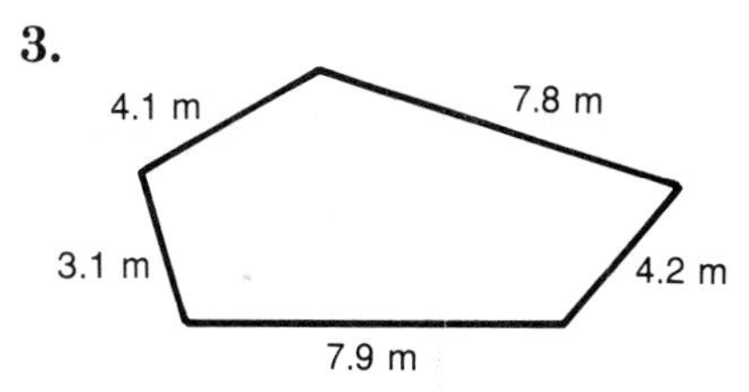

Find the perimeter of each rectangle described below. Remember, add the length twice and the width twice to find the perimeter.

4. length, 17 cm; width, 8 cm

5. length, 4 ft; width, 2.5 ft

6. length, 50.6 in.; width, 8.5 in.

7. length, 0.3 km; width, 0.29 km

Find the perimeter of each of the following regular polygons.

8.

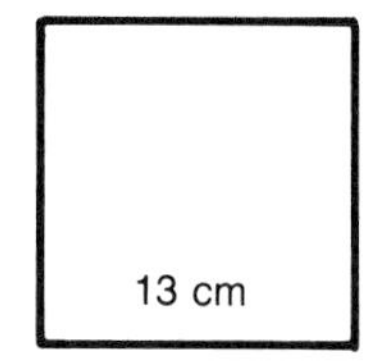

9.

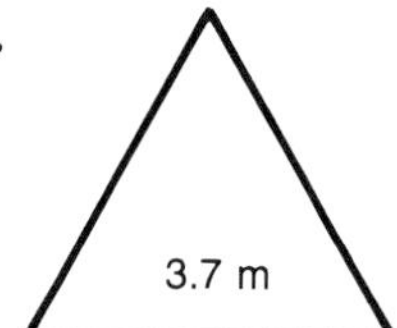

10.

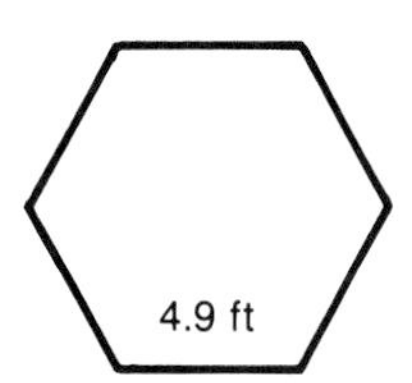

11. square; side 24 cm

12. pentagon; side, 10.1 in.

11-2 Area of Rectangles and Parallelograms

Nearly one-half of the surface of the United States is covered with farmland.

Area is the number of square units that cover a surface.

One common unit of area is the square centimeter.

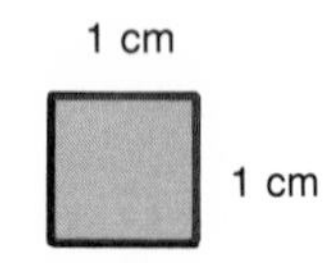

1 square centimeter (cm^2)

What is the area of this rectangle?

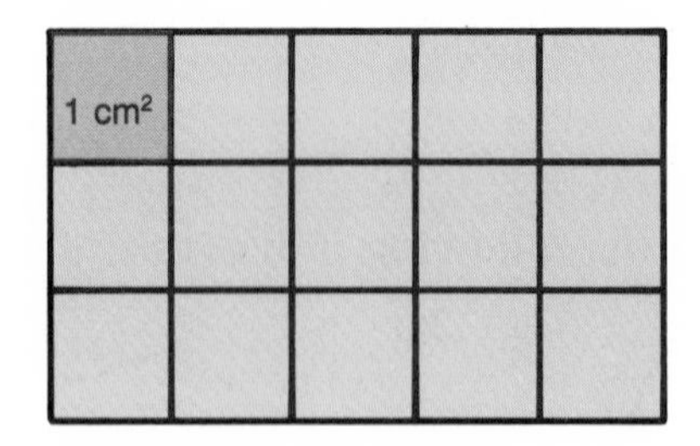

The area (A) of any rectangle can be found by multiplying the measures of the length (l) and the width (w).

$$\mathbf{A = l \times w}$$

$$\mathbf{A = 5 \times 3}$$

$$\mathbf{A = 15}$$

The area of the rectangle is 15 cm^2.

The area of a parallelogram can be found by using the area of a rectangle.

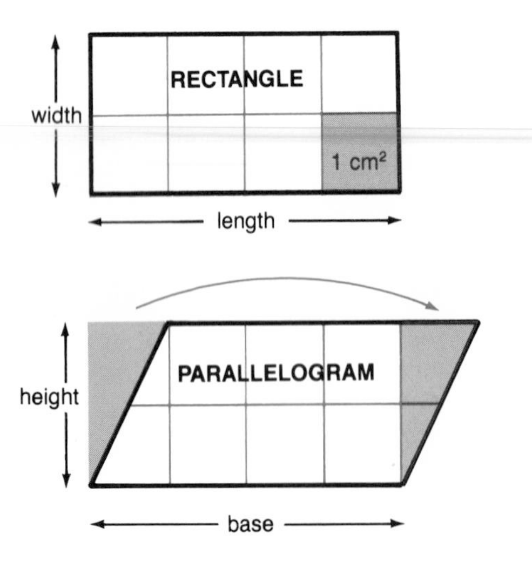

You can change the rectangle into a parallelogram by moving the triangle as shown at the left.

What is the area of the rectangle? What is the area of the parallelogram?

The area of any parallelogram can be found by multiplying the measures of the base (b) and the height (h).

$$\mathbf{A = b \times h}$$

EXERCISES ***Find the area of each rectangle described below.***

1.

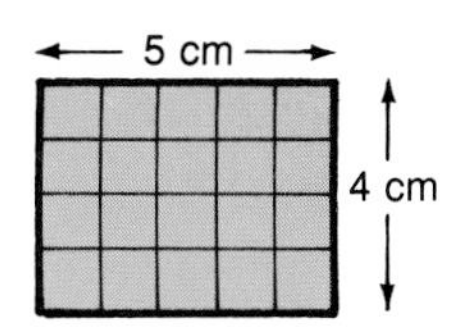

2.

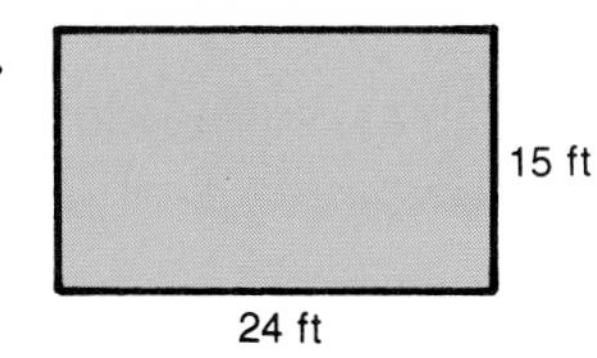

3.

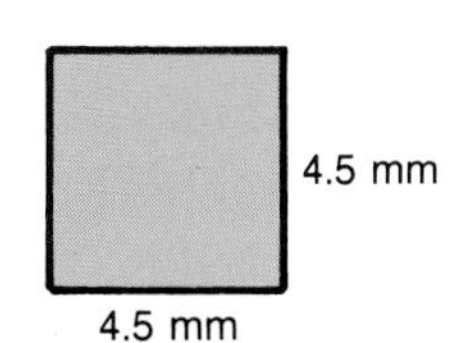

4. length, 15 m; width, 11 m

5. length, 39 in.; width 39 in.

6. length, 70 yd; width, 60.5 yd

7. length, 7.6 cm; width, 5.9 cm

8. length, 2.8 cm; width, 2.8 cm

9. length, 38.3 ft; width, 18.4 ft

Find the area of each parallelogram described below.

10.

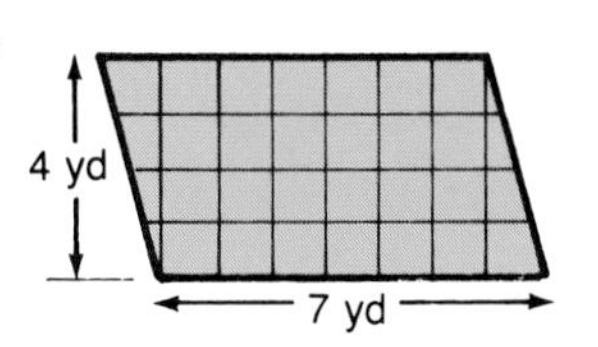

11.

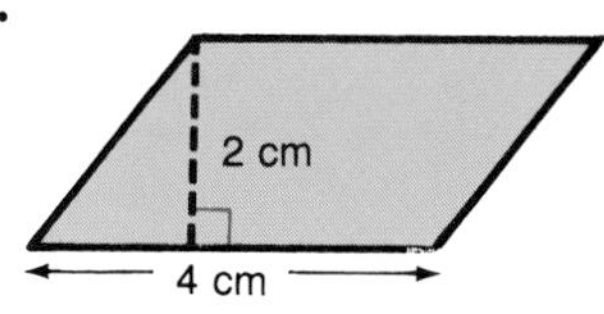

12.

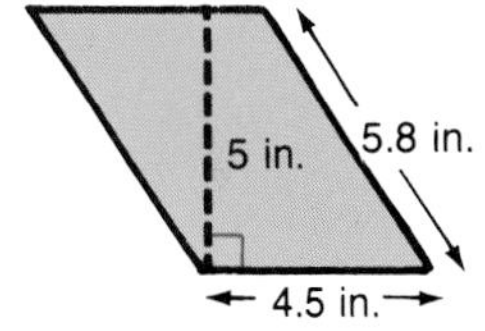

13. base, 12 cm; height, 4 cm

14. base, 3 ft; height, 4.5 ft

15. base, 10 mm; height, 15.5 mm

16. base, 9 m; height, 6.3 m

17. base, 1.5 yd; height, 3.7 yd

18. base, 10.1 in.; height, 9.6 in.

Solve.

19. The floor of Bob Cooper's barn is a rectangle 85 feet by 150 feet. Find the area of the floor.

20. The area of a rectangular field is 414,200 square feet. The length of the field is 760 feet. What is the width?

CONVERTING METRIC UNITS OF AREA

Change 18,400 square centimeters to square meters.

100 cm = 1 m	**18,400 cm^2 = ▒ m^2**
(100 cm)^2 = (1 m)^2	**18,400 ÷ 10,000 = 1.8400**
10,000 cm^2 = 1 m^2	**18,400 cm^2 = 1.84 m^2**

Move the decimal point 4 places to the left. Why?

Complete each of the following.

1. 240,000 cm^2 = ▒ m^2

2. 2.8 m^2 = ▒ cm^2

3. 500 mm^2 = ▒ cm^2

11-3 Area of Triangles and Trapezoids

Marnita paints the gables of her barn. She needs to know the area of the gables before buying the paint. Each gable of the barn is a triangle.

Two congruent triangles form a parallelogram. The area of each triangle is one-half the area of the parallelogram.

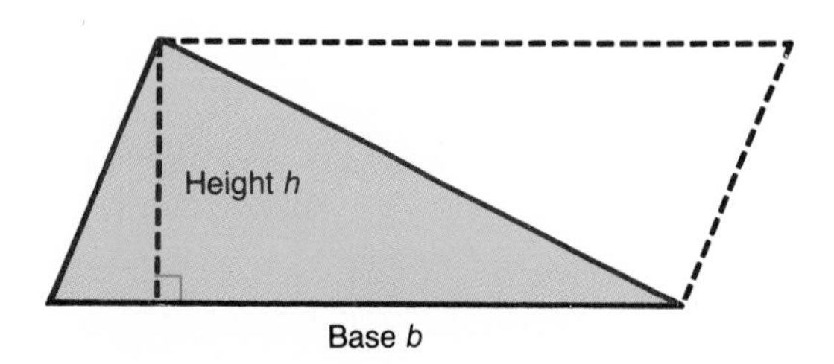

area of parallelogram: $\mathbf{b} \times \mathbf{h}$

area of triangle: $\frac{1}{2} \times \mathbf{b} \times \mathbf{h}$

The area of a triangle is equal to one-half times the measure of the base times the measure of the height.

$$\mathbf{A} = \frac{1}{2} \times \mathbf{b} \times \mathbf{h}$$

Find the area of this triangle.

$\mathbf{A} = \frac{1}{2} \times \mathbf{b} \times \mathbf{h}$

$\mathbf{A} = \frac{1}{2} \times \mathbf{3} \times \mathbf{7}$

$\mathbf{A} = \mathbf{1.5} \times \mathbf{7}$

$\mathbf{A} = \mathbf{10.5}$

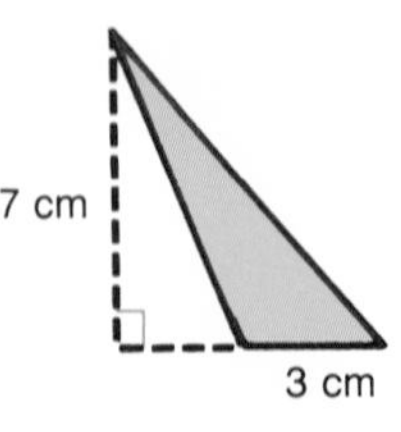

The area is 10.5 cm^2.

Two congruent trapezoids form a parallelogram. The area of each trapezoid is one-half the area of the parallelogram.

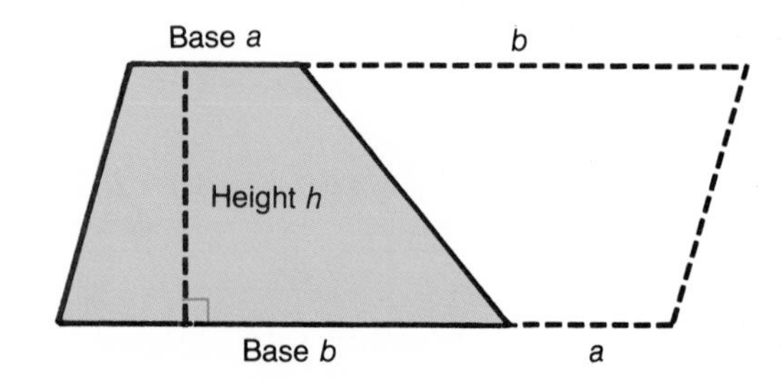

base of parallelogram: $\mathbf{a} + \mathbf{b}$

area of parallelogram: $(\mathbf{a} + \mathbf{b}) \times \mathbf{h}$

area of trapezoid: $\frac{1}{2} \times (\mathbf{a} + \mathbf{b}) \times \mathbf{h}$

The area of a trapezoid is equal to one-half times the measure of the height times the sum of the measures of the bases.

$$\mathbf{A} = \frac{1}{2} \times \mathbf{h} \times (\mathbf{a} + \mathbf{b})$$

Find the area of this trapezoid.

$\mathbf{A} = \frac{1}{2} \times \mathbf{h} \times (\mathbf{a} + \mathbf{b})$

$\mathbf{A} = \frac{1}{2} \times \mathbf{8} \times (\mathbf{10} + \mathbf{15})$

$\mathbf{A} = \mathbf{4} \times \mathbf{25}$

$\mathbf{A} = \mathbf{100}$

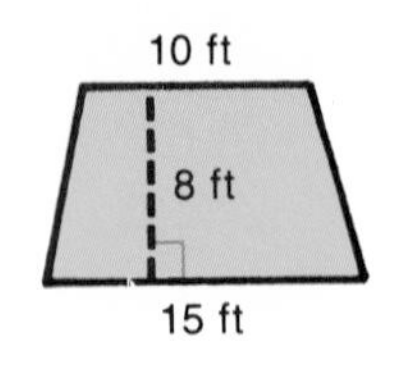

The area is 100 ft^2.

EXERCISES ***Find the area of each triangle described below.***

1. 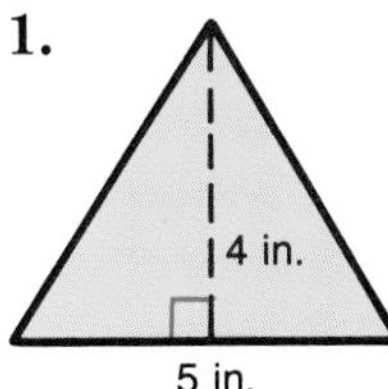

2. 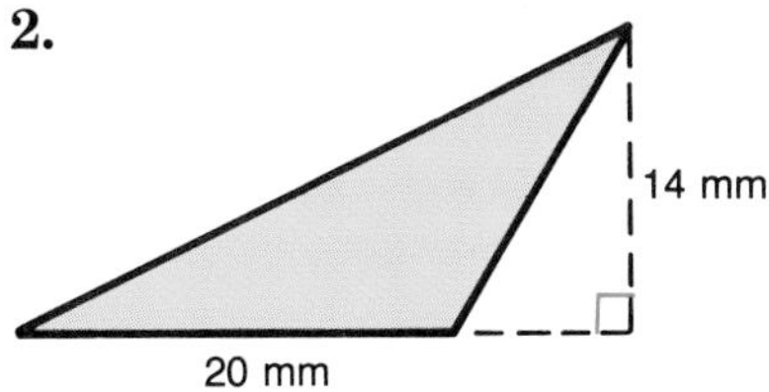

3. 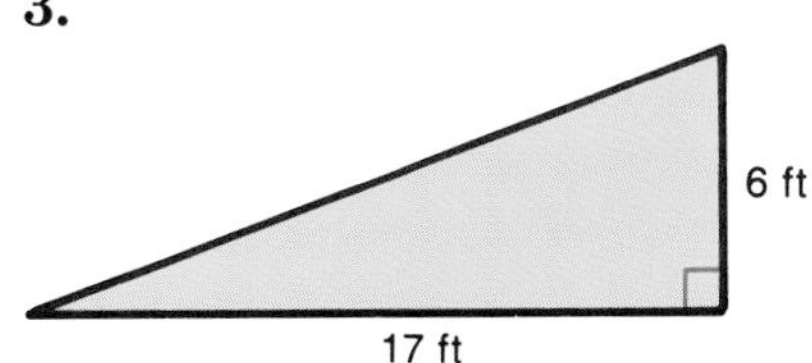

4. base, 23 m; height, 14 m
5. base, 15 in.; height, 8 in.
6. base, 7.4 cm; height, 6 cm
7. base, 23.5 yd; height, 8 yd
8. base, $2\frac{1}{2}$ ft; height, $1\frac{1}{4}$ ft
9. base, 2 m; height, 0.95 m

Find the area of each trapezoid described below.

10. 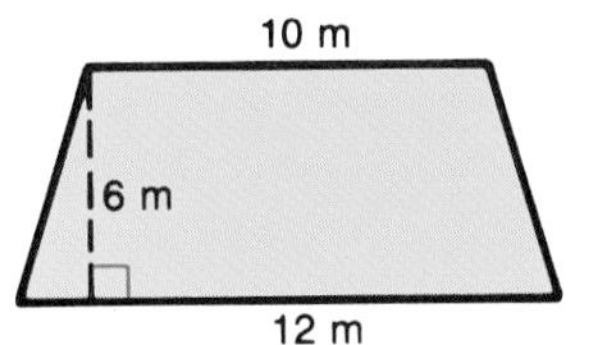

11. 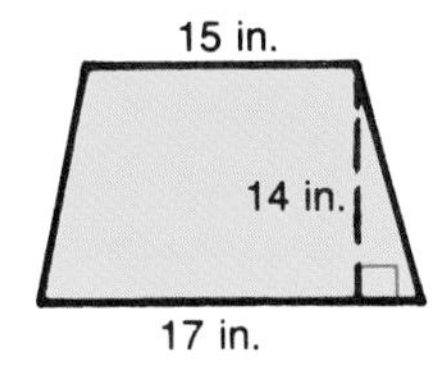

12. 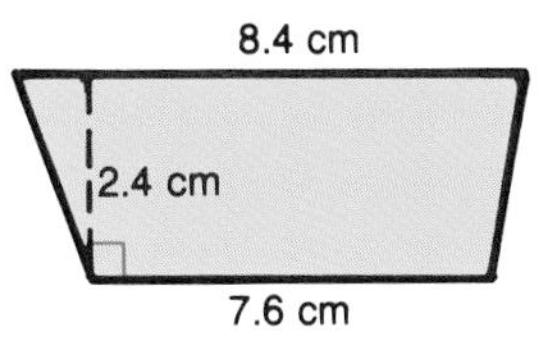

13. base (a), 8 ft; base (b), 16 ft; height, 10 ft
14. base (a), 29 cm; base (b), 51 cm; height, 17 cm
15. base (a), 6 m; base (b), 5.2 m; height, 7.4 m
16. base (a), 36 in.; base (b), 25 in.; height, 9.5 in.

Find the area of each figure shown below.

17. 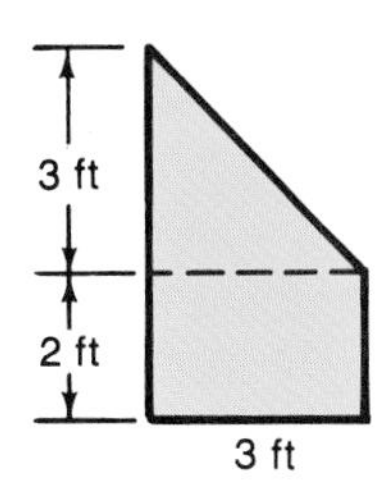

18. 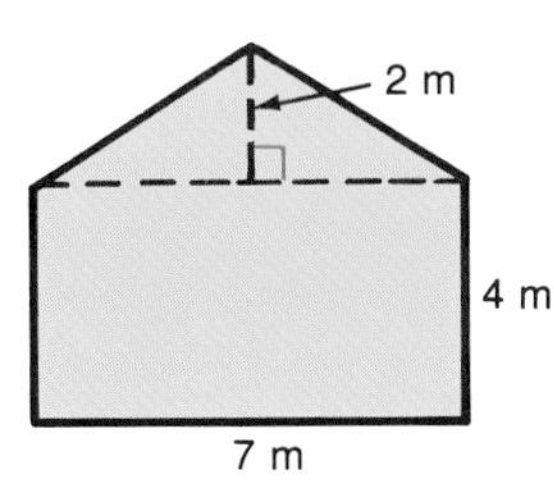

19. 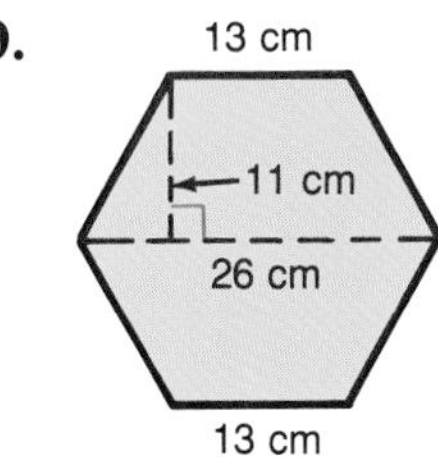

Solve.

20. The area of a triangular sign on a tractor is 143 square inches. The base is 13 inches. What is the height?

21. One side of a shed is shaped like a trapezoid. Its area is 11.16 m^2. The base lengths are 4 m and 3.2 m. What is the height?

11-4 Circumference and Area of Circles

The distance around a circle is its **circumference.** Suppose a tractor tire makes one complete turn. The distance it travels is the same as the circumference of the tire.

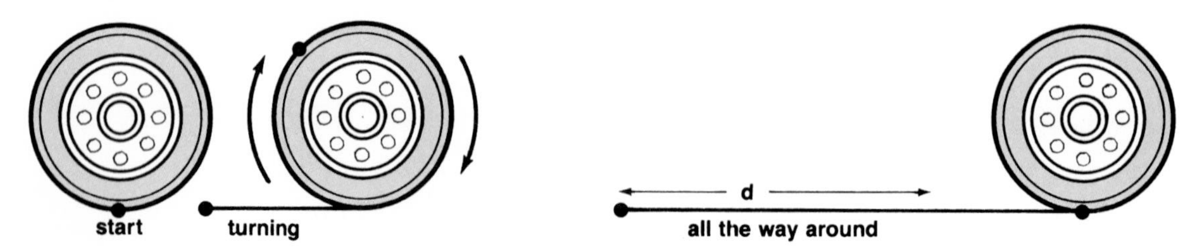

The ratio of the measure of the circumference (C) of a circle to the measure of its diameter (d) is the same for all circles. The Greek letter π (pi) stands for this ratio. An approximation for π is 3.14.

$$\frac{C}{d} = \pi \quad \Rightarrow \quad C = \pi d$$

How is the second formula obtained?

The circumference of a circle is equal to π times the diameter.

The diameter (d) of a circle is twice the length of the radius (r).

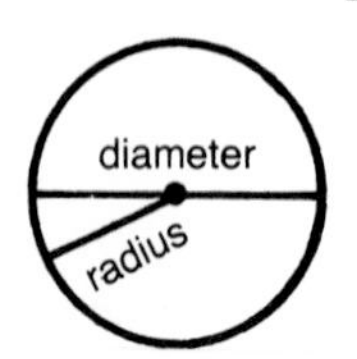

Since $d = 2r$, another formula for circumference is $\mathbf{C = 2\pi r}$.

Each circular disc on a harrow has a diameter of 25 cm. What is the circumference of each disc? Use 3.14 for π.

$C = \pi d$

$C \approx 3.14 \times 25$ $\approx$ means *is approximately equal to.*

$C \approx 78.5$ The circumference is about 78.5 cm.

EXERCISES ***Find the circumference of each circle described below. Use 3.14 for π.***

1.

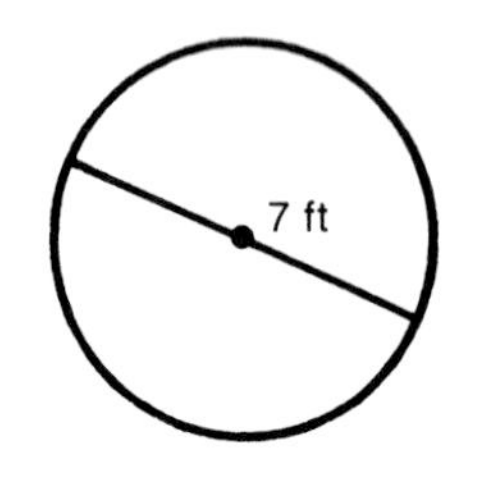

2.

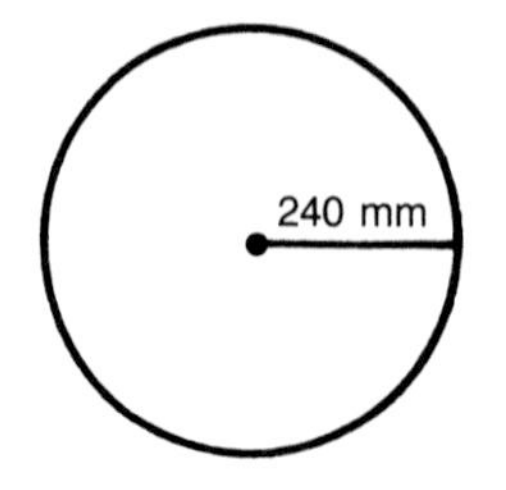

3. diameter, 86 km

4. radius, 4.2 ft

5. radius, 6.7 in.

6. diameter, 35.1 cm

7. radius, 87.5 mm

Suppose you want to find the area of a circle. You can separate a circle into parts and make a figure that looks like a parallelogram. The circle has the same area as that figure.

$\mathbf{A = b \times h}$	area of a parallelogram
$\mathbf{A = (\frac{1}{2} \times C) \times r}$	Why?
$\mathbf{A = \frac{1}{2} \times (2\pi r) \times r}$	Remember, $C = 2\pi r$.
$\mathbf{A = \pi \times r \times r}$	How is this obtained?
$\mathbf{A = \pi r^2}$	area of a circle

Find the area of a circle with a radius 14 feet long. Use 3.14 for π.

$\mathbf{A = \pi r^2}$

$\mathbf{A \approx 3.14 \times 14 \times 14}$

$\mathbf{A \approx 615.44}$ The area is about 615.44 square feet.

EXERCISES ***Find the area of each circle described below. Use 3.14 for π.***

8.

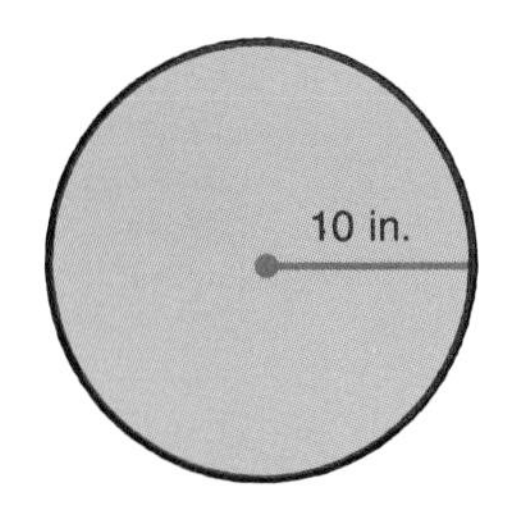

9.

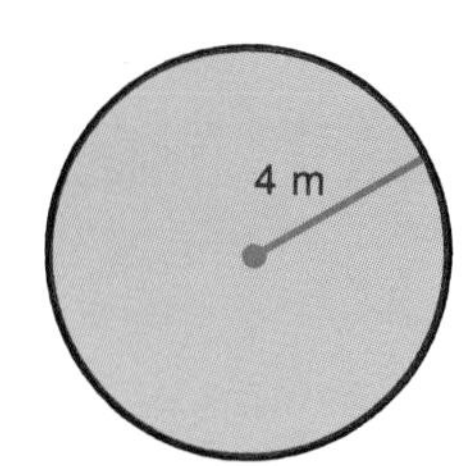

10. radius, 56 ft

11. radius, 6.1 cm

12. diameter, 62 in.

13. diameter, 83 yd

14. diameter, 10.3 mm

Solve. Use 3.14 for π.

15. The circular floor of a corncrib has a radius of 3.2 meters. Find the circumference.

16. The base of a storage silo is shaped like a circle. The radius is 26 feet. Find the area.

CALCULATOR π

Some calculators have a key labeled π. If not, the fraction $\frac{355}{113}$ provides a close approximation for π. An easy way to remember this fraction is to write 113355 and divide as shown: $113\overline{)355}$.

11-5 Surface Area of Prisms and Pyramids

The bin on a machine that picks cotton is a rectangular prism. A rectangular prism is an example of a solid. A solid encloses part of space. A solid with flat surfaces (faces) is a **polyhedron.**

A **prism** is a polyhedron with two parallel congruent bases that are shaped like polygons. The faces of a prism are shaped like parallelograms. A prism is named by the shape of its bases.

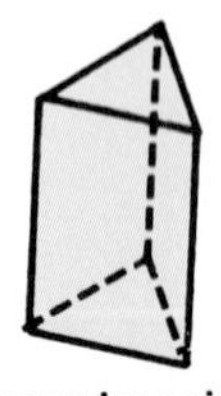

triangular prism

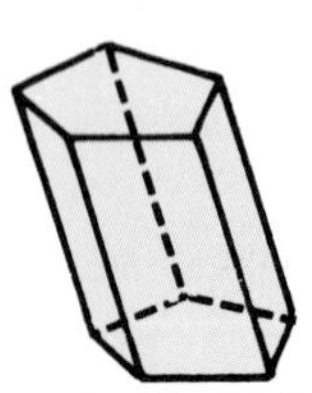

pentagonal prism

A **pyramid** is a polyhedron with one base that is shaped like a polygon. The faces of a pyramid are triangular. A pyramid is named by the shape of its base.

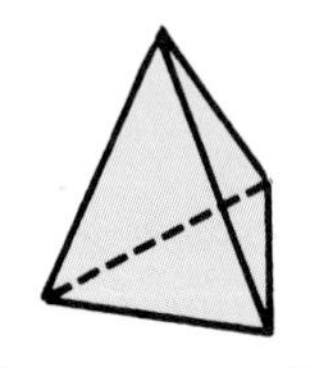

triangular pyramid

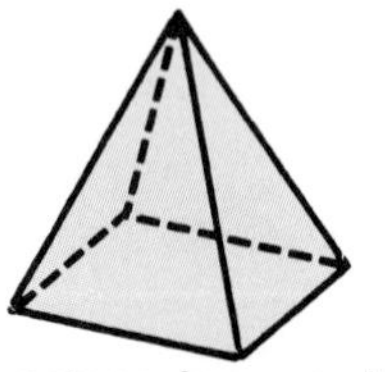

rectangular pyramid

The **surface area** (**S**) of a polyhedron is the sum of the areas of all the faces. What is the surface area of the rectangular prism shown below?

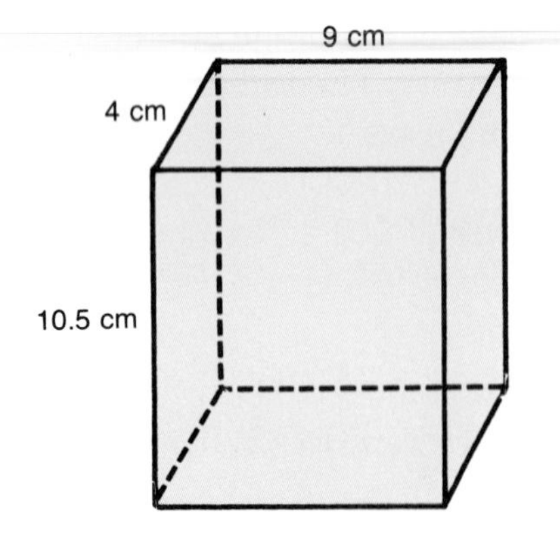

front	**9 × 10.5**	**94.5**
back	**9 × 10.5**	**94.5**
top	**4 × 9**	**36**
bottom	**4 × 9**	**36**
sides	**4 × 10.5**	**42**
	4 × 10.5	**+ 42**
		S = 345

The surface area is 345 cm^2.

EXERCISES ***Find the surface area of each polyhedron.***

1.

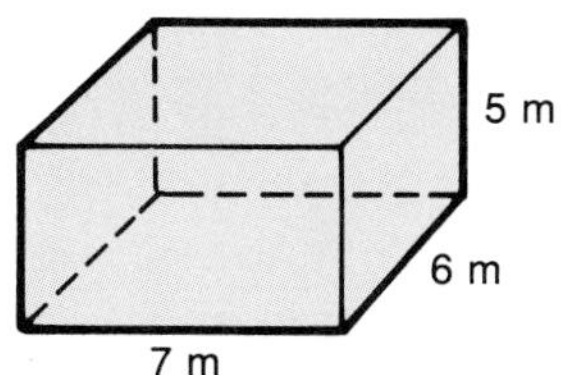

2.

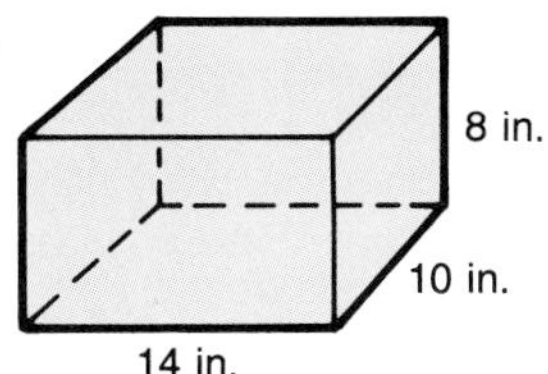

3.

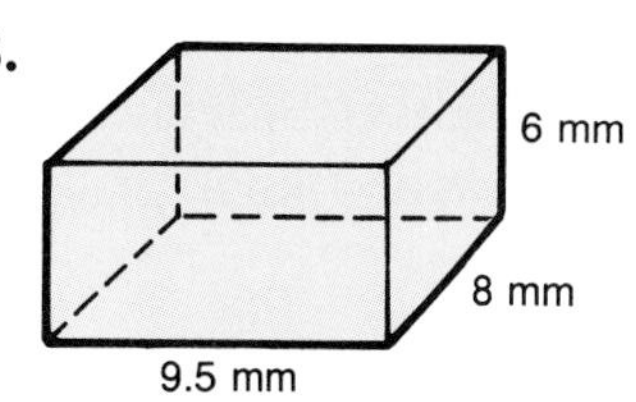

4.

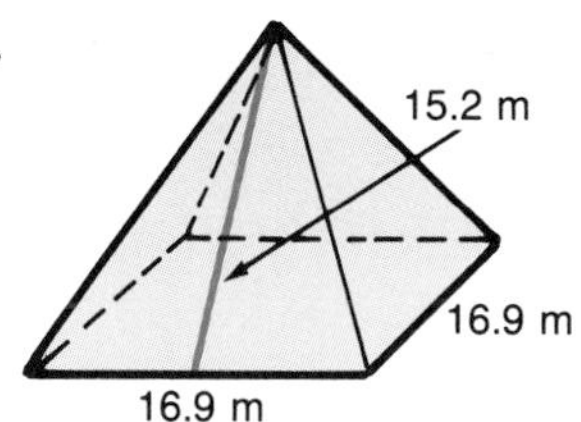

5.

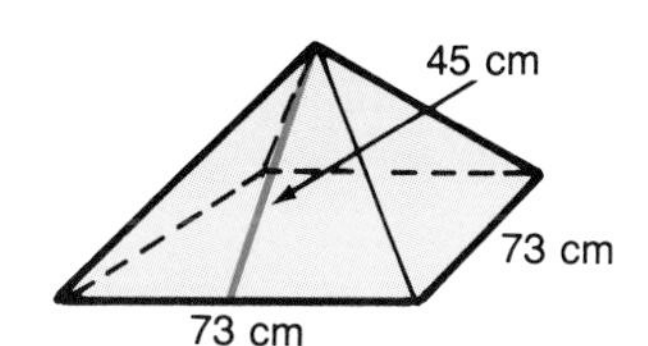

6.

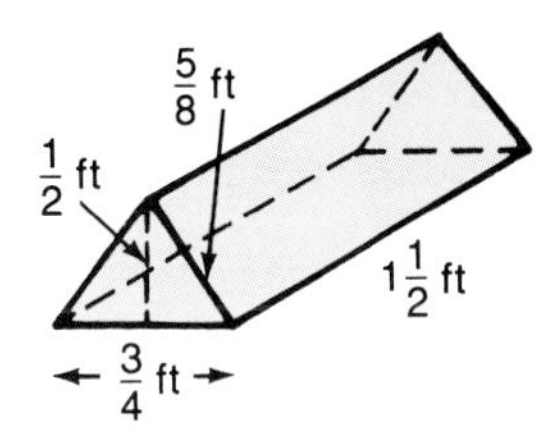

Solve.

7. A fruit crate is 30 cm wide by 60 cm long by 40 cm deep. Find its surface area.

8. The paint in a tube will cover 24 square inches. How many tubes are needed to paint a cube 4 inches on each edge?

Make a sketch of each of the following.

9. hexagonal prism

10. octagonal prism

11. Copy and complete the table.

Polyhedron	Number of Faces (F)	Number of Vertices (V)	Number of Edges (E)
Triangular Prism	5	6	9
Rectangular Prism		8	12
Pentagonal Prism			15
Hexagonal Prism			
Octagonal Prism			

12. What is the sum of F and V for a triangular prism? How does this compare to E?

13. What is the sum of F and V for a pentagonal prism? How does this compare to E?

14. A polyhedron has 14 faces and 24 vertices. How many edges does it have?

15. Write a formula to show the relationship between the number of faces, vertices, and edges that a polyhedron has.

11-6 Surface Area of Cylinders and Cones

Rex's Fertilizer Service uses a tank shaped like a cylinder.

To find the surface area of a cylinder, add the measures of the areas of its circular bases and its curved surface.

Find the surface area of the cylinder shown below. Use 3.14 for π.

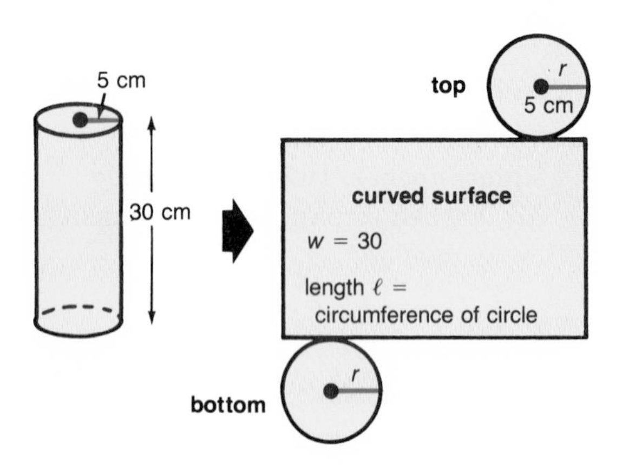

top	3.14×5^2	**78.5**
bottom	3.14×5^2	**78.5**
curved surface	$\underbrace{2 \times 3.14 \times 5}_{\text{circumference}} \times 30$	**+ 942.0**
		$S \approx 1{,}099$

The surface area is about 1,099 cm^2.

To find the surface area of a cone, add the area of its circular base and the area of its curved surface.

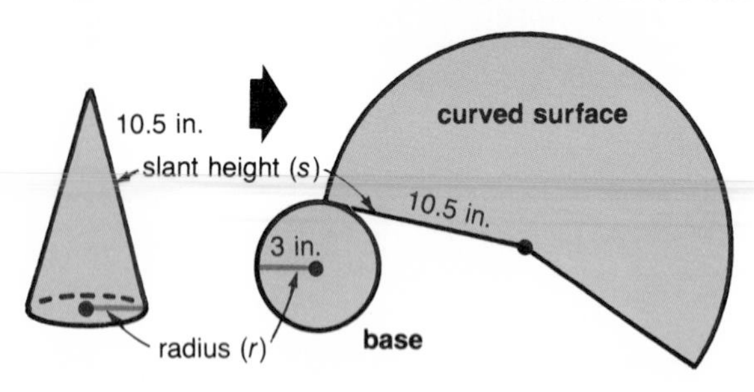

The area of the base is πr^2. The area of the curved surface is πrs.

Find the surface area of the cone shown above. Use 3.14 for π.

base	$3.14 \times 3 \times 3$	**28.26**
curved surface	$3.14 \times 3 \times 10.5$	**+ 98.91**
		$S \approx 127.17$

The surface area is about 127.17 in^2.

EXERCISES ***Find the surface area of each cone and cylinder described below.***

1.

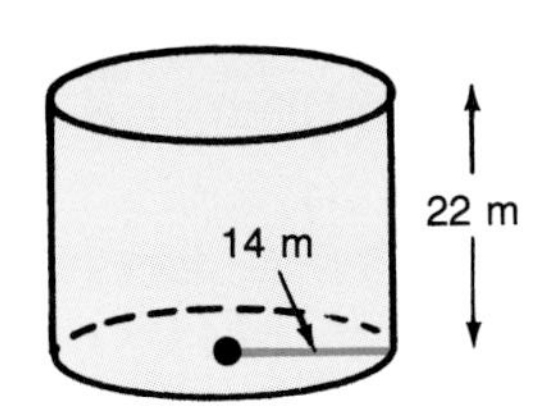

2.

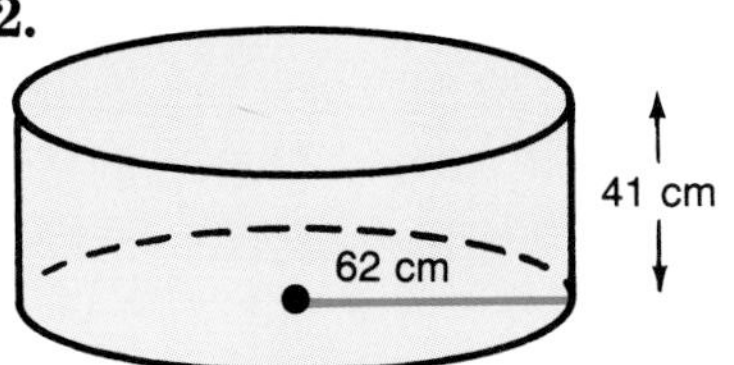

3.

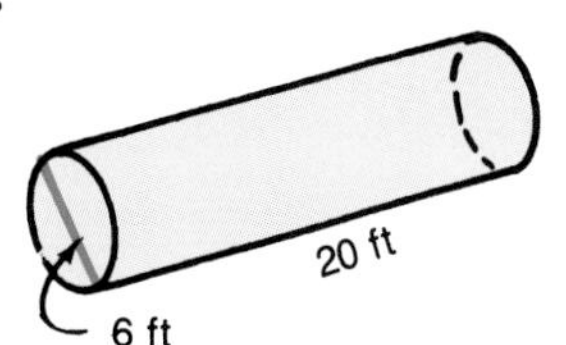

4.

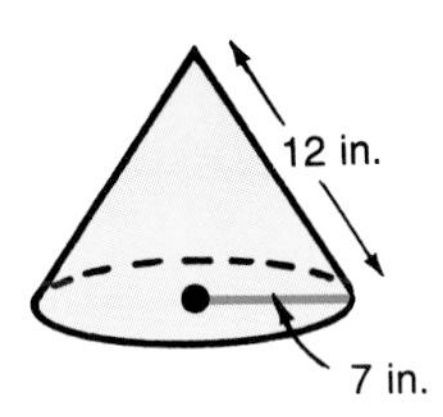

5.

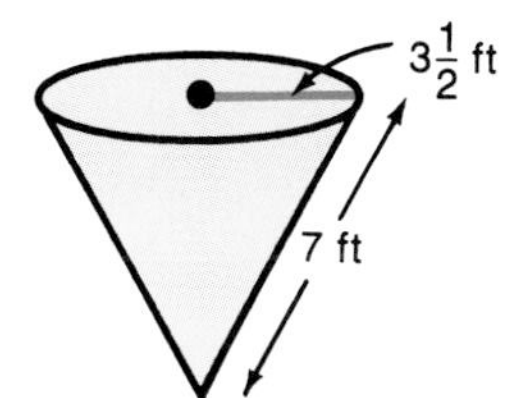

6.

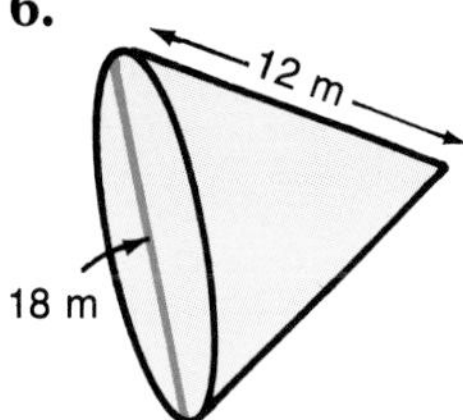

Solve.

7. The height of a cylindrical milk tank is 1.4 m. The radius is 0.4 m. Find the surface area.

8. How many square inches of metal are used to make a closed can $2\frac{1}{2}$ in. wide and $4\frac{1}{2}$ in. tall?

Skills Review: Pages 279–289

Find the perimeter or circumference of each figure. Use 3.14 for π.

1.

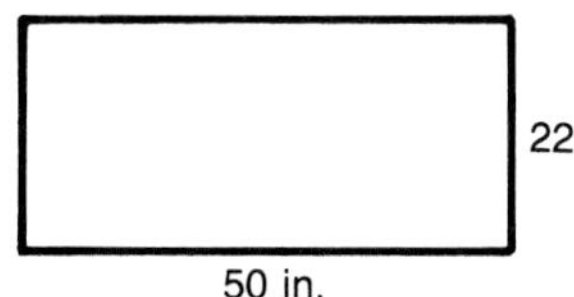

2.

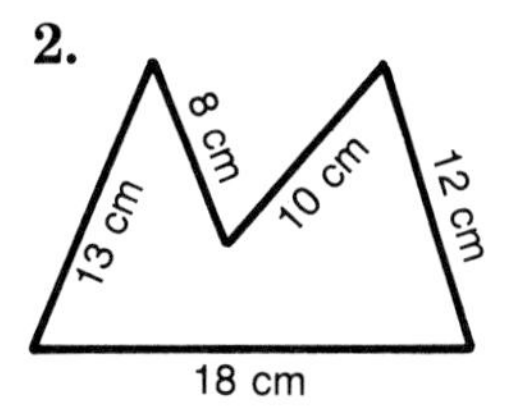

3.

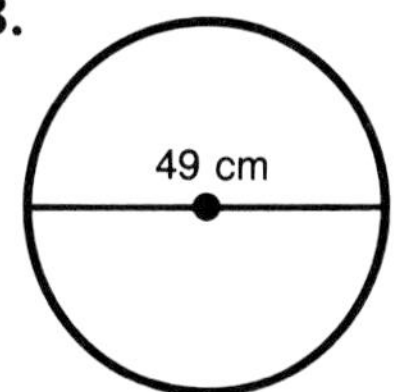

4.

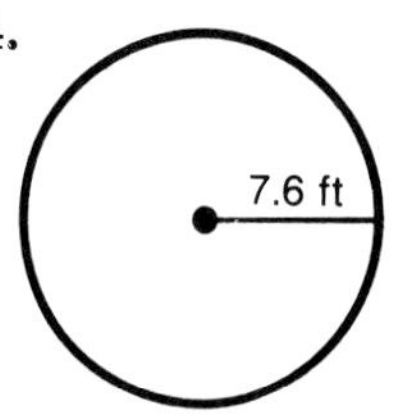

Find the area of each figure. Use 3.14 for π.

5. rectangle: length, 11 m; width, 8.2 m
6. parallelogram: base, 28 in.; height, 16 in.
7. triangle: base 4.7 cm; height, 2.2 cm
8. trapezoid: base (a), 14 ft; base (b), 20 ft; height, 10 ft
9. circle: radius, 35 in.
10. circle: diameter, 4.6 m

Find the surface area of each solid. Use 3.14 for π.

11.

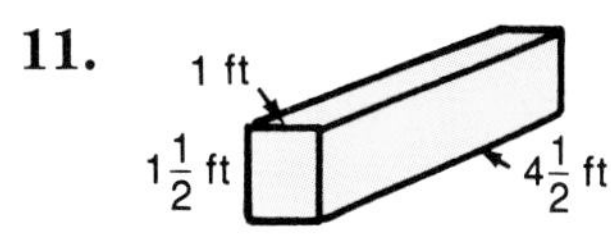

12.

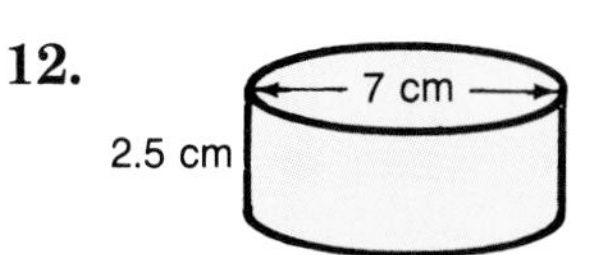

Cumulative Review

Estimate.

1. $\begin{array}{r} 5.147 \\ +\ 9.278 \\ \hline \end{array}$
2. $\begin{array}{r} 9{,}421 \\ -\ 4{,}908 \\ \hline \end{array}$
3. $\begin{array}{r} 82.6 \\ \times\ 0.41 \\ \hline \end{array}$
4. $71\overline{)5{,}083}$
5. $2.9\overline{)1.852}$

Add, subtract, multiply, or divide.

6. $\begin{array}{r} 12.9 \\ +\ 28.75 \\ \hline \end{array}$
7. $\begin{array}{r} \$52.00 \\ -\ 16.35 \\ \hline \end{array}$
8. $\begin{array}{r} 0.09 \\ \times\ 0.36 \\ \hline \end{array}$
9. $\begin{array}{r} 0.947 \\ \times\ \ 2.41 \\ \hline \end{array}$
10. $3.6\overline{)19.8}$

11. $3.36\overline{)23.1}$
12. $8 + {}^-11$
13. ${}^-12 + {}^-34$
14. $8 - 14$
15. ${}^-15 - 13$
16. ${}^-24 - {}^-16$
17. 161×10
18. $12 \times {}^-6$
19. ${}^-11 \times {}^-11$
20. $24 \div {}^-12$
21. ${}^-28 \div 7$
22. ${}^-60 \div {}^-15$

Find the greatest common factor (GCF) for each group of numbers.

23. 10, 25
24. 12, 35
25. 36, 48, 54

Find the least common multiple (LCM) for each group of numbers.

26. 3, 21
27. 8, 12
28. 9, 12, 18

Add, subtract, multiply, or divide. Write each answer in simplest form.

29. $\frac{3}{8} + \frac{3}{4}$
30. $6\frac{1}{5} + 7\frac{7}{10}$
31. $6\frac{5}{6} + 5\frac{7}{8}$
32. $\frac{11}{12} - \frac{1}{3}$
33. $12\frac{5}{6} - 8\frac{5}{12}$
34. $10\frac{1}{4} - 6\frac{4}{5}$
35. $\frac{4}{9} \times 3$
36. $3\frac{8}{9} \times \frac{3}{7}$
37. $2\frac{4}{7} \times 2\frac{11}{12}$
38. $\frac{8}{15} \div \frac{2}{5}$
39. $3\frac{8}{9} \div 2\frac{2}{9}$
40. $7 \div 4\frac{2}{3}$

Solve each equation. Check your solution.

41. $a - 60 = 165$
42. $b + 75 = 42$
43. ${}^-2c = 16$
44. $f - 7 = {}^-16$
45. $\frac{r}{6} = 6$
46. $10 = 6e - 12$
47. $6g + 5 = {}^-13$
48. $16 = 7 + \frac{h}{2}$

Solve.

49. What number is 35% of 80?
50. 7.9% of 60 is what number?
51. What percent of 40 is 1.6?
52. 7.2 is 90% of what number?

Complete each of the following.

53. 5.2 m = ▒ cm
54. 710 m = ▒ km
55. 6,950 mL = ▒ L
56. 4.5 L = ▒ mL
57. 0.62 kg = ▒ g
58. 39 mg = ▒ g

Evaluate each expression if a = 4, b = ⁻3, and c = $\frac{1}{2}$.

59. $a + b$
60. $b - c$
61. ac
62. $\frac{b}{c} + 1$

Solve.

63. Kathy telephones Fran four times a month. Each call costs the same. The total monthly cost is \$7.40. How much does each call cost?

64. Three men complete half of a job in 20 days. At this rate, how long would it take twelve men to complete the job?

Mathematics Lab

Draw parallel lines two centimeters apart across a piece of paper. Now drop a stick one centimeter long on the paper. Continue to drop the stick 30 times. Count the number of times the stick touches a line. Divide the number of times the stick is dropped by the number of times the stick touches a line. Your answer should be approximately π.

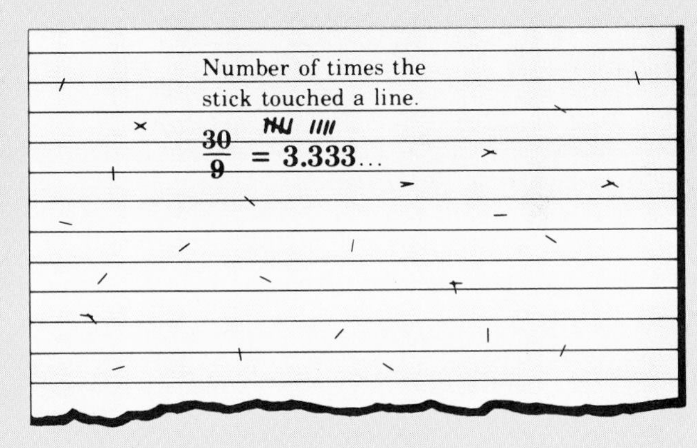

$\frac{30}{9} = 3.333\ldots$

Repeat the experiment dropping the stick the number of times indicated.

1. 20 times
2. 50 times
3. 70 times
4. 90 times
5. Combine your results in problems 1–4.
6. Combine your results in problem 5 with your classmates' results.

11-7 Volume of Prisms and Pyramids

A cistern is an underground tank for storing rainwater.

Volume is the amount of space that a solid contains. Volume is measured in cubic units.

One common unit of volume is the cubic centimeter.

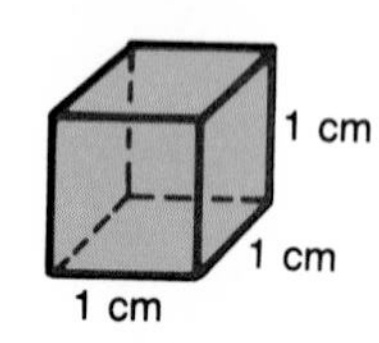

1 cubic centimeter (cm^3)

What is the volume of the rectangular prism shown below?

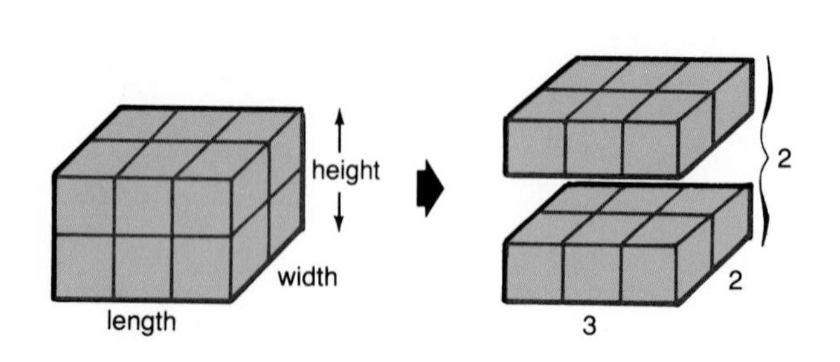

The volume (V) of a rectangular prism can be found by multiplying the measures of the length (l), width (w), and height (h).

$$V = lwh$$

$$V = 3 \times 2 \times 2$$

$$V = 12$$

The volume of the rectangular prism is 12 cubic units.

The volume of any prism can be found by multiplying the measures of the area of the base (B) and the height (h).

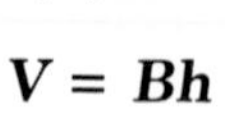

$$V = Bh$$

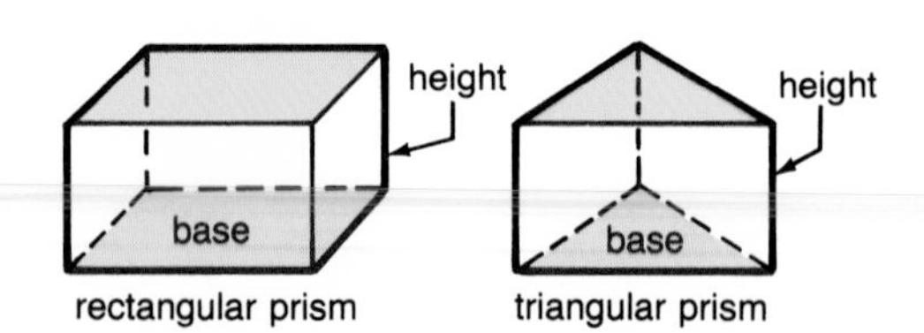

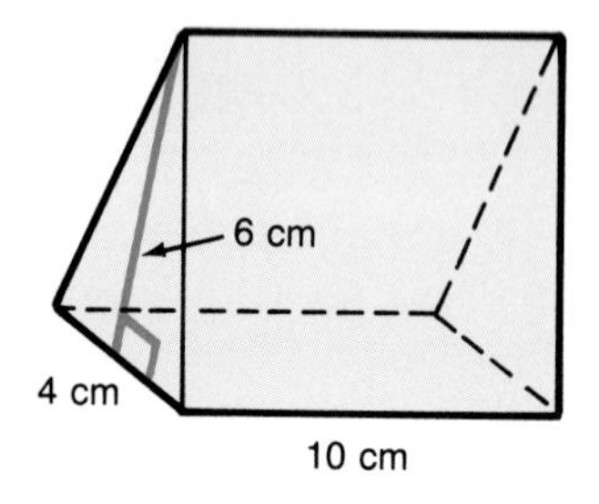

Find the volume of the prism shown at the left.

$V = Bh$ — The base is triangular.

$V = (\frac{1}{2} \times 4 \times 6) \times 10$ — The area of a triangle is $\frac{1}{2} \times b \times h$.

$V = 12 \times 10$

$V = 120$ The volume is 120 cm^3.

The volume of a pyramid is one-third the volume of a prism with the same base and height as the pyramid.

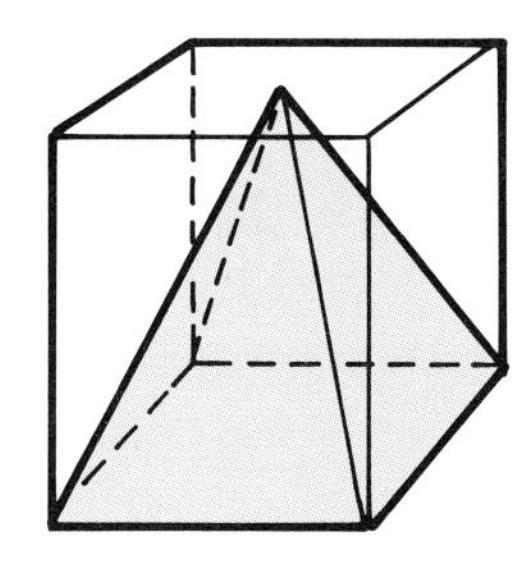

$V = \frac{1}{3}lwh$

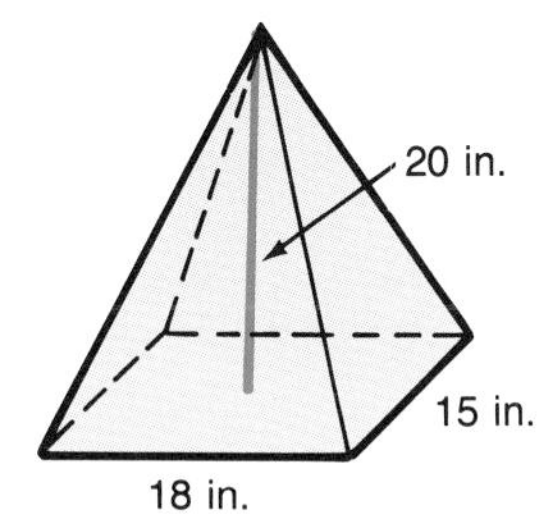

Find the volume of the pyramid at the left.

$V = \frac{1}{3} \times l \times w \times h$

$V = \frac{1}{3} \times 18 \times 15 \times 20$

$V = 1{,}800$ The volume is 1,800 in^3.

EXERCISES Find the volume of each prism and pyramid described below.

1.

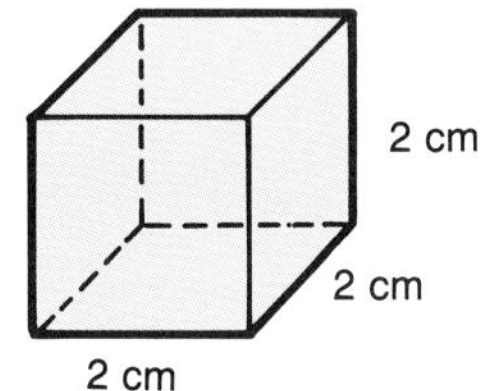

2.

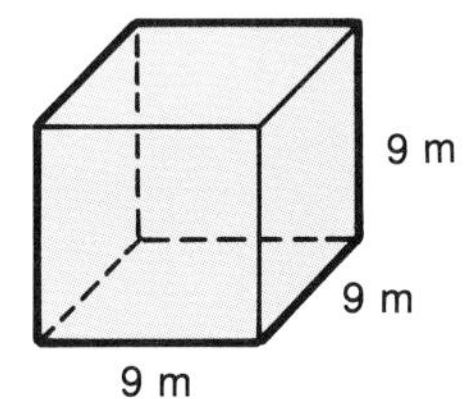

3.

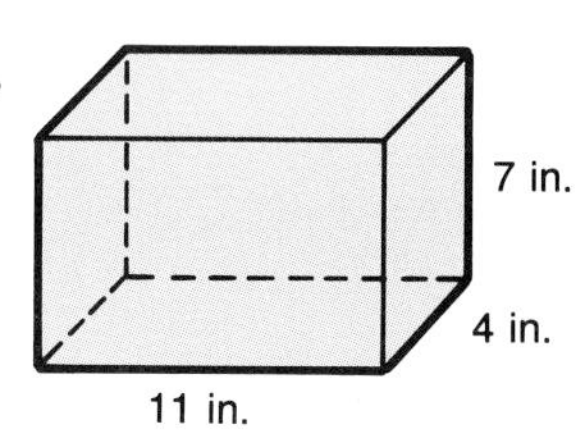

4.

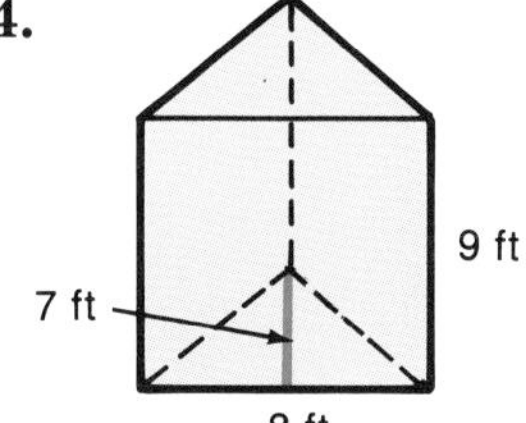

5.

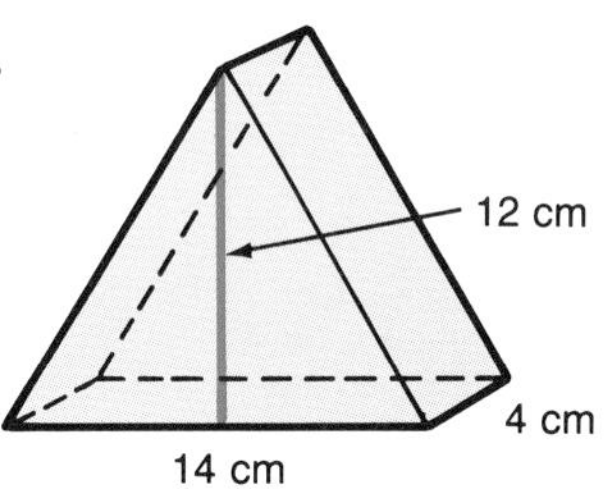

6.

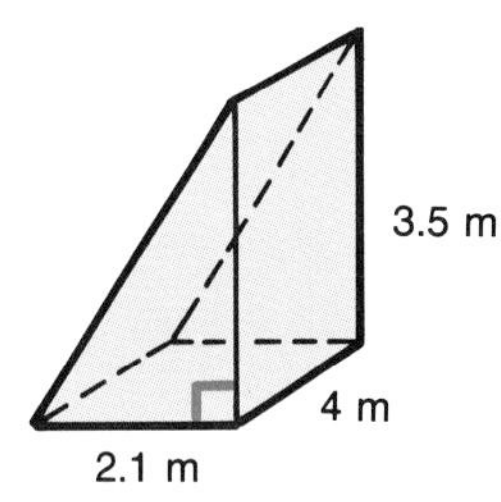

7.

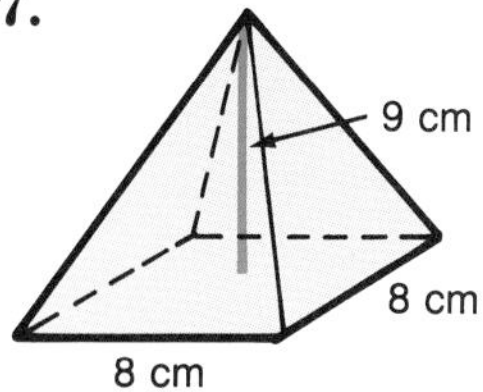

8.

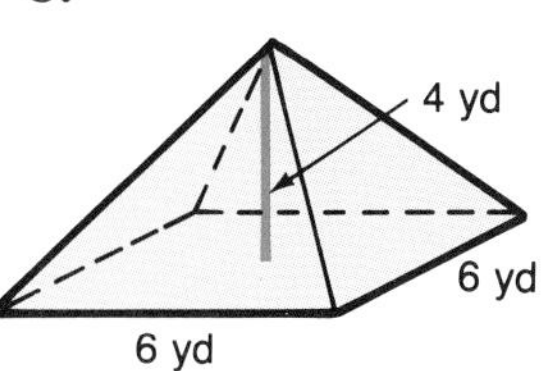

9. **10.**

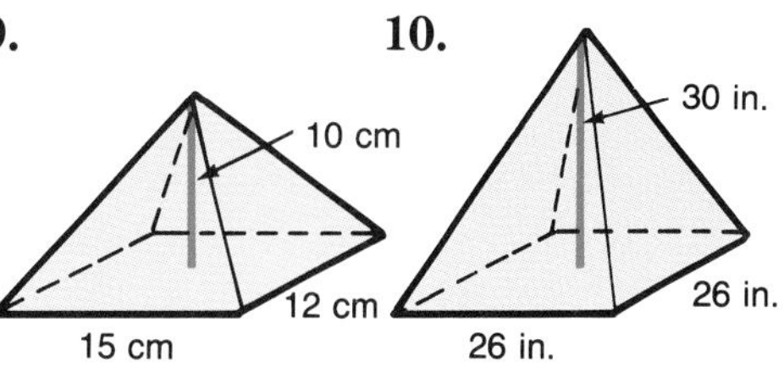

11. rectangular prism: length, 37.1 ft; width, 25.9 ft; height, 64 ft

12. hexagonal prism: base, 13.5 m^2; height, 7 m

13. pyramid: length, 8.2 in.; width, 10 in.; height; 15 in.

11-8 Volume of Cylinders and Cones

Hillsdale Nursery grows plants in containers shaped like cylinders. The volume of a cylinder is found by multiplying the measures of the area of the base and the height.

$\boldsymbol{V = Bh}$

Since the area of a circle is πr^2,

$\boldsymbol{V = \pi r^2 h.}$

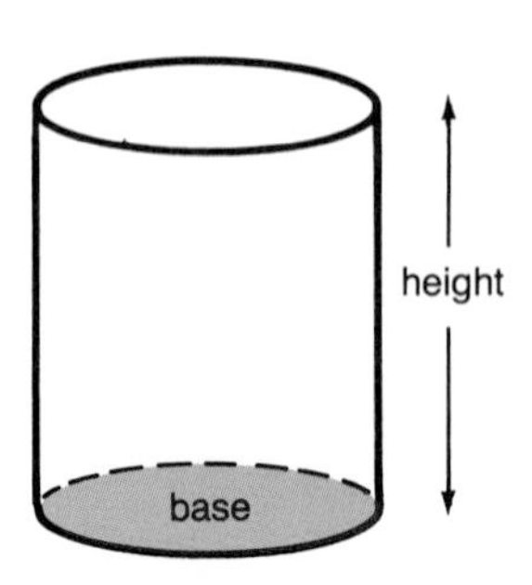

A cylindrical container has a height of 17 centimeters and a radius of 8 centimeters. Find the volume. Use 3.14 for π.

$\boldsymbol{V = \pi r^2 h}$

$\boldsymbol{V \approx 3.14 \times 8 \times 8 \times 17}$

$\boldsymbol{V \approx 3{,}416.32}$

The volume is about 3,416.32 cm^3.

The volume of a cone is one-third the volume of a cylinder with the same radius and height as the cone.

$\boldsymbol{V = \frac{1}{3}\pi r^2 h}$

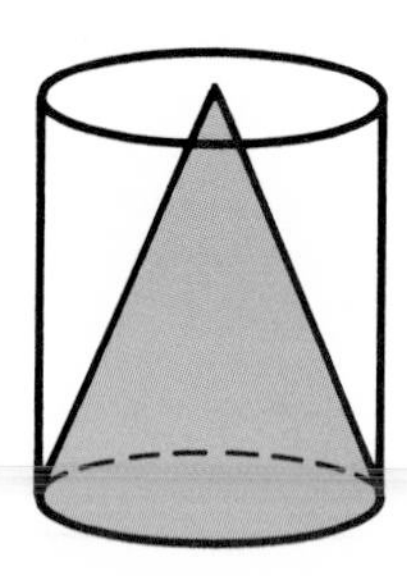

Find the volume of the cone at the right. Use 3.14 for π.

$\boldsymbol{V = \frac{1}{3}\pi r^2 h}$

$\boldsymbol{V \approx \frac{1}{3} \times 3.14 \times 7 \times 7 \times 18}$

$\boldsymbol{V \approx 923.16}$

The volume is about 923.16 ft^3.

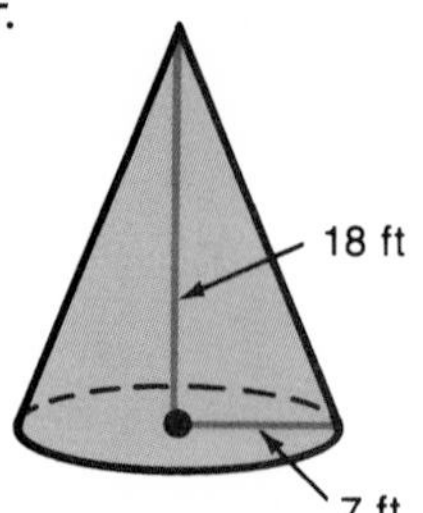

EXERCISES ***Find the volume of each cylinder and cone described below. Use 3.14 for π.***

1.

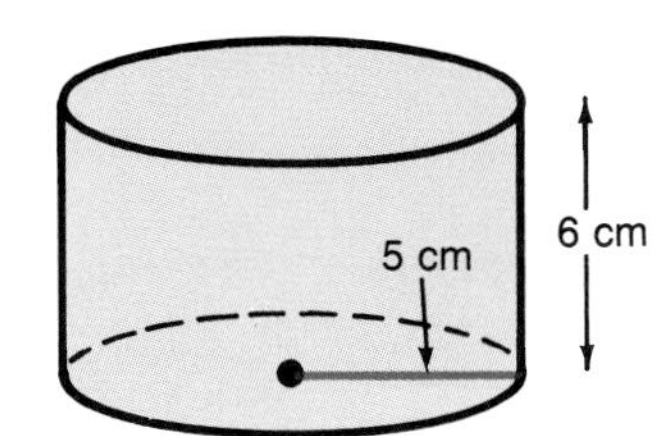

2.

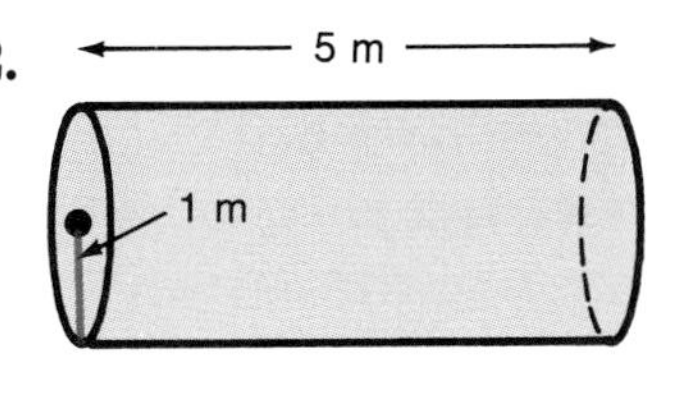

3.

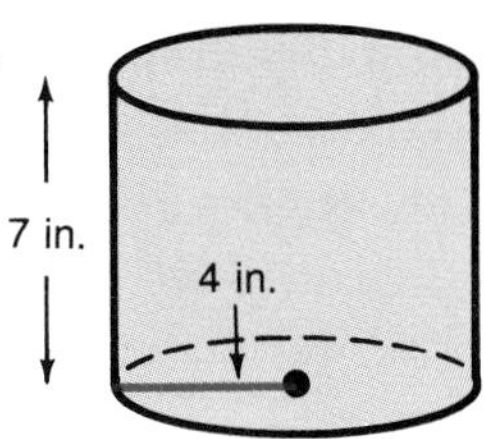

4.

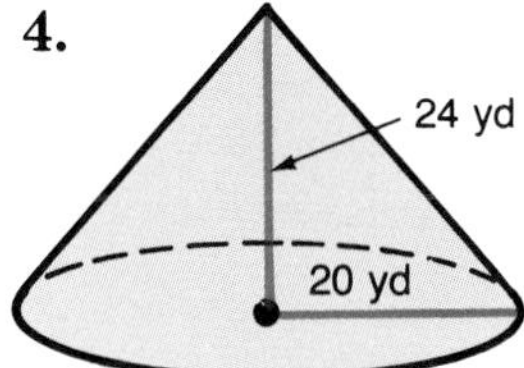

5.

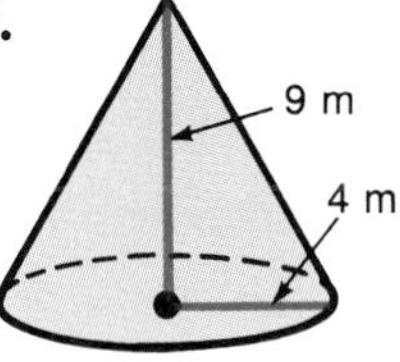

6.

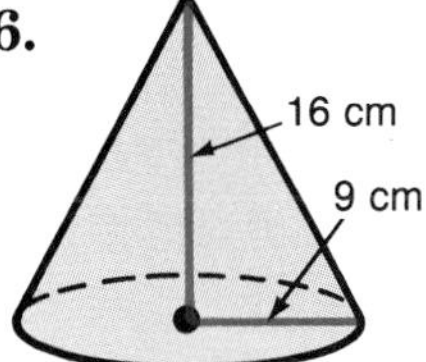

7.

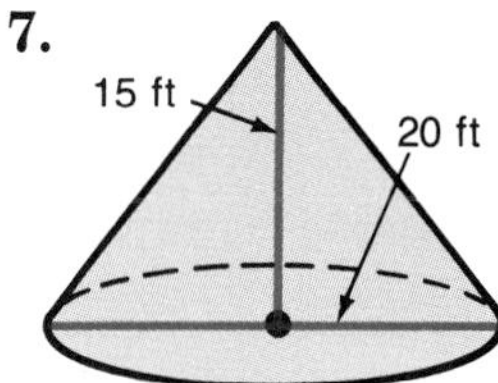

8. cylinder: radius, 2.3 cm; height, 13.6 cm
9. cylinder: diameter, 15 in.; height, 8 in.
10. cone: radius, 6 yd; height, 8 yd
11. cone: diameter, 29.2 m; height, 39.2 m

Solve.

12. A cylindrical gasoline can is 18 in. high and has a diameter of 16 in. Find the volume.

13. A cone-shaped funnel has a radius of 4 inches and a height of $7\frac{1}{2}$ inches. Find the volume.

VOLUME, CAPACITY, AND MASS

The volume, capacity, and mass of water are related. Study the chart shown at the right.

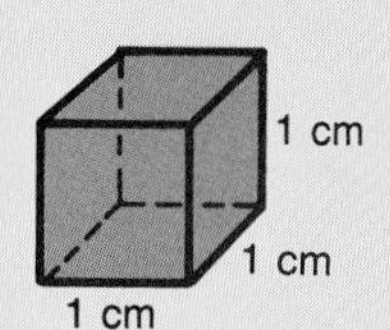

volume = 1 cm^3
capacity = 1 mL
mass = 1 g

Solve.

1. How many milliliters of water have a mass of 65 grams?

2. What is the mass in grams of the water in a 3.4 m^3 container?

3. How many liters of water have a mass of 825 grams?

4. What is the mass in kilograms of 8 liters of water?

11-9 Problem Solving: Using Perimeter, Area, and Volume

A circular pond is in the center of a pasture. The diameter of the pond is 130 feet. The pasture is shaped like a trapezoid with a height of 260 feet and bases of 400 feet and 360 feet. Find the grazing area of the pasture.

Read the problem. You need to find the grazing area of the pasture. You know the dimensions of the circular pond inside the pasture and the dimensions of the pasture.

Decide what to do. Make a diagram of the pasture and pond. Find the area of the pond. Then find the total area of the pasture. Subtract the area of the pond from the total area to find the grazing area.

Solve the problem.

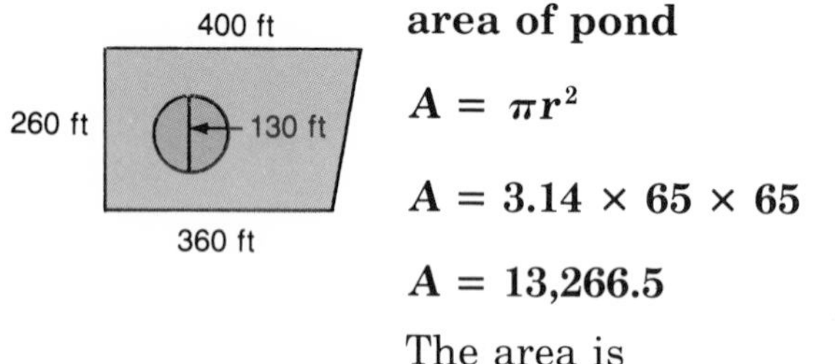

area of pond

$\mathbf{A = \pi r^2}$

$\mathbf{A = 3.14 \times 65 \times 65}$

$\mathbf{A = 13{,}266.5}$

The area is 13,266.5 ft^2.

area of pasture

$\mathbf{A = \frac{1}{2}h(a + b)}$

$\mathbf{A = \frac{1}{2} \times 260(400 + 360)}$

$\mathbf{A = 98{,}800}$

The area is 98,800 ft^2.

$$\underbrace{\text{grazing area}}_{\mathbf{A}} = \underbrace{\text{area of the pasture}}_{\mathbf{98{,}800}} - \underbrace{\text{area of pond}}_{\mathbf{13{,}266.5}}$$

$$\mathbf{A = 85{,}533.5}$$

The grazing area is 85,533.5 ft^2.

Examine the solution. The area of the pond plus the grazing area should equal the total area.

13,266.5 + 85,533.5 = 98,800 ✓

The answer is correct.

Solve. Make a diagram.

1. The radius of a circular flower garden and its border is 2.8 meters. Without the border, the radius is 2.3 meters. Find the area of the border.

2. All but one corner of a rectangular field 180 m by 250 m is planted in soybeans. The corner is a right triangle 60 m by 60 m. Find the area planted in soybeans.

3. A steam roller is 3 feet wide and has a diameter of 2 feet. About how many square feet of pavement can it cover in one complete roll?

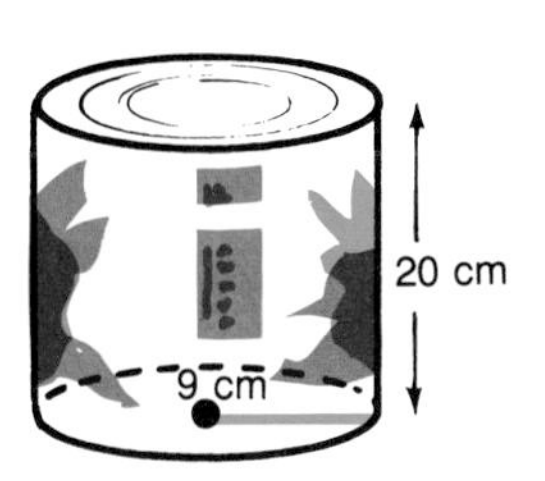

Solve.

4. The can shown at the left is packed in a box 18 cm by 18 cm by 20 cm. Find the volume of space remaining in the box.

5. Find the volume of the barn shown at the right.

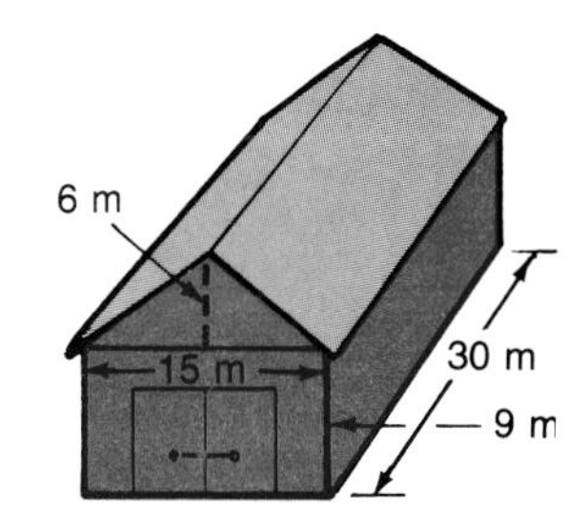

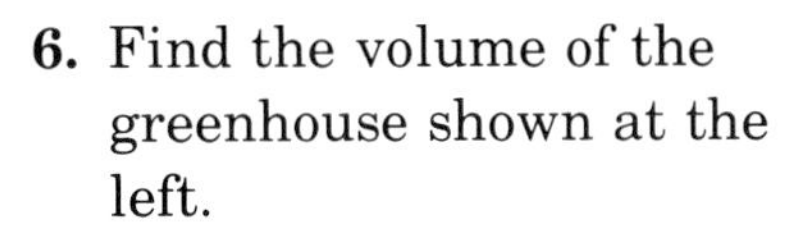

6. Find the volume of the greenhouse shown at the left.

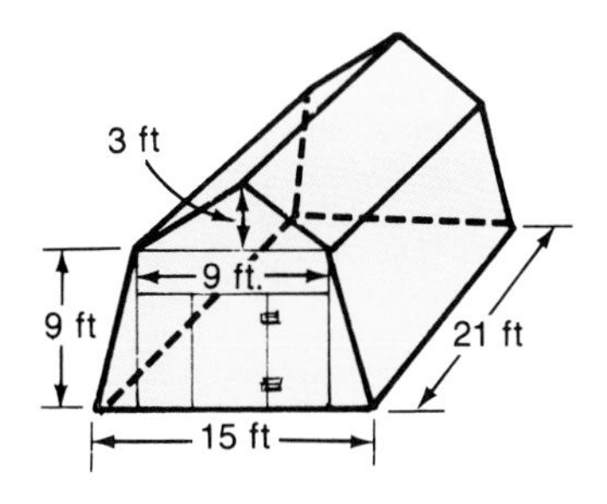

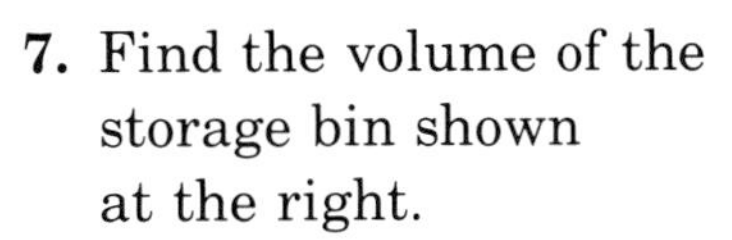

7. Find the volume of the storage bin shown at the right.

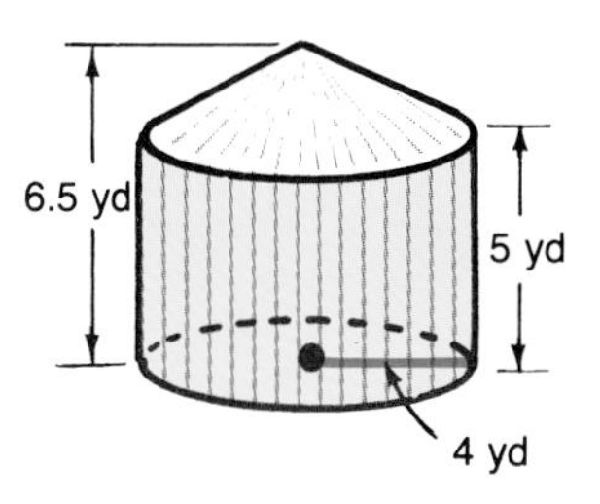

Skills Review: Pages 292–297

Find the volume of each solid. Use 3.14 for π.

1. rectangular prism: length, 83 mm; width, 34 mm; height, 10 mm
2. prism: base, 58 ft^2; height, 21 ft
3. cylinder: base, 76 cm^2; height, 5.9 cm
4. cylinder: radius, 9 ft; height, 5 ft
5. pyramid: length, 45 in.; width, 45 in.; height, 40 in.
6. cone: radius, 25 cm; height, 36 cm
7. A grain elevator is shaped like a cylinder attached to a cone. The height of the cylindrical part is 4 m. The height of the conical part is 1.5 m. The radius is 2 m. Find the volume of the grain elevator.

Mathematics and Science

Two wooden blocks that are the same size are placed in a container of water. One sinks and the other floats. Why?

Although the volume of the two blocks is the same, the density is different. The **density** of a substance is the mass per unit of volume.

$$\textbf{density} = \frac{\textbf{mass (g)}}{\textbf{volume (cm}^3\textbf{)}}$$

Suppose the blocks each have a volume of 120 cm^3. The mass of the first block is 150 g. The mass of the second block is 96 g. Find the density of each block.

$$\textbf{density} = \frac{\textbf{mass (g)}}{\textbf{volume (cm}^3\textbf{)}}$$

first block

$\textbf{density} = \frac{150}{120}$ **or 1.25**

second block

$\textbf{density} = \frac{96}{120}$ **or 0.80**

The density of water is 1.00. The first block sinks because its density is greater than the density of water. The second block floats because its density is less than the density of water.

EXERCISES* *Find the density of each of the following objects. Tell whether the object would float or sink in water.

1. chunk of ice: mass, 74 g; volume, 86 cm^3

2. styrofoam insulation: mass, 255 g; volume, 830 cm^3

3. rock: mass, 300 g; volume, 180 cm^3

Solve.

4. Find the volume of corn syrup that has a density of 1.08 and a mass of 10.8 grams.

5. A soap bar, 10 cm by 7.2 cm by 2.4 cm, weighs 160 grams. Find its density. Will it float in water?

Chapter 11 Review

VOCABULARY

perimeter (279) | area (280)
circumference (284) | polyhedron (286) | prism (286)
pyramid (286) | surface area (286) | volume (292)

EXERCISES Find the perimeter or circumference for each of the following. Use 3.14 for π. (279, 284)

1.

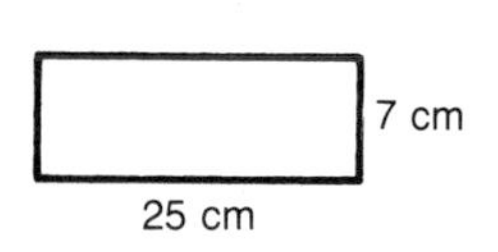

2.

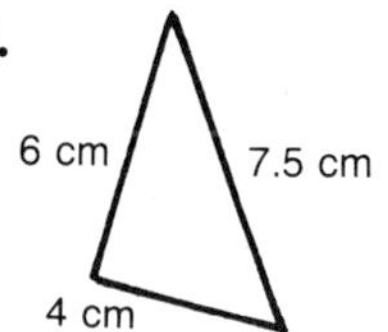

3.

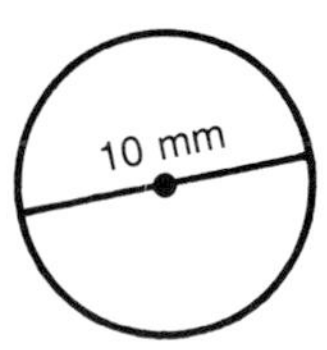

4.

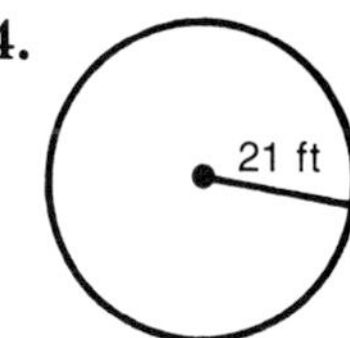

Find the area of each figure described below. Use 3.14 for π. (280–285)

5. rectangle: length, 13.5 cm; width, 9.4 cm

6. square: side, 16 in.

7. triangle: base, 17 ft; height, 7.6 ft

8. circle: diameter, 28 in.

9. parallelogram: base, 42 cm; height, 37 cm

10. trapezoid: height, 15 ft; base (a), 3 ft; base (b), 81 ft

Find the surface area of each solid. Use 3.14 for π. (286–289)

11.

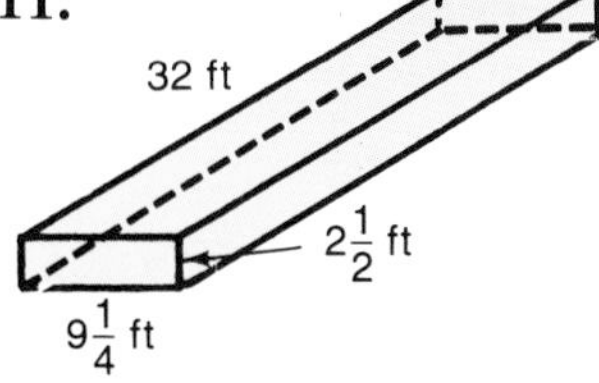

12.

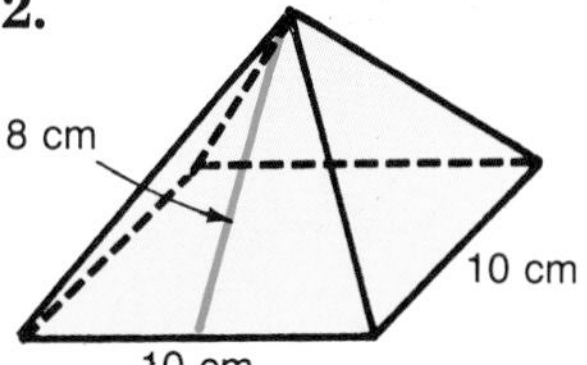

13.

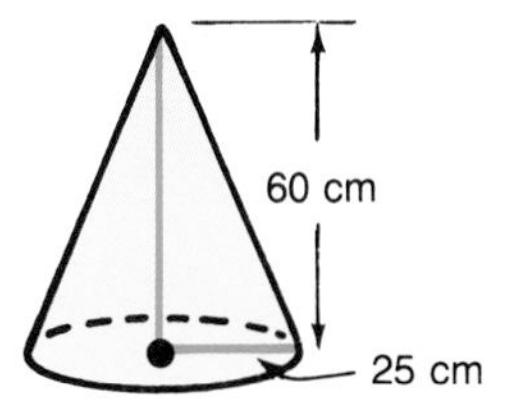

Find the volume of each solid. Use 3.14 for π. (292–295)

14.

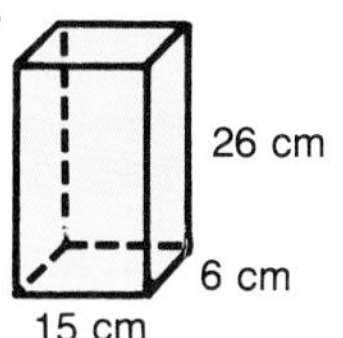

15.

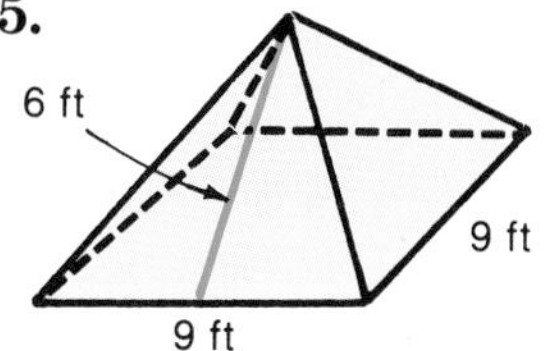

16.

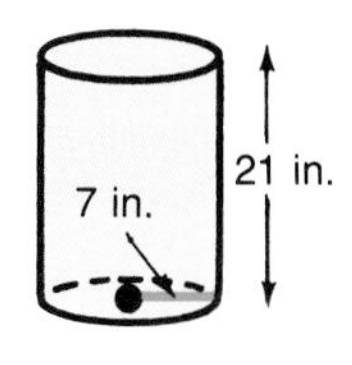

Solve. Use 3.14 for π. (296)

17. A machine part is cylindrical with identical cones on each end. Find the volume.

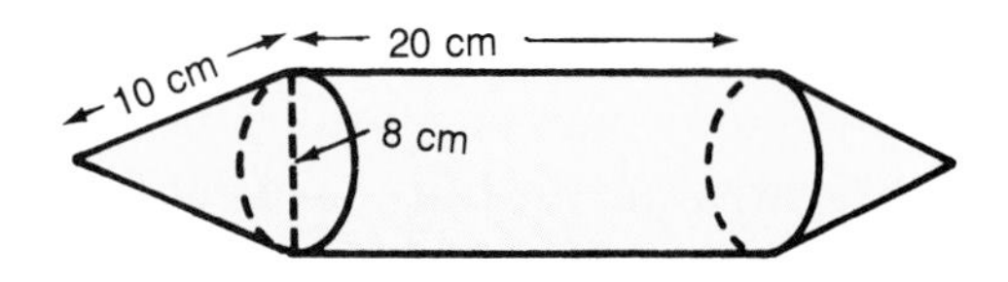

Chapter 11 Test

Find the perimeter or circumference of each figure shown below. Use 3.14 for π.

1.

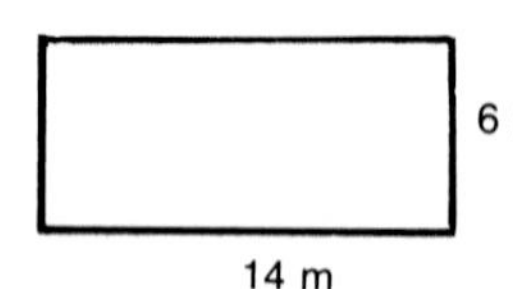

2.

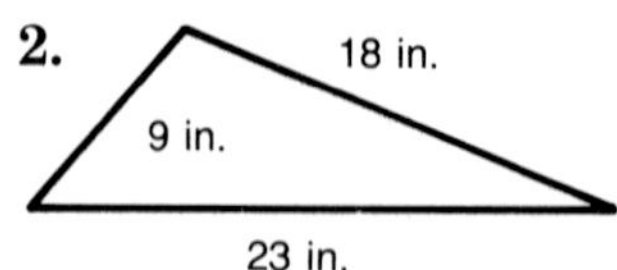

3.

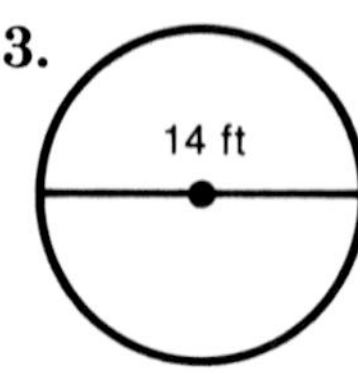

4.

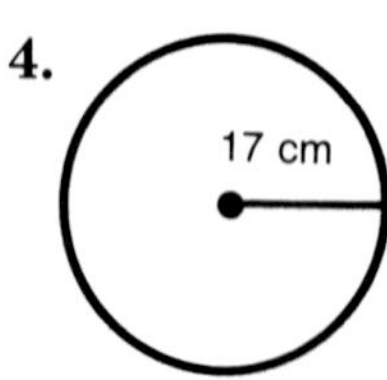

Find the area of each figure described below. Use 3.14 for π.

5. rectangle: length, 12.9 cm; width, 6.2 cm

6. parallelogram: base, 27 yd; height, 36 yd

7. triangle: base, 16 cm; height, 12 cm

8. trapezoid: base (a), 10 m; base (b), 16.2 m; height, 5.5 m

9. circle: radius, 6.3 cm

10. circle: diameter, 5 in.

Find the surface area of each solid shown below. Use 3.14 for π.

11.

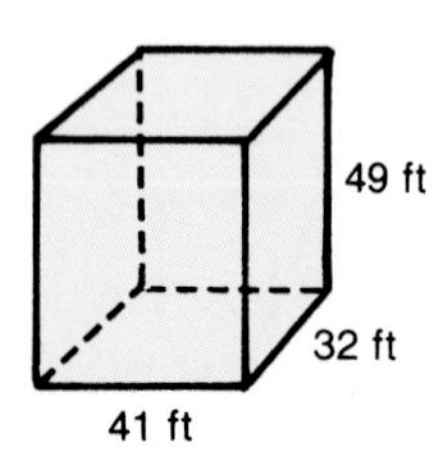

12.

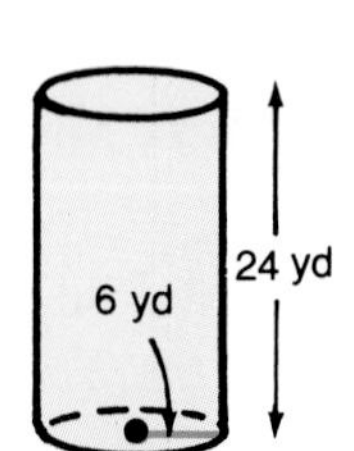

13.

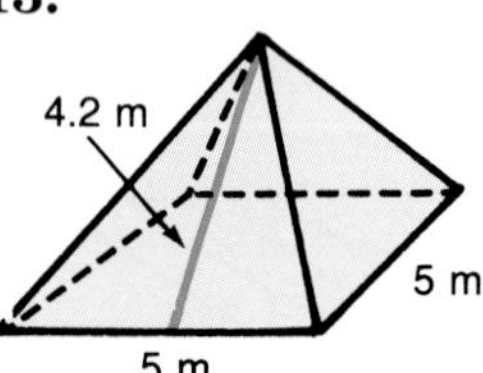

Find the volume of each solid described below. Use 3.14 for π.

14. rectangular prism: length, 6.5 yd; width, 4 yd; height, 3.1 yd

15. cylinder: base, 92.7 cm^2; height, 5.4 cm

16. cylinder: radius, 4 m; height, 10.2 m

17. pyramid; length, 9 in., width, 4 in., height, 11 in.

18. cone: radius, 5 ft; height, 12 ft

19. prism: base, 93 cm^2; height, 26 cm

Solve. Use 3.14 for π.

20. A circular part of a square field 600 m by 600 m is irrigated. The irrigated part has a radius of 300 m. Find the area of the field that is not irrigated.

Enrichment

A **sphere** is a solid with all points the same distance from a given point called the **center.** A line segment from any point on the sphere to the center is called the **radius** (r).

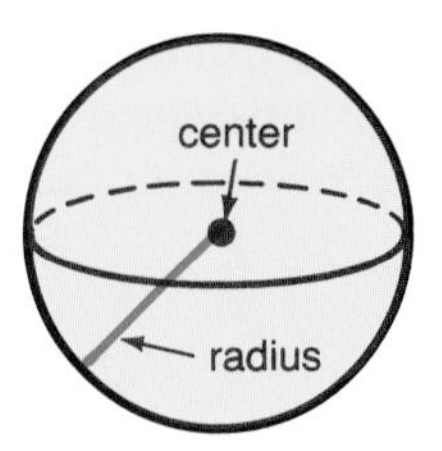

To find the surface area of a sphere, use the formula $\mathbf{S = 4\pi r^2}$.

To find the volume of a sphere, use the formula $\mathbf{V = \frac{4\pi r^3}{3}}$.

Find the surface area and volume of a sphere with a radius of 5 meters, to the nearest whole number.

$\mathbf{S = 4\pi r^2}$

$\mathbf{S \approx 4 \times 3.14 \times 5^2}$

$\mathbf{S \approx 314}$

The surface area is about 314 m^2.

$\mathbf{V = \frac{4\pi r^3}{3}}$

$\mathbf{V \approx \frac{4 \times 3.14 \times 5^3}{3}}$

$\mathbf{V \approx \frac{1{,}570}{3} \approx 523}$

The volume is about 523 m^3.

***EXERCISES** Find the surface area and volume of each sphere described below. Round each answer to the nearest whole number. Use 3.14 for π.*

1.

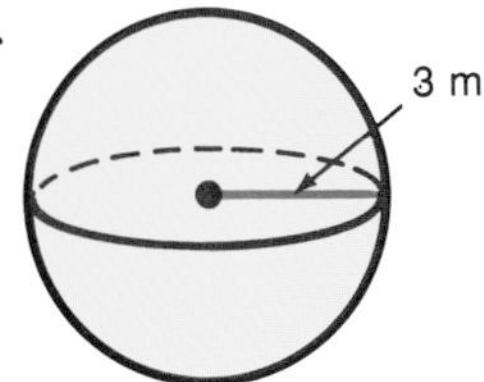

2.

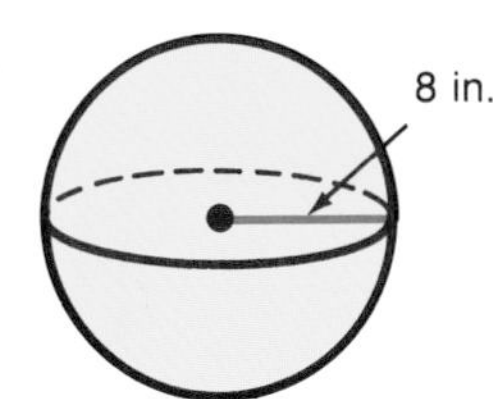

3.

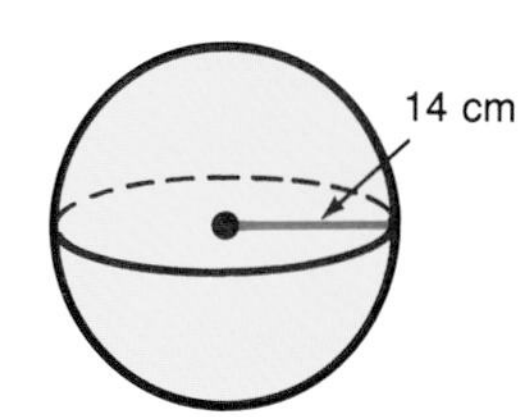

4. radius, 60 km

5. radius, 710 km

6. radius, 940 ft

***Solve.** Use 3.14 for π.*

7. The shape of Earth is almost a perfect sphere. The radius is about 6.4 megameters (million meters). Find the surface area to the nearest square megameter.

8. About 45 square megameters of land on Earth is used for farming. What percent of the surface area is used for farming? Round your answer to the nearest percent.

Skills Test, Chapters 1–11

Standardized Format

Directions Work each problem on your own paper. Choose the letter of the correct answer. If the correct answer is not given, choose the letter for *none of the above*. Make no marks in this book.

1. Rounded to the nearest hundred, what is 72,118?

- **a** 72,000
- **b** 72,100
- **c** 70,000
- **d** *none of the above*

2. Estimate.

$$\begin{array}{r} \$32.19 \\ -\ 19.78 \\ \hline \end{array}$$

- **e** \$20
- **f** \$12.41
- **g** \$10
- **h** *none of the above*

3. Multiply.

$$\begin{array}{r} 98.3 \\ \times\ 0.02 \\ \hline \end{array}$$

- **a** 0.1966
- **b** 19.66
- **c** 196.6
- **d** *none of the above*

4. Divide.

$$1.47\overline{)36.897}$$

- **e** 25.1
- **f** 2.51
- **g** 251
- **h** *none of the above*

5. Which pair of numbers has 24 as its least common multiple?

- **a** 4, 6
- **b** 2, 12
- **c** 8, 12
- **d** *none of the above*

6. What is the greatest common factor of 4, 6, and 32?

- **e** 2
- **f** 6
- **g** 4
- **h** *none of the above*

7. Add.

$$3\tfrac{3}{4} + 9\tfrac{7}{10}$$

- **a** $12\frac{10}{14}$
- **b** $12\frac{1}{2}$
- **c** $13\frac{3}{5}$
- **d** *none of the above*

8. Subtract.

$$8\tfrac{2}{3} - 4\tfrac{7}{9}$$

- **e** $3\frac{1}{3}$
- **f** $3\frac{8}{9}$
- **g** $3\frac{5}{6}$
- **h** *none of the above*

9. Divide.

$$1\tfrac{2}{3} \div \tfrac{1}{2}$$

- **a** $3\frac{1}{3}$
- **b** $1\frac{1}{3}$
- **c** $\frac{5}{6}$
- **d** *none of the above*

10. Which statement is always true about vertical angles?

- **e** They are perpendicular.
- **f** They are complementary.
- **g** They are congruent.
- **h** *none of the above*

11. The sentence "Six more than x is nine" written as an equation is what?

- **a** $6 = x + 9$
- **b** $6 + 9 = x$
- **c** $6 + x = 9$
- **d** *none of the above*

12. Solve.

$$7 + m = 16$$

- **e** 11
- **f** 23
- **g** $^{-}9$
- **h** *none of the above*

GO ON TO THE NEXT PAGE

13. Solve.

$8y - 2 = 18$

a $2\frac{1}{2}$

b 2

c $4\frac{1}{4}$

d *none of the above*

14. What is the ratio 18 : 22 changed to a fraction in simplest form?

e $\frac{18}{22}$

f $\frac{9}{11}$

g $\frac{11}{9}$

h *none of the above*

15. 90 is 60% of what number?

a 54

b 144

c 140

d *none of the above*

16. A shirt costs $21.95. The sales tax is $5\frac{1}{2}$%. How much tax must be paid?

e $1.14

f $5.50

g $1.21

h *none of the above*

17. Add.

$^{-}8 + 7$

a $^{-}15$

b $^{-}1$

c 15

d *none of the above*

18. Multiply.

$^{-}15 \times {}^{-}\frac{1}{3}$

e 5

f $^{-}5$

g 45

h *none of the above*

19. A container holds 2,010 mL of water. How many liters is this?

a 0.201

b 2,010,000

c 2.01

d *none of the above*

20. What is the perimeter of the figure shown at the right?

e 28 cm

f about 32.56 cm

g about 45.12 cm

h *none of the above*

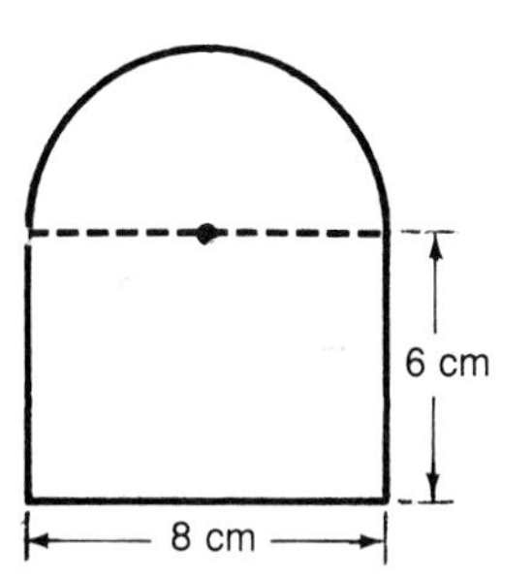

21. Chad's quiz scores are 19, 15, 16, and 16. What must he score on the next quiz to have an average score of 17?

a 16

b 17

c 18

d *none of the above*

22. How many more points did Jenelle score in the second game than in the fifth?

e 1

f 3

g 4

h *none of the above*

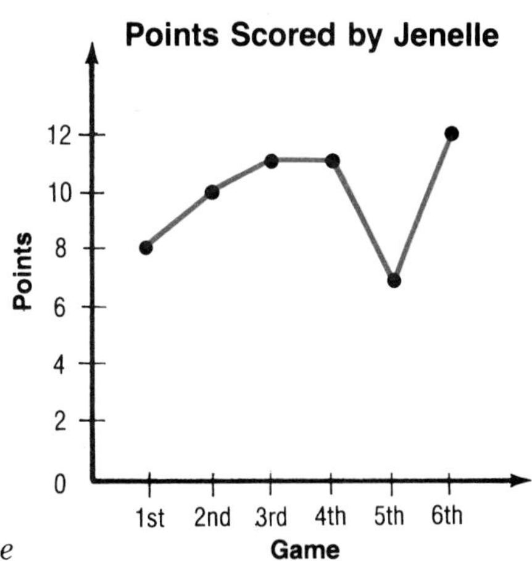

STOP

12 Probability and Statistics

At the beginning of a football game a coin is tossed. The visiting team has the choice of kicking or receiving if they call the toss of the coin correctly.

12–1 Counting Outcomes Using Tree Diagrams

When a coin is tossed, there are two possible **outcomes.** The coin can come up either heads (H) or tails (T). Each outcome is equally likely.

Suppose a penny and a nickel are tossed at the same time. How many possible outcomes are there?

You can use a **tree diagram**, such as the one at the right, to find *all* possible outcomes.

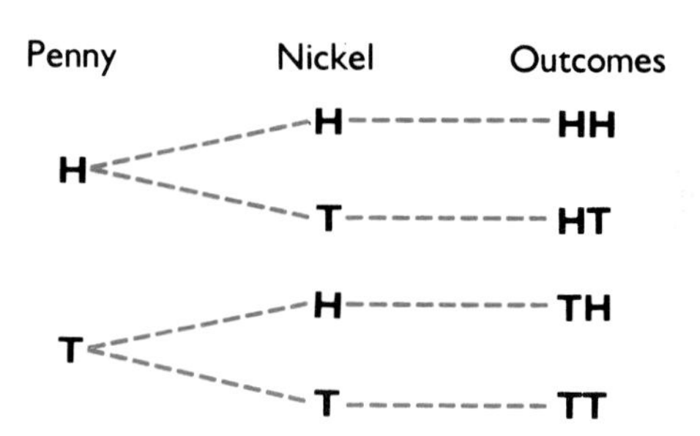

The possible outcomes are HH, HT, TH, and TT. How does HT differ from TH?

There are four possible outcomes.

EXERCISES ***State the number of possible outcomes for each of the following.***

1. rolling a die

2. spinning the spinner

Draw a tree diagram for each of the following. Then state the number of possible outcomes.

3. tossing a penny, a nickel, and a dime

4. spinning each spinner once

5. a choice of cake, pie, or fruit with a choice of milk or tea
6. tossing a quarter, rolling a die, and tossing a penny
7. a choice of a desk or a wall phone in white, black, green, or tan
8. a choice of two skirts, a choice of two blouses, and a choice of three scarves

12-2 Counting Outcomes Using Multiplication

Wesley spends a day at the Holiday Amusement Park. At 2:00 P.M. he can see a dolphin show, a lion show, or an elephant show. At 9:30 P.M. he can go to a rodeo, watch fireworks, or hear a band. How many possible combinations or outcomes are there?

You can use a tree diagram to find the number of possible outcomes.

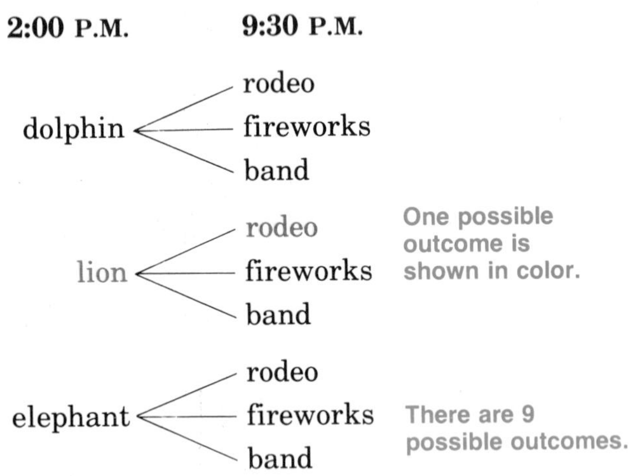

Another way to find the number of outcomes is to use multiplication.

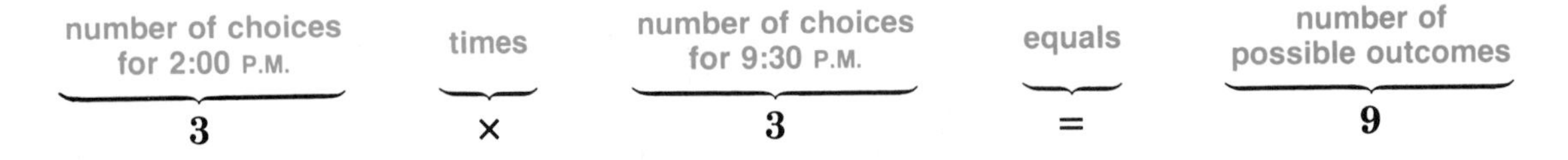

EXERCISES ***Use multiplication to find the number of outcomes.***

1. Four coins are tossed. How many outcomes are possible?
2. Three dice are rolled. How many outcomes are possible?
3. The Panthers have 8 pitchers and 3 catchers. How many pitcher-catcher combinations are possible?
4. Mieko has 5 blouses, 3 skirts, and 3 scarves. How many outfits are possible?
5. A menu offers the choice of 7 salads, 12 main dishes, and 6 desserts. How many three-course dinners are possible?
6. Meyer Ford offers a choice of 6 vinyl-top colors, 18 body colors, and 7 upholstery colors. How many color combinations are possible?

Luis, Tom, and Joel play trumpet. They are trying out for the three chairs in concert band. How many ways can they be seated?

There is a choice of three persons to sit in the first chair. Then either of the remaining two persons may sit in the second chair. Only one person remains to sit in the third chair. There are $3 \times 2 \times 1$ or 6 ways for them to be seated.

Suppose Paul tries out also. How many ways can the four boys be seated in the four chairs?

choices for first chair		choices for second chair		choices for third chair		choices for fourth chair		number of ways they can be seated
4	×	3	×	2	×	1	=	24

The symbol for $4 \times 3 \times 2 \times 1$ is 4! It is read *four* **factorial.**

Evaluate 6!.

$$
\begin{aligned}
\mathbf{6!} &= \mathbf{6 \times 5 \times 4 \times 3 \times 2 \times 1} \\
&= \mathbf{720}
\end{aligned}
$$

EXERCISES ***Evaluate each of the following.***

7. 5! **8.** 2! **9.** 3! **10.** 7! **11.** $6! - 2!$ **12.** $(6 - 2)!$

Solve.

13. How many ways can six books be arranged in a row on a shelf?

14. How many ways can ten people line up to buy concert tickets?

15. Five majorettes are having their picture taken. How many ways can the photographer arrange them in a row?

16. Four persons are speaking at a program. How many ways can they be seated at the speakers' table?

17. Suppose you are forming 5-place numerals with the digits 2, 3, 4, 5 and 6. How many can you form if no digit is used more than once?

18. Suppose you are forming 4-place numerals between 2,000 and 5,000 with the digits 2, 3, 7, and 9. How many can you form if no digit is used more than once?

12-3 Probability

Dorothy and Sandy are playing a game. The spinner stops on one of four colors.

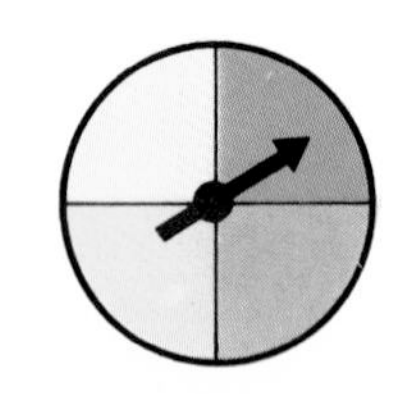

$$\text{probability of an event} = \frac{\text{number of ways the event can occur}}{\text{number of possible outcomes}}$$

What is the probability that it stops on yellow? This can be written as P(yellow).

$$\text{P(yellow)} = \frac{1}{4} \begin{array}{l} \leftarrow \text{number of ways to spin yellow} \\ \leftarrow \text{number of possible outcomes} \end{array}$$

Suppose you choose one marble from those shown at the right. What is the probability of choosing a blue marble?

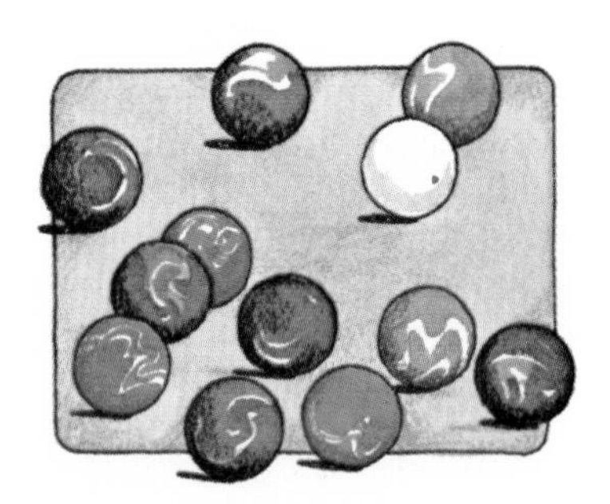

$$\text{P(blue)} = \frac{2}{12} \begin{array}{l} \leftarrow \text{number of ways to choose blue} \\ \leftarrow \text{number of possible outcomes} \end{array}$$

$$= \frac{1}{6}$$

EXERCISES ***A die is rolled. Find the probability for each of the following.***

1. a 1 **2.** a 3 **3.** a 6 **4.** a 0

5. a 1 or a 2 **6.** a 2, a 3, or a 4 **7.** *not* a 1 **8.** an odd number

9. a prime number **10.** a number less than 7 **11.** an odd prime number

Choose a marble from those above. Find the probability for each of the following.

12. a red marble **13.** a black marble **14.** *not* a blue marble

15. a blue or a black marble **16.** *not* a red or a black marble

The spinner at the right is equally likely to stop at any of the 20 numbers. Find the probability that it stops at each of the following.

17. the 2 **18.** *not* the 14

19. the 9 or the 10 **20.** *not* the 17 or the 6

21. an odd number **22.** a multiple of 3

23. a factor of 48 **24.** a number less than 10

25. a prime number **26.** a number *not* greater than 6

The chart lists the possible outcomes of a roll of two dice.

27. Copy and complete the chart.

6	6,1	▒	6,3	▒	▒	6,6
5	▒	5,2	▒	▒	▒	5,6
4	4,1	▒	▒	4,4	4,5	▒
3	3,1	3,2	▒	▒	▒	3,6
2	▒	▒	2,3	2,4	▒	▒
1	▒	1,2	1,3	▒	1,5	▒
	1	**2**	**3**	**4**	**5**	**6**

Suppose the dice are rolled once. Find the probability for each of the following. Use the completed chart.

28. 6,1

29. 2,1 or 5,3

30. *not* 5,5

31. both numbers odd

32. a 1 on both dice

33. a sum of 8

34. *not* a sum of 12

35. a sum of 7 or 11

36. a sum less than 5

Solve. Use the marbles shown on page 308.

37. Roberto chooses a red marble and keeps it. Then Matt chooses a marble. What is the probability that it is blue?

38. Mindy chooses a black marble and keeps it. Then Julie chooses a marble. What is the probability that it is black?

PASCAL'S TRIANGLE

Toss one coin. There are 2 possible outcomes.

Toss two coins. There are 4 possible outcomes.

Toss three coins. There are 8 possible outcomes.

Toss four coins. How many possible outcomes are there?

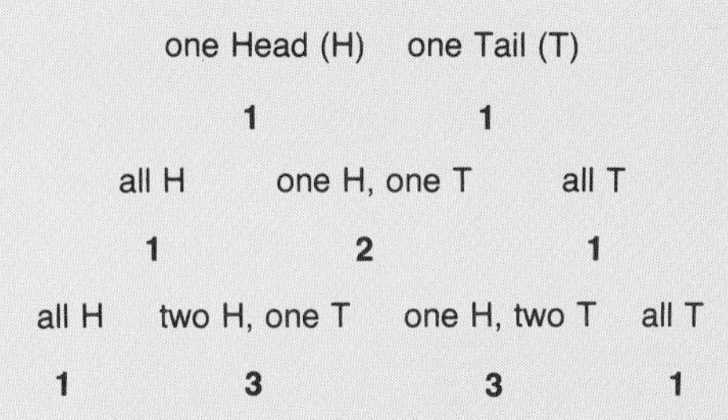

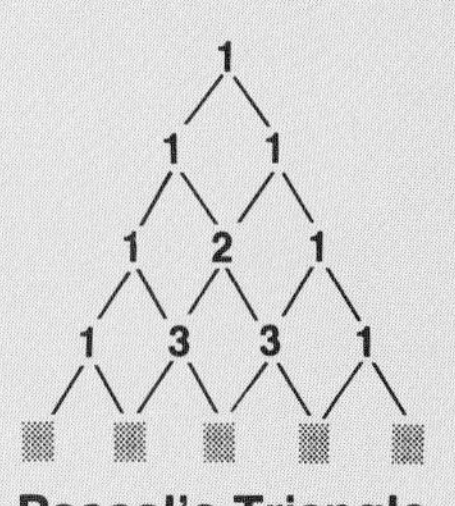

Pascal's Triangle

Copy Pascal's triangle as shown above.

1. Replace the boxes in the last row with numerals.

2. Write the next six rows of Pascal's triangle.

3. When three coins are tossed, there are 1 + 3 + 3 + 1 or 8 possible outcomes. Compute the number of possible outcomes for 8 coins.

12-4 Multiplying Probabilities

Chris collects coins for a hobby. She has six dimes in a drawer. One dime was minted in 1920, two in 1924, and three in 1925. Suppose she draws a dime, replaces it, and draws another dime. What is the probability that she draws a 1924 dime both times?

Draw a dime.	Replace the dime.	Draw another dime.
P(1924) $= \frac{2}{6}$ **or** $\frac{1}{3}$		**P(1924)** $= \frac{2}{6}$ **or** $\frac{1}{3}$

Multiply to find the probability.

probability of drawing a 1924 dime both times $= \frac{1}{3} \times \frac{1}{3} = \frac{1}{9}$

Since the first dime is replaced, the second draw is *not* affected by the first draw. These events are **independent.**

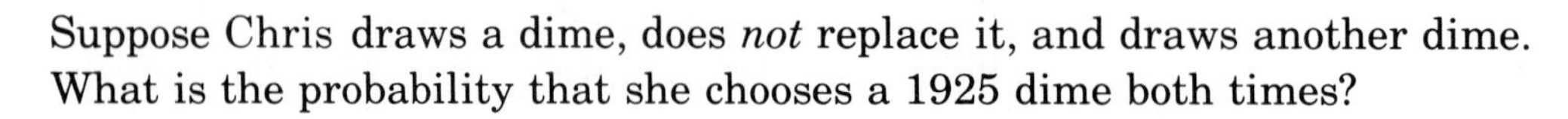

Suppose Chris draws a dime, does *not* replace it, and draws another dime. What is the probability that she chooses a 1925 dime both times?

Draw a dime.	Do not replace the dime.	Draw another dime.
P(1925) $= \frac{3}{6}$ **or** $\frac{1}{2}$		**P(1925)** $= \frac{2}{5}$ Why?

probability of drawing a 1925 dime both times $= \frac{1}{2} \times \frac{2}{5} = \frac{1}{5}$

Since the first dime is *not* replaced, the second draw *is* affected by the first draw. These events are **dependent.**

EXERCISES ***Find the probability for drawing each of the following. Refer to the six dimes shown above. Each dime drawn is replaced.***

1. the 1920 dime two times
2. a 1925 dime two times
3. a 1925 dime, then a 1924 dime
4. the 1920 dime, then a 1924 dime
5. the 1920 dime three times
6. a 1925 dime three times

Find the probability for drawing each of the following. Refer to the six dimes shown above. Each dime drawn is not replaced.

7. a 1924 dime two times
8. the 1920 dime two times
9. the 1920 dime, then a 1925 dime
10. a 1925 dime, then a 1924 dime
11. a 1925 dime three times
12. a 1924 dime three times

A bag contains 4 white marbles, 3 blue marbles, and 5 red marbles. Find the probability of drawing each of the following. Each marble drawn is not replaced.

13. a red marble, then a white marble

14. a blue marble, then a red marble

15. 2 white marbles in a row

16. 3 red marbles in a row

17. a red marble, then a blue marble, then a white marble

The Great Fumbo says he can magically pull a white rabbit from a hat containing 4 white rabbits and 2 brown rabbits. But he actually chooses rabbits at random. If he pulls out a brown rabbit, he does not replace it. Find the probability of each of the following.

18. a white rabbit on the first try

19. a brown rabbit, then a white rabbit

20. a brown rabbit twice, then a white rabbit

Solve.

21. Kim's drawer contains 3 navy blue socks and 6 black socks. She chooses two at random. What is the probability that the socks are blue?

22. Suppose Kim chooses three socks at random. What is the probability that she gets a matching pair?

CONDITIONAL PROBABILITY

Suppose the numbers 1 through 10 are written on cards and placed in a box. Amber draws a card and tells you the number is even. What is the probability that it is a 2? This is called **conditional probability** because you are already given one condition; that is, the card drawn has an even number.

probability of 2 given that the number is even $= \frac{1}{5}$ ← only one way to choose a 2 (numerator); ← number of possible even outcomes (denominator)

Solve. Use the cards described above.

1. If the card drawn is a prime number, what is the probability that it is odd?

2. If the card drawn is greater than 3, what is the probability that it is 9?

12-5 Adding Probabilities

Celia enjoys reading books. Ten books are on a shelf. Three of the books are novels, one is a biography, and the others are science fiction. Celia chooses a book at random. What is the probability that it is a novel *or* a biography?

P(novel) $\frac{3}{10}$

P(biography) $\frac{1}{10}$

P(novel or biography)

$\frac{4}{10}$ ← ways to choose a novel or a biography; ← possible outcomes

Notice that $\frac{3}{10} + \frac{1}{10} = \frac{4}{10}$. The probability of a novel *or* a biography is the *sum* of the probability of a novel and the probability of a biography. The probability of choosing a novel or a biography is $\frac{4}{10}$ or $\frac{2}{5}$.

Suppose you spin the spinner shown at the left. What is the probability of spinning red *or* a number greater than 8?

P(red) $\frac{6}{12}$

P(number greater than 8) $\frac{4}{12}$

Notice that 9 and 11 satisfy both conditions. They are each red and greater than 8. So you must subtract the probability of the outcomes that are counted twice.

$$P(\text{red}) + P\left(\begin{array}{c}\text{number greater}\\ \text{than 8}\end{array}\right) - P\left(\begin{array}{c}\text{red } \textit{and} \text{ number}\\ \text{greater than 8}\end{array}\right) = P\left(\begin{array}{c}\text{red } \textit{or} \text{ number}\\ \text{greater than 8}\end{array}\right)$$

$$\frac{6}{12} + \frac{4}{12} - \frac{2}{12} = \frac{8}{12}$$

The probability of spinning red or a number greater than 8 is $\frac{8}{12}$ or $\frac{2}{3}$.

EXERCISES ***The names Jacob, Jason, Jane, Maria, Mark, Rob, and Sally are written on slips of paper and placed in a box. A slip of paper is chosen from the box. Find the probability of choosing each of the following.***

1. a boy's name
2. a girl's name
3. a 6-letter name
4. a name ending with Y
5. a name beginning with J or M
6. a 5-letter name beginning with M
7. a 3-letter name beginning with J
8. a name containing 5 letters or beginning with M
9. a name containing 3 letters or beginning with J

Find the probability of spinning each of the following.

10. green
11. yellow or blue
12. number less than 7
13. multiple of 5
14. blue or number greater than 5
15. red or an even number
16. a prime number or yellow
17. green or an odd number
18. a prime or a multiple of 4
19. a multiple of 2 or a multiple of 3

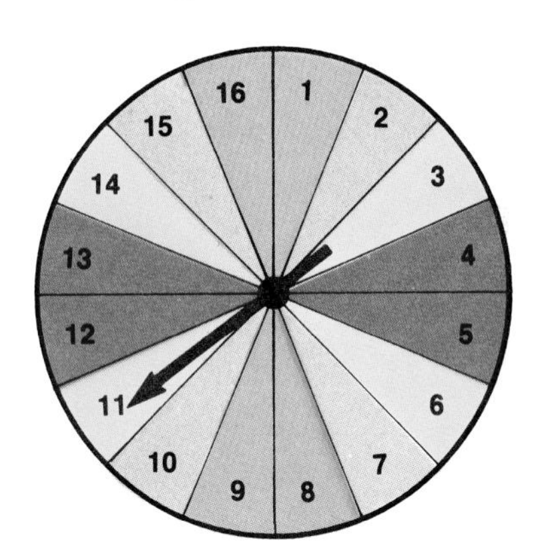

Two dice are rolled. Find the probability of each of the following.

20. doubles (matching numbers)
21. doubles or sum of 11
22. doubles or sum of 10
23. sum of 8 or sum of 9
24. sum is greater than 9
25. sum is less than 6

The table lists the dogs in the Central Animal Shelter. Eva chooses a dog at random. Find the probability of choosing each of the following.

26. a spotted dog
27. a female dog
28. a red dog or a female dog
29. a female dog or a tan dog
30. a brown dog or a female dog

Name	Sex	Color
Brighty	F	brown
Echo	M	tan
Gidget	F	brown
Lady	F	tan
Matti	F	tan
Phideaux	M	spotted
Rocky	M	brown
Shane	M	red
Sparky	M	brown
Trixie	F	spotted

12-6 Odds

Lisa shoots free throws. She makes 35 free throws and misses 15. From this information, Lisa can find the **odds** that she will make the next free throw.

$$\textbf{odds for an event} = \frac{\textbf{number of ways that event can occur}}{\textbf{number of ways that event cannot occur}}$$

odds of making free throw $= \frac{35}{15}$ She made 35. She missed 15.

$= \frac{7}{3}$

The odds that Lisa will make the next free throw are $\frac{7}{3}$ or 7 to 3.

What are the odds that she will miss the next free throw?

EXERCISES During another practice, Lisa makes 42 free throws and misses 28. Find the odds for each of the following.

1. making the next free throw
2. missing the next free throw

A coin is tossed. Find the odds for each of the following.

3. for tails
4. *not* for heads
5. *not* for tails
6. for heads

A die is rolled. Find the odds for each of the following.

7. for a 1
8. for a 5
9. *not* for a 6
10. *not* for a 2
11. for a prime number
12. *not* for an odd number
13. for a 2 or a 5
14. *not* for a number less than 4

Suppose you draw a card from those shown at the right. Find the odds for drawing each of the following.

15. a GM card

16. a Ford card

17. a Chrysler card

18. *not* an AMC card

19. *not* a Ford card

20. *not* a GM card

21. an AMC card or a Chrysler card

22. a Ford card or an AMC card

23. *not* a GM card or a Ford card

24. *not* a Chrysler card or a GM card

Two dice are rolled. Find the odds for each of the following.

25. for a sum of 7

26. *not* for a sum of 6

27. *not* for a sum of 2

28. for a sum of 10

29. for a sum of 3 or 11

30. for a sum of 5 or 4

31. for an odd sum

32. for both dice the same

33. for a sum of 8 and for a 6 on one die

34. for a sum of 9 and for a 4 on one die

35. for an odd sum or a sum less than 7

Skills Review: Pages 305-315

Solve.

1. A menu offers the choice of orange, grapefruit, or tomato juice and bacon or ham. Draw a tree diagram for this.
2. A die is rolled and a coin is tossed. How many outcomes are possible?
3. How many ways can five books be stacked in a pile?

A bag contains 5 red marbles, 3 green marbles, and 2 yellow marbles. Find the probability for each of the following.

4. draw a red marble
5. draw a green marble, replace it, draw a green marble
6. draw a yellow marble, do not replace, draw a red marble
7. draw a yellow marble or a green marble

8. A die is rolled. Find the odds that a 3 is rolled.

Cumulative Review

Estimate.

1. $\begin{array}{r} \$27.59 \\ +\ 82.06 \\ \hline \end{array}$
2. $\begin{array}{r} 29{,}641 \\ -\ 6{,}073 \\ \hline \end{array}$
3. $\begin{array}{r} 86.7 \\ \times\ 2.94 \\ \hline \end{array}$
4. $\begin{array}{r} 0.406 \\ \times\ 0.029 \\ \hline \end{array}$
5. $12.1\overline{)3.831}$

Add, subtract, multiply, or divide.

6. $\begin{array}{r} 4.8 \\ -\ 0.97 \\ \hline \end{array}$
7. $\begin{array}{r} 438.5 \\ +\ 909.8 \\ \hline \end{array}$
8. $\begin{array}{r} \$0.49 \\ \times\ \ \ 27 \\ \hline \end{array}$
9. $\begin{array}{r} 2.016 \\ \times\ 10.8 \\ \hline \end{array}$
10. $26\overline{)275.6}$

11. $0.11\overline{)10.56}$
12. $^-14 + 12$
13. $3 + {^-9}$
14. $66 - {^-19}$
15. $^-3 \times 8$
16. $^-5 \times {^-10}$
17. $18 \div {^-6}$
18. $^-72 \div {^-9}$
19. $^-8.3 + {^-0.9}$
20. $^-9.7 - 2.4$
21. $12.1 \times {^-5}$
22. $^-17 \div 5$

Find the greatest common factor (GCF) for each group of numbers.

23. 15, 21
24. 16, 20
25. 36, 24, 18

Find the least common multiple (LCM) for each group of numbers.

26. 9, 6
27. 10, 12
28. 2, 5, 15

Add, subtract, multiply, or divide. Write each answer in simplest form.

29. $\frac{8}{15} + \frac{4}{15}$
30. $\frac{5}{6} + \frac{2}{9}$
31. $4\frac{3}{4} + 3\frac{1}{3}$
32. $\frac{11}{12} - \frac{5}{12}$
33. $\frac{5}{8} - \frac{1}{6}$
34. $12\frac{5}{8} - 2\frac{4}{5}$
35. $\frac{2}{3} \times \frac{4}{5}$
36. $2\frac{1}{4} \times \frac{2}{3}$
37. $\frac{4}{21} \times 1\frac{3}{4}$
38. $\frac{2}{7} \div 3$
39. $\frac{9}{16} \div 2\frac{1}{10}$
40. $1\frac{13}{15} \div 4\frac{1}{5}$

Solve each equation. Check your solution.

41. $b + 7 = 19$
42. $3 + x = 2$
43. $71 = y - 46$
44. $5c = {^-8}$
45. $\frac{2}{5}x = 22$
46. $\frac{w}{3} = {^-12}$
47. $3a + 25 = 67$
48. $\frac{h}{7} - 4 = 1$

Solve each problem.

49. 6 is what percent of 8?
50. 12 is 50% of what number?
51. What number is 18% of 65?
52. 110% of what number is 66?

Complete each of the following.

53. 296 mm = ▒ m **54.** 11 cm = ▒ mm **55.** 0.17 g = ▒ mg

56. 823 g = ▒ kg **57.** 49 mL = ▒ L **58.** 4.1 kL = ▒ L

Solve.

59. A box of detergent contains 20 cups. How many loads of laundry can be washed if each load uses $\frac{3}{4}$ cup of detergent?

60. It takes Teresita 12 minutes to saw a log into three pieces. How long would it take her to saw a log into 4 pieces?

Mathematics Lab

Suppose you are going to roll a die 60 times. About how many 1's can you expect to roll? To find the number of 1's expected, you can multiply as follows.

probability of a 1 — number of rolls — expected number of 1's

$$\frac{1}{6} \times 60 = 10$$

Now actually roll the die 60 times. Record your results in a table like the one shown. Do the results of your experiment seem reasonable?

⚀	𝍸 III	8
⚁	𝍸 𝍸 III	13
⚂	𝍸 𝍸	10
⚃	𝍸 𝍸 II	12
⚄	𝍸 IIII	9
⚅	𝍸 III	8
	TOTAL	60

Suppose you roll a die 360 times. How many rolls would you expect to have each of the following outcomes?

1. a 6 **2.** a 2 **3.** *not* a 4

4. a 5 or a 6 **5.** an odd number **6.** a prime number

7. a number less than 7 **8.** a number greater than 2

9. Suppose you toss a coin and roll a die. One possible outcome is heads on the coin and a 3 on the die (H,3). List all the possible outcomes.

10. Toss a coin and roll a die 120 times. Record your results in a table.

11. How many results had heads on the coin? Is this reasonable?

12. How many results had a 1 on the die? Is this reasonable?

12-7 Statistics

Numerical information is called **data. Statistics** involves collecting, analyzing, and presenting data.

Charlie Oney owns a music shop. He keeps a tally of the type of records that are bought. Each day he organizes the data into a **frequency table** like the one shown below.

Type of Record	Tally	Frequency
Children's	𝍸 𝍸 ||	12
Classical	𝍸 𝍸 𝍸 𝍸 𝍸 𝍸 𝍸 |	36
Country	𝍸 𝍸 𝍸 𝍸 𝍸 𝍸 𝍸 𝍸 𝍸	45
Folk	𝍸 𝍸 𝍸 𝍸 𝍸	25
Instrumental	𝍸 𝍸 𝍸 𝍸 𝍸 𝍸 𝍸 |||	38
Jazz	𝍸 𝍸 𝍸 𝍸 𝍸 𝍸 𝍸 𝍸	40
Rock	𝍸 𝍸 𝍸 𝍸 𝍸 𝍸 𝍸 𝍸 𝍸 𝍸 ||||	54

The information in a frequency table can be represented by a graph called a **histogram.** Each vertical bar represents the frequency or number of a type of record sold.

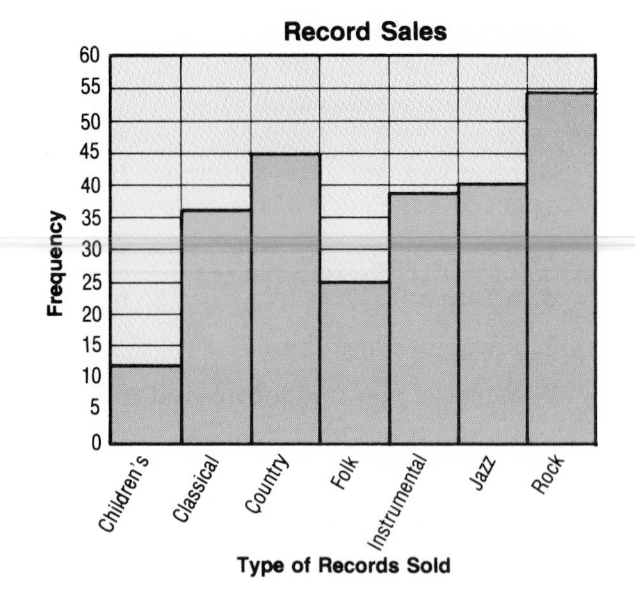

Mr. Oney can use these statistics to answer questions about his sales.

What type of records were sold the most on this particular day?

How many records were sold on this particular day?

What is the ratio of jazz records sold to folk records sold?

Solve. Use the data given.

1. Copy the table and complete the frequency column.
2. How many people gave information for this survey?
3. What is the ratio of people who chose football to people who chose track?
4. What percent chose golf?
5. Make a histogram of the data in the frequency table.

Favorite Sport	Tally	Frequency
baseball	𝍸 𝍸 III	13
basketball	𝍸 𝍸 IIII	▒
football	𝍸 𝍸 𝍸 III	▒
golf	𝍸 𝍸 𝍸	▒
soccer	𝍸 𝍸	▒
tennis	𝍸 𝍸	▒
track	𝍸 𝍸 II	▒
wrestling	𝍸 III	▒

Solve. Use the data given below.

Number of Records Owned by Band Members

3	6	7	4	3	5	4	1
5	4	5	2	3	6	8	5
0	2	5	4	7	4	5	8
5	4	2	7	3	1	6	2
6	2	1	5	3	5	0	6

6. Make a frequency table for the set of data.
7. What is the greatest number of records that a band member owns?
8. What is the least number of records that a band member owns?
9. Make a histogram of the data in the frequency table.

NORMAL CURVE

The heights of all eighth-grade boys at a certain school are recorded. The data are presented in a histogram.

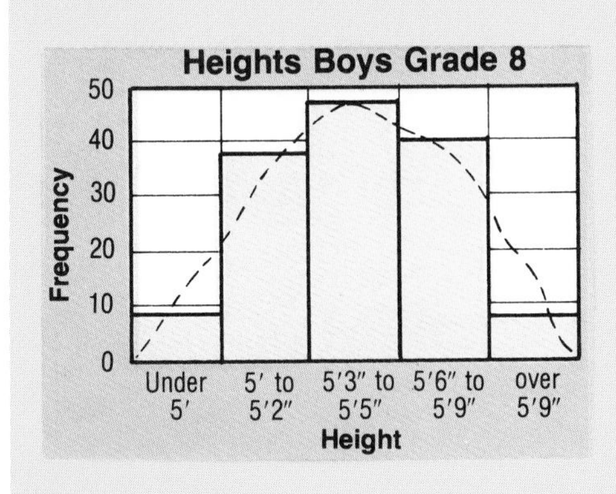

Notice the curve formed by connecting the middle of each frequency bar. This is called a **normal curve.** Many sets of data have the same pattern.

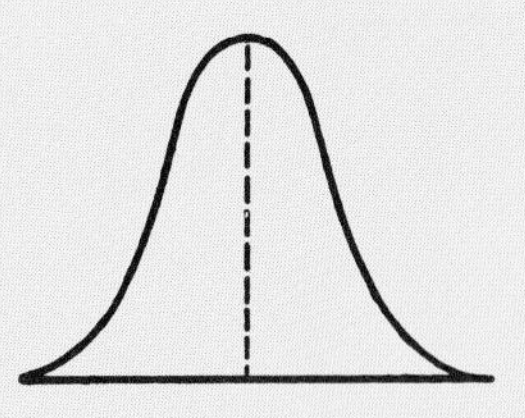

Name some sets of data that have this pattern.

12-8 Using Statistical Graphs

Graphs are used to present data. Different kinds of graphs are used for different purposes.

The **line graph** can be used to show trends or changes.

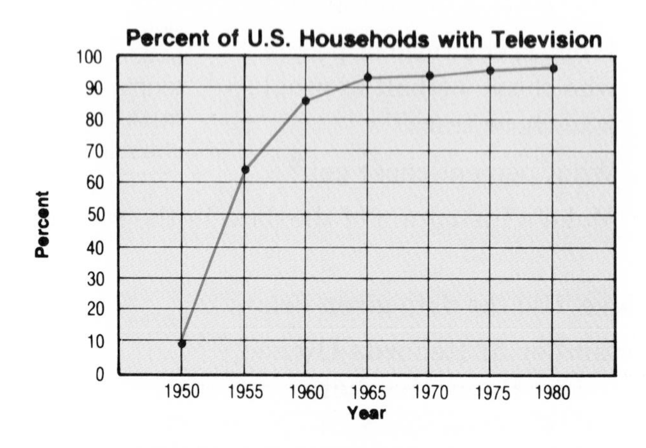

The **bar graph** can be used to show how different quantities compare.

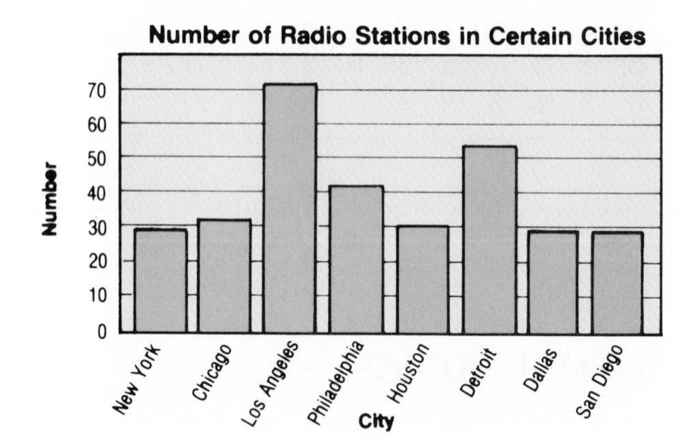

The **pictograph** can be used to present data in an appealing way.

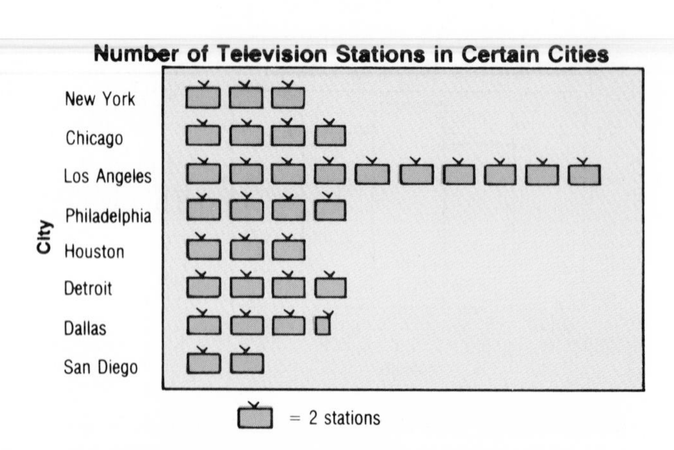

The **circle graph** can be used to compare parts of a whole.

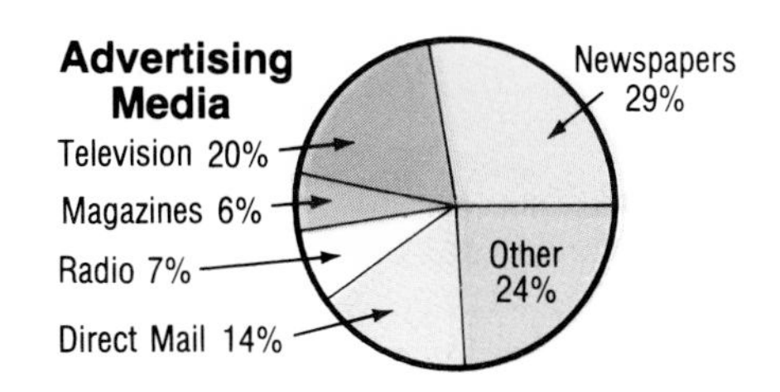

EXERCISES Each of the following is a title for a graph. State whether a line graph, bar graph, pictograph, or circle graph would be best to present the data for each of the following.

1. Number of Cars Produced by Four Car Manufacturers in 1983

2. Population of Iowa from 1920-1980 (10-year intervals)

3. The Budget of Newark City Parks and Recreation

4. Wheat Production in Ten Midwest States

Solve. Use the bar graph.

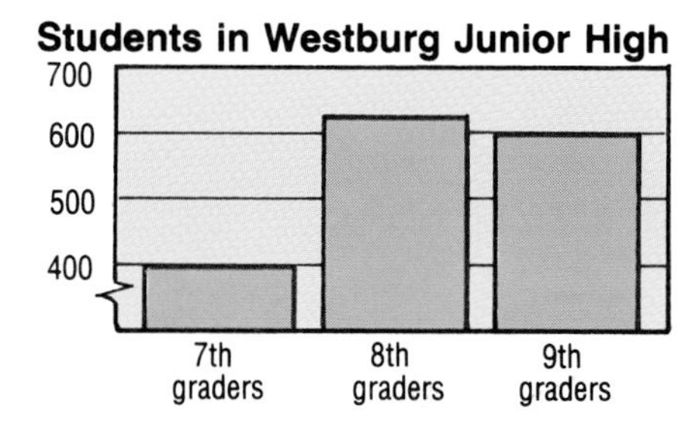

5. About how many seventh graders are there?

6. About how many more eighth graders are there than ninth graders?

7. What is the ratio of seventh graders to ninth graders?

Solve. Use the pictograph.

8. About how many apples did the Adams Orchard produce?

9. About how many more apples did the Lynd Orchard produce than the Smith Orchard?

10. What is the ratio of apples produced in the Cooley Orchard to those produced in the Adams Orchard?

Solve. Use the circle graph.

11. What percent of the Bennetts' income is spent on clothing?

12. Suppose the Bennetts' annual income is \$22,500. How much do they spend on rent?

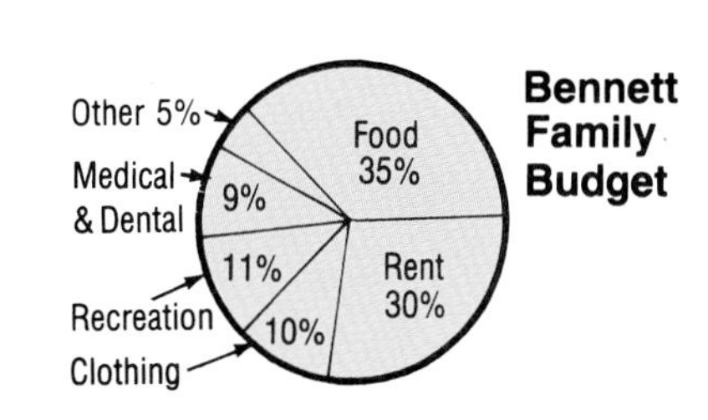

12-9 Problem Solving: Using Statistics

Art Michals takes a poll of 30 people at a concert. Of the 30 people, 10 bought albums, 3 bought T-shirts, and 17 bought nothing. The 30 people polled are a **sample** of all the people at the concert. The results of the poll can be used to predict the number of people who buy items at the concert.

Suppose there are 6,754 at the concert. Mr. Michals needs to predict about how many people buy T-shirts.

Read the problem. You know how many people are at the concert. You also know that of the 30 people polled, 3 bought T-shirts. You need to predict or estimate how many people buy T-shirts.

Decide what to do. The sample is representative of all the people at the concert. Set up a proportion to show two equivalent ratios. Let n represent the total number of people that buy T-shirts.

Solve the problem.

$$\frac{3}{30} = \frac{n}{6{,}754} \quad \Rightarrow \quad \frac{\overset{1}{\cancel{3}}}{\underset{10}{\cancel{30}}} = \frac{n}{6{,}754}$$

Solve for n.

$$1 \times 6{,}754 = 10 \times n \quad \text{Cross products are equal.}$$

$$6{,}754 = 10n$$

$$\frac{6{,}754}{10} = \frac{10n}{10}$$

$$675.4 = n$$

The solution is 675.4.
Mr. Michals predicts that about 675 people buy T-shirts.

Examine the solution. Of the 30 people polled, 3 people or $\frac{1}{10}$ of the people bought T-shirts. Mr. Michals predicts that of the 6,754 people at the concert, about $\frac{1}{10}$ of the people or 675 people buy T-shirts. The answer is reasonable.

Solve. Use the poll shown below.

Favorite Season of the Year	
Spring	16
Summer	13
Autumn	22
Winter	9

1. How many people are in the sample?
2. What part of the sample chose autumn as their favorite season?
3. What percent of the sample chose winter as their favorite season?
4. Suppose 600 people are polled. How many do you predict would choose spring as their favorite season?

Solve. Use the poll shown at the right.

Support for City Council Candidates	
Laura Arthur	24
Gary Hawk	38
Ginny Hobensack	26
Randy Jones	12

5. How many people are in the sample?
6. What part of the sample support Ms. Arthur?
7. What percent support Mr. Jones?
8. Suppose there are 150,000 people in the city. How many do you predict would support Mr. Hawk?
9. Suppose there are 9,040 people in the city. How many do you predict would support Ms. Hobensack?

When a sample is selected, it is usually selected in a random way. The sample also must be representative of the general population. For example, suppose you need to know how much money is spent by a typical American family to heat its home. A sample of only families in Arizona would *not* be representative of the general population.

State whether each of the locations given would be a good place to find a representative sample for the poll given.

	Poll	Location
10.	favorite candidate	Republican headquarters
11.	favorite detergent	laundromat
12.	number of books read	library
13.	number of dogs owned	apartment building
14.	favorite carpet color	carpet store
15.	favorite lunch	school cafeteria

12-10 Range, Mean, Median, and Mode

The Emerick family enjoys camping on weekends. They always compare rates at various campgrounds.

Campground	Rate (dollars per day)
Jackson Lake	15
Camp Tawa	12
Berkshire Campgrounds	10
Skyview Farm	18
Wilderness Trace	12
Lake Buckeye	12
Springpoint Place	27
Sunnydale Camp	15
Dunn Campgrounds	14

Listing the data from least to greatest makes it easier to compare the rates.

RATES in Order
10
12
12
12
14
15
15
18
27

The **range** of a set of data is the difference between the greatest and the least number. What is the range for the data given above?

$\mathbf{27 - 10 = 17}$ The range is 17.

The **mean** of a set of data is the sum of the numbers divided by the number of addends. What is the mean for the set of data given above?

$$\frac{10 + 12 + 12 + 12 + 14 + 15 + 15 + 18 + 27}{9} = \frac{135}{9} \text{ or } 15$$

The mean is 15. The mean is often called the average.

The **median** of a set of data is the middle number when the data is listed in order. If there are two middle numbers, the median is the mean of those two numbers. What is the median for the set of data given above? The middle number is 14. The median is 14.

The **mode** of a set of data is the number that appears most often. What is the mode for the set of data given above? The number 12 appears most often. The mode is 12.
There may be no mode or more than one mode.

***EXERCISES* Find the range, mean, median, and mode for each set of data. Round to the nearest tenth.**

1. 1, 3, 4, 4, 7, 9, 14
2. 58, 61, 58
3. 47, 34, 43, 40, 40
4. 14, 13, 10, 9, 13, 6, 5
5. 45, 31, 40, 38, 45
6. 21, 18, 24, 21
7. 10, 9, 7, 5, 3
8. 16, 16, 14, 19, 13, 15
9. 92, 87, 97, 80, 95
10. 79, 84, 81, 84, 73, 84
11. 75, 80, 78, 84, 79, 87
12. 43, 28, 43, 23, 23, 27
13. 25, 34, 19, 31, 29, 37, 21
14. 3.4, 1.8, 2.6, 1.8, 2.3, 3.1
15. 41, 45, 53, 49, 57, 38, 50
16. 133, 124, 127, 131, 127, 137

Solve.

17. Garcia's mean score in French this month is 77. His first two scores are 75 and 79. He forgets his other score. What is it?

18. Seven employees earn $10,000, 3 earn $12,000, and 2 earn $40,000. List the salaries of the employees. Find the mean, median, and mode.

19. A set of data is 2, 7, 9, 6, 7, 10, 8, and 3. What is the mean? What is the median?

20. Substitute 300 for 3 in the data in problem 19. What is the mean? What is the median?

21. Which is affected more by very great or very small numbers, the mean or median?

PERCENTILES

On various nationwide tests, a **percentile** may be used to describe the score. For example, the 82nd percentile is the point at or below which 82% of the scores fall. Suppose your test score is 85. Your score is at the 75th percentile. This means that 75% of the scores are at or below your score.

Test Scores	
	←100th percentile
96	
86	
	← 75th percentile
85	
80	
	← 50th percentile
78	
74	
	← 25th percentile
73	
65	

Solve. Use the list. For problems 3 and 4, add 86, 67, 82, and 93 to the list.

1. Suppose your score is 78. At what percentile is your score?

2. Suppose your score is 96. At what percentile is your score?

3. What score is at the 75th percentile?

4. Suppose your score is 73. At what percentile is your score?

12-11 Focus on Problem Solving

Using Venn Diagrams

Hope Wilcoxon owns an ice cream store. In a recent poll of 50 people, 25 people liked chocolate, 28 liked vanilla, and 8 liked both. How many people did not like either chocolate or vanilla?

Read the problem. You know how many people were polled. You also know some results of the poll. You need to find the number of people who did not like either chocolate or vanilla.

Decide what to do. Find the total number of people who liked chocolate or vanilla or both. Then subtract this from 50 to find the number who did not like either. Use a **Venn diagram** to show all the possibilities.

Solve the problem. Draw a Venn diagram. The rectangle represents all 50 people. Each circle represents a flavor. The intersection of the circle represents both flavors.

Flavor of Ice Cream Liked

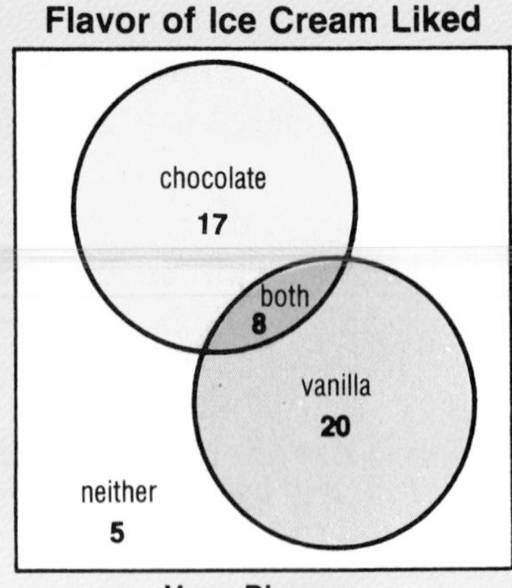

Venn Diagram

The number of people who liked *only* chocolate is 25 − 8 or 17. The number of people who liked *only* vanilla is 28 − 8 or 20. The number of people who liked one flavor or both is found as follows.

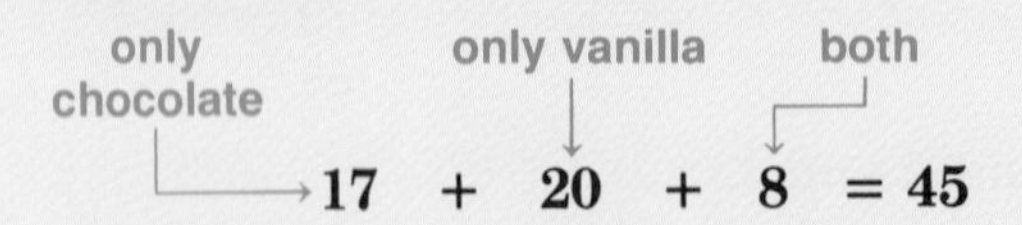

So the number of people who did not like either flavor is 50 − 45 or 5.

Examine the solution. The total of all the possibilities should be 50.

5 + 17 + 20 + 8 = 50 The answer is reasonable and correct.

Solve. Use the Venn diagram.

Letters Received at Sports Banquet

Cross Country only	39
Basketball only	9
Softball only	12
Cross Country and Basketball only	0
Cross Country and Softball only	3
Basketball and Softball only	1
All three	2

1. How many athletes received letters?
2. How many athletes received letters in cross country only?
3. How many athletes received letters in basketball and softball?
4. How many athletes received letters in all three sports?

Solve. Use a Venn diagram.

5. At a buffet, 24 persons chose beef and 20 chose pork. Ten persons chose both beef and pork. Each person at the buffet chose at least one of the two meats. How many people were served at the buffet?

Solve. Use any strategy.

6. Jeff buys a dog for $100 and sells it for $110. Then he buys it back again for $120 and sells it for $130. How much money does he make or lose?
7. Max and Fran have $6.50 all together. If Max borrows 25¢ from Fran, they will each have the same amount. How much does each person have now?

Skills Review: Pages 318-327

Solve. Use the data given below.

Scores on a History Quiz

14	12	19	14	20	14	13	15
16	16	14	12	17	12	13	17
17	16	17	19	20	13	15	17

1. Make a frequency table for the set of data.
2. Find the range for the data.
3. Find the mean for the data.
4. Find the median for the data.
5. Find the mode for the data.
6. Would a circle graph or a bar graph better present the data?

Solve.

7. Of 40 people polled, 18 have a blue car, 13 have a green car, and 6 have a blue car *and* a green car. How many have neither a blue car nor a green car?

Mathematics and Careers

Mary Stashwick is an insurance agent. She uses statistics to find rates for automobile insurance. Liability insurance covers injury to others and their property caused by the person insured. The chart below lists some statistics showing why liability insurance is higher for younger drivers.

Age of Youngest Driver	Average Number of Claims per 100 Drivers	Average Cost of Claim
under 21	12.6	$1,046
21-24	11.0	$1,039
over 24	5.7	$856

Suppose the insurance company insures 10,000 drivers who are at least 25 years old. How many claims can they expect?

The average number of claims for each 100 drivers over 24 is 5.7. Set up a proportion to find the number of claims for each 10,000 drivers.

$$\frac{5.7}{100} = \frac{n}{10{,}000}$$

$$5.7 \times 10{,}000 = 100 \times n$$

$$57{,}000 = 100n$$

$$\frac{57{,}000}{100} = \frac{100n}{100}$$

$$570 = n$$

The company can expect about 570 claims.

Solve.

1. Suppose the insurance company insures 5,550 drivers, ages 21-24. How many claims can they expect?
2. Suppose the insurance company insures 10,500 drivers under 21. How many claims can they expect?
3. Suppose the insurance company insures 10,500 drivers under 21. What would be their cost to pay all the expected claims?
4. Suppose the insurance company insures 3,500 drivers under 21, 4,400 drivers, ages 21-24, and 26,000 drivers over 24. What would be their cost to pay all the expected claims?

Chapter 12 Review

VOCABULARY outcome (305) tree diagram (305) probability (308) independent (310) dependent (310) odds (314) data (318) statistics (318) frequency table (318) histogram (318) line graph (320) bar graph (320) pictograph (320) circle graph (321) range (324) mean (324) median (324) mode (324)

EXERCISES ***Solve. (305-306)***

1. A penny is tossed and a die is rolled. How many outcomes are possible?

2. How many ways can four candles be arranged in a row?

A box contains three 1977 pennies, five 1980 pennies, and four 1983 pennies. Find the probability for each of the following. (308-313)

3. draw a 1980 penny

4. draw a 1983 penny or a 1980 penny

5. draw a 1977 penny, replace it, draw a 1983 penny

Find the odds for each of the following. Refer to the pennies above. (314)

6. for a 1983 penny

7. *not* for a 1977 penny

Solve. Use the data given below, (319, 325)

High Temperature (°C) for Atlanta for a 20-day Period				
21	25	16	18	18
26	21	17	19	21
22	24	26	21	22
17	16	17	20	25

8. Make a histogram of the data.

9. Would a line graph or a bar graph better present the data?

10. Find the range for the data.

11. Find the mean for the data.

12. Find the median for the data.

Ray Burkholder records the weather on 30 random days in a year. It rains on 12 days. The sun shines on 17 days. It neither rains nor does the sun shine on 6 days. Solve. (323)

13. Draw a Venn diagram to represent the situation.

14. How many days does it rain *and* the sun shine?

15. About how many days in a year do you predict there will be sunshine *and* no rain?

Chapter 12 Test

A die is rolled once and the spinner shown at the right is spun once.

1. Draw a tree diagram to show the possible outcomes.
2. State how many outcomes are possible.

Solve.

3. How many ways can five photos be lined up in a photo album?
4. Two die are rolled. What are the odds of rolling a sum of 6?

The letters in the word PARIS are written on slips of paper and placed in a hat. A slip of paper is drawn from the hat. Find the probability for each of the following.

5. an R
6. a Q
7. not an R
8. an R or a vowel
9. an R or a consonant
10. draw an A, do not replace it, draw a vowel

Fifty people were polled about the kind of laundry detergent they use. Of the 50 people, 24 used Soilfree, 8 used Neatnix, 5 used Surprise, and 13 used First Place.

11. Make a histogram for the set of data.
12. Would a pictograph or a circle graph better present the data?

Find the range, mean, median, and mode for each set of data. Round to the nearest tenth.

13. 5, 4, 6, 10, 3, 6, 6
14. 8, 8, 8, 2, 0, 4

Solve. Use the poll.

15. What part of the sample supports Goldberg?
16. Out of 1,440 people, how many do you predict support Underwood?

Whom do you support for council?	
Miller	13
Goldberg	24
Underwood	23

17. Mrs. Santiago has 25 students in her class. Nine have blonde hair and 16 have brown eyes. Five have blonde hair and brown eyes. How many have blonde hair but not brown eyes?

Enrichment

Scattergrams show how two things are related. Terry Wilder wants to know if the number of cars a family has is related to the size of the family. He collected the data presented in the chart.

Family size	2	2	2	3	3	2	5	3	2	5	3	3	6	1	4	4	4	1
Number of cars	1	2	1	3	2	2	3	2	1	2	1	1	3	1	2	4	2	0

Make a scattergram as follows. Plot the point that represents a family of 2 and 1 car. Start at the lower left. This point is shown by the black dot.

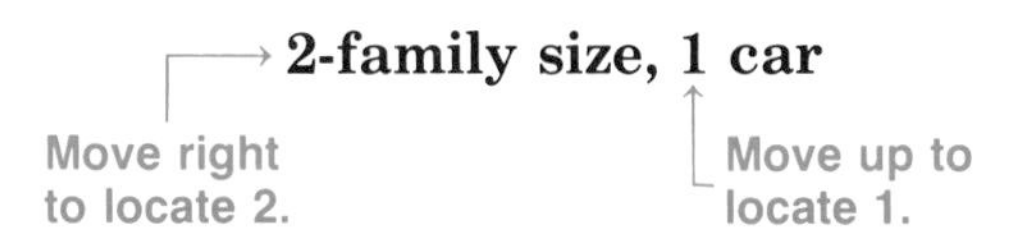

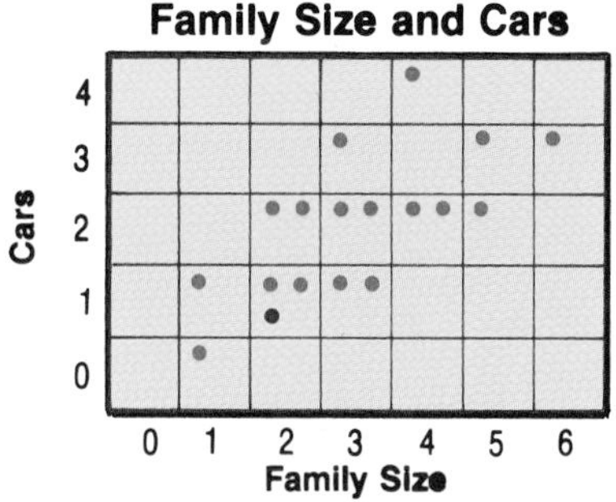

The rest of the data is plotted.

Solve. Use the scattergram above.

1. How many families have 3 or more cars?
2. How many families have a size of 3?
3. What does the scattergram tell you about how the size of a family and the number of cars are related?

Draw a scattergram for the following data. Then tell how the two groups of data are related.

4.

Age (months)	12	123	181	46	170	183	34	151	218	105	60	1	213	60	78
Height (cm)	71	152	157	99	157	168	86	147	183	142	101	53	170	102	107

Explain how you think each of the following things may be related.

5. outside temperature, heating bill
6. sales per salesperson, years of experience per salesperson
7. test score, height of student
8. miles per gallon, weight of car
9. height, weight
10. amount of fertilizer, crop yield

13 Real Numbers and Graphing

Barbara and Gary Sewell plan a trip to the Wisconsin Dells. They use a square map that has 9 units along each side. The area of the map is 9×9 or 81 square units. You say 81 is the *square* of 9, or 9 **squared** is 81 ($9^2 = 81$).

13–1 Squares and Square Roots

The region the square map represents has an area of 81 square miles. What is the length of each side of the region?

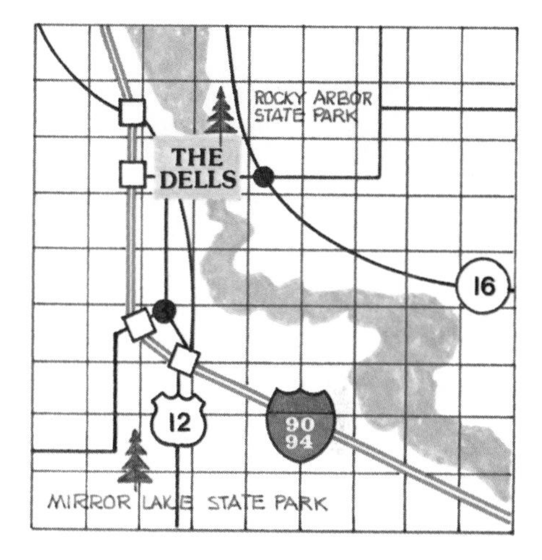

$\mathbf{A = s^2}$ This is the formula for the area of square.

$\mathbf{81 = s \times s}$

What number multiplied by itself gives 81? Since $81 = 9 \times 9$, $s = 9$. The length of each side of the region is 9 miles.

Since $9 \times 9 = 81$, a **square root** of 81 is 9.

$\mathbf{\sqrt{81} = 9}$ The positive square root of 81 is 9.

Since $^-9 \times {}^-9 = 81$, another square root of 81 is $^-9$. Notice that a negative sign is used to indicate the negative square root.

$\mathbf{^-\sqrt{81} = {}^-9}$ The negative square root of 81 is $^-9$.

***EXERCISES* Find the square of each number.**

1. 2 **2.** 5 **3.** 14 **4.** 25 **5.** 81 **6.** 144

Find each of the following.

7. $\sqrt{4}$ **8.** $\sqrt{49}$ **9.** $\sqrt{25}$ **10.** $\sqrt{16}$ **11.** $\sqrt{121}$ **12.** $\sqrt{225}$

13. $^-\sqrt{9}$ **14.** $^-\sqrt{64}$ **15.** $^-\sqrt{1}$ **16.** $^-\sqrt{144}$ **17.** $^-\sqrt{100}$ **18.** $\sqrt{625}$

19. $\sqrt{4} + \sqrt{9}$ **20.** $^-\sqrt{49} + \sqrt{36}$ **21.** $\sqrt{144} \div \sqrt{1}$ **22.** $\sqrt{100} \times \sqrt{16}$

23. $\sqrt{\frac{4}{49}}$ **24.** $\sqrt{\frac{25}{36}}$ **25.** $\sqrt{5^2}$ **26.** $\sqrt{(^-2)^2}$

Solve.

27. Rosa makes a square rug that has an area of 400 square inches. What is the length of each side of the rug?

13-2 Approximating Square Roots

Patrick has a map of Madison with a square inset map of its downtown in the corner. This region has an area of 20 square kilometers. What is the length of each side of this region?

$$\mathbf{A = s^2}$$

$$\mathbf{20 = s \times s}$$

$$\mathbf{\sqrt{20} = s}$$

$\sqrt{20} > 4$ because $4 \times 4 = 16$.
$\sqrt{20} < 5$ because $5 \times 5 = 25$.
So $\sqrt{20}$ is between 4 and 5.

A square root table can be used to find the approximation of square roots. The following example shows how to use the table on page 422 to find the square root of 20.

For $N = 20$
$\sqrt{N} \approx 4.472$

N	N^2	$\sqrt{N}$
19	361	4.359
20	400	4.472
21	441	4.583

If the square root is a whole number, you can use the table to find square roots up to 10,000.

Think $\sqrt{N^2} = N$.
For $N^2 = 4{,}624$,
$\sqrt{N^2} = \sqrt{4{,}624}$ and $N = 68$.

N	N^2	$\sqrt{N}$
67	4489	8.185
68	4624	8.246
69	4761	8.307

Some calculators have a key labeled $\sqrt{x}$. You can use this key to find the positive square root of a number.

Enter 20. `20.`
Press the square root key. `4.472136`

You can use the square root table to solve equations. Study the example below.

$$\mathbf{c^2 = 75}$$

$\sqrt{c^2} = \sqrt{75}$ Take the square root of each side.

$c \approx 8.660$ Find 75 in the N-column. Then, find the corresponding entry in the $\sqrt{N}$-column.

The table only shows positive square roots. The opposite of 8.660 is also a solution.

$c \approx 8.660$ or $^-8.660$ The solutions are about 8.660 *and* about $^-8.660$.

EXERCISES ***State whether each of the following is an integer.***

1. $\sqrt{3}$ **2.** $\sqrt{16}$ **3.** $\sqrt{51}$ **4.** $^-\sqrt{18}$ **5.** $^-\sqrt{81}$ **6.** $^-\sqrt{90.5}$

State two consecutive integers between which each of the following lies.

7. $\sqrt{8}$ **8.** $\sqrt{56}$ **9.** $\sqrt{85}$ **10.** $^-\sqrt{24}$ **11.** $^-\sqrt{52}$ **12.** $^-\sqrt{117}$

Use the table on page 422 to find each square root.

13. $\sqrt{8}$ **14.** $\sqrt{13}$ **15.** $\sqrt{34}$ **16.** $\sqrt{45}$ **17.** $\sqrt{78}$ **18.** $\sqrt{93}$

19. $^-\sqrt{3}$ **20.** $^-\sqrt{24}$ **21.** $^-\sqrt{39}$ **22.** $^-\sqrt{56}$ **23.** $^-\sqrt{62}$ **24.** $^-\sqrt{96}$

25. $\sqrt{484}$ **26.** $\sqrt{841}$ **27.** $\sqrt{6,889}$ **28.** $^-\sqrt{361}$ **29.** $^-\sqrt{2,401}$ **30.** $^-\sqrt{3,844}$

Solve each equation.

31. $a^2 = 64$ **32.** $b^2 = 49$ **33.** $c^2 = 81$ **34.** $d^2 = 100$

35. $e^2 = 22$ **36.** $f^2 = 37$ **37.** $g^2 = 40$ **38.** $h^2 = 59$

39. $m^2 + 9 = 25$ **40.** $a^2 + 64 = 100$ **41.** $k^2 - 15 = 70$

Solve.

42. Find all numbers between 1 and 200 whose square roots are integers.

43. Wei-Min makes a square quilt that has an area of 100 square feet. It has 25 square blocks each the same size. What is the length of each side of a block?

44. Jamee's living room is square. It has an area of 225 square feet. How many square yards of carpeting does it take to carpet the room?

13-3 Real Numbers

You know about integers and rational numbers. Integers are numbers such as 3, 0, $^{-}5$, and 91. Rational numbers are numbers that can be named as the quotient of two integers.

Rational numbers, like 144, 81, and $\frac{36}{121}$, whose square roots are rational numbers are called **perfect squares.** Consider the square roots of numbers which are *not* perfect squares.

2 is not a perfect square.	$\sqrt{2} = 1.4142136\ldots$	This decimal continues forever without any pattern of repeating digits.

A number which can be named by a nonterminating, nonrepeating decimal is called an **irrational number.** Irrational numbers together with rational numbers form the set of **real numbers.** Study the following examples.

Real Numbers	Irrational Numbers	Rational Numbers	Integers
$^{-}7$		$^{-}7$	$^{-}7$
$0.12121212\ldots$		$0.12121212\ldots$	
$\sqrt{14}$	$\sqrt{14}$		
$0.1011011101111\ldots$	$0.1011011101111\ldots$		
$\sqrt{9}$		$\sqrt{9}$	$\sqrt{9}$

EXERCISES ***Name the set or sets of numbers to which each number belongs, the integers, rationals, irrationals, or reals.***

1. $^{-}6$ **2.** $\frac{1}{2}$ **3.** $\frac{9}{3}$ **4.** 15 **5.** $^{-}0.3333\ldots$

6. $\sqrt{12}$ **7.** $\sqrt{25}$ **8.** 0.125 **9.** 0.36945 **10.** $0.\overline{53}$

11. 0.6125 **12.** $3.1416\ldots$ **13.** $\sqrt{\frac{100}{36}}$ **14.** $^{-}\sqrt{16}$ **15.** $^{-}\sqrt{43}$

16. 1.123124125 **17.** $0.\overline{571428}$ **18.** $2.9\overline{36}$ **19.** $5.45445444\ldots$

State whether each of the following is true or false.

20. Every rational number is a real number.

21. Every number is a rational number.

22. The number $^{-}2.4$ is irrational.

23. The number 0 is real.

Mathematics and Science

The distance you can see from an airplane in clear weather is given by the following formula.

$D = 3.56\sqrt{A}$

D represents distance in kilometers.
A represents altitude in meters.

Suppose Vaughn flies in a plane at an altitude of 5,000 meters. How far can he see?

$D = 3.56\sqrt{A}$

$D = 3.56 \times \sqrt{5{,}000}$ Replace *A* with 5,000.

$D \approx 3.56 \times 70.71$ Use a calculator to find $\sqrt{5{,}000}$.

$D \approx 252$ To the nearest kilometer, Vaughn can see 252 km.

EXERCISES ***Find D when A has each of the following values.***

1. 1,000 meters
2. 3,000 meters
3. 10,000 meters
4. 12 kilometers
5. At what altitude can you see a distance of 500 kilometers?

The following formula can be used to find the time it takes for an object to fall a certain distance.

$t = \frac{\sqrt{d}}{4}$ *t* represents time in seconds.
d represents distance in feet.

Find t when d has each of the following values.

6. 100 feet
7. 400 feet
8. 1,000 feet
9. 1 mile

Solve.

10. An apple falls from a tree branch that is 16 feet from the ground. In how many seconds does it hit the ground?

13-4 Inequalities

Jim Batey is an air traffic controller. For every aircraft within a certain radius of the control tower, there is a corresponding mark on the screen.

Likewise, for every real number, rational or irrational, there is a corresponding point on the number line. You have graphed rational numbers on the number line before. Irrational numbers can be graphed by using their decimal approximations.

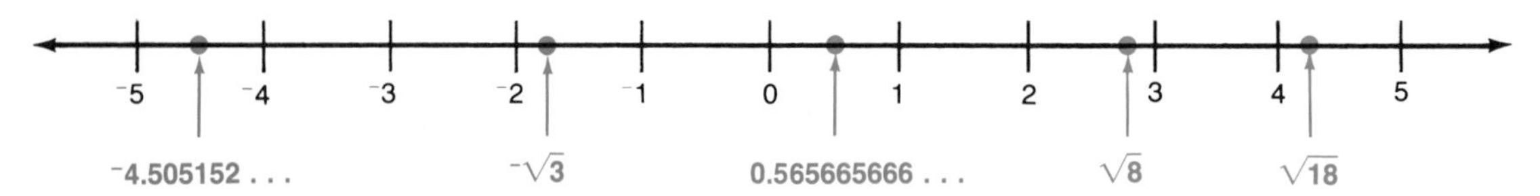

A mathematical sentence that contains a symbol as $<$, $>$, $\leq$, $\geq$, or $\neq$ is called an **inequality.** You can use a number line to show the solutions to an inequality. Consider the inequality $x > {}^-2$. It has many solutions. Every real number greater than ⁻2 is a solution.

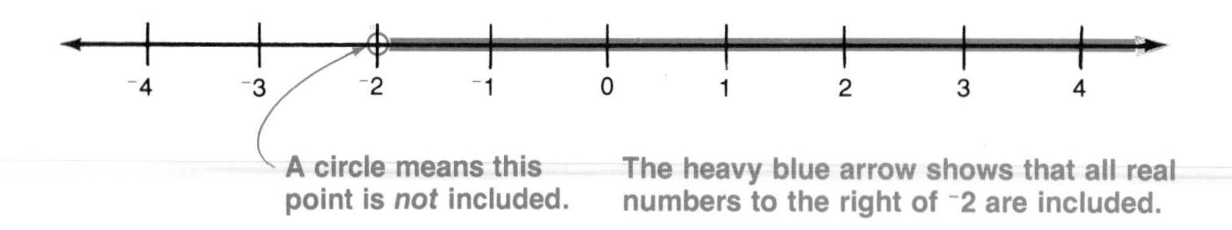

Use a number line to show the solutions to $a \leq \frac{1}{2}$.

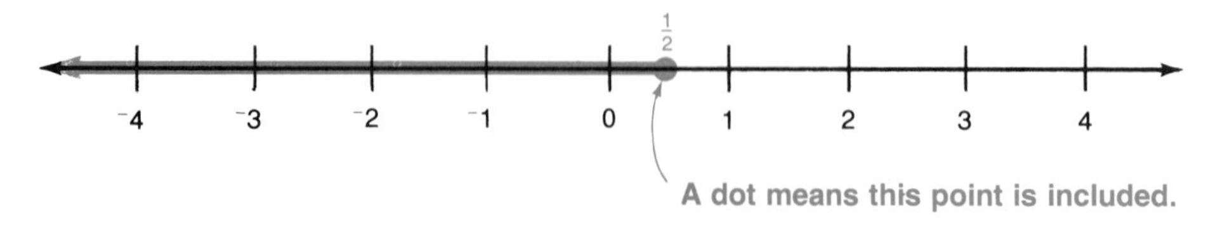

You can solve inequalities like you solve equations.

$$\mathbf{n - 7 > 5}$$
$$\mathbf{n - 7 + 7 > 5 + 7}$$
$$\mathbf{n > 12}$$

To check the solution, replace n with any number greater than 12. For example, use 13.

$$\mathbf{n - 7 > 5}$$
$$\mathbf{13 - 7 \overset{?}{>} 5}$$
$$\mathbf{6 > 5} \checkmark$$

The solution is any number greater than 12 ($n > 12$).

$$\mathbf{2p \le 14}$$
$$\mathbf{\frac{2p}{2} \le \frac{14}{2}}$$
$$\mathbf{p \le 7}$$

To check the solution, replace p with any number less than or equal to 7. For example, use 6.

$$\mathbf{2p \le 14}$$
$$\mathbf{2 \times 6 \overset{?}{\le} 14}$$
$$\mathbf{12 \le 14} \checkmark$$

The solution is any number less than or equal to 7 ($p \le 7$).

EXERCISES Write the inequality for each of the following.

1. 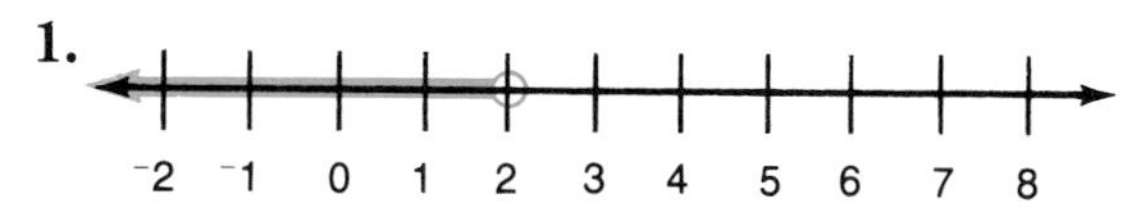

2. 

3. 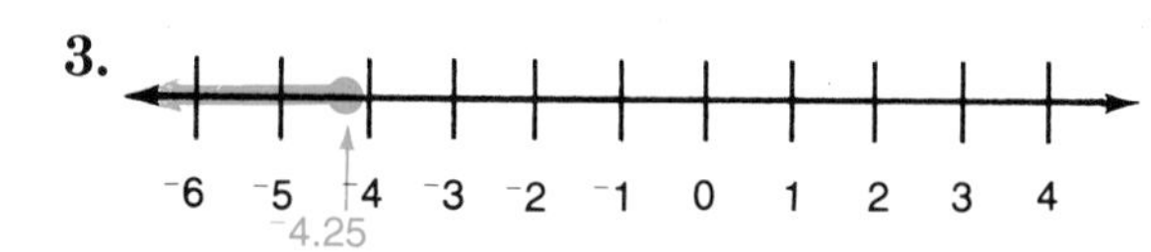

4. 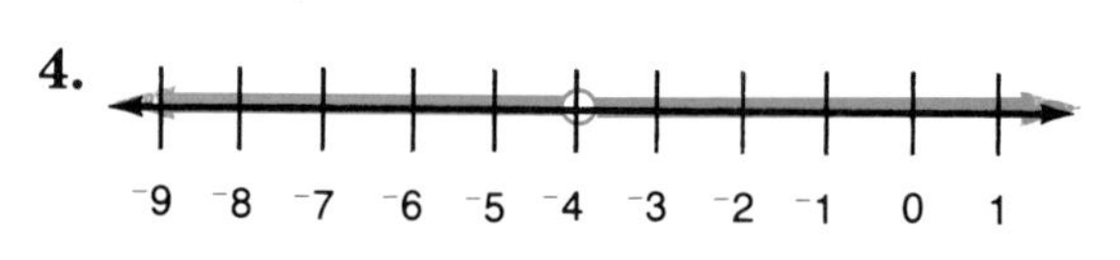

Use a number line to show the solutions to each of the following inequalities.

5. $y > 2$ **6.** $x < {}^{-}3$ **7.** $m \le {}^{-}1$ **8.** $y < 6$

9. $x \ge {}^{-}5$ **10.** $t \ge 0$ **11.** $x \ne 4$ **12.** $n \le {}^{-}1.5$

Solve each inequality. Check your solution.

13. $m - 7 < 6$ **14.** $n - 8 > 5$ **15.** $x + 4 > 9$ **16.** $p + 5 < 10$

17. $6t < 96$ **18.** $5m > 45$ **19.** $\frac{b}{3} > 2$ **20.** $\frac{k}{6} > 14$

Solve.

21. Scott needs to buy at least 7 pairs of socks. They come in packages of 3 pairs. What is the least number of packages he should buy?

13–5 The Coordinate System

Anna Rodriquez is hiking in Shawnee Forest. The forest has been mapped using a **coordinate system.** In a coordinate system, two perpendicular number lines are used. The horizontal number line is called the **x-axis.** The vertical number line is called the **y-axis.** The point where the number lines cross is called the **origin.** The number lines separate a plane into four **quadrants.**

Each point on the coordinate system has an **x-coordinate** and a **y-coordinate.** The coordinates of each point are named as an **ordered pair.** Use the ordered pair (2, 4) to locate Pinehill Peak.

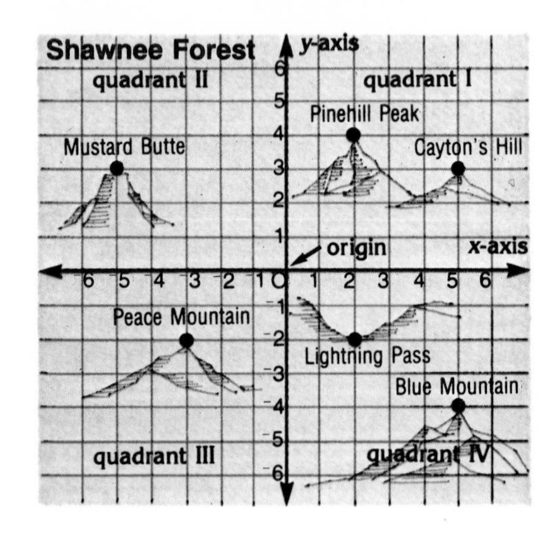

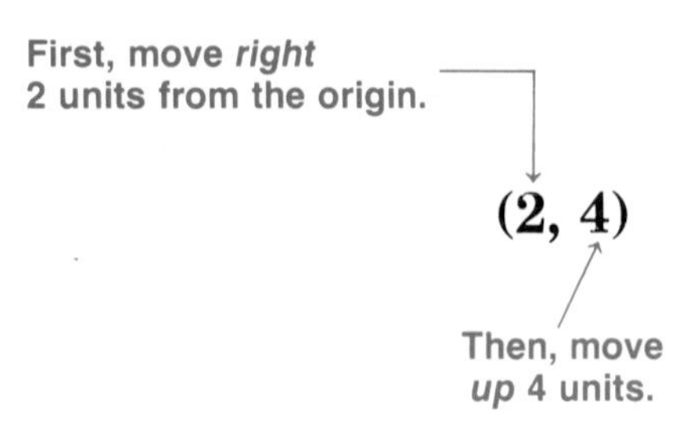

What are the coordinates of Blue Mountain?

***EXERCISES* Use the coordinate system shown below. Name the letter for each ordered pair.**

1. $(^-4, 2)$	**2.** (1, 3)	**3.** $(^-3, ^-2)$
4. $(2, ^-1)$	**5.** (3, 5)	**6.** $(^-1, 4)$
7. $(4, ^-5)$	**8.** $(^-5, 0)$	**9.** $(^-2, ^-3)$

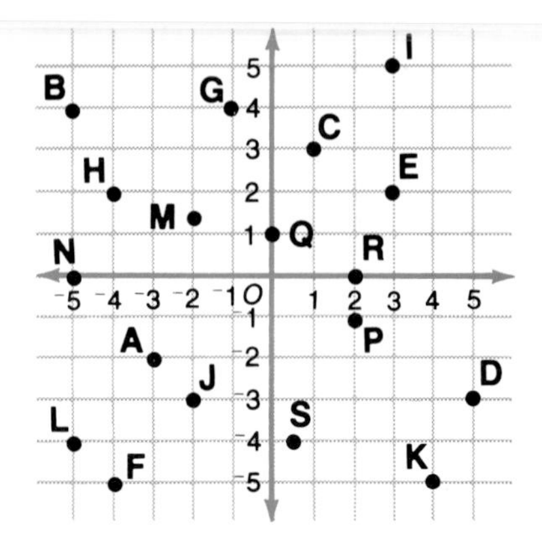

Name the ordered pair for each letter.

10. E	**11.** F	**12.** B
13. D	**14.** L	**15.** Q
16. S	**17.** M	**18.** R

State which quadrant contains the graph of each of the following.

19. $(^{-}3, 2)$
20. $(1, 1)$
21. $\left(4\frac{1}{2}, 5\right)$
22. $(^{-}6, ^{-}3)$
23. $(7, ^{-}4)$
24. $\left(5, ^{-}8\frac{1}{2}\right)$
25. $(^{-}2, ^{-}3)$
26. $(^{-}7, 2)$

On graph paper, draw a coordinate system. Then graph and label each of the following ordered pairs.

27. $J(0, 5)$
28. $L(^{-}5, 0)$
29. $N(^{-}4, 2)$
30. $P(^{-}3, ^{-}5)$
31. $Q(5, ^{-}2)$
32. $R(1, 3)$
33. $S\left(^{-}4\frac{1}{2}, ^{-}4\right)$
34. $T(3, ^{-}3.5)$

Solve.

35. Larry rides his bicycle 14 blocks west and 8 blocks south to the store. Then he rides 5 blocks east, 2 blocks north, and 9 blocks east. How many blocks is he from home?

36. Rachel hikes 3 kilometers north, then 2 kilometers west, then 4 kilometers south, and finally 2 kilometers east. How far is she from where she started?

37. Jody's house and school are shown on the map. How many different routes can she take to school? (Assume she does not backtrack or go on a diagonal.)

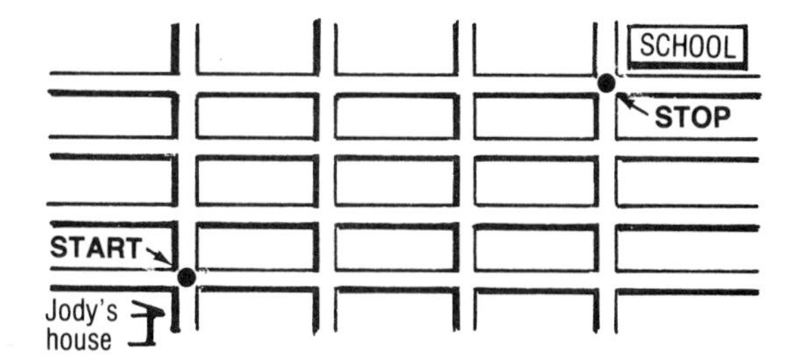

WHAT IS IT?

Graph and label each of the following ordered pairs. Then connect the points in alphabetical order.

$A(0, ^{-}5)$	$B(2, ^{-}4)$	$C(1, ^{-}1)$	$D(3, ^{-}1)$	$E(8, 4)$	$F(3, 4)$
$G(1, 2)$	$H(1, 3)$	$I(2, 4)$	$J(0, 6)$	$K(^{-}1, 2)$	$L(^{-}3, 4)$
$M(^{-}8, 4)$	$N(^{-}3, ^{-}1)$	$O(^{-}1, ^{-}1)$	$P(^{-}2, ^{-}4)$	$Q(0, ^{-}5)$	

13-6 Using Coordinates

Vince Marinacci spends a weekend at Hocking Lake. When the water in the lake is calm, he can see reflections of things on the shore.

Consider the triangle shown on the coordinate system at the right. It has vertices at points A(1, 3), B(4, 4), and C(3, 1).

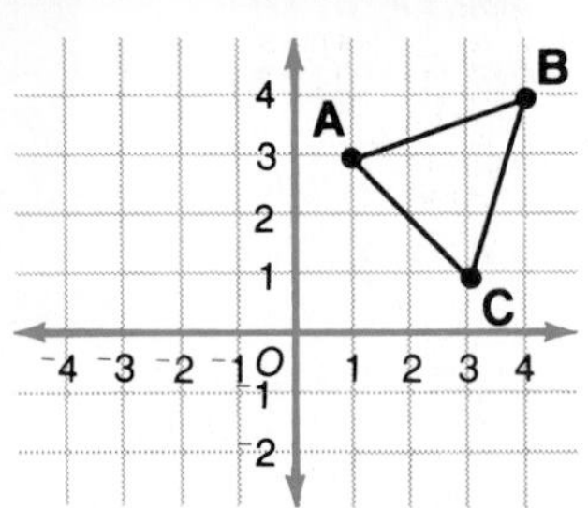

Suppose you multiply the x-coordinate of each point by $^{-}1$.

A(1, 3) → D($^{-}1$, 3)

B(4, 4) → E($^{-}4$, 4)

C(3, 1) → F($^{-}3$, 1)

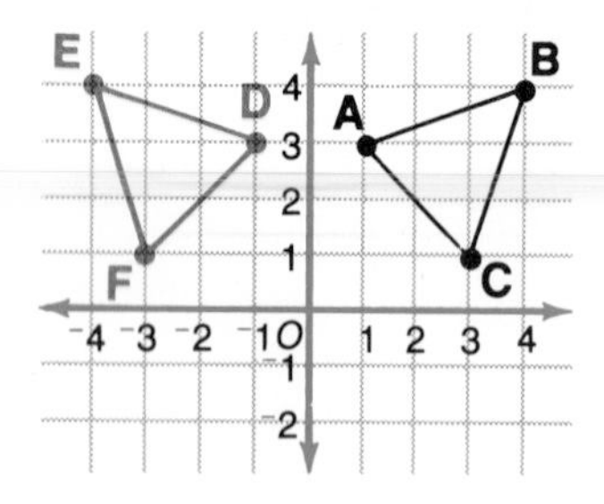

Triangle DEF is a **reflection** of triangle ABC about the y-axis.

Suppose you add $^{-}3$ to the y-coordinate of each point.

A(1, 3) → G(1, 0)

B(4, 4) → H(4, 1)

C(3, 1) → I(3, $^{-}2$)

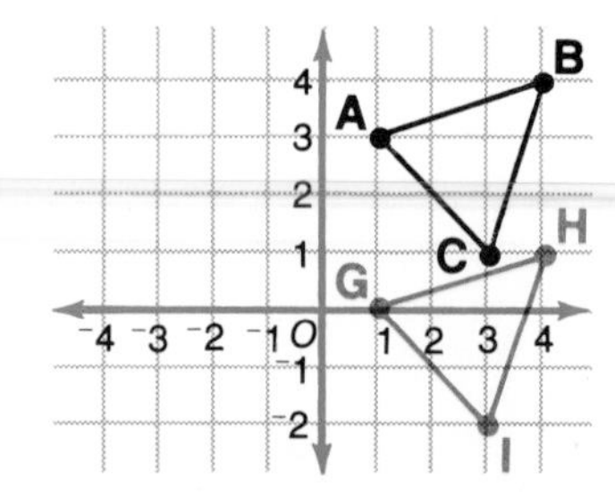

Triangle GHI is a **translation** of triangle ABC down 3 units.

In a reflection or a translation, the size and shape of the original figure is *not* affected.

EXERCISES ***Copy triangle JKL on graph paper. Then draw the triangle you get by doing each of the following.***

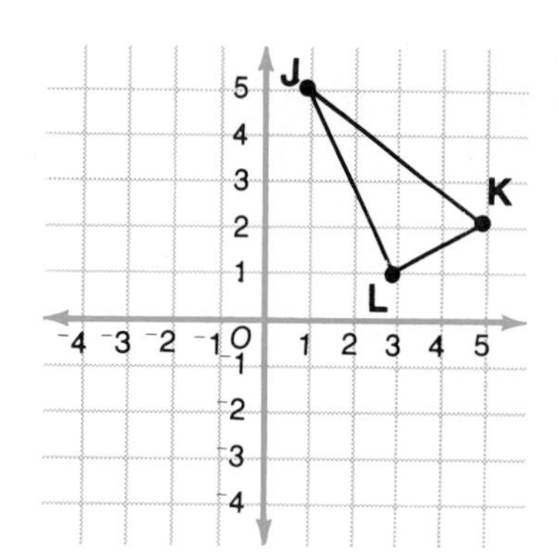

1. Multiply the y-coordinate of each vertex by $^-1$.
2. Multiply both coordinates of each vertex by $^-1$.
3. Add $^-3$ to the y-coordinate of each vertex.
4. Add $^-2$ to the x-coordinate and 1 to the y-coordinate of each vertex.
5. On graph paper, graph the points A(1, 6), B(2, 2), and C(5, 4). Reflect each point over the x-axis. Write the coordinates of each new point.
6. On graph paper, graph the points P($^-2$, 4), Q(1, 3), and R($^-1$, $^-2$). Translate each point 2 units up. Write the coordinates of each new point.
7. On graph paper, graph the points K($^-3$, 3), L($^-1$, 3), M(0, 1), and N($^-4$, 1). Translate each point right 5 units. Then reflect each point over the x-axis. Write the coordinates of each resulting point.

Skills Review: Pages 333-343

Find each of the following. Use the table on page 422 if necessary.

1. $\sqrt{64}$ **2.** $^-\sqrt{49}$ **3.** $^-\sqrt{85}$ **4.** $\sqrt{43}$ **5.** $\sqrt{2{,}304}$ **6.** $^-\sqrt{5{,}041}$

State whether each of the following is rational or irrational.

7. 14.1 **8.** 0.5454 . . . **9.** $\sqrt{19}$

Use a number line to show the solutions to each of the following inequalities.

10. $x > {}^-1$ **11.** $2b \leq 4$

Use the coordinate system shown at the right. Name the ordered pair for each letter.

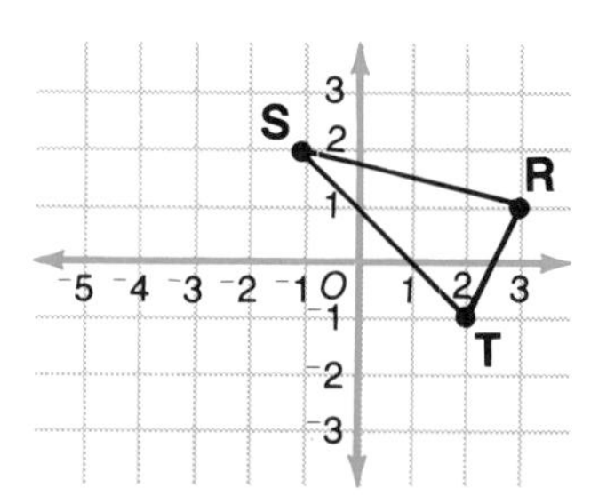

12. R **13.** S **14.** T

15. Copy triangle RST on graph paper. Add $^-4$ to the x-coordinate of each vertex. Then draw the new triangle.

Cumulative Review

Estimate.

1. $\begin{array}{r} 4.96 \\ + 7.854 \\ \hline \end{array}$ **2.** $\begin{array}{r} 65.85 \\ - 19.09 \\ \hline \end{array}$ **3.** $\begin{array}{r} 52.7 \\ \times \ 6.9 \\ \hline \end{array}$ **4.** $398\overline{)2,145}$ **5.** $9.2\overline{)284.6}$

Add, subtract, multiply, or divide.

6. $\begin{array}{r} 92.7 \\ + 34.35 \\ \hline \end{array}$ **7.** $\begin{array}{r} 62.39 \\ - \ 8.954 \\ \hline \end{array}$ **8.** $\begin{array}{r} 0.087 \\ \times \ 0.03 \\ \hline \end{array}$ **9.** $\begin{array}{r} 0.968 \\ \times \ 3.49 \\ \hline \end{array}$ **10.** $16\overline{)11}$

11. $15.5\overline{)96.1}$ **12.** $12 + {}^{-}9$ **13.** $5 - 11.5$ **14.** ${}^{-}25 - {}^{-}15$

15. ${}^{-}8.2 \times 9$ **16.** $14 \times {}^{-}0.2$ **17.** $32 \div {}^{-}8$ **18.** ${}^{-}90 \div {}^{-}30$

Find the greatest common factor (GCF) for each group of numbers.

19. 14, 21 **20.** 24, 36 **21.** 6, 24, 39

Find the least common multiple (LCM) for each group of numbers.

22. 10, 25 **23.** 4, 16 **24.** 6, 8, 10

Add, subtract, multiply, or divide. Write each answer in simplest form.

25. $\frac{5}{6} + \frac{5}{12}$ **26.** $4\frac{3}{4} + 6\frac{1}{8}$ **27.** $3\frac{3}{4} + 2\frac{1}{6}$ **28.** $\frac{11}{15} - \frac{2}{5}$

29. $7\frac{3}{4} - 4\frac{3}{8}$ **30.** $14\frac{2}{3} - 6\frac{3}{4}$ **31.** $\frac{7}{8} \times 2$ **32.** $4\frac{4}{9} \times \frac{3}{5}$

33. $2\frac{2}{7} \times 4\frac{1}{12}$ **34.** $\frac{7}{16} \div \frac{1}{4}$ **35.** $2\frac{5}{8} \div 1\frac{7}{8}$ **36.** $14 \div 5\frac{3}{5}$

Solve each equation. Check your solution.

37. $d + 40 = 27$ **38.** $a - 4 = 32$ **39.** $10z = 5$

40. $\frac{x}{7} = 12$ **41.** $\frac{2}{3}r = {}^{-}24$ **42.** $\frac{y}{3} + 6 = {}^{-}9$

Solve.

43. What number is 65% of 60? **44.** What percent of 75 is 30?

45. 70 is 35% of what number? **46.** 5.4% of 80 is what number?

Find the range, mean, median, and mode for each of the following.

47. 36, 28, 35, 37, 24, 35, 29 **48.** 384, 638, 596, 972, 430

Complete each of the following.

49. 16.4 m = ▒ cm
50. 238 m = ▒ km
51. 2.65 g = ▒ mg
52. 1,150 g = ▒ kg
53. 49 mL = ▒ L
54. 6.7 kL = ▒ L

Solve.

55. Benito Diaz builds a tool box. It is 1.1 m long, 0.6 m wide, and 0.4 m deep. Find its surface area and volume.

56. A waitress earned $22.65 one day in tips. She worked from 6:30 A.M. to 2:00 P.M. How much did she average per hour?

Mathematics Lab

One method for approximating square roots is called the **divide-and-average method.** The steps below show how to approximate $\sqrt{18}$.

Step 1 Locate 18 between consecutive perfect squares.

$$\mathbf{16 < 18 < 25}$$
$$\mathbf{\sqrt{16} < \sqrt{18} < \sqrt{25}}$$
$$\mathbf{4 < \sqrt{18} < 5}$$

Choose 4 as the first approximation because 18 is closer to 16.

Step 2 Divide the number by the approximation. Carry the quotient to *twice* as many digits as the divisor.

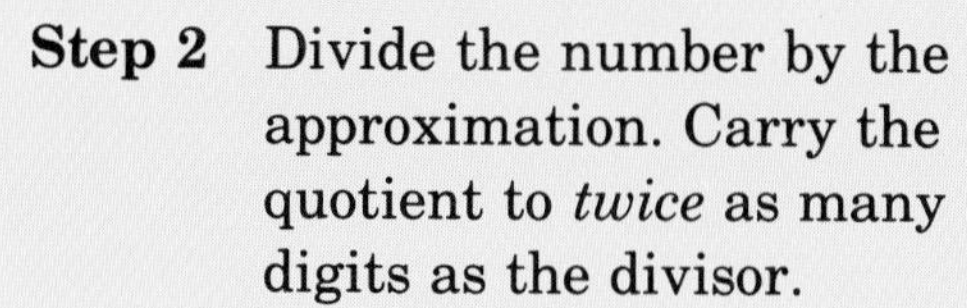

Step 3 Average the quotient and the divisor. Carry the average to the same number of digits as the quotient. Do not round.

4.2 is the new approximation.

Step 4 Repeat steps 2 and 3 using the new approximation.

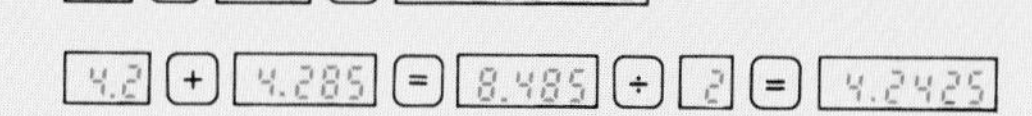

An approximation for $\sqrt{18}$ is 4.242. More accurate approximations may be made by continuing the divide-and-average method.

Use the divide-and-average method twice to approximate each square root.

1. $\sqrt{11}$ **2.** $\sqrt{30}$ **3.** $^{-}\sqrt{51}$ **4.** $\sqrt{277}$ **5.** $\sqrt{848}$ **6.** $\sqrt{1,209}$

13-7 Equations with Two Variables

The Primms are retired and like to travel. Mr. Primm drives about one-half of the time. Suppose x represents the total driving time and y represents Mr. Primm's driving time. Since Mr. Primm drives one-half of the time, $y = \frac{1}{2}x$.

Day	Total Driving Time	One-half of Total Driving Time	Mr. Primm's Driving Time
	x	$\frac{1}{2}x$	y
Monday	4	$\frac{1}{2} \times 4$	2
Wednesday	6	$\frac{1}{2} \times 6$	3
Friday	7	$\frac{1}{2} \times 7$	$3\frac{1}{2}$

Equations with two variables, like $y = \frac{1}{2}x$, have infinitely many solutions. For every value that is substituted for x, there is a corresponding value for y. Each x-value with its corresponding y-value can be expressed as an ordered pair (x, y).

Consider the equation $y = 2x + 1$. You can find an ordered pair that makes a true equation as follows.

$y = 2x + 1$ Suppose $x = 4$.

$y = 2 \times 4 + 1$ Replace x with 4.

$y = 8 + 1$

$y = 9$

When $x = 4$, $y = 9$. So, the ordered pair $(4, 9)$ *satisfies* the equation $y = 2x + 1$.

Can you find other ordered pairs that satisfy the equation?

Ordered pairs that satisfy an equation can be found by using a table like the one shown at the right. How can you check that the ordered pairs (0, 1) and (2, 5) satisfy the equation $y = 2x + 1$?

$\mathbf{y = 2x + 1}$

x	$2x + 1$	y
4	$2 \times 4 + 1$	9
0	$2 \times 0 + 1$	1
2	$2 \times 2 + 1$	5

EXERCISES ***State which of the ordered pairs satisfy the given equation.***

1. $y = x + 1$
- **a.** (1, 1)
- **b.** (1, 0)
- **c.** (0, 1)

2. $y = 5 - x$
- **a.** $(^-3, 8)$
- **b.** $(0, ^-5)$
- **c.** (1, 6)

3. $y = 2x - 5$
- **a.** $(0, ^-4)$
- **b.** $(1, ^-3)$
- **c.** (3, 2)

4. $y = \frac{1}{2}x + 2$
- **a.** (6, 9)
- **b.** $(^-4, 0)$
- **c.** $(3, 3\frac{1}{2})$

Copy. ***Complete the table for each equation.***

5. $y = 3x$

x	$3x$	y
0	3×0	0
1	3×1	▒
3	3×3	▒

6. $y = x + 2$

x	$x + 2$	y
2	$2 + 2$	▒
4	▒ $+ 2$	▒
6	▒ $+ 2$	▒

7. $y = x - 5$

x	$x - 5$	y
$^-1$	$^-1 - 5$	▒
2	▒ $- 5$	▒
5	▒ $- 5$	▒

8. $y = x$

x	y
0	▒
$^-2$	▒
2	▒
$^-3$	▒

9. $y = x + 4$

x	y
$^-2$	▒
$^-1$	▒
0	▒
1	▒

10. $y = 4 + 2x$

x	y
$^-5$	▒
0	▒
3	▒
2	▒

11. $y = {^-2}x$

x	y
$^-2$	▒
$^-1$	▒
3	▒
4	▒

Find four ordered pairs that satisfy each equation.
Use x-values greater than $^-5$ and less than 5.

12. $y = 2x$

13. $y = x + 5$

14. $y = 8 - x$

15. $y = x - 3$

16. $y = 4x$

17. $y = 3x - 1$

Solve.

18. One year in a dog's life is equivalent to about 7 years in a human's life. Felipe is 28 years old. What is the equivalent age for a dog?

19. Carolyn and her mother agree to give $1 each week to a charity. If she gives $0.50, what does her mother give? Write an equation to show this relationship.

13-8 Graphing Equations

Karen Wheeler is a navigator for a large airline. She uses data from the control tower and radar to plot the plane's course. A plane usually flies in a straight line from one city to another.

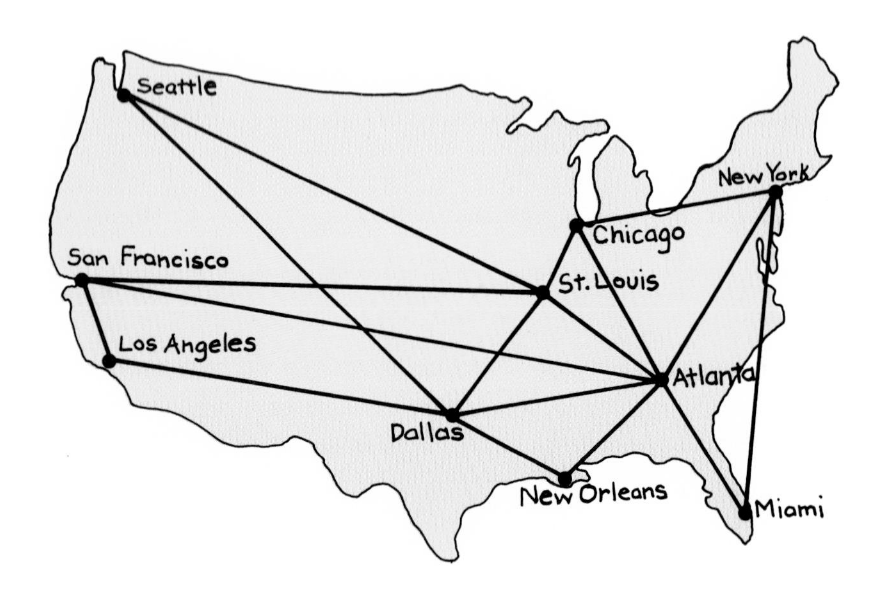

Some equations have graphs that are straight lines. To draw the graph of the equation $y = x + 3$, you would do the following.

First, find several ordered pairs that satisfy the equation.

$y = x + 3$

x	y	(x, y)
$^-2$	1	$(^-2, 1)$
$^-1$	2	$(^-1, 2)$
0	3	$(0, 3)$
1	4	$(1, 4)$

Next, graph those ordered pairs.

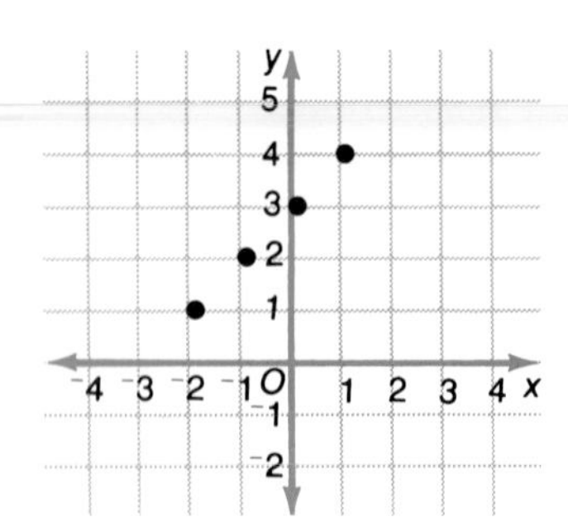

Then, use a straightedge to draw a line through the points.

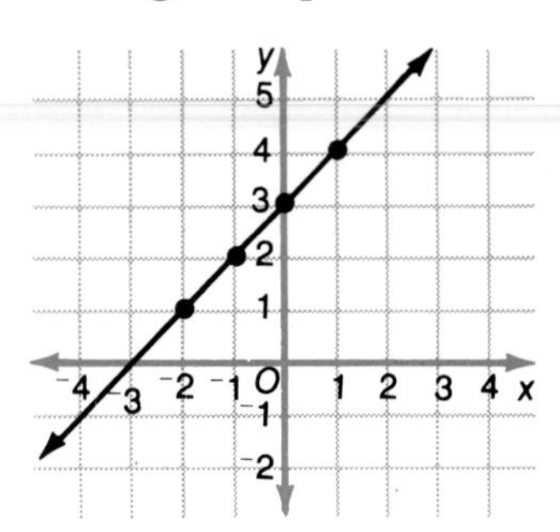

The line drawn is the graph of the equation $y = x + 3$. The coordinates of any point on the line will *satisfy* the equation.

EXERCISES ***Copy and complete each table. Then graph each equation on graph paper.***

1. $y = x$

x	y
0	0
1	▒
2	▒
3	▒

2. $y = x - 4$

x	y
$^{-}1$	$^{-}5$
0	▒
1	▒
2	▒

3. $y = 2x - 3$

x	y
$^{-}2$	$^{-}7$
0	▒
2	▒
4	▒

4. $y = 7 - 3x$

x	y
$^{-}1$	▒
0	▒
1	▒
2	▒

Graph each of the following equations on graph paper.

5. $y = {}^{-}1x$ **6.** $y = 3x$ **7.** $y = 2x + 1$ **8.** $y = 2x + 5$

9. $y = x - 5$ **10.** $y = 4 - x$ **11.** $y = 2 - x$ **12.** $y = 3x + 1$

13. $y = 6 - 3x$ **14.** $y = 2 - 2x$ **15.** $y = \frac{1}{2}x$ **16.** $y = x - \frac{1}{2}$

Answer each of the following. Assume the x-axis and y-axis do not lie in any quadrant.

17. Can a straight line graph ever pass through all four quadrants?

18. What is the least and greatest number of quadrants a straight line graph passes through?

WRITE AN EQUATION

Suppose you wish to know the equation of a straight line graph. First make a table of ordered pairs that names points on the line.

(x, y)
$(0, {}^{-}3)$
$(1, {}^{-}2)$
$(3, 0)$

To write an equation of the line, compare the coordinates. Notice that you can get each y-coordinate by subtracting 3 from each x-coordinate. An equation is $y = x - 3$.

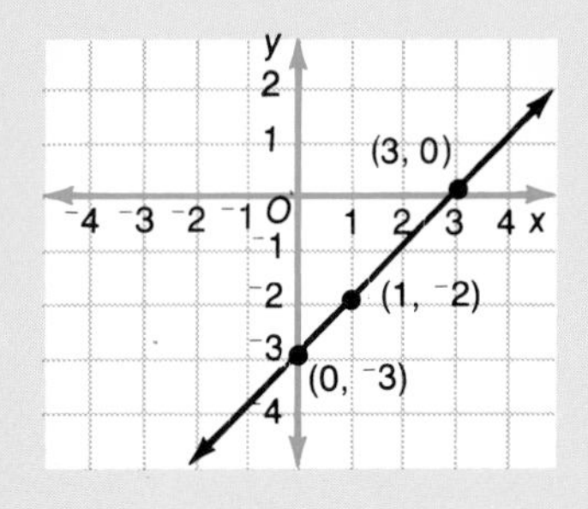

Write an equation for each set of ordered pairs.

1. (2, 5), (3, 6), (4, 7)

2. (5, 3), (7, 5), (2, 0)

3. (4, 3), (6, 4), (8, 5)

4. (4, 7), (6, 11), (7, 13)

13-9 Graphing Two Equations

Kevin Gratz rents buses and vans for Hanthorn Travel Agency. In a recent week, he rented a total of 9 vehicles. Twice as many buses as vans were rented. How many buses and vans did Mr. Gratz rent?

Let x represent the number of vans.

Let y represent the number of buses.

The following equations describe the situation.

number of vans	plus	number of buses	equals	9
x	$+$	y	$=$	9

number of buses	equals	twice	number of vans
y	$=$	$2 \times$	x

Now graph both equations on the same coordinate system. The graphs intersect at (3, 6). Since this point lies on the graph of each equation, its coordinates are a solution to each equation. You can check this solution by substituting each value of the ordered pair in both equations.

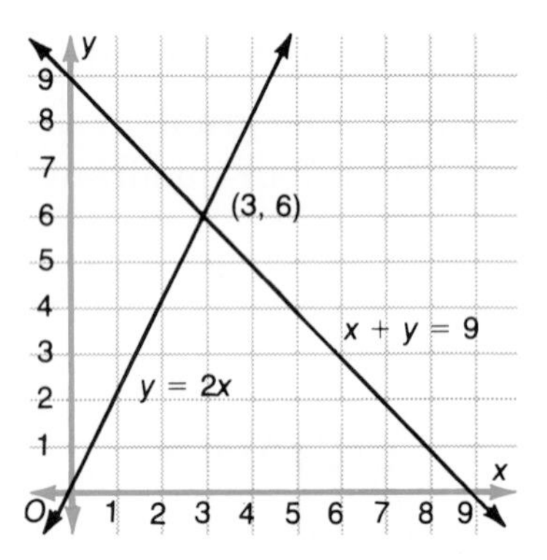

$$x + y = 9$$
$$3 + 6 \stackrel{?}{=} 9$$
$$9 = 9 \checkmark$$

$$y = 2x$$
$$6 \stackrel{?}{=} 2 \times 3$$
$$6 = 6 \checkmark$$

So, $x = 3$ and $y = 6$. Mr. Gratz rents 3 vans and 6 buses.

EXERCISES ***Copy and complete each table. Then graph the two equations in each exercise and state the solution as an ordered pair.***

1. $y = x - 1$ $\qquad$ $y = 11 - x$

x	y
1	0
3	
5	

x	y
0	11
2	
4	

2. $2y = 3 - x$ $\qquad$ $x + y = 0$

x	y
$^{-}3$	
$^{-}1$	
1	

x	y
$^{-}1$	
0	
1	

Graph the two equations in each exercise on the same coordinate system. State the solution as an ordered pair.

3. $y = 6 - x$
$y = x - 2$

4. $y = 4x$
$x + y = 5$

5. $x + y = 3$
$y = 1 + x$

6. $x - 2y = {}^{-}5$
$y = x + 3$

7. $x + y = 3$
$2x + y = 4$

8. $2x + y = 7$
$x - y = 5$

Solve.

9. The perimeter of a rectangular garden is 46 meters. The length is 3 meters longer than the width. Write two equations to describe the situation. Graph the equations on the same coordinate system. What is the length and width of the garden?

INEQUALITIES WITH TWO VARIABLES

The graph of the equation $y = x + 1$ is a line that separates the coordinate system into two regions.

The graph of $y > x + 1$ is the region *above* and *not* including the line.

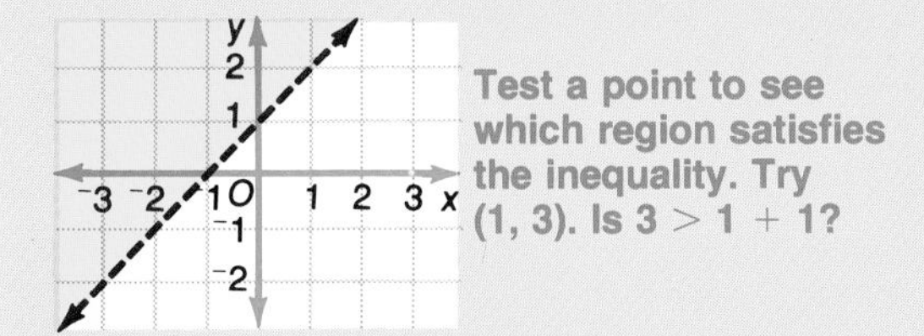

The graph of $y \leq x + 1$ is the region *below* and including the line.

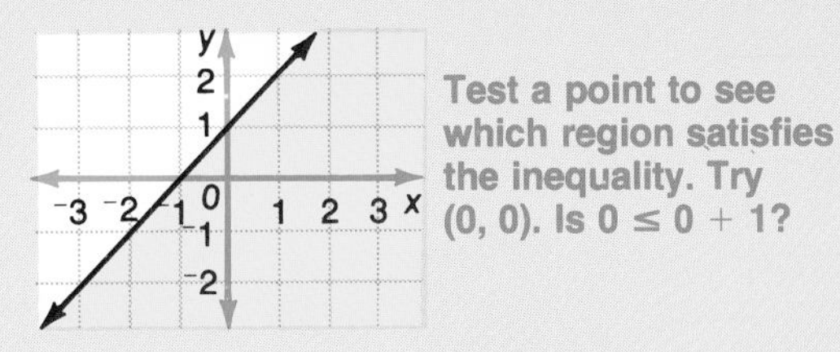

Draw the graph of each inequality.

1. $x + y > 1$ $\qquad$ **2.** $x + y < 2$ $\qquad$ **3.** $y \geq x - 1$

13–10 Curved Graphs

Liz Peroski is a pilot of a jet plane. The plane takes off down the runway. The distance the plane has traveled after a certain number of seconds can be shown on a graph.

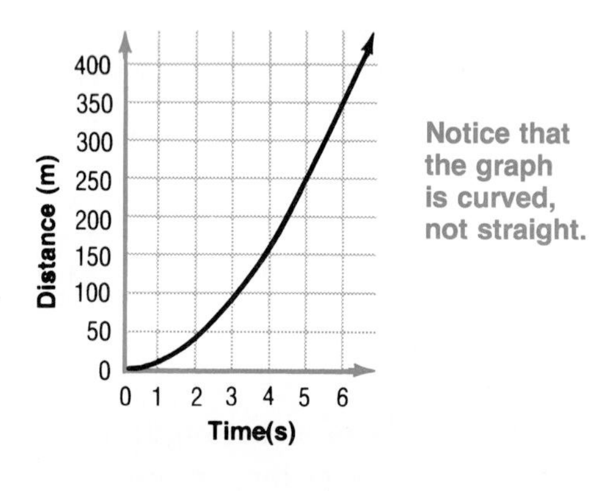

The graphs of some equations are curved. Consider the equation $y = x^2$.

First, find several ordered pairs that satisfy the equation.

x	y	(x, y)
$^-3$	9	$(^-3, 9)$
$^-2$	4	$(^-2, 4)$
$^-1$	1	$(^-1, 1)$
0	0	$(0, 0)$
1	1	$(1, 1)$
2	4	$(2, 4)$
3	9	$(3, 9)$

Next, graph those ordered pairs.

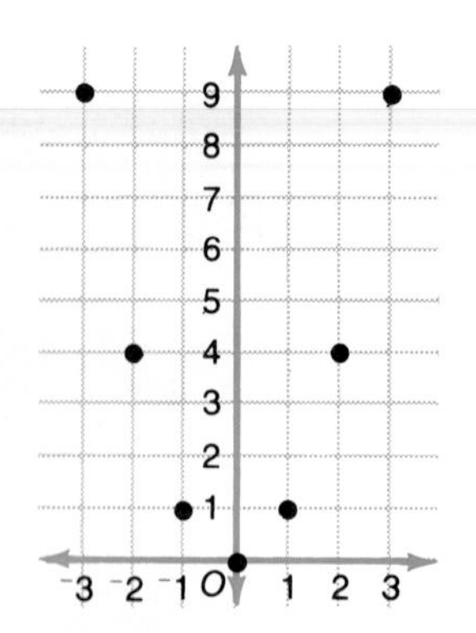

Then, connect the points with a smooth curve.

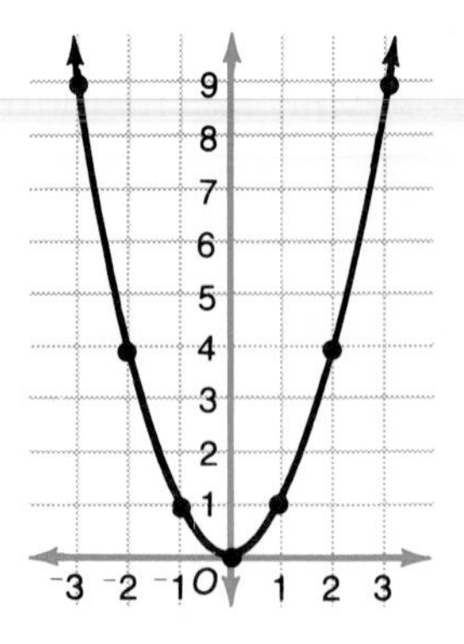

The resulting graph is called a **parabola.**

EXERCISES ***Copy and complete each table. Then graph each equation on graph paper.***

1. $y = x^2 - 1$

x	y
$^-1$	0
0	$^-1$
1	▒
2	▒

2. $y = x^2 + 2$

x	y
$^-1$	3
0	▒
1	▒
2	▒

3. $y = 1 - x^2$

x	y
$^-1$	▒
0	▒
1	▒
2	▒

4. $y = 2x^2$

x	y
$^-1$	▒
0	▒
1	▒
2	▒

Graph each of the following equations on graph paper.

5. $y = x^2 + 1$

6. $y = x^2 - 3$

7. $y = \frac{1}{2}x^2$

8. Draw a graph to show typical hourly temperatures for a spring day (24 hours) where you live.

CURVE STITCHING

Draw an acute angle making each line 10 centimeters long. For each line, start at the vertex and place dots at one centimeter intervals. On one line, number the dots starting at the dot nearest the vertex. On the other line, number the dots starting at the dot farthest from the vertex. Now draw a straight line connecting the dots numbered 1. Then connect the dots numbered 2, and so on. Notice the curve formed by the straight lines.

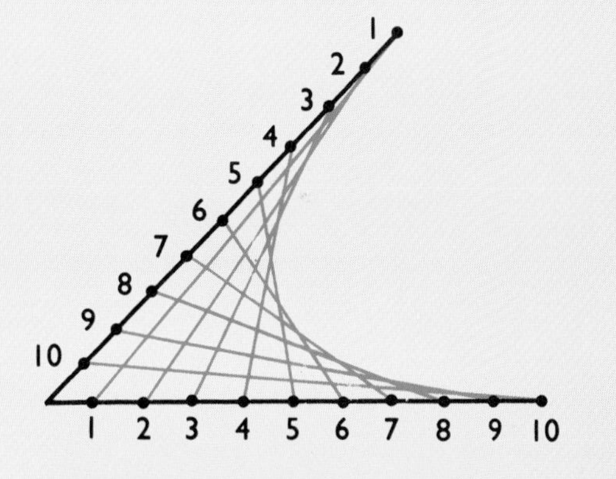

Now try a right angle and an obtuse angle. Then, try marking one of the sides of an angle in half centimeter intervals and other in centimeter intervals. Experiment with overlapping angles. If you find a design you like, try stitching the design on material.

13–11 Problem Solving: Using Graphs

A small plane can carry 2,060 pounds of people, cargo, and fuel. The more people and cargo it carries, the less fuel it carries. This decreases the flying time. A graph of the pounds of fuel needed to fly a certain number of hours is shown below.

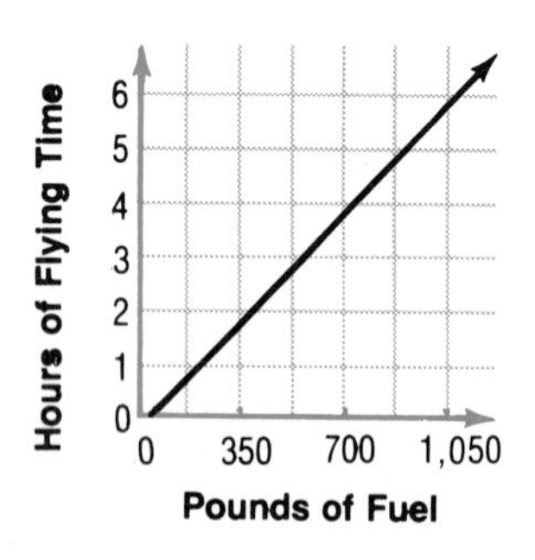

Suppose a plane carries 410 pounds of cargo and six people that weigh a total of 950 pounds. The rest of the weight is fuel. How many hours of flying time does the plane have?

Read the problem. You know the plane can carry a total of 2,060 pounds. You also know the weight of the people and cargo it carries. You need to find the weight of the fuel and how much flying time it allows.

Decide what to do. First, find the pounds of fuel the plane can carry. Then, use the graph to find the hours of flying time.

Solve the problem.

410	pounds of cargo	2,060 (regrouped: 1 10)	total pounds allowed
+ 950	pounds of people	− 1,360	pounds of cargo and people
1,360		700	pounds of fuel

Find 700 on the horizontal scale of the graph. Then move up to the line. From this point, move left and read the hours of flying time. The plane has 4 hours of flying time.

Examine the solution. You can check the solution by working backwards. Assume that the plane has 4 hours of flying time. Find how much fuel is needed and the pounds of people and cargo allowed. The solution does check.

Solve. Use the graph. He earns a base salary of $300 a week and makes a commission of 5% on all sales.

1. What are Mr. Lewis's total earnings if his sales are $1,000?
2. Mr. Lewis needs to make $450 this week. How much must his sales be?
3. Write an equation to describe the graph. Use x for Mr. Lewis's sales and y for his total earnings.

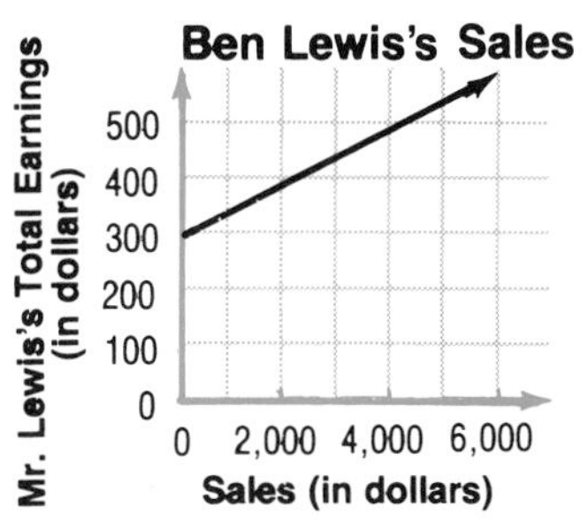

Solve. Use the graph on the previous page.

4. A plane carries 770 pounds of cargo and 4 people who weigh 765 pounds. The rest of the weight is fuel. How many hours of flying time does the plane have?
5. A plane must fly 4 hours to reach its destination. The pilot and co-pilot each weigh 145 pounds. There are no passengers. How many pounds of cargo can the plane carry?

Ace Repair Shop has a chart for its employees to use in computing customers' bills.

Hours	0.5	0.75	1	1.25	1.5	2
Charge	$29	$33.50	$38	$42.50	$47	$56

6. Draw a graph to show the relationship given in the chart.
7. What is the charge for a job that takes 2.25 hours?

Skills Review: Pages 346-355

Copy. Complete the table for each equation. Then graph each equation on graph paper.

1. $y = 2x - 1$

x	y
$^-1$	▒
1	▒
3	▒

2. $y = x^2 - 2$

x	y
$^-1$	▒
0	▒
1	▒

3. Graph the equations below on the same coordinate axis. State the solution as an ordered pair.

$y = 3x + 1$

$x + y = 9$

4. An inch of rain is equivalent to 10 inches of snow. Draw a graph to show this relationship.

Mathematics and Consumers

There are many types and methods of investing money. One common investment is a certificate of deposit (CD). It usually yields a higher rate of interest than a passbook savings account.

Several time periods and annual rates are shown at the right. The annual yield is based on the reinvestment of the principal and interest earned at the given annual interest rate.

Time Period	Annual Rate	Annual Yield
3 months	8.5%	8.87%
1 to 3 years	9.75%	10.24%
4 to 7 years	11.25%	11.91%
8 to 10 years	11.5%	12.19%

Tony Perez has a 3-year CD for $2,000. At the end of each year, the interest is reinvested with the principal. How much interest does he earn in three years?

$2,000 CD
× 0.0975 annual rate (9.75% = 0.0975)
$195.00 first year interest → **$2,000.00 + 195.00 = $2,195.00** CD after 1 year

$2,195.00
× 0.0975 annual rate
$214.01 second year interest → **$2,195.00 + 214.01 = $2,409.01** CD after 2 years

$2,409.01
× 0.0975 annual rate
$234.88 third year interest

Mr. Perez earns $195.00 + $214.01 + $234.88 or $643.89 in three years.

EXERCISES ***Find the interest earned on each of the following certificates of deposit. If the time period is over 1 year, the interest is invested with the principal. Use the chart above.***

1. $1,500; 2 years
2. $6,000; 2 years
3. $10,000; 3 years
4. $5,800; 3 years
5. $2,000; 3 months
6. $10,000; $2\frac{1}{2}$ years
7. Cheryl Edens has a 2-year CD for $1,800. Kent Williams has a 3-year CD for $1,000. Which person earns more interest?

Chapter 13 Review

VOCABULARY square (332) square root (333) perfect square (336) irrational number (336) real number (336) inequality (338) coordinate system (340) x-coordinate (340) y-coordinate (340) x-axis (340) y-axis (340) origin (340) quadrant (340) ordered pair (340) reflection (342) translation (342) parabola (352)

EXERCISES ***Find each of the following. Use the table on page 422 if necessary. (333–335)***

1. $\sqrt{81}$ **2.** $^-\sqrt{100}$ **3.** $^-\sqrt{35}$ **4.** $\sqrt{14}$ **5.** $\sqrt{2,916}$

Use a number line to show the solutions to each of the following inequalities. (338)

6. $a > 2$ **7.** $b \leq {}^-1$ **8.** $3 + x \geq 4$ **9.** $2y < 12$

Use the coordinate system shown at the right. Name the letter for each ordered pair. (340)

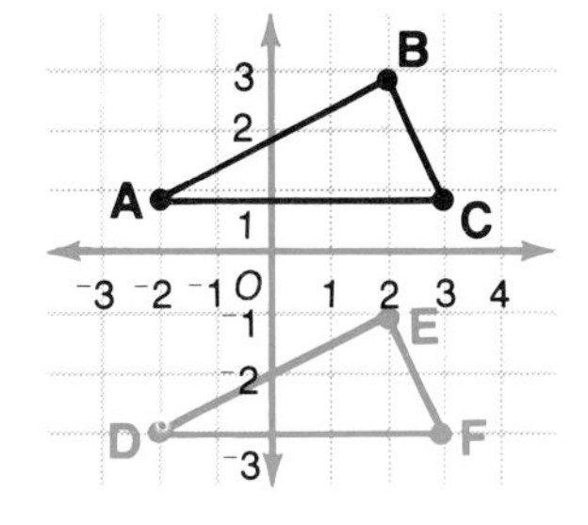

10. $(^-2, {}^-3)$ **11.** $(2, 3)$ **12.** $(^-2, 1)$

13. Is triangle DEF a reflection or translation of triangle ABC? (342)

Copy. Complete the table for each equation. Then graph each equation on graph paper. (346–349, 352)

14. $y = 3 + x$

x	y
$^-1$	
0	
1	

15. $y = x - 1$

x	y
$^-2$	
0	
2	

16. $y = 2x + 1$

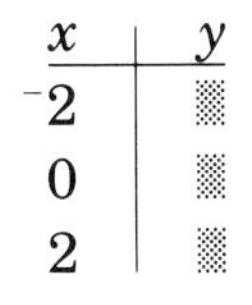

x	y
$^-2$	
0	
2	

17. $y = x^2 + 3$

x	y
$^-2$	
0	
2	

18. Graph the equations on the same coordinate axis. State the solution as an ordered pair. (350)

$$y = 3x - 2$$

$$x + y = 6$$

19. Each game of bowling at Al's Lanes costs \$1.25. Draw a graph to show this relationship. (354)

20. Neva can spend \$4 for bowling. She rents shoes for 25¢. How many games can she bowl?

Chapter 13 Test

Find each of the following.

1. $^-\sqrt{64}$
2. $\sqrt{144}$
3. $\sqrt{32}$
4. $^-\sqrt{17}$
5. $^-\sqrt{5{,}776}$

Solve each equation.

6. $y^2 = 4$
7. $t^2 = 36$
8. $k^2 = 45$

State whether each of the following numbers is rational or irrational.

9. $\frac{4}{3}$
10. $\sqrt{18}$
11. 0.010010001 . . .
12. $^-\sqrt{25}$
13. 3.4141

Use a number line to show the solutions to each of the following inequalities.

14. $x > 4$
15. $x + 5 < 10$
16. $6 + x \leq 24$

Use the coordinate system shown at the right. Name the ordered pair for each letter.

17. P
18. Q
19. R

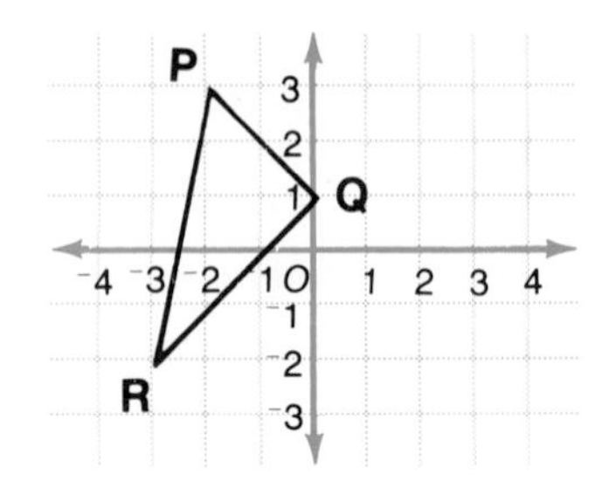

20. Copy triangle PQR on graph paper. Multiply the x-coordinate of each vertex by $^-1$. Then draw the new triangle.

Graph each of the following equations on graph paper.

21. $y = 3 - x$
22. $y = x$
23. $y = 3x - 4$
24. $y = x^2 + 2$

25. Graph the equations on the same coordinate axis. State the solution as an ordered pair.

$$y = x + 2$$
$$y = 3x$$

26. The cost of telephone service in Branson is related to the number of calls a customer makes.

Calls	0	5	10	20	40
Cost	\$12	\$12.50	\$13	\$14	\$16

Draw a graph to show this relationship.

27. Mrs. Pantera's telephone bill is \$13.80. Use the graph in exercise 26 to find how many calls were made on her telephone.

Enrichment

A road sign may warn drivers of steep downgrades or upgrades. It means that for every 5 feet, there is a rise of 1 foot. The ratio of vertical distance to horizontal distance is called **slope.**

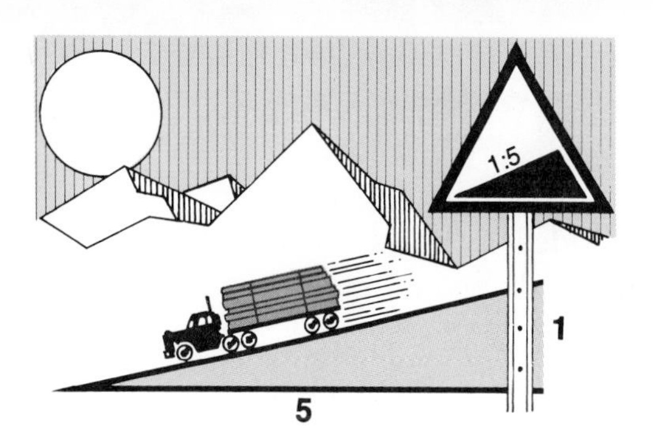

In a coordinate system, the slope of a line is the ratio of the change in y to the corresponding change in x.

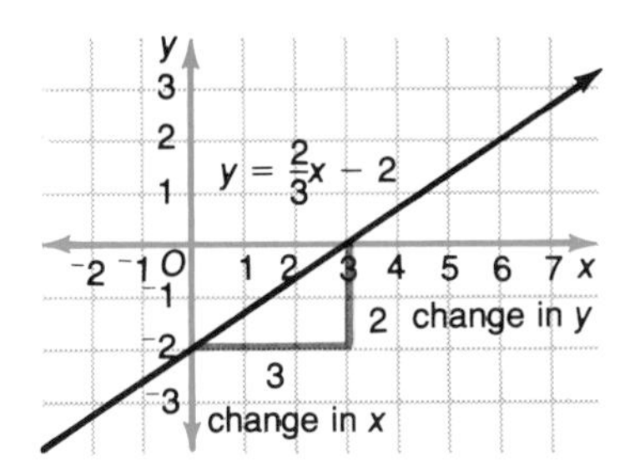

$$\textbf{slope} = \frac{\textbf{change in y}}{\textbf{change in x}}$$

$$\textbf{slope} = \frac{2}{3}$$

Notice where the line crosses the y-axis. The y-coordinate of this point is called the **y-intercept** of the line.

The slope of the line whose equation is $y = \frac{2}{3}x - 2$ is $\frac{2}{3}$. The y-intercept is $^-2$. How might you find the slope and y-intercept of the graph of an equation like $y = \frac{2}{3}x - 2$ without drawing the graph?

EXERCISES ***Find the slope and y-intercept of each of the following.***

1. $y = x + 2$

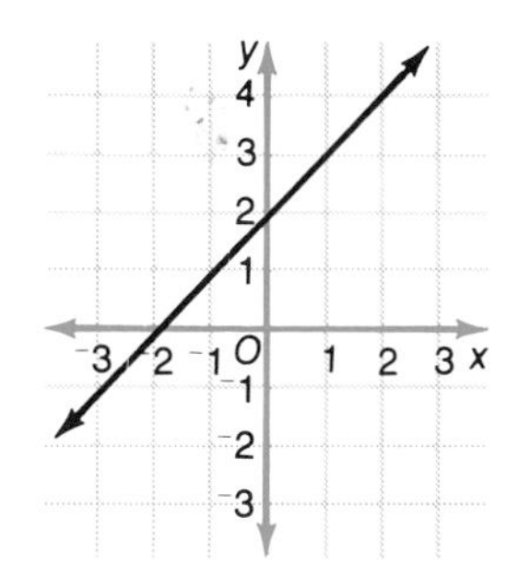

2. $y = 3x - 3$

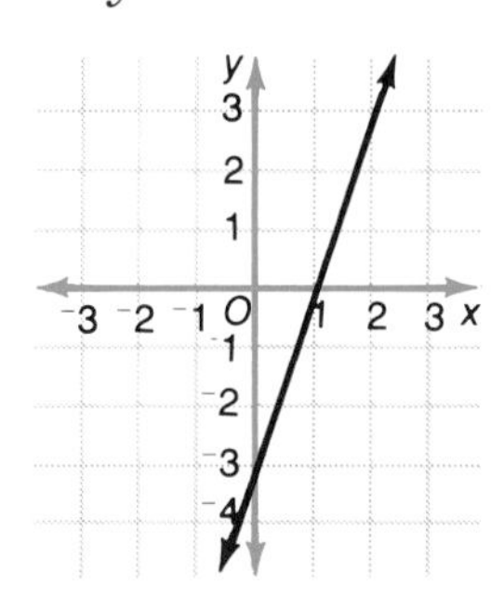

3. $y = x - 5$

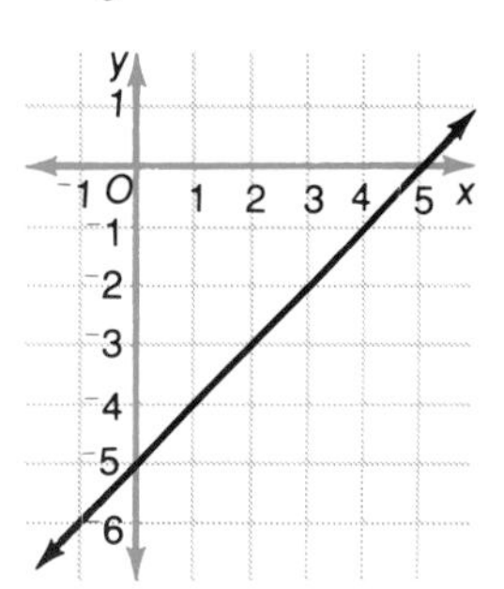

Find the slope and y-intercept of the graph of each of the following.

4. $y = \frac{3}{4}x + 5$

5. $y = 2x - 3$

6. $y = x + \frac{3}{2}$

14 Right Triangles

Two sides of the sail meet to form a right angle. The sail has the shape of a right triangle.

14–1 Right Triangles

In a right triangle, the side opposite the right angle is called the **hypotenuse.** The other two sides are called **legs.**

Triangle ABC is a right triangle. Angle C is the right angle. The hypotenuse is $\overline{AB}$. The legs are $\overline{AC}$ and $\overline{BC}$. Each side can also be named by a lowercase letter that corresponds to the letter for the opposite angle. For example, $\overline{AC}$ is opposite angle B. So $\overline{AC}$ may be named b.

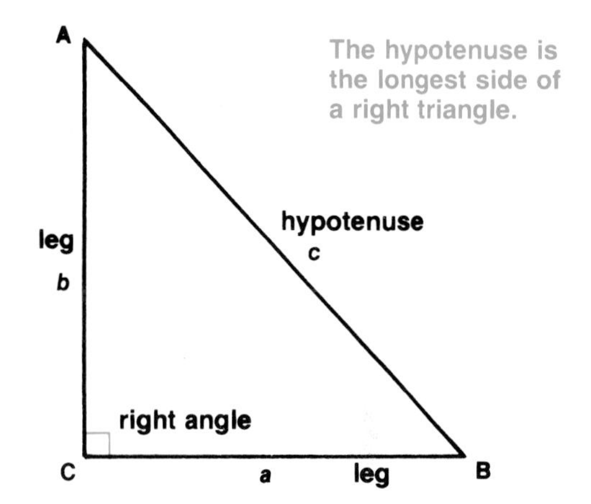

EXERCISES ***Name the hypotenuse and legs of each right triangle.***

1.

2.

3.

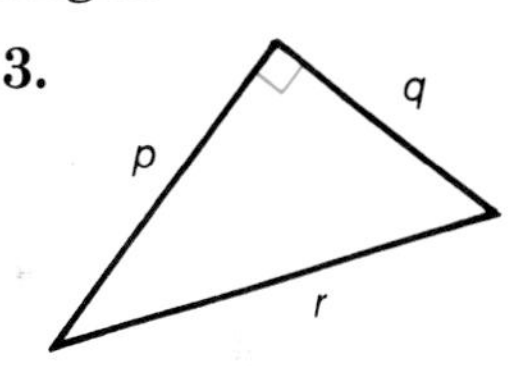

Use the rectangle JKLM to answer each of the following.

4. Name two right triangles formed by diagonal $\overline{KM}$ and the sides of the rectangle.

5. Are the two right triangles congruent?

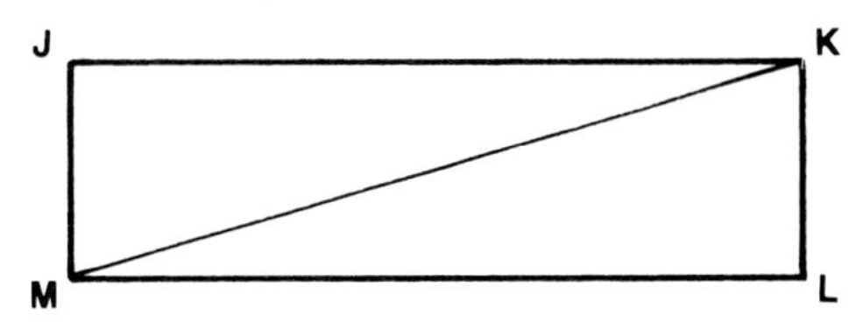

Complete the following.

6. Use a compass to draw a circle. Then draw a triangle so that one side is the diameter and the vertex of the opposite angle is on the circle. Do you think this is a right triangle?

7. Draw two other triangles in the circle where one side of each triangle is a diameter. The vertex of the opposite angle should be on the circle. Are both of these triangles right triangles?

8. What conclusion can you make about triangles drawn in this way in a circle?

14–2 The Pythagorean Theorem

Mike Molina helped survey the three subdivisions in Royalton that bound Crockett Park. Since Alamo Avenue and Bowie Street meet at a right angle, $\triangle ABC$ is a right triangle. Study the drawing below and find the area of each subdivision to discover an important property of right triangles.

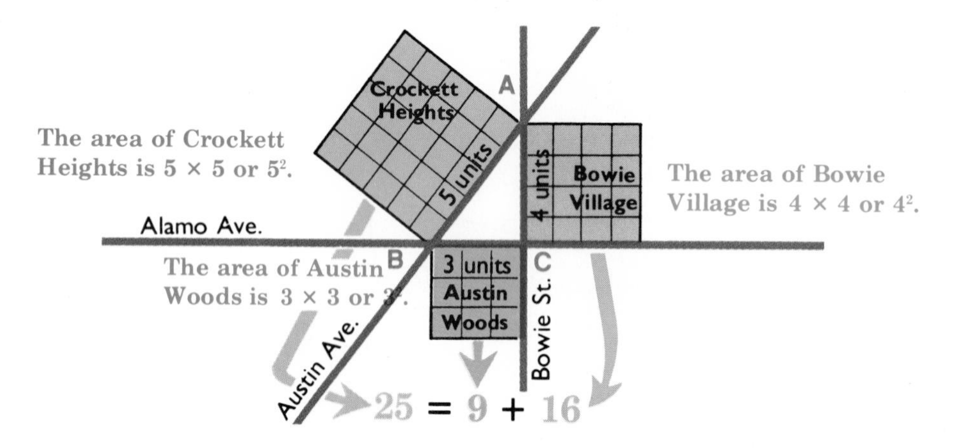

Add the areas of Austin Woods and Bowie Village. Does the sum equal that of Crockett Heights? This is example of a property of right triangles called the **Pythagorean theorem.**

In a right triangle, the square of the length of the hypotenuse is equal to the sum of the squares of the lengths of the other two sides.

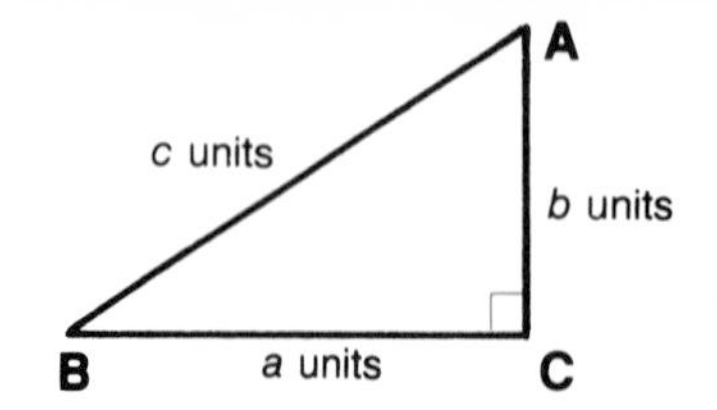

$$c^2 = a^2 + b^2$$

You can use the Pythagorean theorem to find the length of the hypotenuse of a right triangle.

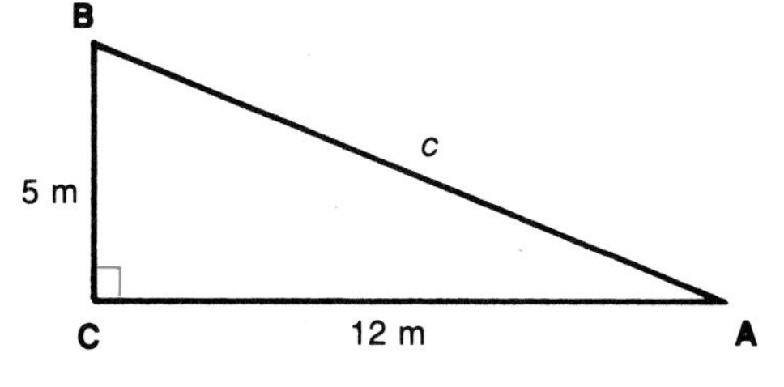

$$c^2 = a^2 + b^2$$
$$c^2 = 5^2 + 12^2$$
$$c^2 = 25 + 144$$
$$c^2 = 169$$
$$\sqrt{c^2} = \sqrt{169}$$
$$c = 13$$ The hypotenuse is 13 meters long.

EXERCISES ***Use the Pythagorean theorem to write an equation for each triangle. If necessary, round answers to the nearest hundredth. Use the table on page 422.***

1.

2.

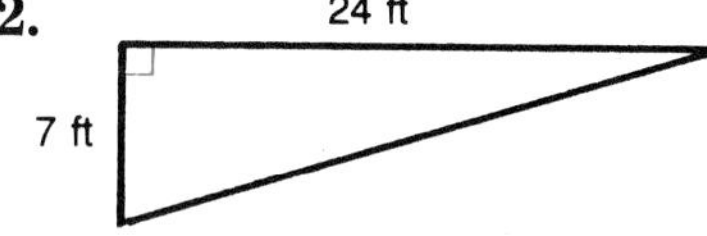

3.

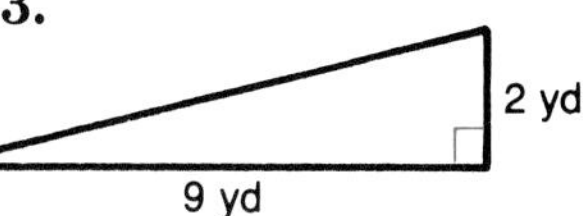

Use the Pythagorean theorem to find the length of the hypotenuse of each right triangle. The length of each leg is given.

4. a, 3 in.; b, 4 in.
5. a, 8 m; b, 6 m
6. a, 9 ft; b, 40 ft
7. a, 12 cm; b, 9 cm
8. a, 12 m; b, 5 m
9. a, 7 yd; b, 7 yd
10. a, 2 m; b, 5 m
11. a, 7 cm; b, 3 cm
12. a, 15 in.; b, 36 in.
13. Which rectangle has the longer diagonal?

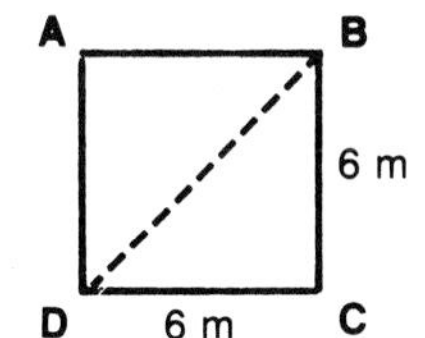

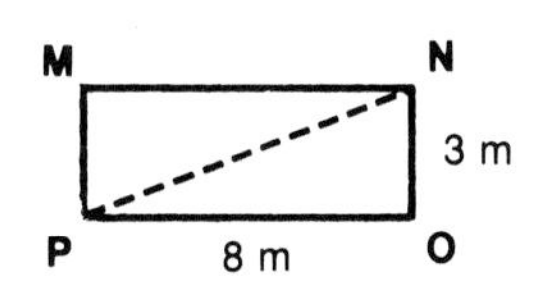

PYTHAGOREAN TRIPLES

Three numbers that satisfy the Pythagorean theorem are called **Pythagorean triples.** The set of numbers 5, 12, and 13 is a Pythagorean triple because $5^2 + 12^2 = 13^2$.

State whether each set of numbers is a Pythagorean triple.

1. 3, 4, 5
2. 8, 10, 13
3. 45, 75, 60
4. 100, 240, 260

14-3 Using the Pythagorean Theorem

Russell Gossman makes a map of Royalton and Lake Royal. He must find the distance across the lake. First, he finds the lengths of $\overline{AB}$ and $\overline{AC}$. Then, he uses the Pythagorean theorem to find the length of $\overline{BC}$.

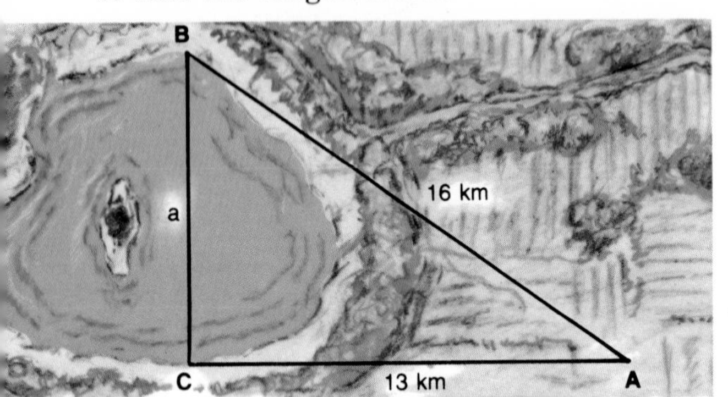

$$c^2 = a^2 + b^2$$
$$16^2 = a^2 + 13^2$$
$$256 = a^2 + 169$$
$$256 - 169 = a^2 + 169 - 169$$ Subtract 169 from both sides.
$$87 = a^2$$
$$\sqrt{87} = \sqrt{a^2}$$
$$9.33 \approx a$$ Use the table on page 422.

The distance across the lake is about 9.33 km.

***EXERCISES* Use the Pythagorean theorem to find the missing length for each right triangle.**

1. a, 15 ft; c, 17 ft
2. a, 40 in.; c, 41 in.
3. b, 80 m; c, 89 m
4. b, 7 m; c, 9 m
5. a, 21 yd; b, 28 yd
6. a, 15 cm; b, 36 cm

Solve. Round each answer to two decimal places.

7. How high is the television screen?

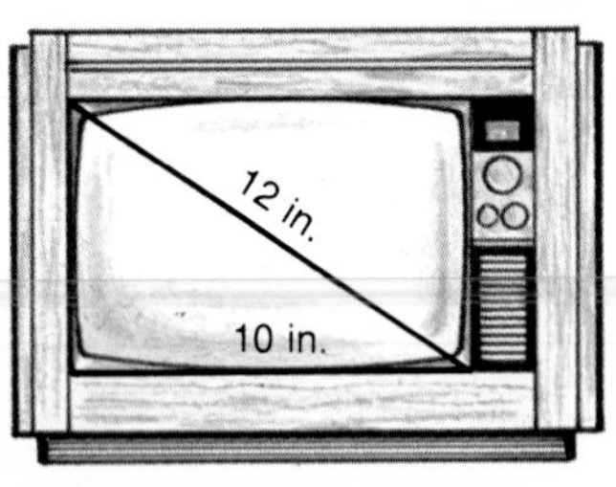

8. How far above the ground is the kite?

kite
125 m
75 m
ground

9. How long is the brace on the gate?

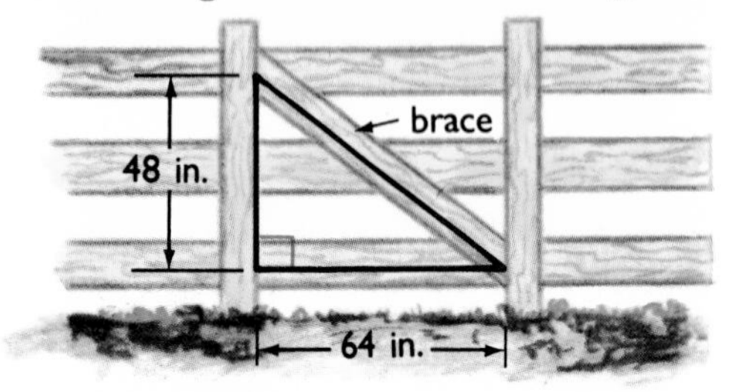

10. How long is the longest side of the sail?

5 m
3 m

11. How far is the weather balloon from the weather station?

12. How far above the ground does the ladder touch the house?

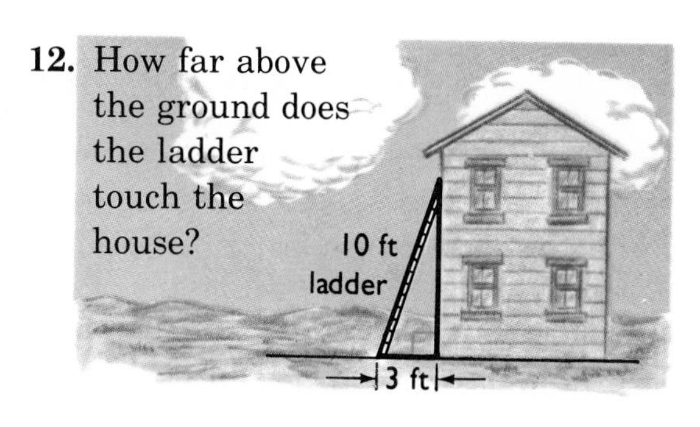

13. What is the distance between the feet of the sawhorse?

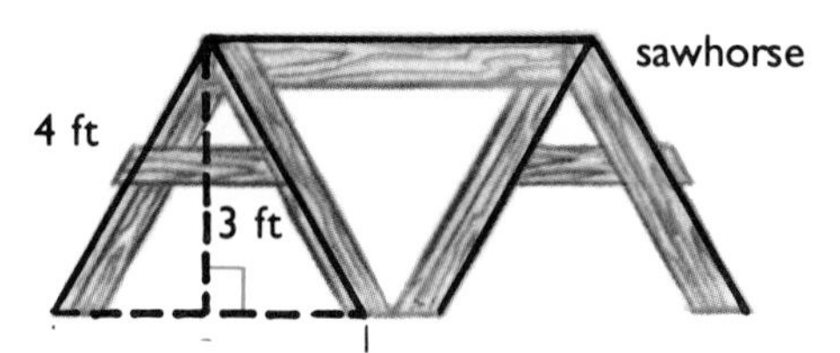

14. How long is each rafter?

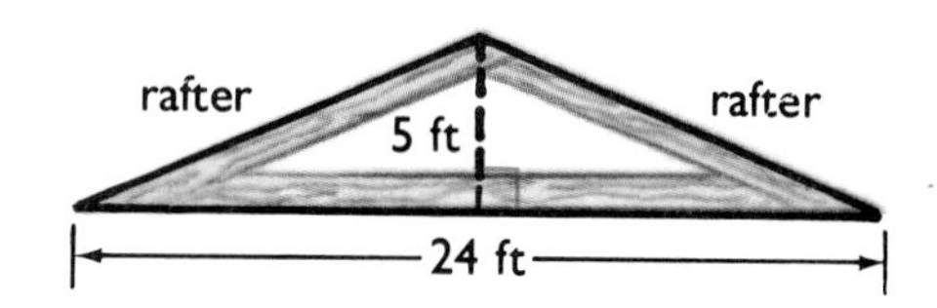

CONSTRUCTING IRRATIONAL NUMBERS

It is possible to construct segments whose measures are irrational numbers using only a compass, straightedge, and a given unit measure. Suppose you wish to construct a segment whose measure is $\sqrt{2}$.

Step 1 On a straight line, mark off 1 unit measure. Label the endpoints A and C.

Step 2 Construct a line perpendicular to $\overline{AC}$ at C. Mark off 1 unit measure on this line. Label this point B.

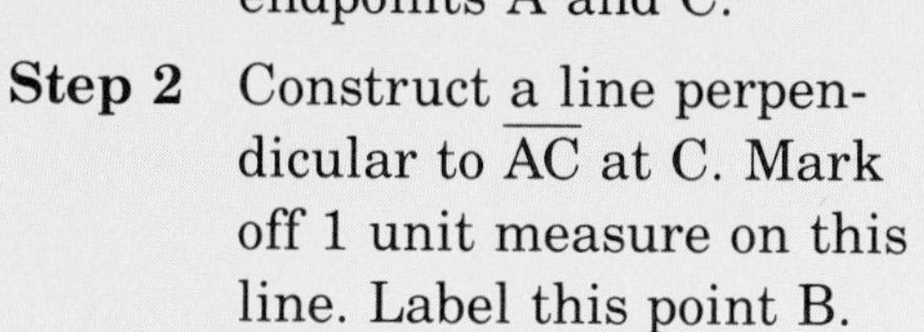

Step 3 Draw $\overline{AB}$.

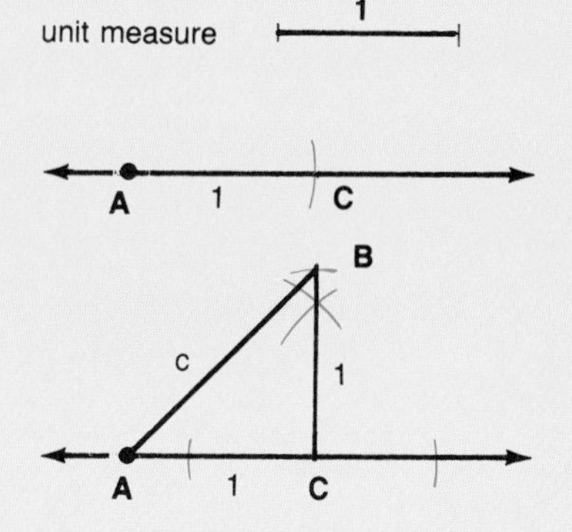

Triangle ABC is a right triangle. Why? Now apply the Pythagorean theorem.

$$c^2 = a^2 + b^2$$
$$c^2 = 1^2 + 1^2$$
$$c^2 = 2$$
$$c = \sqrt{2}$$

The measure of $\overline{AB}$ is $\sqrt{2}$.

You use this procedure to construct a segment whose measure is $\sqrt{5}$.

14–4 30°-60° Right Triangles

Royalton City Council appointed a committee to design wooden playground equipment. To make the design for a swing set, Pedro Muñoz constructed a bisector of an angle of an equilateral triangle. The two triangles formed are congruent.

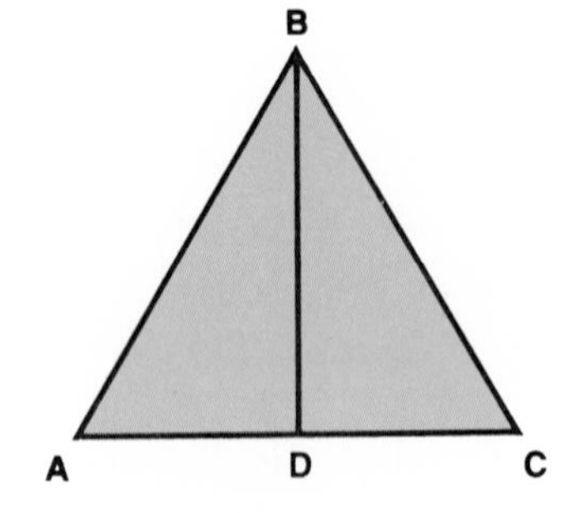

What kind of a triangle is $\triangle ABD$?

$m\angle A = 60$ $\triangle ABC$ is an equilateral triangle.

$m\angle ABD = 30$ $\angle ABC$ is bisected to form $\angle ABD$ and $\angle CBD$.

$m\angle ADB = 90$ $m\angle ADB + m\angle CDB$ is 180 and these angles are congruent. (corresponding parts of congruent triangles)

So, $\triangle ABD$ is a right triangle. More specifically, it is called a **30°-60° right triangle.** Study the following to learn an important property of such triangles.

$\overline{AD}$ and $\overline{DC}$ are corresponding parts of congruent triangles. So, $\overline{AD} \cong \overline{DC}$, or the length of $\overline{AD}$ is one-half the length of $\overline{AC}$. Since $\overline{AC} \cong \overline{AB}$, the length of $\overline{AD}$ (the side opposite the 30° angle of $\triangle ABD$) is one-half the length of $\overline{AB}$ (the hypotenuse).

In any 30°-60° right triangle, the length of the side opposite the 30° angle is one-half the length of the hypotenuse.

Find the length of the side opposite the 30° angle in the triangle below.

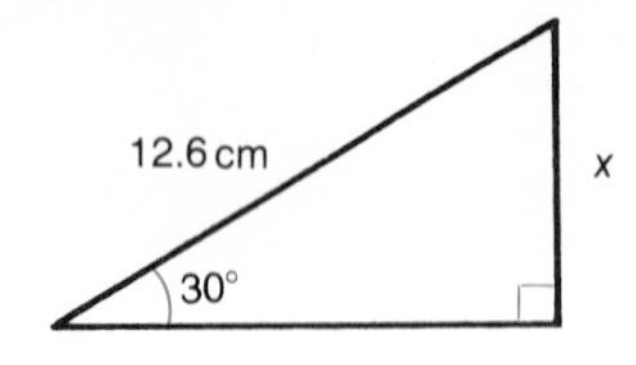

$\mathbf{x = 0.5 \times 12.6}$

$\mathbf{x = 6.3}$ The side opposite the 30° angle is 6.3 cm long.

Find the length of the hypotenuse in the triangle below.

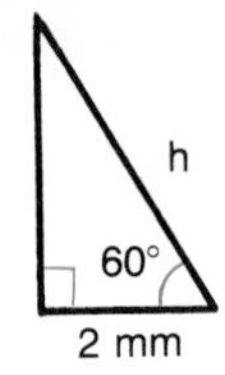

$\mathbf{2 = 0.5 \times h}$

$\frac{2}{0.5} = \frac{0.5h}{0.5}$ Divide both sides by 0.5.

$\mathbf{4 = h}$ The hypotenuse is 4 mm long.

EXERCISES ***The length of the hypotenuse of a 30°-60° right triangle is given. Find the length of the side opposite the 30° angle.***

1. 8 m **2.** 6.7 cm **3.** 4.59 mm **4.** 4.5 mi

5. $6\frac{5}{8}$ in. **6.** 4.47 m **7.** $17\frac{1}{2}$ in. **8.** $3\frac{1}{3}$ yd

9. 48 km **10.** 26.48 mm **11.** 122 km **12.** 4.38 in.

The length of the side opposite the 30° angle of a right triangle is given. Find the length of the hypotenuse.

13. 9 m **14.** 6.9 in. **15.** 4.27 km **16.** 13.2 mm

17. $4\frac{1}{2}$ in. **18.** $5\frac{3}{8}$ in. **19.** 12 m **20.** 4.39 m

21. $2\frac{1}{3}$ yd **22.** $9\frac{1}{2}$ mi **23.** 8.5 cm **24.** $14\frac{1}{2}$ mm

Find the length of the red side of each triangle.

25.

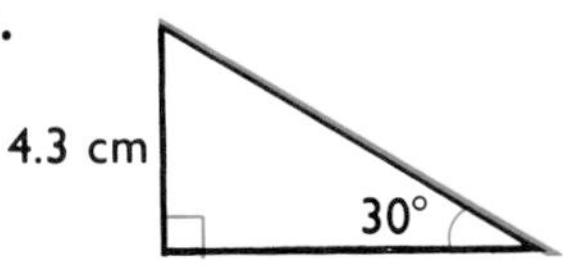

26.

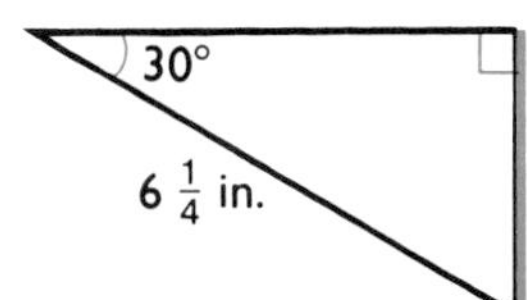

27.

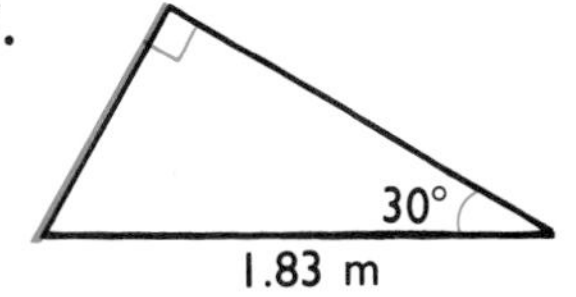

28.

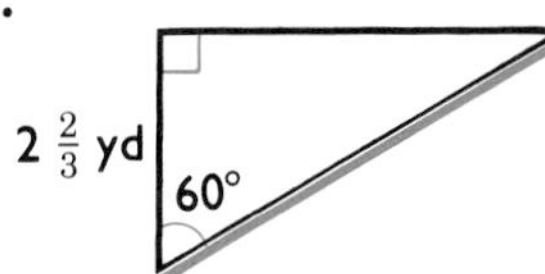

29.

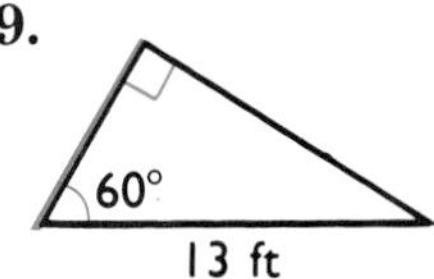

30.

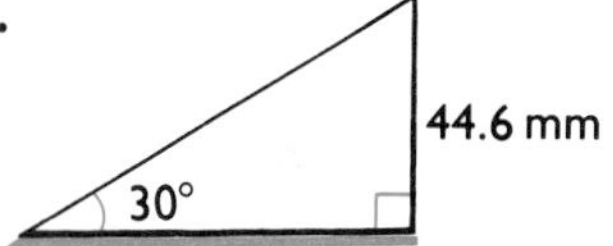

Solve.

31. How long is each rafter?

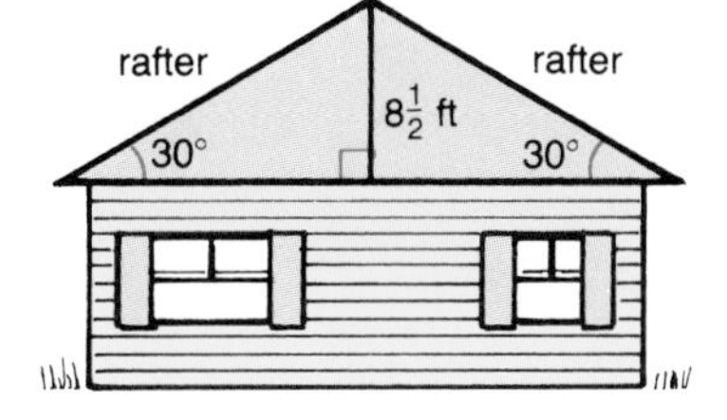

32. How tall is the water tower?

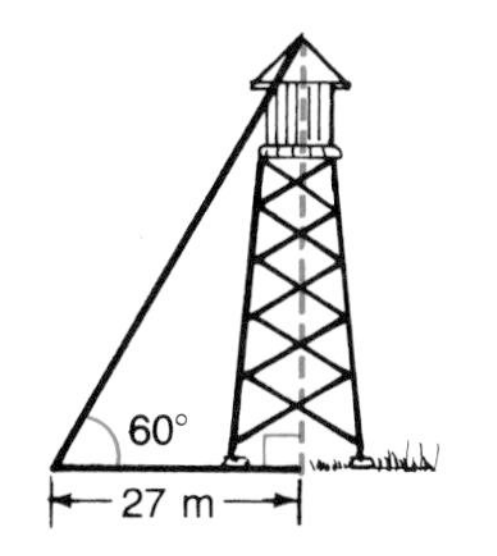

14-5 Similar Triangles

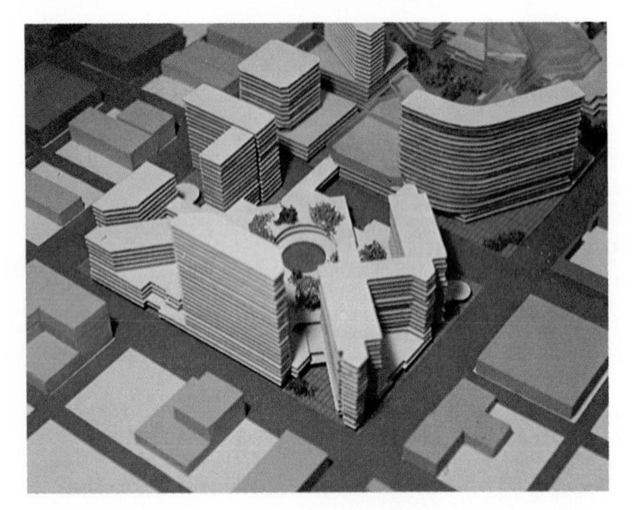

Elsie Frank built a model of the new Royalton Civic Center. The model has the same shape as the actual building, but the model is much smaller.

Similar figures have the same shape, but may differ in size. Triangles ABC and DEF below are similar.

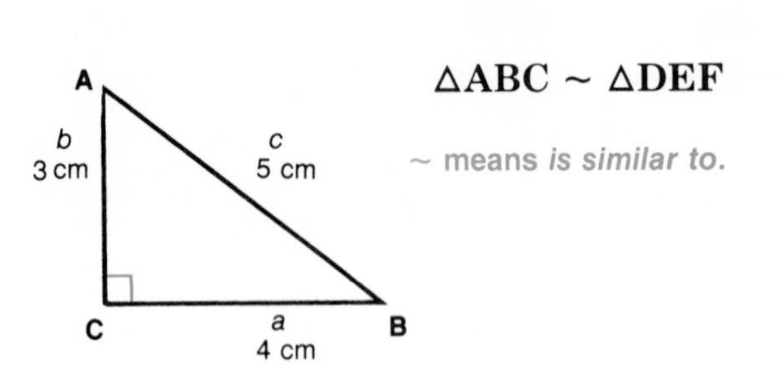

$\triangle ABC \sim \triangle DEF$

~ means *is similar to.*

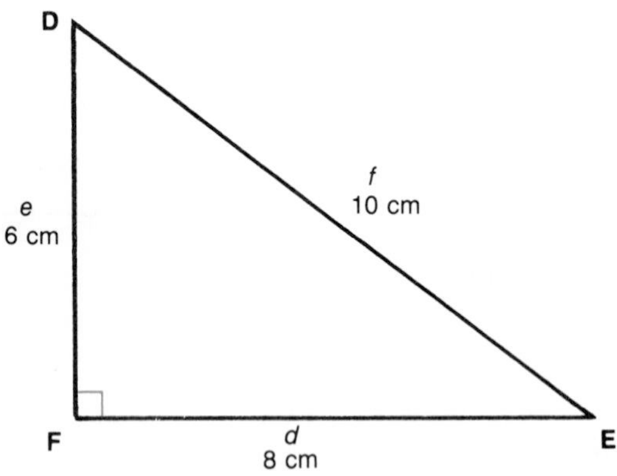

Measure the angles of $\triangle ABC$. Compare these measures with the measures of the angles of $\triangle DEF$. What do you discover?

If two triangles are similar, their corresponding angles are congruent.

If two triangles are similar, the sides opposite congruent angles are called **corresponding sides.** For example, $\overline{CB}$ corresponds to $\overline{FE}$. Compare the measures of the corresponding sides.

$\frac{3}{6} = \frac{1}{2}$ $\quad$ $\frac{4}{8} = \frac{1}{2}$ $\quad$ $\frac{5}{10} = \frac{1}{2}$ $\quad$ What do you discover?

If two triangles are similar, the measures of their corresponding sides are proportional.

The triangles shown at the right are similar. Find the length of side x by setting up and solving a proportion.

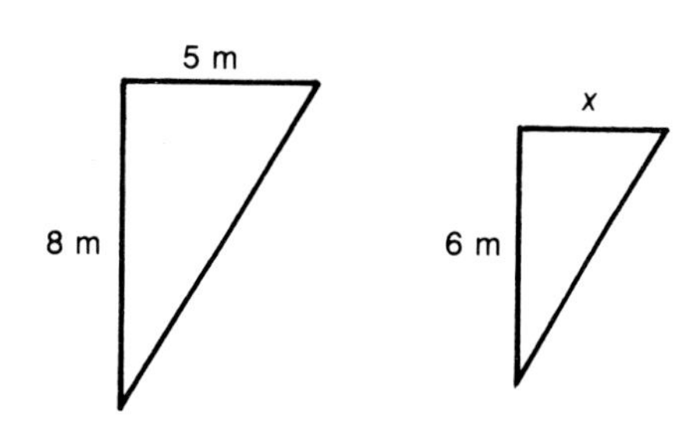

$$\frac{8}{6} = \frac{5}{x}$$

$$8 \times x = 6 \times 5 \quad \text{Cross products are equal.}$$

$$8x = 30$$

$$\frac{8x}{8} = \frac{30}{8} \quad \text{Divide both sides by 8.}$$

$$x = 3.75 \quad \text{The length of side } x \text{ is 3.75 m.}$$

EXERCISES ***Use the similar triangles shown at the right to complete each of the following.***

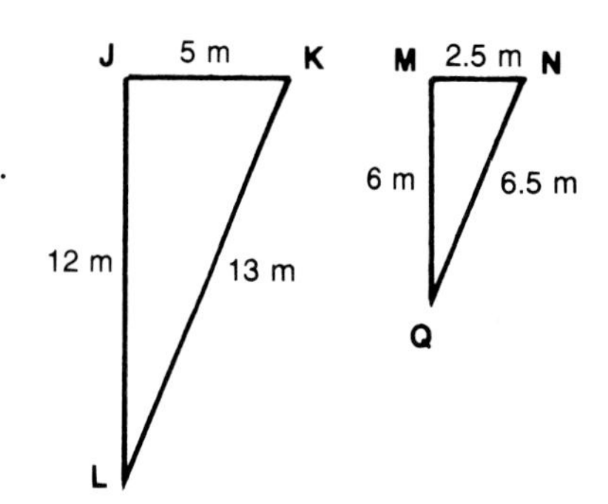

1. $\overline{JL}$ corresponds to ▒.
2. $\overline{NQ}$ corresponds to ▒.
3. The ratio of the measure of $\overline{JK}$ to the measure of $\overline{MN}$ is ▒.
4. The ratio of the measure of $\overline{LK}$ to the measure of $\overline{QN}$ is ▒.

For each pair of similar triangles, use a proportion to find the length of side x.

5.

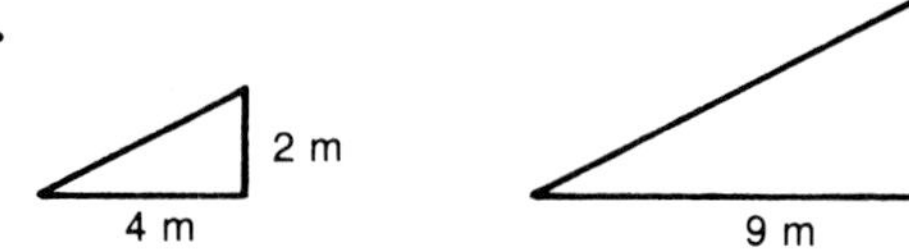

6.

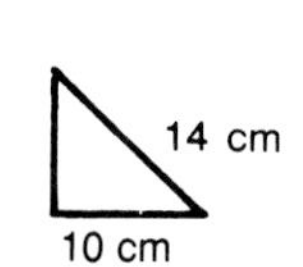

x

22 cm

7.

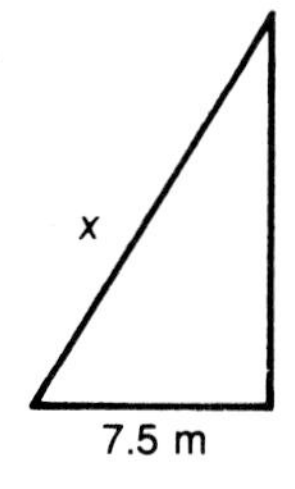

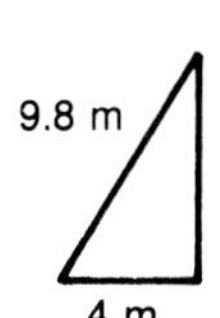

8.

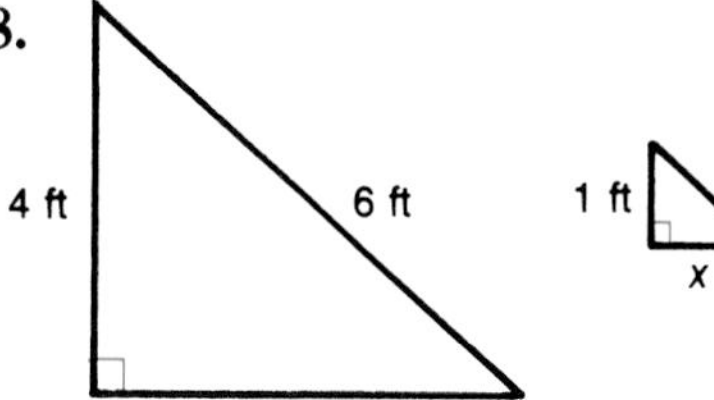

Solve.

9. Find the length of the ladder.

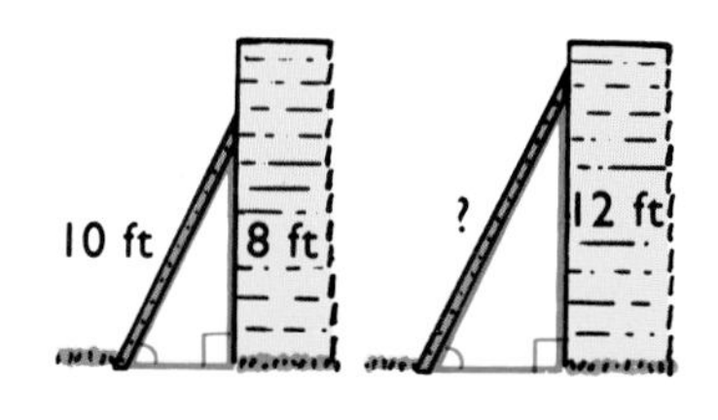

10. Find the distance across the stream.

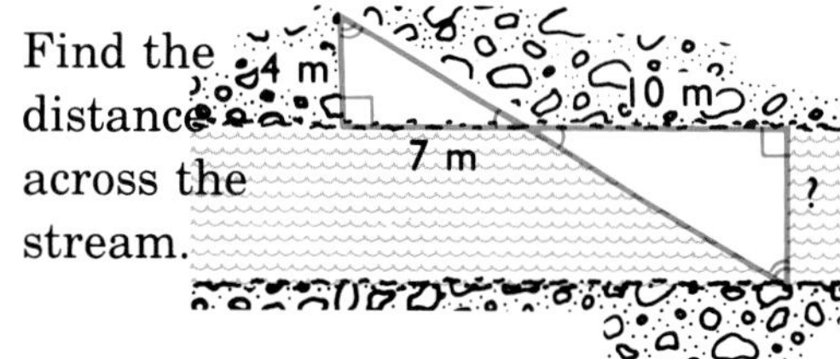

14-6 Indirect Measurement

Royalton Construction Company is clearing land for a new housing development. Any tree under 6 meters tall is cut down. Felicia Loomis uses a method involving similar triangles to find the height of a tree.

Miss Loomis holds a meter stick perpendicular to the ground. Then she measures its shadow and the shadow of the tree.

The two triangles that are formed are similar. Why?

Miss Loomis then uses a proportion to find the height of the tree.

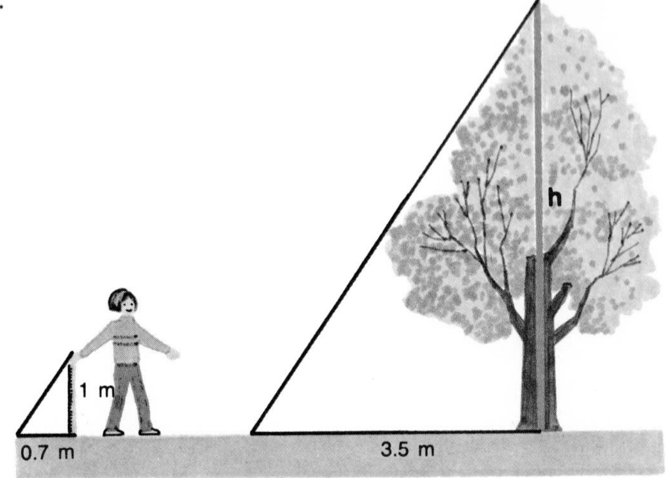

shadow of stick → 0.7; height of stick → 1

shadow of tree → 3.5; height of tree → h

$$\frac{0.7}{3.5} = \frac{1}{h}$$

$0.7 \times h = 3.5 \times 1$ Cross multiply. Cross products are equal.

$\frac{0.7h}{0.7} = \frac{3.5}{0.7}$ Divide both sides by 0.7.

$h = 5$ The tree is 5 meters tall.

EXERCISES ***The shadow of a meter stick measures 0.8 m. The lengths of the shadows of trees measured at the same time are given below. Use a proportion to find the height of each tree to the nearest tenth of a meter.***

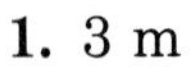

1. 3 m **2.** 9 m

3. 11.4 m **4.** 5.1 m

5. 6.6 m **6.** 13.5 m

Solve. Use a proportion.

7. A tree casts a shadow of 24 feet while Ralph casts a shadow of 8 feet. If Ralph is 6 feet tall, how tall is the tree?

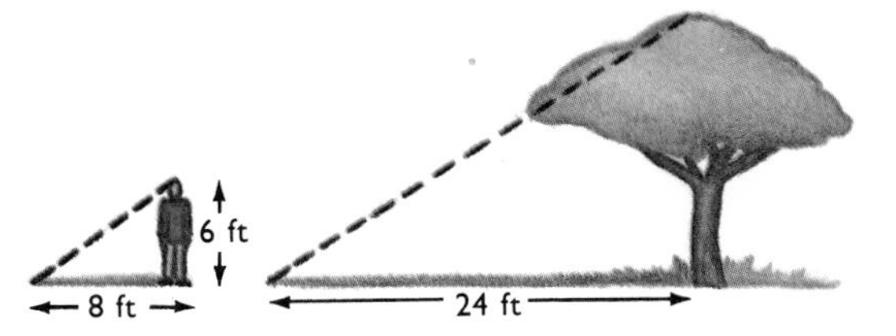

8. Corinne is 5 feet tall and casts a shadow of 2 feet. How high is the building that casts a shadow of 26 feet?

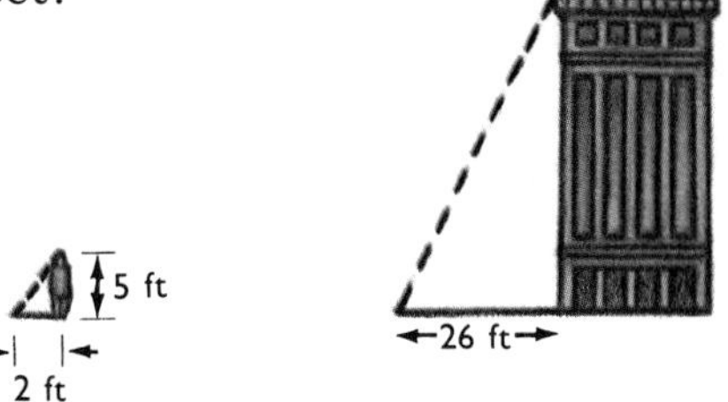

9. Find the length of Kingly Lake.

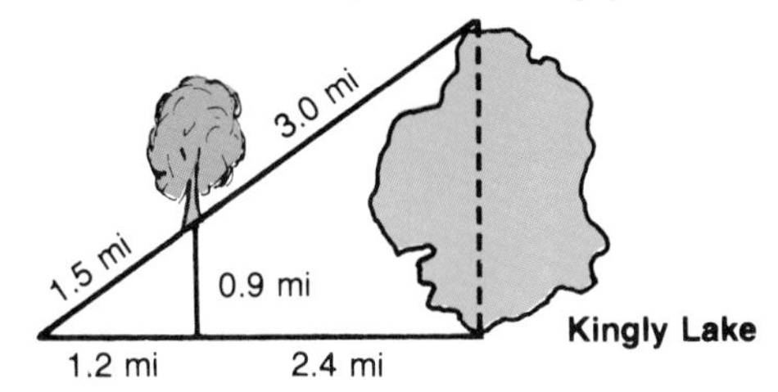

10. Find the length of the brace.

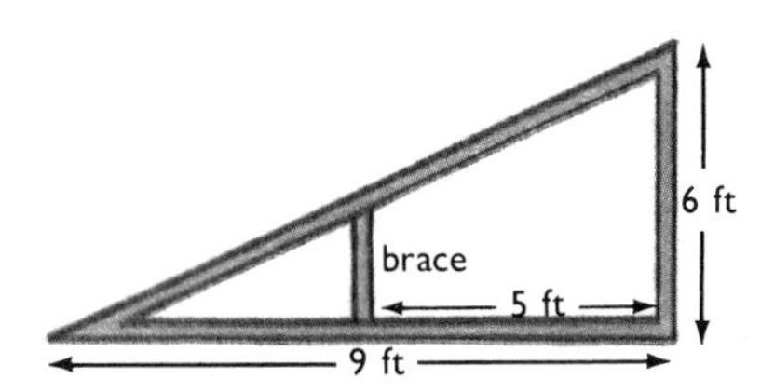

11. A flagpole casts a shadow of 9 meters. At the same time, a 2-meter signpost casts a shadow of 2.6 meters. How tall is the flagpole?

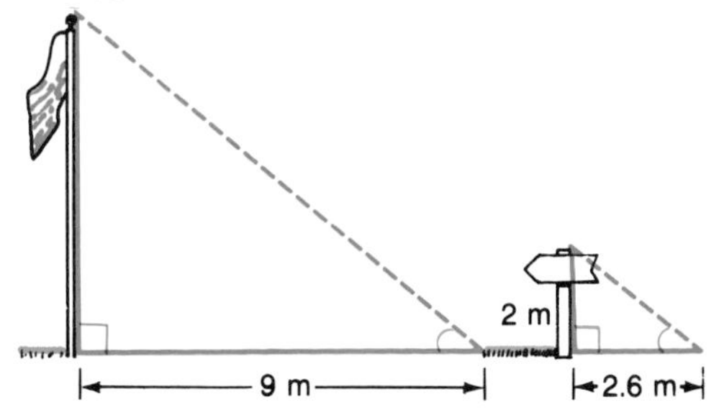

12. Maple Drive and Oak Street meet at a right angle. Cedar Lane is parallel to Walnut Avenue. Find the length of Cedar Lane.

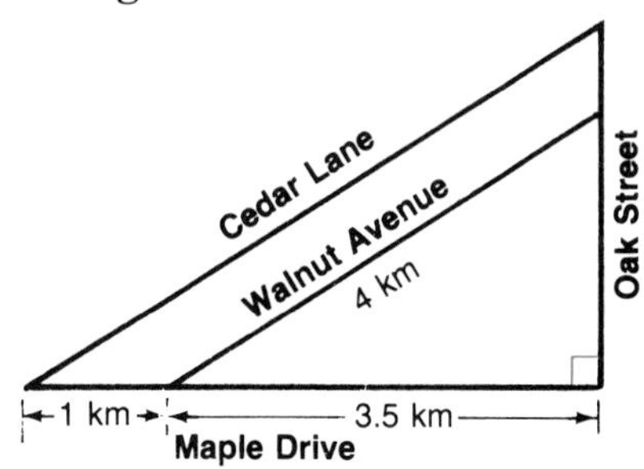

13. A tower casts a shadow of 32 meters. At the same time, a 2-meter pole nearby casts a shadow of 8 meters. How high is the tower?

14. Rich is 1.5 meters tall and casts a 0.75-meter shadow. At the same time, a nearby flagpole casts a 3-meter shadow. How tall is the flagpole?

15. Pam is 58 inches tall and Rory is 63 inches tall. They are standing by a lamppost. Pam's shadow is 78 inches long. How long is Rory's shadow?

14-7 Problem Solving: Right Triangles

Mel takes a shortcut to school by walking diagonally across an empty lot. The rectangular lot is 20 meters wide and 40 meters long. How much shorter is the shortcut than a route on the sides of the lot?

Read the problem. The lot that Mel uses as a shortcut is a rectangle 20 meters wide and 40 meters long. The shortcut is a diagonal of the rectangle.

Decide what to do. Make a drawing to illustrate the problem.

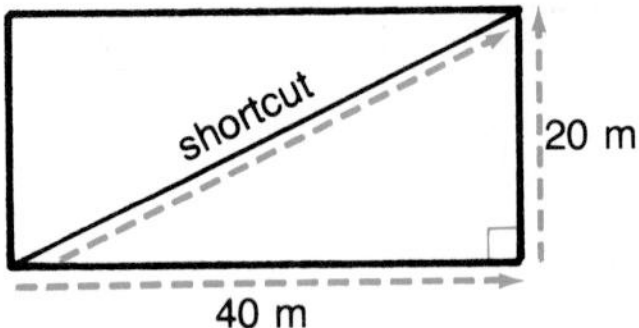

Notice that the diagonal and sides form a right triangle. You can use the Pythagorean theorem to find the length of the diagonal.

Solve the problem.

$$a^2 + b^2 = c^2$$ Pythagorean theorem

$$20^2 + 40^2 = c^2$$ Replace *a* with 20 and *b* with 40.

$$400 + 1{,}600 = c^2$$

$$2{,}000 = c^2$$

$$44.7 \approx c$$ Use the table on page 422.

The shortcut is 44.7 meters. The route on the sides is 20 + 40 or 60 meters. Subtract to find how much shorter the shortcut is.

60.0 meters
− 44.7 meters
15.3 meters The shortcut is 15.3 meters shorter.

Examine the solution. The shortcut should be longer than either side, but shorter than both sides together. The solution is reasonable.

Solve. Round answers to the nearest tenth.

1. Anita hikes seven miles due east and then three miles due north. How far is she from the starting point?
2. An airplane flies due south 65 kilometers and due west 72 kilometers. How far is the plane from its starting point?
3. A baseball diamond is a square. The distance from home plate to first base is 90 feet. Find the distance from home plate to second base.
4. Wire is stretched from the top of a 26-foot pole to a point on the ground that is 15 feet from the bottom of the pole. How long is the wire?
5. The foot of a ladder is placed 5 feet from a building. The ladder is 13 feet long. How high does the ladder reach on the building?
6. Mr. Sisk makes a gate for his picket fence. It is 1 meter wide and 1.5 meters long. How long is the diagonal brace for the gate?
7. A clock has a minute hand that is 1.5 m long and an hour hand that is 1.2 m long. What is the distance between the ends of the hands at 9 o'clock?
8. When Jerome stands 3 feet from a lamppost, his shadow is 4 feet long. If Jerome is 6 feet tall, how tall is the lamppost?

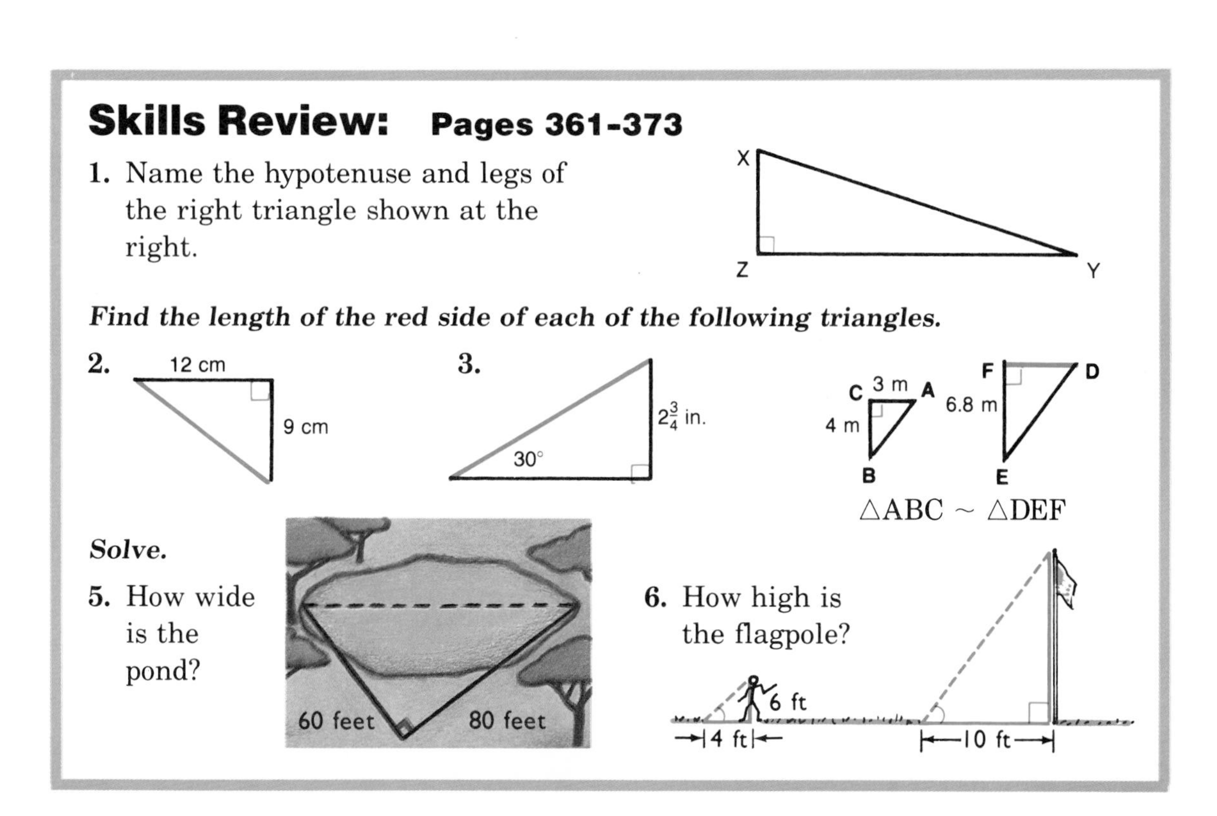

Skills Review: Pages 361-373

1. Name the hypotenuse and legs of the right triangle shown at the right.

Find the length of the red side of each of the following triangles.

2.

3.

Solve.

5. How wide is the pond?
6. How high is the flagpole?

Cumulative Review

Estimate.

1. $\begin{array}{r} 7{,}846 \\ +\ 3{,}782 \\ \hline \end{array}$

2. $\begin{array}{r} 4{,}180 \\ -\ 1{,}347 \\ \hline \end{array}$

3. $\begin{array}{r} 278 \\ \times\ 44 \\ \hline \end{array}$

4. $278\overline{)11{,}964}$

5. $4.1\overline{)3.55}$

Add, subtract, multiply, or divide.

6. $\begin{array}{r} \$49.03 \\ -\ 17.26 \\ \hline \end{array}$

7. $\begin{array}{r} 47.5 \\ 8.74 \\ +\ 0.198 \\ \hline \end{array}$

8. $\begin{array}{r} 10.362 \\ -\ 4.77 \\ \hline \end{array}$

9. $\begin{array}{r} \$35.50 \\ 4.99 \\ +\ 19 \\ \hline \end{array}$

10. $\begin{array}{r} 27.2 \\ -\ 8.88 \\ \hline \end{array}$

11. $\begin{array}{r} 42 \\ \times\ 8.4 \\ \hline \end{array}$

12. $\begin{array}{r} 0.47 \\ \times\ 0.02 \\ \hline \end{array}$

13. $\begin{array}{r} 54.7 \\ \times\ 3.48 \\ \hline \end{array}$

14. $\begin{array}{r} 33.78 \\ \times\ 5.9 \\ \hline \end{array}$

15. $\begin{array}{r} 6{,}700 \\ \times\ 0.24 \\ \hline \end{array}$

16. $0.6\overline{)5.94}$

17. $12\overline{)27}$

18. $4.6\overline{)9.2}$

19. $28\overline{)565.6}$

20. $0.72\overline{)4.68}$

21. $^{-}9 + {}^{-}7$

22. $^{-}8 + 5.1$

23. $^{-}2 - {}^{-}7$

24. $6 - 12$

25. $^{-}4 \times {}^{-}9.5$

26. $^{-}2 \times 7$

27. $^{-}16 \div 2$

28. $^{-}72 \div {}^{-}1.8$

Find the greatest common factor (GCF) for each group of numbers.

29. 20, 36

30. 32, 45

31. 45, 60

32. 12, 18, 24

Find the least common multiple (LCM) for each group of numbers.

33. 6, 8

34. 8, 18

35. 5, 15

36. 2, 3, 10

Add, subtract, multiply, or divide. Write each answer in simplest form.

37. $\frac{7}{9} + \frac{1}{4}$

38. $5\frac{1}{2} + 2\frac{5}{8}$

39. $\frac{4}{5} - \frac{1}{6}$

40. $2\frac{1}{7} - 1\frac{2}{3}$

41. $\frac{5}{8} \times \frac{4}{15}$

42. $2\frac{2}{3} \times 3\frac{3}{4}$

43. $\frac{3}{8} \div \frac{3}{4}$

44. $5\frac{1}{2} \div 2$

Solve each equation. Check your solution.

45. $a - 8 = 25.5$

46. $17 + w = 65$

47. $5.9 = h - 8.6$

48. $9r = 10$

49. $\frac{t}{7} = 6.05$

50. $2s + 5 = 13$

Solve.

51. What number is 44% of 65?

52. What percent of 52 is 13?

Complete each of the following.

53. 43 cm = ▒ mm

54. 9.01 km = ▒ m

55. 67 mL = ▒ L

56. 0.08 kg = ▒ g

57. ▒ L = 6.5 kL

58. 9,406 mg = ▒ g

Solve.

59. Find the perimeter and area of the rectangle shown at the right.

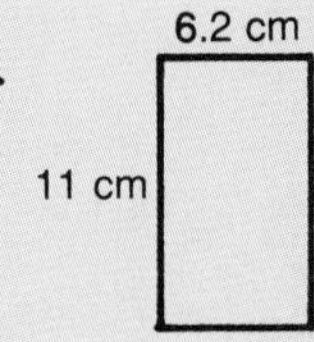

60. Find the surface area and volume of a rectangular prism whose base is 7 ft by 8 ft and whose height is 12 ft.

61. The price of a gallon of regular gasoline at five service stations was $1.299, $1.239, $1.339, $1.249 and $1.309. Find the average price to the nearest tenth of a cent.

62. Graph the equations on a coordinate axis. State the solution as an ordered pair.

$y = x + 3 \qquad y = 4x$

Mathematics Lab

A **stadia** like the one shown at the right can be used to find the height of an object. Hold the stadia to your eye. Back away from the object until the top and bottom of the object are in line with the strings. Now record the two readings where the strings appear to cross the stick. Notice that two similar triangles are formed. You can use a proportion to find the height of the tree.

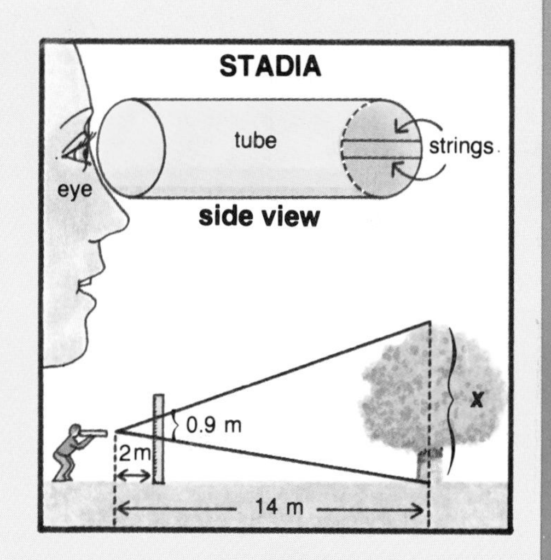

1. Set up a proportion to find the height of the tree shown in the diagram.
2. Solve the proportion for x. What is the height of the tree?
3. Find an object such as a building, tree, or a flagpole. Use a stadia and a measuring stick to find the height of the object. Remember to measure the distances between yourself and the stick and between yourself and the object.

14-8 Tangent, Sine, and Cosine Ratios

The measures of the sides of right triangles form special ratios.

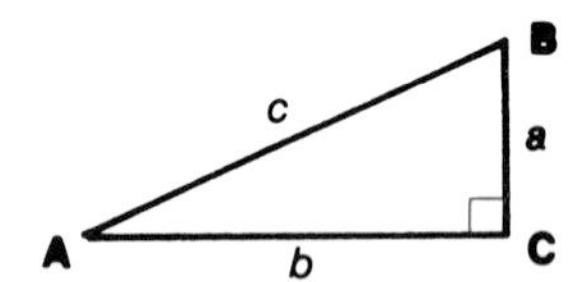

$$\text{sine of } \angle A = \frac{\text{measure of the side opposite } \angle A}{\text{measure of the hypotenuse}} \quad \text{or } \sin A = \frac{a}{c}$$

$$\text{cosine of } \angle A = \frac{\text{measure of the side adjacent to } \angle A}{\text{measure of the hypotenuse}} \quad \text{or } \cos A = \frac{b}{c}$$

$$\text{tangent of } \angle A = \frac{\text{measure of the side opposite } \angle A}{\text{measure of the side adjacent to } \angle A} \quad \text{or } \tan A = \frac{a}{b}$$

For $\triangle ABC$ shown below, express sin A, cos A, tan A, sin B, cos B, and tan B to three decimal places.

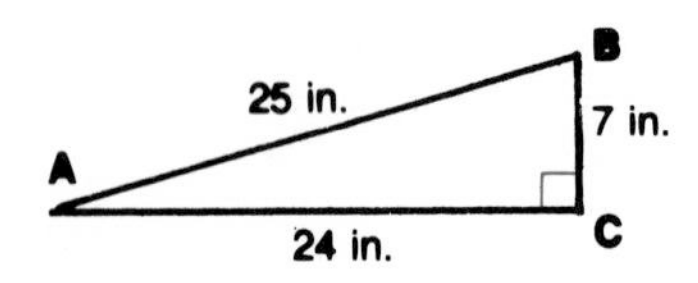

Angle	Opposite Side	Adjacent Side
$\angle A$	$\overline{BC}$	$\overline{AC}$
$\angle B$	$\overline{AC}$	$\overline{BC}$

$\sin A = \frac{7}{25} = 0.280$ $\quad \cos A = \frac{24}{25} = 0.960$ $\quad \tan A = \frac{7}{24} \approx 0.292$

$\sin B = \frac{24}{25} = 0.960$ $\quad \cos B = \frac{7}{25} = 0.280$ $\quad \tan B = \frac{24}{7} \approx 3.429$

The value of each ratio depends only on the measure of the acute angle. For example, the sine of angle D is equal to the sine of angle G even though $\triangle DEF$ is smaller than $\triangle GHI$.

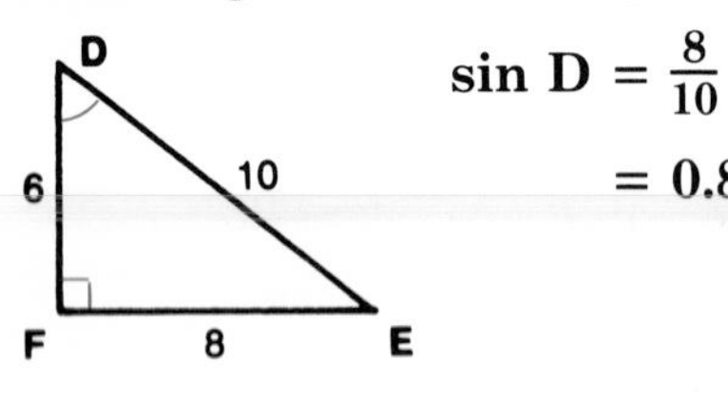

$\sin D = \frac{8}{10}$

$= 0.800$

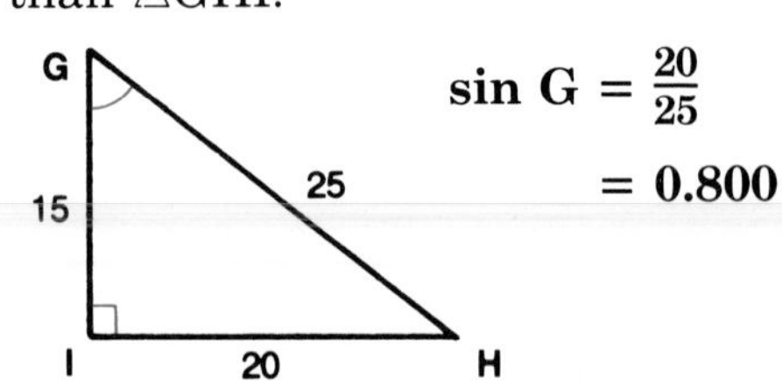

$\sin G = \frac{20}{25}$

$= 0.800$

EXERCISES ***Express each ratio to three decimal places.***

1. sin J **2.** cos J

3. tan J **4.** sin L

5. cos L **6.** tan L

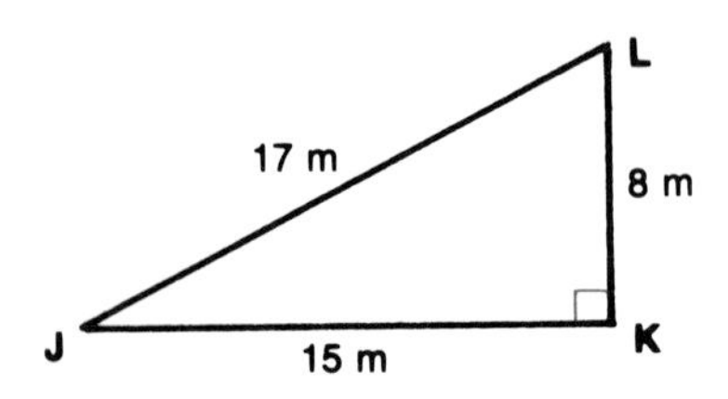

The table on page 423 can be used to find decimal approximations of the sine, cosine, and tangent ratios. Study how to use the table to find tan 53°.

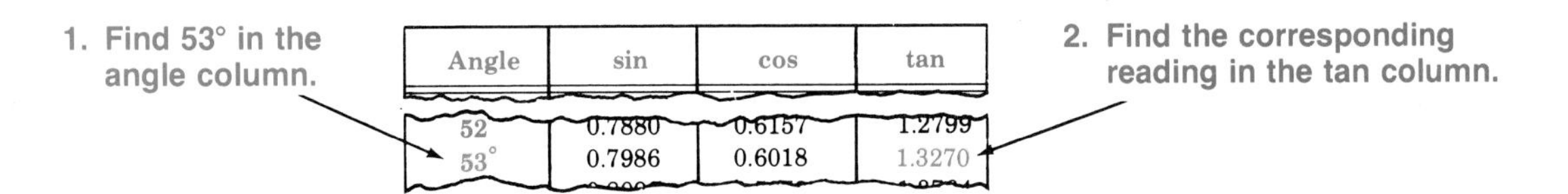

Tan 53° is approximately 1.3270.

Suppose you know one of the ratios. For example, you know that the length of the side opposite an angle is twice the side adjacent to it. In other words, the tangent of the angle is 2. You can use the tables to find the measure of the angle. First express the ratio as a decimal (2 = 2.0000).

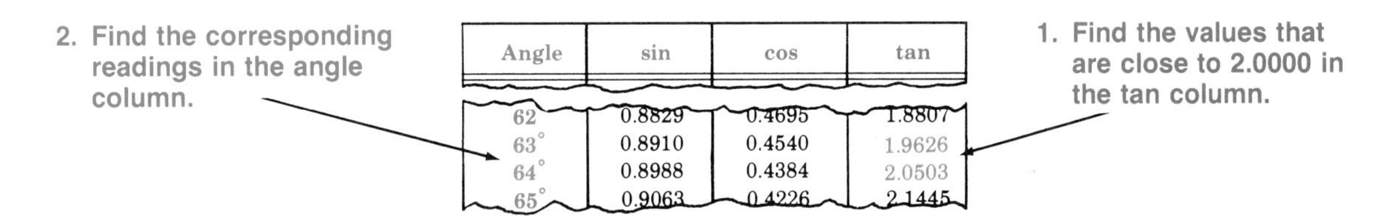

The angle is between 63° and 64°. Since 2.0000 is closer to 1.9626 than to 2.0503, the measure of the angle is about 63.

EXERCISES ***Use the table on page 423 to find the value of each ratio.***

7. sin 30° **8.** cos 30° **9.** tan 38° **10.** sin 51°

11. cos 45° **12.** cos 72° **13.** tan 24° **14.** cos 0°

Use the table on page 423 to find the measurement of each angle.

15. sin M = 0.8660 **16.** tan N = 0.5000 **17.** cos F = 0.7071

18. tan E = 0.5774 **19.** sin V = 0.0523 **20.** cos G = 0.7660

21. sin A = $\frac{1}{2}$ **22.** cos T = $\frac{4}{5}$ **23.** tan Z = $\frac{3}{4}$

14-9 Using Tangent, Sine, and Cosine

Jean Newton works for the WROY radio station in Royalton. She needs to verify the height of the broadcasting tower. Suppose the tower casts a shadow 40 meters long. The angle measures 47°. The tangent ratio may be used to find the height of the tower.

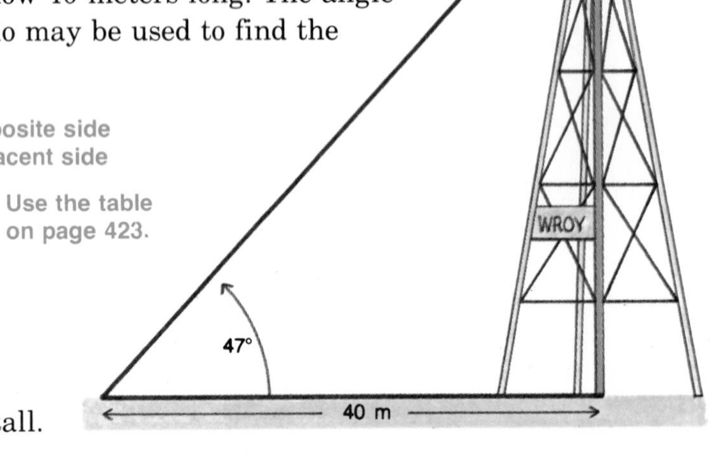

$$\tan 47° = \frac{x}{40} \quad \begin{matrix}\leftarrow \text{opposite side} \\ \leftarrow \text{adjacent side}\end{matrix}$$

$$1.0724 \approx \frac{x}{40}$$

Use the table on page 423.

$$1.0724 \times 40 \approx \frac{x}{40} \times 40$$

$$42.896 \approx x$$

The tower is about 43 meters tall.

Why was the tangent ratio used instead of the sine ratio or the cosine ratio?

You can find the degree measures of angles A and B using either the sine ratio or the cosine ratio.

$$\sin A = \frac{5}{13}$$

$$\approx 0.3846$$

B

13 in.

5 in.

A

12 in.

C

$$\cos A = \frac{12}{13}$$

$$\approx 0.9231$$

Using the table, you see that by either method the degree measure of angle A is approximately 23. Then the measure of angle B is approximately 90 − 23 or 67.

EXERCISES ***Find the missing measures of each of the following triangles.***

1. A, 42°, 15 cm, B, C

2. 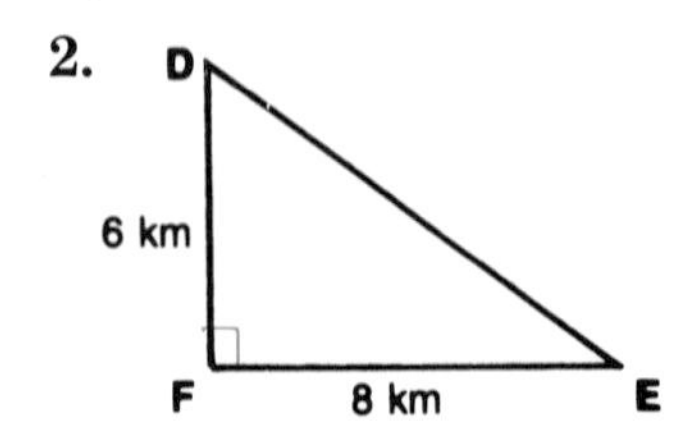

3. 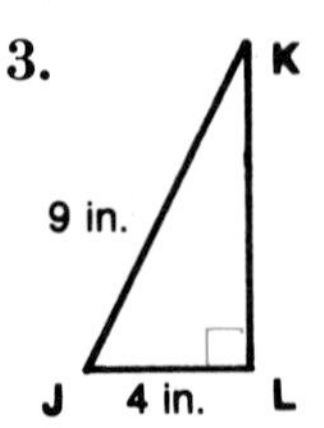

Solve. Round answers to the nearest unit.

4. How high is the kite?

5. How long is the guide wire?

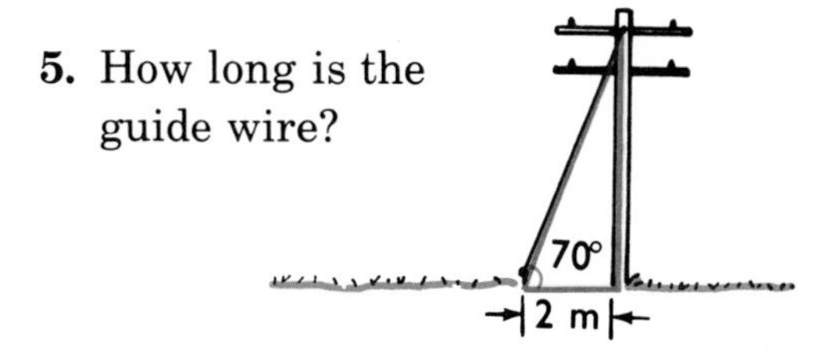

6. Mei and Ed are flying kites in Crockett Park. When Mei is 30 meters from Ed, Mei's kite is directly over Ed. The kite string makes an angle of 58° with the ground. How high is the kite?

7. The path of a cable car connecting Piney Peak and Smokey Peak rises 20 meters for every 100 meters of horizontal distance. What is the measurement of the angle the cable makes with the horizontal?

INTERPOLATION

To find a closer approximation of the measure of the angle whose tangent is 2.0000, you can use a proportion of differences. This process of finding a close approximation is called **interpolation.**

$$\tan 63^\circ = 1.9626$$

$A - 63^\circ = x$ $\qquad$ $2.0000 - 1.9626 = 0.0374$

$$\tan A = 2.0000$$

$64^\circ - 63^\circ = 1^\circ \text{ or } 60'$ $\qquad$ $2.0503 - 1.9626 = 0.0877$

$$\tan 64^\circ = 2.0503$$

$$\frac{x}{60} = \frac{0.0374}{0.0877}$$

$$0.0877 \times x = 2.244$$

$$\frac{0.0877 \times x}{0.0877} = \frac{2.244}{0.0877}$$

$$x \approx 26'$$

$$A - 63^\circ = 26'$$

$$A - 63^\circ + 63^\circ = 26' + 63^\circ$$

$$A = 63^\circ 26'$$

Angle A measures approximately 63°26′.

Use interpolation to find the approximate measurement of each angle.

1. $\sin T = 0.7000$ $\qquad$ **2.** $\tan G = 3.5000$ $\qquad$ **3.** $\sin W = 0.8200$

Focus on Problem Solving

14-10 Solve a Similar Problem

The Royalton Garden Club takes care of a square flower bed in the park. They plant two different kinds of flowers in a checkerboard pattern as shown below. How many squares are there?

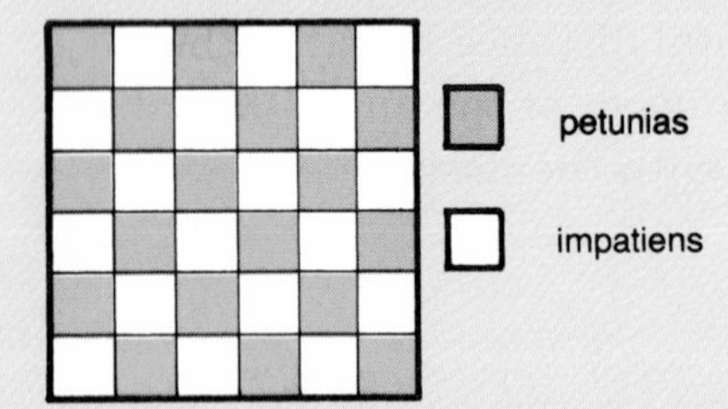

Read the problem. The flower bed is a 6×6 square with two types of flowers alternating each way. You need to find the total number of squares of all sizes.

Decide what to do. Find the number of squares in a 1×1 square, a 2×2 square, and a 3×3 square. Look for a pattern that you can extend to a 6×6 square.

Solve the problem.

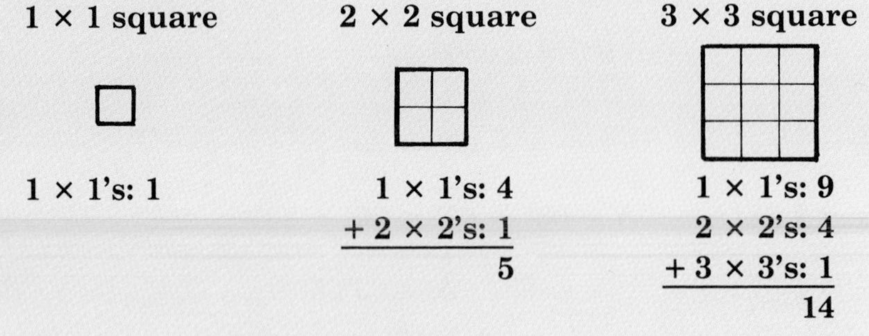

Notice that the number of squares is the sum of the numbers squared up to that point. For a 6×6 square, there would be $1 + 4 + 9 + 16 + 25 + 36$ or a total of 91 squares.

Examine the solution. You can check the solution by actually continuing to list the number of squares for each size up to a 6×6 square. The answer is correct.

Solve.

1. How many numbers from 10 to 1,000 read the same forward or backward?

2. Suppose you add the digits of a number. How many numbers from 0 to 1,000 have a sum of 10?

3. The width of a rectangle is 105 feet. Its length is 140 feet. How long is the diagonal?

4. Find the sum of the numbers 1 through 1,000.

5. The Royalton Express seats 132 passengers. On a recent trip, there was one empty seat for every three passengers. How many passengers were on the trip?

Solve. Use any strategy.

6. Mrs. Trimmer grades a 20-question test. Each correct answer is $^{+}2$ points. Each wrong answer is $^{-}1$ point. Lana's score is 25. How many of her answers are correct?

7. Jose cuts a bolt of material that is 50 yards long into pieces that are 1 yard long. Each cut takes one minute. How long will it take Jose to make all the cuts?

8. The area of a garden is 250 square meters. Its perimeter is 65 meters. What are the length and width of the garden?

Skills Review: Pages 376-381

Express each ratio to three decimal places.

1. sin A **2.** cos A

3. tan B **4.** sin B

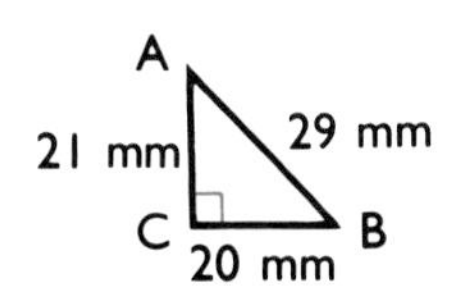

Use the table on page 423 to find the value of each ratio.

5. tan 42° **6.** cos 17°

Solve.

9. How far up the wall does the ladder reach?

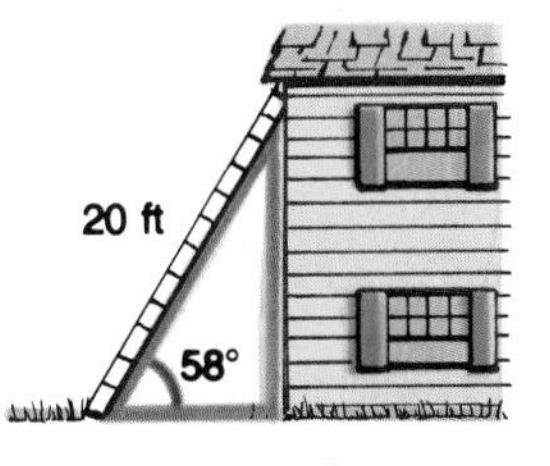

Use the table on page 423 to find the measurement of each angle.

7. sin N = 0.2419

8. tan P = 2.3559

10. Find the total number of squares in the figure at the right.

Mathematics and Geography

Any point on Earth can be located by an imaginary grid of lines called **latitude** and **longitude**. Latitude and longitude are expressed in degrees because they are measures of angles formed from the center of Earth.

Lines of latitude are parallel to each other and to the equator. The equator has 0° latitude. Any point on Earth is a certain number of degrees either north or south of the equator. For example, point A is located at 40° N. latitude.

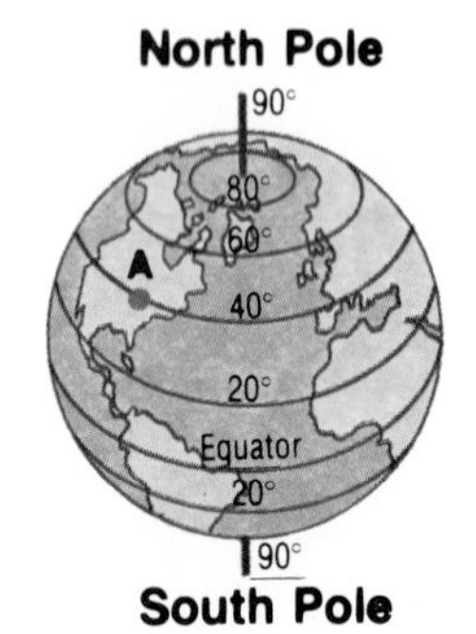

Lines of longitude run in a north-south direction from pole to pole. The prime meridian passes through Greenwich, England. It has 0° longitude. Any point on Earth is a certain number of degrees either east or west of the prime meridian. For example, point B is located at 60°W. longitude.

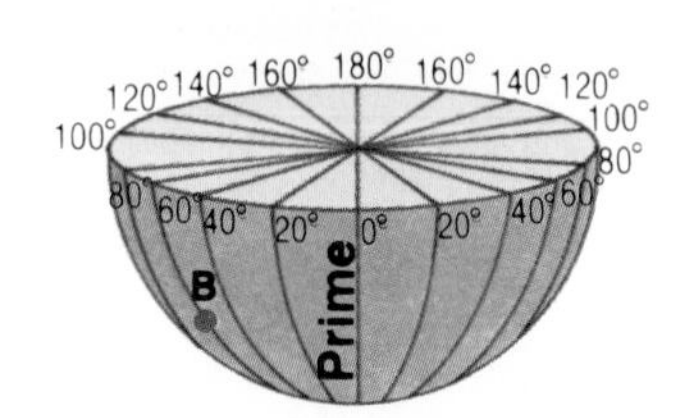

EXERCISES ***Estimate the latitude and longitude of each of the following points.***

1. C	**2.** D	**3.** E	**4.** F
5. G	**6.** H	**7.** I	**8.** J

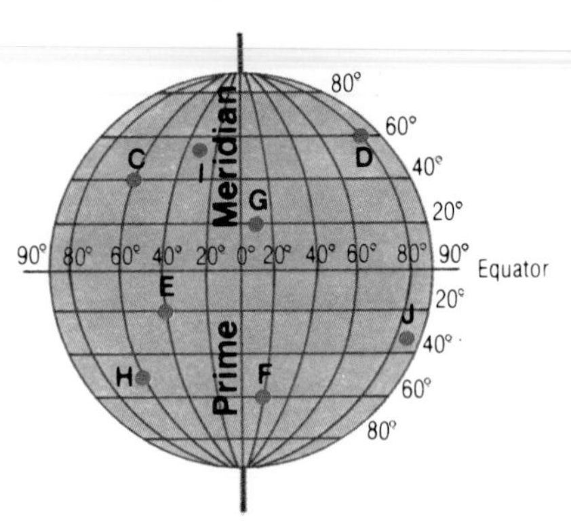

Use a globe to estimate the latitude and longitude of each of the following.

9. Washington, D.C. **10.** Stockholm

11. Rio de Janeiro **12.** Sydney

13. where you live

Chapter 14 Review

VOCABULARY	hypotenuse (361)	legs (361)
Pythagorean theorem (362)	Pythagorean triples (363)	30°-60° right triangle (366)
similar figures (368)	corresponding sides (368)	ratios (376)

EXERCISES

1. Name the hypotenuse and legs of the right triangle shown at the right. (361)

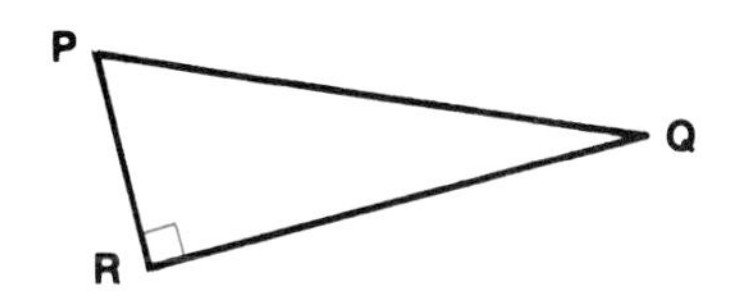

Find the length of the red side of each of the following triangles. (362–369)

2.

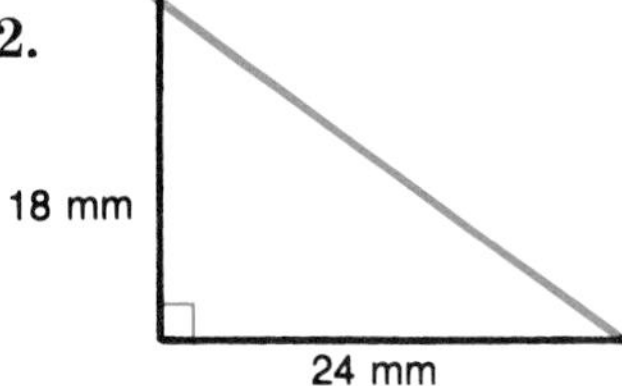

3.

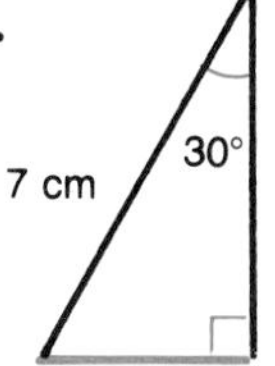

4.

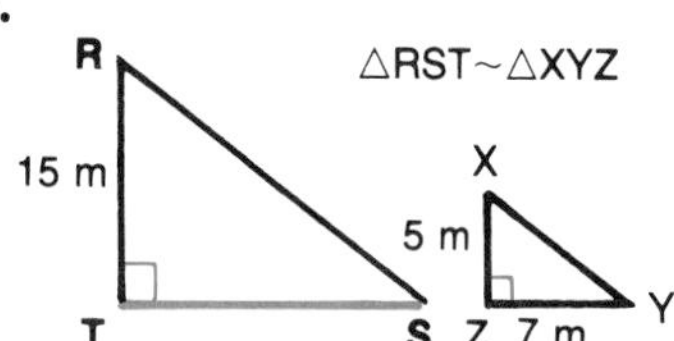

Solve. (370–373)

5. Find the length of the support.

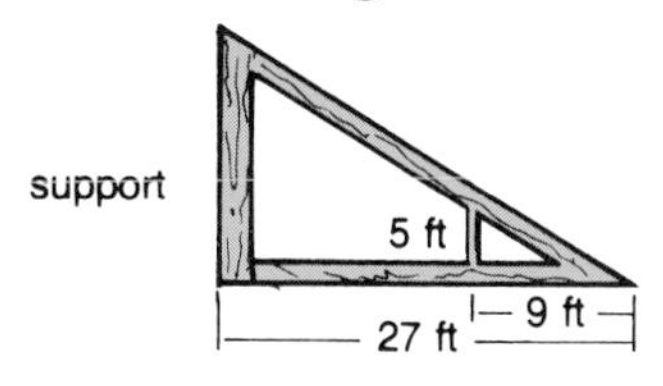

6. Archie is standing 28 feet from a point directly below his kite. The string attached to the kite is 53 feet long. How high is the kite flying?

Express each ratio to three decimal places. (376)

7. sin J
8. tan K

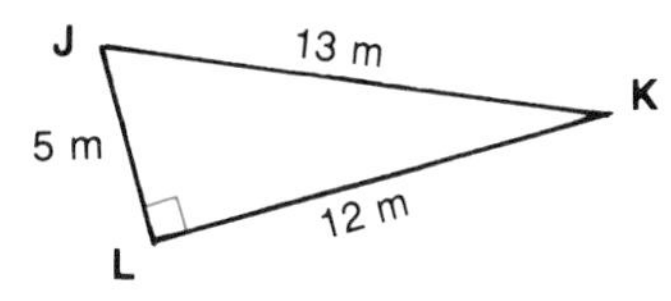

Use the table on page 423 to find the measurement of each angle. (376)

9. tan A = 0.3443
10. cos B = 0.1908

Solve. (378–380)

11. How high is the lamp post?

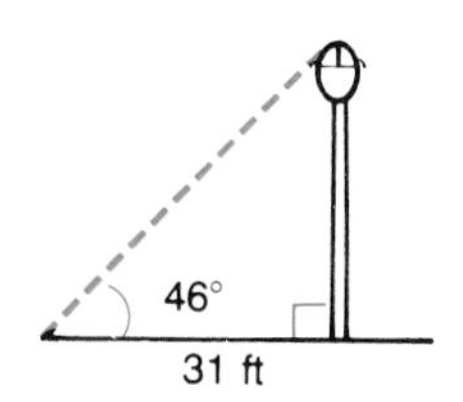

12. Find the sum of the numbers 1 through 500.

Chapter 14 Test

Find the length of the red side of each of the following triangles.

1.

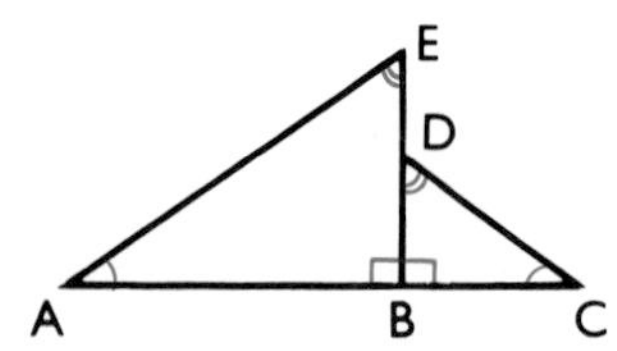

2.

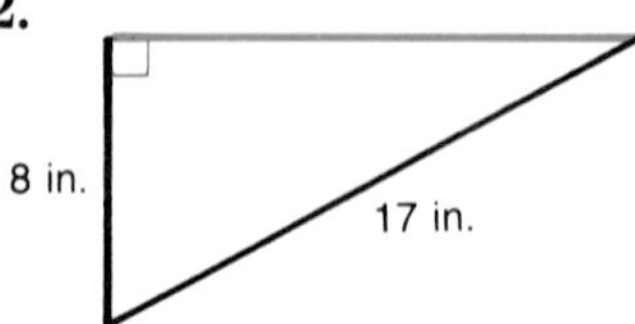

3.

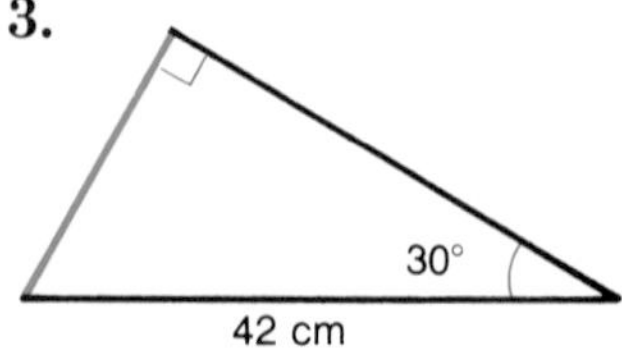

4. Name corresponding angles and sides of the similar triangles.

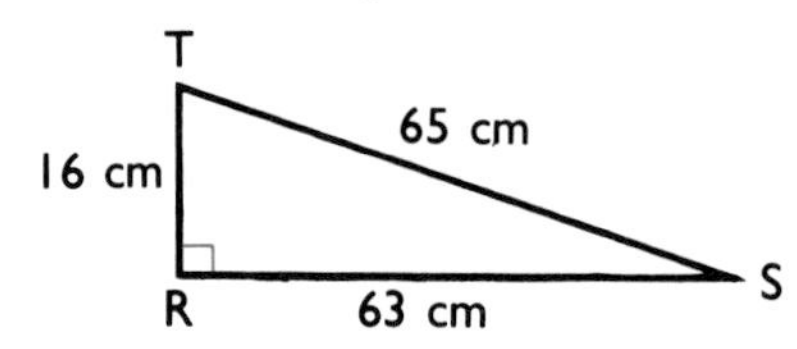

5. Express sin T, cos T, and tan T to three decimal places.

Use the table on page 423 to find the value of each ratio.

6. sin 71°

7. cos 15°

8. tan 34°

Solve.

9. What is the missing length of the side of the sail?

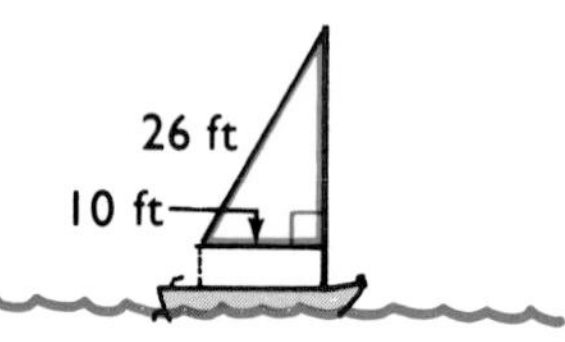

10. What is the height of the triangle?

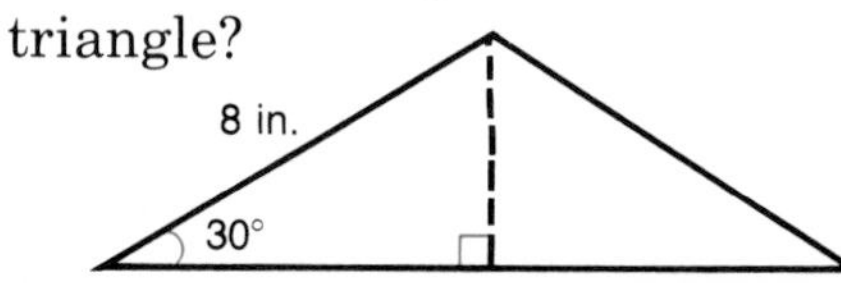

11. What is the distance across the pond?

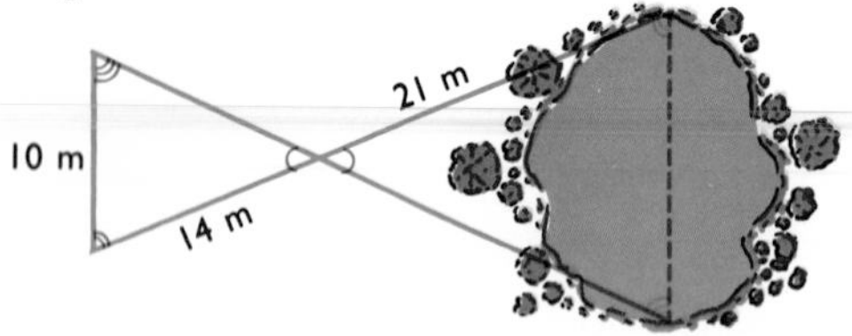

12. How high is the building?

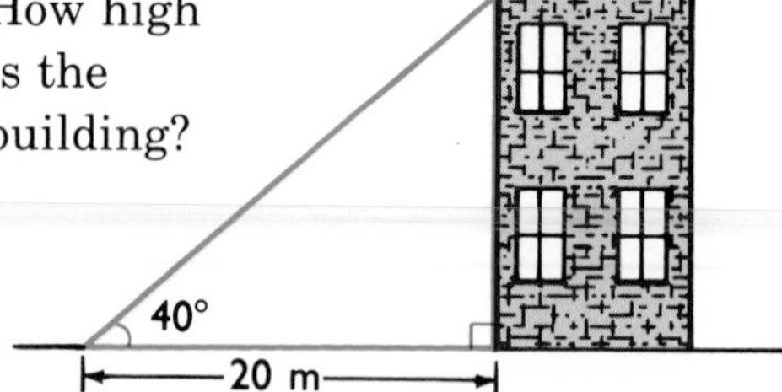

13. A parade balloon flies 60 feet above the ground. Guy wires each 68 feet in length are attached to floats on either side of the balloon. How far apart are the floats?

14. A drainpipe is 50 meters long. A spider climbs up 5 meters during the day but falls back 4 meters during the night. The spider begins at the bottom of the pipe. What day does it get to the top?

Enrichment

Suppose a geometric figure is enlarged or reduced. The figure does *not* change its shape. However, it is altered in size. This is called a **dilation.** The dilation image is similar to the original figure.

In the figure at the right, $\triangle$DEF is the dilation image of $\triangle$ABC. The measure of the distance from P to a point on $\triangle$DEF is two times the measure of the distance from P to the corresponding point of $\triangle$ABC.

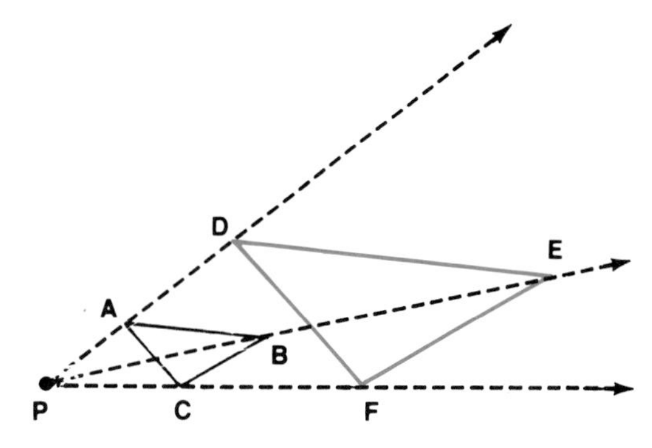

PD = 2(PA)

PE = 2(PB)

PF = 2(PC)

This dilation has center P and a scale factor of 2.

Find the dilation image of $\triangle$PQR with center C and a scale factor of $\frac{3}{4}$.

Draw rays CP, CQ, and CR. Find X, Y, and Z so that CX $= \frac{3}{4}$(CP), CY $= \frac{3}{4}$(CQ), and CZ $= \frac{3}{4}$(CR). $\triangle$XYZ is the dilation image of $\triangle$PQR.

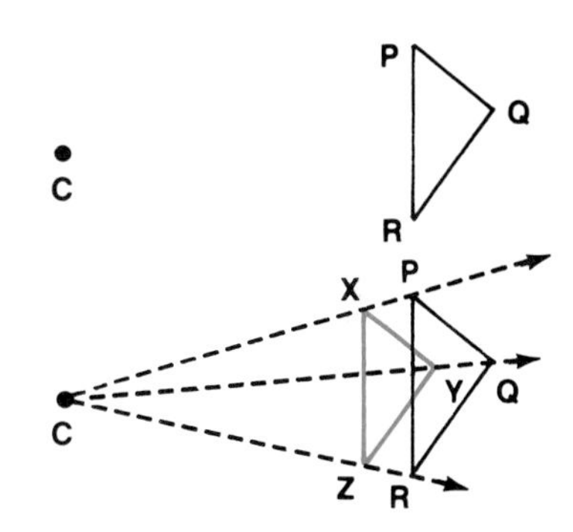

EXERCISES ***Copy the figure shown at the right. Then draw the dilation image of $\triangle$JKL for the given scale factor and center.***

1. scale factor, 2; center, B

2. scale factor, $\frac{1}{2}$; center B

3. scale factor, 2; center A

Graph each of the following ordered pairs. Connect the points in order. Draw the dilation image of each figure with the origin as the center and a scale factor of 2.

4. (0, 2), (4, 0)

5. (3, $^-3$), ($^-2$, $^-2$)

6. (6, 2), (4, 2), (3, 7)

7. (1, $^-2$), (4, $^-3$), (2, 3)

Skills Test, Chapters 1-14

Standardized Format

Directions Work each problem on your own paper. Choose the letter of the correct answer. If the correct answer is not given, choose the letter for *none of the above*. Make no marks in this book.

1. Which of the following is 4.675 rounded to the nearest tenth?

a 5
b 4.68
c 4.7
d *none of the above*

2. Add.

$$\begin{array}{r} 11.8 \\ 45.37 \\ +\ 27.64 \\ \hline \end{array}$$

e 84.71
f 84.81
g 847.1
h *none of the above*

3. Subtract.

$6.07 – $2.59

a $3.58
b $3.48
c $8.66
d *none of the above*

4. Multiply.

825×43

e 35,265
f 35,475
g 35,275
h *none of the above*

5. Divide.

$6.8\overline{)207.4}$

a 30.5
b 3.05
c 305
d *none of the above*

6. What is the greatest common factor of 24 and 16?

e 48
f 4
g 2
h *none of the above*

7. Which of the following is $\frac{16}{12}$ in simplest form?

a $1\frac{4}{12}$
b $2\frac{1}{3}$
c $\frac{4}{3}$
d *none of the above*

8. Add.

$\frac{4}{9} + \frac{2}{3}$

e $\frac{1}{2}$
f $1\frac{1}{9}$
g $\frac{8}{27}$
h *none of the above*

9. Subtract.

$2\frac{1}{4} - 1\frac{2}{5}$

a $\frac{17}{20}$
b $1\frac{17}{20}$
c $3\frac{13}{20}$
d *none of the above*

10. Multiply.

$4.3 \times {}^-8$

e 34.4
f $^-34.4$
g 3.44
h *none of the above*

11. Divide.

$2\frac{5}{8} \div 2\frac{5}{8}$

a 0
b $\frac{1}{8}$
c 1
d *none of the above*

12. Solve.

$\frac{w}{9.1} = 27.3$

e 248.43
f 3
g 18.2
h *none of the above*

GO ON TO THE NEXT PAGE

13. Solve.

$\frac{2.5}{t} = \frac{0.5}{8.6}$

a 4.3

b 47

c 40

d *none of the above*

14. What is the measure of an angle that is supplementary to a 49° angle?

e 41

f 121

g 131

h *none of the above*

15. Which of the following is equivalent to 80%?

a 8

b 0.08

c 0.8

d *none of the above*

16. What percent of 16 is 12?

e 25%

f 75%

g $133\frac{1}{3}\%$

h *none of the above*

17. The mass of one nickel is 5 grams. What is the mass of 40 nickels?

a 0.02 kg

b 0.2 kg

c 0.002 kg

d *none of the above*

18. What number has a square root of 9?

e $^{-}81$

f 18

g 81

h *none of the above*

19. If $y = 2x - 4$, what number will complete the table?

x	y
14	24
20	36
26	?

a 40

b 44

c 48

d *none of the above*

20. Mr. Jhin bought a TV for $480. He paid 20% of the cost at the time of purchase. He paid the rest of the cost in 10 equal payments. How much was each payment?

e $9.60

f $48

g $38.40

h *none of the above*

21. Suppose you draw a ball, replace it and draw another ball. What is the probability that both balls drawn are black?

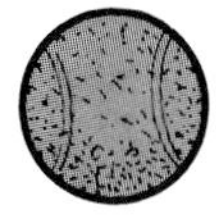
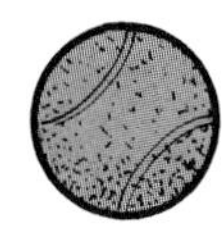
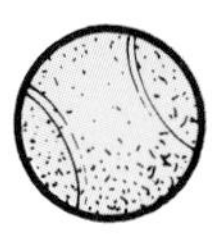
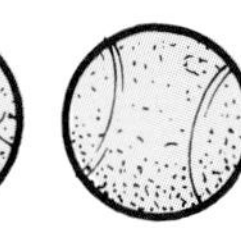

a $\frac{1}{2}$

b $\frac{1}{6}$

c $\frac{1}{4}$

d *none of the above*

22. What is the length of the hypotenuse of the right triangle?

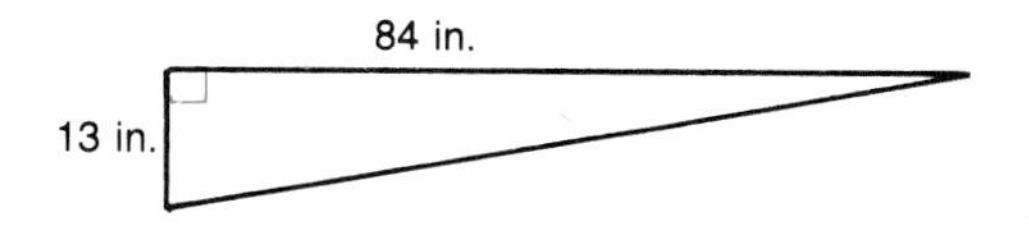

e 85 in.

f 86 in.

g 83 in.

h *none of the above*

STOP

Appendix: BASIC

Lesson 1 The Language of BASIC

The computer language **BASIC** uses symbols similar to those used in mathematics.

Operation	Mathematics	BASIC
addition	+	+
subtraction	−	−
multiplication	×	*
division	÷	/
raising to a power	x^2	X↑2

The symbols above can be used to translate mathematical expressions into BASIC and vice-versa.

Mathematics	BASIC
$a - 3$	A−3
$7w$	7*W
$c \div 6 + 4$	C/6+4
$n^5 - 2.1$	N↑5−2.1
$4 \times (b + \frac{9}{7})$	4*(B+9/7)

Notice that all variables are represented by capital letters in BASIC.

EXERCISES ***Translate each of the following into a mathematical expression.***

1. B+5
2. A↑4
3. 6/G
4. A*B/C
5. (D+1)↑3
6. H−(8/4+3)
7. X+Y/2
8. L*W*H
9. (R+D)/(B+R)

Translate each of the following into BASIC.

10. $7 - 3$
11. z^3
12. $d \div 4.89$
13. $6t + 3$
14. $(4 - p) \times 6$
15. $(c - 3)^4$
16. $3 - \frac{x^2}{3}$
14. $\frac{1}{4}y + 2$
18. $\frac{1}{2}h \times (a + b)$

The order of operations is the same in BASIC as in mathematics.

1. Do all operations within parentheses.
2. Evaluate all powers from left to right.
3. Do all multiplications and/or divisions from left to right.
4. Do all additions and/or subtractions from left to right.

Evaluate 4 ↑ 3−2*5/(2+3) as follows.

4 ↑ 3−2*5/(2+3) = 4 ↑ 3−2*5/5	Do operations in parentheses.
= 64−2*5/5	Evaluate all powers.
= 64−10/5	Do multiplications and divisions from left to right.
= 64−2	
= 62	Do the subtraction.

EXERCISES ***Copy. Put numerals under each operation sign to indicate the order in which the operations will be performed. Then evaluate each expression.***

```
54/6+7 ↑ 2 = 58
  2 3  1
```

19. 4 ↑ 3−5
20. 10+8*6
21. (4+9)/13
22. 4+6/2
23. (2*3) ↑ 2
24. 2*3 ↑ 2
25. 2*(4+8)/6
26. 4*7/4−3
27. 6/3+4*5
28. 4 ↑ 2−4*3
29. 4*5−9/3
30. 5 ↑ 2−(7+9)
31. 2 ↑ 3+4 ↑ 2*3
32. (5 ↑ 2+3 ↑ 3)/13
33. (91−3 ↑ 3)/(5 ↑ 2+15)
34. 4*7−5*4+4 ↑ 2
35. (7*5)/4+9−7
36. (−3) ↑ 2+(−4) ↑ 2−2*(−3)*(−4)

Copy. Insert parentheses to make a true statement.

37. 5*6−1 = 25
38. 7+3 ↑ 2 = 100
39. 15/2+3 = 3
40. 8*4/2+5 = 21
41. 6+4 ↑ 2/5+5 = 25
42. 21/7−4*2 = 14
43. 19−4*3 ↑ 2 = 49
44. 2 ↑ 15/5+19 = 27

Lesson 2 Computer Programs

A **computer program** is a series of statements that gives directions to a computer. After the instructions and data **(input)** are given to the computer, it does the calculations and provides results called **output.**

Consider the program shown below.

```
1Ø READ Y,Z
2Ø LET X=4*Y+Z↑2
3Ø PRINT X
4Ø DATA 2,7
5Ø END
RUN
```

The **READ statement** assigns values from the **DATA statement** to the variables Y and Z in order.

$$Y = 2 \qquad Z = 7$$

Each program that has a READ statement must have a DATA statement.

The **LET statement** tells the computer to assign the value of the expression on the right to the variable on the left. For example, $X = 4 \times 2 + 7^2$ or 57.

The **PRINT statement** tells the computer to print the value assigned to X. The output for the program above is 57.

Every program must have an **END statement.** The **RUN command** tells the computer to execute the program. It has no statement number.

EXERCISES ***For each READ and DATA statement below, state the value that the computer will assign to each variable.***

1.
```
1Ø READ A
2Ø DATA 5
```

2.
```
1Ø DATA 1.5, 6
2Ø READ B,C
```

3.
```
3Ø READ D,R,L
95 DATA Ø.9,16,51
```

Find the value assigned to X by each of the following LET statements if A = 2, B = 7, and C = 1.5.

4. `2Ø LET X=A+B+C`

5. `2Ø LET X=4*A`

6. `2Ø LET X=B↑2`

7. `2Ø LET X=A+B*3`

8. `2Ø LET X=C*A+4`

9. `2Ø LET X=B/7+A*C`

10. `2Ø LET X=A↑2−B/7`

11. `2Ø LET X=C−A*3/2`

Determine the output of each of the following programs.

12.
```
1Ø  LET X=4.6
2Ø  LET Y=5.23
3Ø  PRINT X+Y
4Ø  END
```

13.
```
1Ø  LET X=7
2Ø  LET Y=3*X↑2+4*X
3Ø  PRINT Y
4Ø  END
```

14.
```
1Ø  READ A,B
2Ø  LET C=A−B
3Ø  PRINT C
4Ø  DATA 14,8
5Ø  END
```

15.
```
1Ø  LET Y=2
2Ø  LET X=Y+1
3Ø  PRINT X*Y
4Ø  END
```

16.
```
1Ø  READ A,B,C,D
2Ø  DATA 3,4,5,8
3Ø  LET M=(D−C)/(B−A)
4Ø  PRINT M
5Ø  END
```

17.
```
1Ø  READ A,B
2Ø  LET X=A+B
3Ø  LET Y=A*B
4Ø  PRINT X+Y
5Ø  DATA 6.3,7.5
6Ø  END
```

18.
```
1Ø  LET X=6+3
2Ø  LET Y=2
3Ø  LET Z=X↑Y
4Ø  PRINT Z
5Ø  END
```

19.
```
1Ø  LET L=1/8
2Ø  LET M=3*L
3Ø  PRINT M
4Ø  END
```

20.
```
1Ø  READ X
2Ø  LET Y=X↑2
3Ø  PRINT Y
4Ø  DATA 15
5Ø  END
```

21.
```
1Ø  READ N
2Ø  LET S=5*N−6
3Ø  PRINT S
4Ø  DATA 27.3
5Ø  END
```

For each equation, write a LET statement that tells the computer to assign the value of the expression on the right to the variable.

22. $x = 3 + b$

23. $y = (d - 7.9)^2$

24. $r = \frac{1}{2}(cz - 2\frac{3}{4})$

25. $s = 3^2 + g^2$

Lesson 3 IF-THEN Statements and Loops

An **IF-THEN statement** tells the computer to make a comparison. Then it tells the computer what to do based on the results. Study the program shown below.

```
1Ø  LET R=1
2Ø  LET A=3.14*R↑2 ←
3Ø  PRINT A
4Ø  LET R=R+1
5Ø  IF R<11 THEN 2Ø
     ↓ no           yes
6Ø  END
```

This program finds the areas of circles with radii from 1 through 10.

The computer compares the value of *R* with 11. If *R* is less than 11, the computer goes to line 20. If not, the program goes to line 60 and ends.

Since lines 20 through 50 are repeated in the program, they form a **loop.**

The following chart shows how mathematical sentences can be translated into BASIC.

Mathematics	BASIC
$a < b$	A<B
$7c \leq 2$	7*C<=2
$4 > d - 1\frac{3}{4}$	4>D−1.75
$13 \div e \geq f \uparrow 2$	13/E>=F↑2
$g \neq 3$	G<>3

The program shown below counts the multiples of 3 between 10 and 1,000.

```
1Ø  LET K=Ø
2Ø  LET X=12
3Ø  LET K=K+1
4Ø  LET X=X+3
5Ø  IF X<=1ØØØ THEN 3Ø
6Ø  PRINT K
7Ø  END
```

The value of 0 is assigned to *K*, the "counter."
12 is the first multiple of 3 greater than 10.
The counter increases by 1.
The next multiple of 3 is found.
The computer loops back to line 30 until $X > 1,000$.

EXERCISES ***Let A = 5, B = 8, and X = 10. Tell the number of the statement that the computer will execute next.***

1.
```
1Ø  IF A<2Ø THEN 75
15  PRINT B
```

2.
```
15  IF A>=4 THEN 9Ø
2Ø  PRINT 2*A
```

3.
```
1Ø  IF A<>B THEN 5Ø
2Ø  PRINT X
```

4.
```
1Ø  IF (A+B)<X THEN 6Ø
2Ø  PRINT 2*X
```

5.
```
5Ø  IF (A-B)>X THEN 75
6Ø  PRINT B-A
```

6.
```
45  IF (B*X)<A↑3 THEN 1Ø
5Ø  PRINT B*X
```

Tell whether A, B, or both A and B will be printed for each of the following values of A and B. Give the values of any variable printed. Use the program shown below.

```
1Ø  IF A>B THEN 5Ø
2Ø  LET A=A+1Ø
3Ø  LET B=B+2
4Ø  IF A>=B THEN 6Ø
5Ø  PRINT A
6Ø  PRINT B
7Ø  END
```

7. A = 12, B = 12

8. A = 9, B = 21

9. A = 67, B = 37

10. A = 14, B = 19

11. A = 32, B = 40

12. A = 21, B = 5

Determine the output of each of the following programs.

13.
```
1Ø  LET X=1
2Ø  PRINT 4*X
3Ø  LET X=X+1
4Ø  IF X<11 THEN 2Ø
5Ø  END
```

14.
```
1Ø  LET X=3
2Ø  PRINT X+5
3Ø  LET X=X+2
4Ø  IF X<=15 THEN 2Ø
5Ø  END
```

15.
```
1Ø  LET X=1
2Ø  PRINT X, X↑2
3Ø  LET X=X+1
4Ø  IF X<=15 THEN 2Ø
5Ø  END
```

16.
```
1Ø  LET N=1ØØ
2Ø  PRINT N
3Ø  LET N=N-2
4Ø  IF N>=Ø THEN 2Ø
5Ø  END
```

17.
```
1Ø  LET C=Ø
2Ø  LET X=21
3Ø  LET C=C+1
4Ø  LET X=X+7
5Ø  IF X<=1ØØ THEN 3Ø
6Ø  PRINT C
7Ø  END
```

18.
```
1Ø  LET X=1
2Ø  LET S=Ø
3Ø  LET S=S+X
4Ø  LET X=X+1
5Ø  IF X<11 THEN 3Ø
6Ø  PRINT S/1Ø
7Ø  END
```

Lesson 4 Flowcharts

A **flowchart** can be used to plan the steps of a problem. Making a flowchart is often the first step in writing a program. Each shape used in a flowchart has a special meaning.

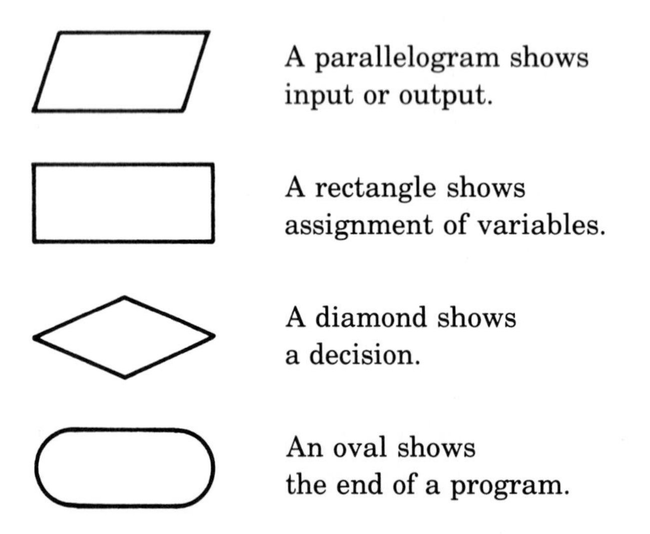

Study the flowchart and program shown below. The output of the program is the integers from 1 through 100 and their squares.

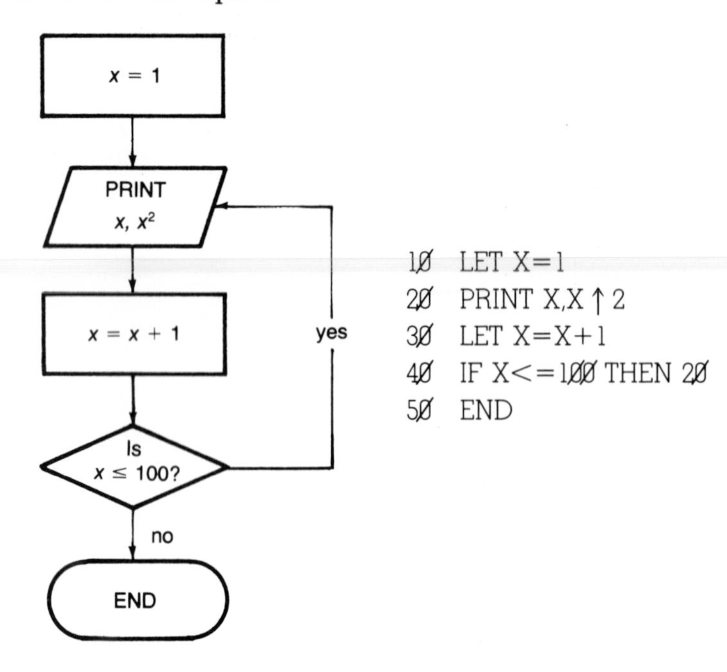

EXERCISES ***Write a program for each flowchart shown below.***

1. Batting Average

T represents the times at bat.
H represents the number of hits.
A represents the batting average.

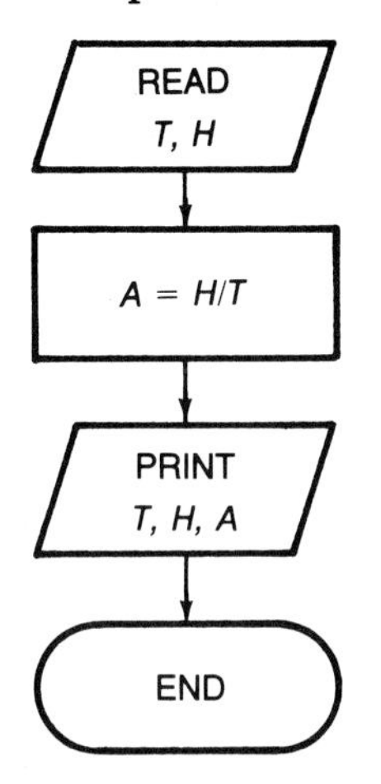

2. Gas Mileage

D represents distance in miles.
G represents gallons of gas.
M represents gas mileage (mpg).

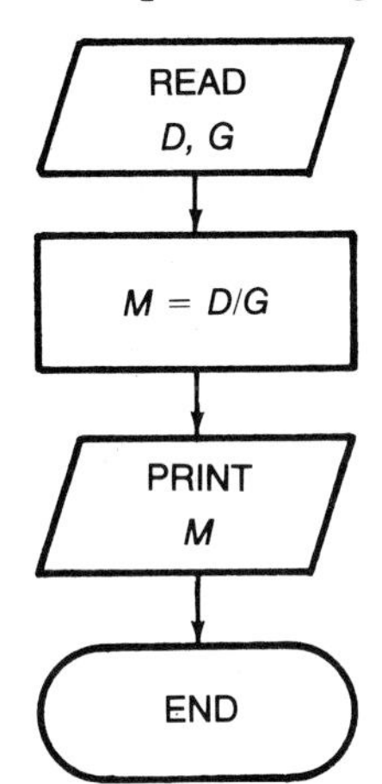

3.

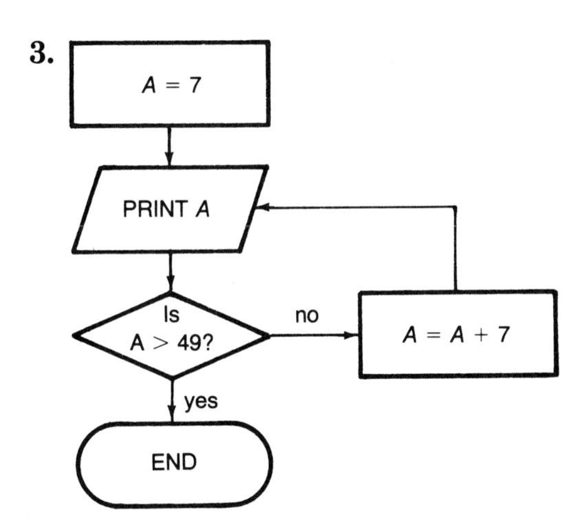

4.

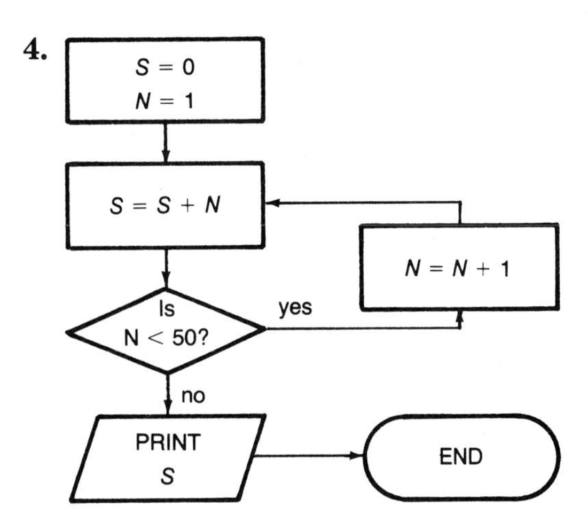

Make a flowchart for each of the following programs.

5.

```
1Ø  LET Y=1
2Ø  PRINT Y,Y ↑ 3
3Ø  LET Y=Y+1
4Ø  IF Y ↑ 3<=1ØØØ THEN 2Ø
5Ø  END
```

6.

```
1Ø  LET S=Ø
2Ø  LET Y=2
3Ø  LET S=S+Y
4Ø  LET Y=Y+2
5Ø  IF Y<1Ø1 THEN 3Ø
6Ø  PRINT S
7Ø  END
```

Lesson 5 Writing Programs

Many problems can be solved by a computer. The program shown below can be used to change degrees Celsius to degrees Fahrenheit.

```
10 PRINT "DEGREES", "DEGREES"
20 PRINT "CELSIUS", "FAHRENHEIT"
30 READ C
40 LET F = 9/5*C+32
50 PRINT C,F
60 GO TO 30
70 DATA -5,8,17,25
80 END
RUN
DEGREES           DEGREES
CELSIUS           FAHRENHEIT
-5                23
8                 46.4
17                62.6
25                77
OUT OF DATA IN LINE 30
```

Anything placed between quotation marks in a PRINT statement will be printed exactly as typed.

The GO TO statement tells the computer to return to line 30 until there is no more data.

output

EXERCISES ***The following proportion is used to solve percent problems.***

$$\frac{\textbf{Percentage}}{\textbf{Base}} = \textbf{Rate} \quad \textbf{or} \quad \frac{\textbf{P}}{\textbf{B}} = \frac{\textbf{r}}{\textbf{100}}$$

Complete each of the following programs.

1.
```
10 PRINT "PERCENTAGE", "BASE",
20 PRINT "RATE"
30 READ P,B
40 LET R=P*100/B
50 PRINT P,B,__
60 GO TO __
70 ____________
80 ____________
```

2.
```
10 PRINT "PERCENTAGE", "BASE",
20 PRINT "RATE"
30 READ B,R
40 LET P=____________
50 PRINT __, __, __
60 ____________
70 ____________
80 ____________
```

3. Write a program in BASIC to find the base given the percentage and rate.

Use the programs in exercises 1-3 to find each of the following.

4. 43% of 78

5. $2\frac{1}{2}$% of 142

6. 0.04% of 2

7. 168% of 96

8. What percent of 120 is 63?

9. What percent of 6 is 5?

10. 2 is what percent of 500?

11. 52 is what percent of 4?

12. 3.15 is 15% of what number?

13. 46 is $11\frac{1}{2}$% of what number?

14. 2,600 is 65% of what number?

15. 0.12 is $1\frac{1}{4}$% of what number?

Write a program in BASIC to solve each of the following.

16. Dean's history test scores are 83, 79, 85, and 90. Find the average of the scores.

17. The Pickerington Tigers baseball team won 13 games and lost 7. Find the percent of games won.

18. Employees at Dee's Floral Shop earn $4.75 an hour. Last week four employees worked 25, 37, 32, and 40 hours. Find how much each employee earned.

19. Mario's living room is 15 ft by 18 ft. He buys carpet that costs $17.95 a square yard. Find how much it costs to carpet the room.

20. Find the sales tax (T) if the cost of an item (C) and the tax rate (R) are given. The output should show the item cost, sales tax, and total cost.

Item	Cost	Tax Rate
toaster	$25.95	$5\frac{1}{4}$%
electric skillet	$34.98	6%
iron	$19.30	$4\frac{1}{2}$%
lamp	$93.69	7%

21. Find the total cost of an order at Hamburger King. The output should show the total cost of the order.

Item	Cost	Number Ordered
hamburger	95¢	7
french fries	55¢	4
soft drink	45¢	5

22. Find the total service charge on a checking account. The output should show the charge per check, the number of checks written, the monthly charge, and the total service charge.

Charge per Check	Number of Checks	Monthly Charge
8¢	23	$2.25
12¢	15	$3.50

Addition

	a.	b.	c.	d.	e.	f.
1.	40 + 30	71 + 20	25 + 12	20 + 37	62 + 33	77 + 21
2.	200 + 80	420 + 50	402 + 70	185 + 12	671 + 27	324 + 62
3.	400 + 500	680 + 300	206 + 101	247 + 602	618 + 321	563 + 226
4.	37 + 5	85 + 9	49 + 8	67 + 26	43 + 37	52 + 18
5.	107 + 87	216 + 44	846 + 28	206 + 606	472 + 218	338 + 327
6.	40 + 70	90 + 50	64 + 70	482 + 36	554 + 194	229 + 280
7.	346 + 78	469 + 83	829 + 91	295 + 636	709 + 196	643 + 167
8.	47 74 69 + 14	65 58 83 + 56	237 94 142 + 80	578 388 367 + 23	554 386 740 + 895	769 936 408 + 687
9.	4327 + 2294	2397 + 4945	7468 + 4923	25,406 + 9 329	4 371 + 17,299	45,646 + 28,475
10.	2765 4283 + 1065	1700 2685 + 7325	8432 1811 + 4255	26,509 8 060 + 11,695	14,680 23,067 + 45,943	94,006 73,885 + 27,642
11.	780,764 + 16,433	435,706 + 73,198	578,644 + 85,480	470,989 + 585,265	623,416 + 777,589	289,455 + 860,950

Subtraction

	a.	b.	c.	d.	e.	f.
1.	90 − 70	40 − 10	69 − 30	87 − 42	98 − 67	47 − 27
2.	890 − 50	650 − 20	293 − 30	147 − 26	978 − 65	367 − 64
3.	400 − 300	590 − 240	735 − 420	1738 − 1226	9459 − 2352	8477 − 2436
4.	67 − 8	94 − 7	28 − 9	62 − 27	80 − 36	50 − 14
5.	575 − 26	782 − 13	645 − 36	755 − 327	970 − 835	840 − 421
6.	427 − 62	284 − 93	635 − 55	748 − 367	510 − 380	484 − 193
7.	284 − 195	625 − 278	847 − 458	973 − 187	420 − 237	641 − 442
8.	515 − 338	812 − 473	914 − 865	403 − 168	200 − 127	800 − 164
9.	4273 − 695	9714 − 426	2344 − 986	6547 − 2488	8173 − 6575	4016 − 2067
10.	8602 − 794	4702 − 946	2013 − 845	2057 − 1987	7001 − 2741	3106 − 1428
11.	11,654 − 8 465	24,605 − 5 637	11,006 − 2 472	25,623 − 20,736	31,409 − 23,010	91,000 − 27,624
12.	812,600 − 74,706	750,290 − 61,499	592,006 − 93,067	413,000 − 324,223	500,000 − 210,486	800,000 − 506,707

Multiplication

	a.	b.	c.	d.	e.	f.
1.	20×8	40×3	90×6	11×8	32×4	71×8
2.	232×3	122×4	612×4	510×9	7032×2	9231×3
3.	23×4	16×8	54×7	73×9	35×6	94×5
4.	105×3	206×7	304×8	505×5	604×6	907×8
5.	143×4	275×2	816×5	9731×3	6666×6	7046×8
6.	23×10	46×10	77×10	231×10	706×10	3421×10
7.	32×20	51×80	70×30	241×60	627×50	6541×40
8.	261×100	749×100	241×100	607×100	590×100	4076×100
9.	224×200	624×300	321×500	473×800	907×700	2409×900
10.	400×200	500×700	7000×900	8000×300	3000×6000	5000×8000
11.	2619×1000	4742×1000	8069×1000	7004×1000	2340×1000	$64,206 \times 1000$
12.	2142×2000	6512×4000	7047×6000	2007×9000	4286×7000	$17,506 \times 5000$

Multiplication

	a.	b.	c.	d.	e.	f.
1.	24 × 11	42 × 22	64 × 12	74 × 21	34 × 42	31 × 95
2.	47 × 12	65 × 17	43 × 36	84 × 91	53 × 42	72 × 84
3.	57 × 22	86 × 34	27 × 52	68 × 64	95 × 46	74 × 89
4.	121 × 11	322 × 24	603 × 32	421 × 43	6023 × 33	5111 × 79
5.	646 × 12	709 × 16	523 × 34	6094 × 14	8432 × 25	7698 × 18
6.	263 × 35	742 × 58	509 × 83	6591 × 76	5083 × 64	9557 × 52
7.	594 × 605	406 × 132	573 × 206	840 × 603	796 × 405	980 × 788
8.	681 × 124	386 × 427	958 × 643	286 × 554	814 × 453	657 × 399
9.	8739 × 111	2705 × 603	7160 × 305	1006 × 246	2781 × 115	6072 × 621
10.	2576 × 222	6509 × 605	9036 × 427	2274 × 362	5719 × 586	8371 × 948
11.	2044 × 2012	7031 × 2015	6403 × 1062	5006 × 8405	4030 × 6105	3608 × 5008
12.	8205 × 2404	9140 × 4151	7006 × 9054	3097 × 8522	5416 × 3460	6009 × 7800

Division

	a.	b.	c.	d.	e.
1.	$9\overline{)63}$	$8\overline{)24}$	$4\overline{)36}$	$3\overline{)39}$	$2\overline{)64}$
2.	$3\overline{)600}$	$2\overline{)242}$	$3\overline{)609}$	$7\overline{)770}$	$4\overline{)888}$
3.	$2\overline{)32}$	$4\overline{)92}$	$3\overline{)228}$	$6\overline{)504}$	$7\overline{)364}$
4.	$6\overline{)726}$	$5\overline{)855}$	$8\overline{)968}$	$9\overline{)3789}$	$7\overline{)5824}$
5.	$7\overline{)1421}$	$9\overline{)2763}$	$6\overline{)7248}$	$5\overline{)5165}$	$6\overline{)6054}$
6.	$10\overline{)90}$	$10\overline{)440}$	$10\overline{)690}$	$10\overline{)5010}$	$10\overline{)6870}$
7.	$30\overline{)90}$	$40\overline{)80}$	$80\overline{)560}$	$50\overline{)4500}$	$70\overline{)4970}$
8.	$11\overline{)33}$	$15\overline{)60}$	$21\overline{)126}$	$65\overline{)325}$	$87\overline{)783}$
9.	$13\overline{)130}$	$22\overline{)220}$	$16\overline{)480}$	$34\overline{)680}$	$23\overline{)920}$
10.	$52\overline{)1040}$	$65\overline{)1950}$	$94\overline{)3760}$	$83\overline{)5810}$	$76\overline{)3800}$
11.	$14\overline{)154}$	$26\overline{)442}$	$51\overline{)918}$	$29\overline{)928}$	$16\overline{)912}$
12.	$31\overline{)1116}$	$83\overline{)5644}$	$91\overline{)6643}$	$42\overline{)8862}$	$59\overline{)7316}$
13.	$55\overline{)11,495}$	$88\overline{)35,288}$	$37\overline{)77,478}$	$27\overline{)97,362}$	$89\overline{)89,534}$
14.	$100\overline{)600}$	$200\overline{)800}$	$310\overline{)930}$	$220\overline{)880}$	$160\overline{)960}$
15.	$208\overline{)624}$	$155\overline{)775}$	$116\overline{)928}$	$874\overline{)5244}$	$712\overline{)6408}$
16.	$131\overline{)1441}$	$255\overline{)4080}$	$172\overline{)3784}$	$205\overline{)7380}$	$197\overline{)9259}$
17.	$352\overline{)14,080}$	$406\overline{)23,548}$	$722\overline{)25,270}$	$384\overline{)51,840}$	$419\overline{)95,951}$
18.	$341\overline{)139,128}$	$517\overline{)314,853}$	$826\overline{)718,620}$	$194\overline{)593,640}$	$253\overline{)760,771}$

Division with Remainders

	a.	b.	c.	d.	e.
1.	$6\overline{)25}$	$8\overline{)60}$	$5\overline{)19}$	$9\overline{)83}$	$7\overline{)54}$
2.	$5\overline{)52}$	$2\overline{)33}$	$4\overline{)83}$	$8\overline{)94}$	$3\overline{)40}$
3.	$7\overline{)214}$	$9\overline{)182}$	$5\overline{)217}$	$8\overline{)500}$	$6\overline{)560}$
4.	$2\overline{)801}$	$3\overline{)902}$	$4\overline{)483}$	$7\overline{)1425}$	$8\overline{)2487}$
5.	$10\overline{)65}$	$30\overline{)98}$	$20\overline{)75}$	$40\overline{)127}$	$30\overline{)428}$
6.	$70\overline{)2162}$	$90\overline{)7030}$	$80\overline{)7700}$	$20\overline{)6330}$	$40\overline{)8974}$
7.	$15\overline{)47}$	$12\overline{)99}$	$22\overline{)90}$	$36\overline{)330}$	$23\overline{)162}$
8.	$42\overline{)425}$	$17\overline{)520}$	$21\overline{)275}$	$74\overline{)985}$	$39\overline{)940}$
9.	$27\overline{)1355}$	$15\overline{)1364}$	$56\overline{)1578}$	$82\overline{)2550}$	$26\overline{)8340}$
10.	$68\overline{)61,250}$	$74\overline{)59,734}$	$48\overline{)29,314}$	$31\overline{)93,600}$	$43\overline{)86,840}$
11.	$100\overline{)809}$	$200\overline{)735}$	$300\overline{)2782}$	$800\overline{)4002}$	$600\overline{)4306}$
12.	$100\overline{)1039}$	$400\overline{)8101}$	$500\overline{)8812}$	$200\overline{)6619}$	$800\overline{)9926}$
13.	$109\overline{)356}$	$156\overline{)795}$	$210\overline{)867}$	$145\overline{)1172}$	$555\overline{)3912}$
14.	$124\overline{)2510}$	$321\overline{)9660}$	$193\overline{)7725}$	$182\overline{)5572}$	$106\overline{)8500}$
15.	$125\overline{)1521}$	$301\overline{)5641}$	$280\overline{)8326}$	$190\overline{)6940}$	$614\overline{)8000}$
16.	$222\overline{)11,150}$	$409\overline{)28,652}$	$847\overline{)13,560}$	$941\overline{)21,068}$	$737\overline{)45,000}$
17.	$181\overline{)18,136}$	$265\overline{)53,116}$	$147\overline{)16,203}$	$360\overline{)72,390}$	$429\overline{)81,642}$
18.	$917\overline{)558,777}$	$544\overline{)516,894}$	$208\overline{)849,400}$	$352\overline{)777,000}$	$196\overline{)588,313}$

Addition of Decimals

	a.	b.	c.	d.	e.	f.
1.	4.76	10.06	6.50	9.24	8.065	0.941
	+ 3.03	+ 8.92	+ 2.38	+ 6.75	+ 2.122	+ 16.052
2.	0.015	1.406	2.1	16.15	202.07	4
	6.202	2.46	15.045	0.6	6.41	0.901
	+ 3.78	+ 5.031	+ 1.84	+ 1.204	+ 21	+ 15.024
3.	6.5	3.25	17.61	26.02	1.06	0.865
	+ 2.7	+ 4.82	+ 9.34	+ 15.98	+ 11.97	+ 9.148
4.	4.06	36.6	1.009	45.25	0.65	1.5
	15.18	8.042	12.65	16.89	1.049	70.081
	+ 20.75	+ 0.577	+ 7.855	+ 18.23	+ 8.652	+ 68.499
5.	$18.50	$20.19	$ 9.16	$140.02	$139.95	$ 8.39
	0.06	6.72	40.82	71.15	9.95	15.99
	+ 2.17	+ 8.04	+ 16.18	+ 9.88	+ 10.59	+ 5.29

	g.	h.	i.
6.	0.42 + 0.06 + 1.11	0.2 + 6.51 + 2.03	7.11 + 0.64 + 1.02
7.	16.4 + 6.5 + 20.6	4.4 + 30.6 + 11.2	5.9 + 18.1 + 19.5
8.	0.614 + 0.95 + 1.001	7.84 + 0.912 + 6.7	0.116 + 9.5 + 8.015
9.	6 + 4.2 + 9	19 + 0.1 + 11	10.2 + 6.1 + 8
10.	5.106 + 4 + 1.5	14 + 1.04 + 0.091	6.501 + 1.1 + 1
11.	2 + 10.01 + 0.006	19.5 + 21.1 + 21	1.6 + 16 + 0.016
12.	0.2 + 0.02 + 0.002	18 + 1.8 + 0.18	42.2 + 4.22 + 0.422
13.	31.596 + 0.04 + 10.112	26.65 + 0.123 + 10.605	0.414 + 1.73 + 30.866
14.	$0.45 + $0.55 + $0.80	$0.95 + $0.29 + $0.78	$0.19 + $0.60 + $0.98
15.	$9 + $0.59 + $6.50	$11.45 + $1.16 + $8	$0.18 + $10.04 + $27
16.	$28 + $45.50 + $36	$50 + $83 + $22.49	$70 + $92.85 + $46

Subtraction of Decimals

	a.	b.	c.	d.	e.	f.
1.	2.7	6.5	9.4	4.6	12.5	26.8
	− 1.4	− 2.4	− 2.4	− 0.5	− 11.4	− 10.8
2.	6.84	64.75	9.006	19.54	6.095	26.706
	− 1.63	− 0.74	− 6.002	− 12	− 6.082	− 6.406
3.	28.2	37.6	41.93	16.58	16.58	26.075
	− 1.6	− 5.7	− 2.92	− 0.49	− 9.52	− 2.651
4.	6.54	9.45	20.48	31.51	40.606	4.768
	− 1.65	− 8.96	− 16.8	− 16.6	− 11.055	− 0.23
5.	6	1.6	24	265.8	21.1	0.9
	− 0.29	− 0.648	− 3.889	− 89.365	− 19.668	− 0.7476
6.	$29.15	$17.84	$28.05	$16.17	$17.00	$21.00
	− 8.90	− 8.80	− 9.95	− 10.49	− 4.32	− 12.48

	g.	h.	i.
7.	9.74 − 6.03	8.65 − 8.42	11.8 − 10.5
8.	27.82 − 18	60.95 − 26	29.45 − 16
9.	25.6 − 4.8	32.5 − 0.9	10.5 − 8.2
10.	14 − 6.5	24 − 1.6	20 − 0.5
11.	18 − 10.45	36 − 0.44	16 − 8.94
12.	28.1 − 0.008	19.5 − 6.274	12.1 − 0.101
13.	0.08 − 0.0734	0.36 − 0.351	0.03 − 0.018
14.	$36.94 − $19.43	$96.22 − $4.96	$114.58 − $19.19
15.	$14.50 − $7.40	$24.16 − $4.19	$95.47 − $0.48
16.	$36.22 − $4	$15.69 − $6	$101.81 − $23
17.	$15 − $0.40	$55 − $5.49	$2 − $1.08

Multiplication of Decimals

Copy. Then place the decimal point in each product.

	a.	b.	c.	d.	e.	f.
1.	9.51	601	2.6	4.86	8.6	12
	× 3	× 0.8	× 1.8	× 8.11	× 2	× 0.4
	2 8 5 3	4 8 0 8	4 6 8	3 9 4 1 4 6	1 7 2	4 8
2.	1.09	0.108	1.95	10.046	0.8	0.09
	× 1.2	× 0.03	× 0.6	× 1.14	× 0.2	× 18
	1 3 0 8	0 0 0 3 2 4	1 1 7 0	1 1 4 5 2 4 4	0 1 6	1 6 2

Multiply.

3	232	421	68	406	2451	4065
	× 0.3	× 0.4	× 0.7	× 0.9	× 0.2	× 0.7
4	6.6	8.4	3.1	11.5	4.68	10.95
	× 5	× 2	× 3	× 22	× 47	× 66
5	12.5	7.52	40.8	11.54	452.2	20.07
	× 0.5	× 0.6	× 0.4	× 4.3	× 0.8	× 9.5
6	16.8	29.9	4.65	25.06	31.24	216.17
	× 0.55	× 0.82	× 1.58	× 1.05	× 8.61	× 9.63
7	47	607	9.06	70.44	3.17	4082
	× 0.98	× 1.52	× 53	× 75	× 285	× 11.85
8	$9.60	$8.94	$24.08	$140.15	$12.08	$16.64
	× 24	× 0.5	× 6.5	× 18.6	× 4.25	× 37.75
9	0.645	4.007	8.265	19.042	2.508	43.616
	× 0.81	× 1.95	× 3.32	× 8.54	× 0.975	× 2.405
10	0.0057	0.904	0.63	0.182	0.0615	0.0036
	× 0.4	× 0.2	× 0.105	× 0.07	× 0.13	× 0.28

Division of Decimals

Copy. Then place the decimal point in each quotient.

	a.	b.	c.	d.	e.
1.	$\begin{array}{r}2\,2\\0.6\overline{)1.32}\end{array}$	$\begin{array}{r}0\,6\,6\\0.8\overline{)0.528}\end{array}$	$\begin{array}{r}1\,9\,6\\2.4\overline{)4.704}\end{array}$	$\begin{array}{r}1\,6\,3\\9.1\overline{)14.833}\end{array}$	$\begin{array}{r}3\,4\,5\\0.3\overline{)1.035}\end{array}$
2.	$\begin{array}{r}0\,1\,8\\5\overline{)0.9}\end{array}$	$\begin{array}{r}7\,5\\8\overline{)60}\end{array}$	$\begin{array}{r}4\,2\,5\\20\overline{)85}\end{array}$	$\begin{array}{r}3\,0\,5\\40\overline{)122}\end{array}$	$\begin{array}{r}4\,5\,3\,5\\80\overline{)3628}\end{array}$
3.	$\begin{array}{r}5\,0\\0.3\overline{)15}\end{array}$	$\begin{array}{r}8\,0\\0.92\overline{)73.6}\end{array}$	$\begin{array}{r}1\,3\,4\\5\overline{)6.7}\end{array}$	$\begin{array}{r}5\,0\,0\\0.06\overline{)30}\end{array}$	$\begin{array}{r}3\,6\,4\\1.25\overline{)4.55}\end{array}$

Divide.

4.	$3\overline{)2.7}$	$8\overline{)4.8}$	$6\overline{)11.4}$	$4\overline{)2.92}$	$9\overline{)42.03}$
5.	$12\overline{)15.6}$	$24\overline{)52.8}$	$51\overline{)428.4}$	$47\overline{)164.97}$	$84\overline{)213.36}$
6.	$0.8\overline{)7.2}$	$0.7\overline{)27.3}$	$0.03\overline{)0.54}$	$0.05\overline{)0.315}$	$0.04\overline{)8.72}$
7.	$1.5\overline{)28.5}$	$4.6\overline{)37.26}$	$0.37\overline{)13.32}$	$4.2\overline{)0.462}$	$0.62\overline{)4.278}$
8.	$10\overline{)62}$	$10\overline{)142}$	$30\overline{)96}$	$90\overline{)288}$	$50\overline{)330}$
9.	$6\overline{)9}$	$4\overline{)42}$	$4\overline{)17}$	$8\overline{)18.6}$	$4\overline{)20.3}$
10.	$10\overline{)7}$	$50\overline{)45}$	$30\overline{)24}$	$60\overline{)36}$	$80\overline{)56}$
11.	$0.9\overline{)81}$	$0.5\overline{)35}$	$4.8\overline{)12}$	$5.8\overline{)95.7}$	$8.2\overline{)7.79}$
12.	$100\overline{)16}$	$300\overline{)99}$	$600\overline{)54}$	$800\overline{)296}$	$900\overline{)774}$
13.	$0.07\overline{)7}$	$0.09\overline{)45}$	$0.01\overline{)8}$	$0.05\overline{)30}$	$0.06\overline{)42}$
14.	$50\overline{)460.5}$	$68\overline{)47.26}$	$8.5\overline{)11.22}$	$0.45\overline{)3.474}$	$6.2\overline{)29.45}$
15.	$0.94\overline{)19.317}$	$1.9\overline{)9.557}$	$0.117\overline{)0.24102}$	$0.966\overline{)9.8049}$	$14.6\overline{)15.33}$
16.	$2.25\overline{)0.1107}$	$5.006\overline{)0.32539}$	$8.18\overline{)0.046626}$	$4.02\overline{)0.1005}$	$99.3\overline{)1.23132}$

Prime Factors, GCF and Equivalent Fractions

Express the prime factorization of each number.

	a.	b.	c.	d.	e.	f.
1.	3	17	7	11	2	5
2.	10	6	4	9	14	15
3.	21	34	28	27	42	50
4.	30	51	56	33	49	75

Find the GCF for each pair of numbers.

5.	10 and 3	6 and 17	4 and 7	9 and 11	2 and 14	5 and 15
6.	3 and 21	17 and 34	7 and 28	11 and 27	2 and 42	5 and 50
7.	3 and 30	17 and 51	7 and 56	11 and 33	2 and 49	5 and 75
8.	10 and 21	6 and 34	4 and 28	9 and 27	14 and 42	15 and 50
9.	10 and 30	6 and 51	4 and 56	9 and 33	14 and 49	15 and 75
10.	21 and 30	34 and 51	28 and 56	27 and 33	42 and 49	50 and 75

Write each fraction in simplest form.

11.	$\frac{2}{6}$	$\frac{2}{4}$	$\frac{7}{14}$	$\frac{5}{10}$	$\frac{6}{12}$	$\frac{3}{9}$
12.	$\frac{2}{10}$	$\frac{9}{12}$	$\frac{6}{9}$	$\frac{6}{10}$	$\frac{8}{12}$	$\frac{6}{8}$
13.	$\frac{11}{22}$	$\frac{8}{24}$	$\frac{6}{18}$	$\frac{6}{16}$	$\frac{10}{25}$	$\frac{9}{15}$
14.	$\frac{16}{36}$	$\frac{6}{21}$	$\frac{12}{32}$	$\frac{16}{24}$	$\frac{35}{50}$	$\frac{20}{32}$

Replace each $\square$ with a number so that the fractions are equivalent.

15.	$\frac{1}{2} = \frac{\square}{4}$	$\frac{1}{3} = \frac{\square}{6}$	$\frac{1}{2} = \frac{\square}{8}$	$\frac{1}{4} = \frac{\square}{12}$	$\frac{1}{3} = \frac{\square}{12}$	$\frac{1}{8} = \frac{\square}{16}$
16.	$\frac{1}{9} = \frac{\square}{27}$	$\frac{2}{5} = \frac{\square}{10}$	$\frac{3}{4} = \frac{\square}{8}$	$\frac{2}{5} = \frac{\square}{15}$	$\frac{2}{3} = \frac{\square}{15}$	$\frac{1}{4} = \frac{\square}{20}$
17.	$\frac{4}{5} = \frac{\square}{20}$	$\frac{8}{9} = \frac{\square}{18}$	$\frac{3}{8} = \frac{\square}{32}$	$\frac{3}{7} = \frac{\square}{35}$	$\frac{7}{10} = \frac{\square}{50}$	$\frac{11}{12} = \frac{\square}{48}$
18.	$\frac{3}{2} = \frac{\square}{6}$	$\frac{5}{4} = \frac{\square}{8}$	$\frac{13}{10} = \frac{\square}{20}$	$\frac{3}{1} = \frac{\square}{5}$	$\frac{5}{2} = \frac{\square}{16}$	$\frac{12}{5} = \frac{\square}{10}$

Fractions, Mixed Numerals, and LCM

Find the LCM for each group of numbers.

	a.	b.	c.	d.	e.
1.	2 and 4	5 and 10	10 and 20	2 and 8	2 and 10
2.	2 and 3	2 and 5	3 and 4	3 and 5	4 and 5
3.	8 and 10	9 and 6	12 and 8	8 and 6	10 and 15
4.	16 and 24	9 and 15	20 and 30	24 and 32	14 and 21
5.	2, 4, and 8	5, 3, and 15	2, 3, and 6	12, 4, and 3	3, 6, and 18
6.	4, 8, and 3	6, 3, and 4	4, 5, and 10	8, 4, and 6	6, 9, and 3
7.	10, 6, and 12	3, 16, and 8	10, 5, and 8	2, 5, and 4	12, 6, and 8

Change each fraction to a mixed numeral in simplest form.

8.	$\frac{3}{2}$	$\frac{4}{3}$	$\frac{5}{4}$	$\frac{8}{7}$	$\frac{13}{12}$
9.	$\frac{5}{2}$	$\frac{7}{4}$	$\frac{4}{2}$	$\frac{7}{3}$	$\frac{8}{5}$
10.	$\frac{11}{4}$	$\frac{15}{4}$	$\frac{10}{3}$	$\frac{21}{8}$	$\frac{37}{10}$
11.	$\frac{6}{4}$	$\frac{8}{6}$	$\frac{15}{10}$	$\frac{10}{8}$	$\frac{12}{10}$
12.	$\frac{15}{12}$	$\frac{14}{8}$	$\frac{24}{10}$	$\frac{34}{12}$	$\frac{57}{24}$

Change each mixed numeral to a fraction.

13.	$1\frac{1}{3}$	$1\frac{1}{4}$	$1\frac{1}{6}$	$1\frac{1}{8}$	$1\frac{1}{12}$
14.	$2\frac{1}{2}$	$6\frac{1}{3}$	$4\frac{1}{4}$	$2\frac{1}{8}$	$8\frac{1}{5}$
15.	$1\frac{2}{5}$	$1\frac{3}{4}$	$1\frac{3}{7}$	$1\frac{5}{12}$	$1\frac{7}{8}$
16.	$3\frac{2}{3}$	$4\frac{3}{4}$	$2\frac{2}{5}$	$5\frac{2}{7}$	$3\frac{5}{12}$
17.	$8\frac{6}{7}$	$10\frac{5}{8}$	$9\frac{5}{12}$	$7\frac{5}{6}$	$10\frac{7}{8}$

Addition of Fractions

Add. Write each sum in simplest form.

	a.	b.	c.	d.	e.
1.	$\frac{1}{7} + \frac{2}{7}$	$\frac{1}{15} + \frac{7}{15}$	$\frac{1}{3} + \frac{1}{3}$	$\frac{2}{9} + \frac{5}{9}$	$\frac{4}{11} + \frac{6}{11}$
2.	$\frac{1}{6} + \frac{1}{6}$	$\frac{1}{4} + \frac{1}{4}$	$\frac{2}{9} + \frac{1}{9}$	$\frac{5}{12} + \frac{1}{12}$	$\frac{3}{10} + \frac{5}{10}$
3.	$\frac{8}{15} + \frac{11}{15}$	$\frac{4}{7} + \frac{6}{7}$	$\frac{5}{9} + \frac{8}{9}$	$\frac{2}{3} + \frac{2}{3}$	$\frac{16}{21} + \frac{10}{21}$
4.	$\frac{7}{12} + \frac{11}{12}$	$\frac{3}{8} + \frac{7}{8}$	$\frac{7}{9} + \frac{5}{9}$	$\frac{11}{18} + \frac{17}{18}$	$\frac{5}{6} + \frac{5}{6}$
5.	$1\frac{1}{5} + \frac{2}{5}$	$\frac{4}{7} + 2\frac{1}{7}$	$4\frac{1}{3} + 1\frac{1}{3}$	$8\frac{1}{9} + 2\frac{1}{9}$	$6\frac{5}{11} + 7\frac{4}{11}$
6.	$\frac{1}{4} + 1\frac{1}{4}$	$2\frac{1}{6} + \frac{1}{6}$	$1\frac{1}{10} + 5\frac{3}{10}$	$2\frac{1}{8} + 7\frac{3}{8}$	$5\frac{1}{12} + 11\frac{7}{12}$
7.	$2\frac{1}{2} + \frac{1}{2}$	$\frac{5}{9} + 1\frac{6}{9}$	$2\frac{2}{3} + 1\frac{2}{3}$	$4\frac{5}{7} + 5\frac{4}{7}$	$5\frac{11}{15} + 2\frac{8}{15}$
8.	$\frac{3}{4} + 5\frac{3}{4}$	$1\frac{10}{21} + 8\frac{17}{21}$	$\frac{5}{6} + 7\frac{5}{6}$	$4\frac{11}{24} + 1\frac{23}{24}$	$1\frac{11}{12} + 7\frac{11}{12}$
9.	$\frac{1}{2} + \frac{1}{4}$	$\frac{1}{3} + \frac{2}{9}$	$\frac{5}{12} + \frac{1}{6}$	$\frac{5}{8} + \frac{1}{4}$	$\frac{2}{3} + \frac{1}{6}$
10.	$\frac{1}{2} + \frac{1}{6}$	$\frac{1}{3} + \frac{1}{6}$	$\frac{5}{12} + \frac{1}{4}$	$\frac{2}{5} + \frac{1}{10}$	$\frac{7}{12} + \frac{1}{4}$
11.	$\frac{5}{6} + \frac{1}{3}$	$\frac{7}{8} + \frac{1}{4}$	$\frac{2}{3} + \frac{5}{12}$	$\frac{17}{20} + \frac{3}{4}$	$\frac{5}{8} + \frac{23}{24}$
12.	$\frac{2}{3} + \frac{5}{6}$	$\frac{7}{12} + \frac{2}{3}$	$\frac{11}{14} + \frac{5}{7}$	$\frac{3}{4} + \frac{7}{12}$	$\frac{5}{6} + \frac{11}{12}$
13.	$\frac{3}{5} + 3\frac{1}{4}$	$6\frac{5}{8} + 3\frac{1}{4}$	$4\frac{2}{3} + 4\frac{1}{5}$	$8\frac{4}{9} + 1\frac{1}{3}$	$5\frac{1}{2} + 2\frac{1}{3}$
14.	$4\frac{1}{3} + \frac{5}{12}$	$\frac{1}{12} + 2\frac{1}{4}$	$1\frac{2}{15} + 3\frac{2}{3}$	$4\frac{1}{10} + 3\frac{13}{20}$	$6\frac{1}{8} + 4\frac{19}{24}$
15.	$6\frac{8}{21} + 4\frac{5}{7}$	$4\frac{8}{9} + 5\frac{1}{2}$	$3\frac{4}{5} + 2\frac{2}{3}$	$1\frac{6}{7} + 6\frac{1}{3}$	$6\frac{3}{4} + 11\frac{7}{9}$
16.	$4\frac{2}{3} + 1\frac{8}{15}$	$4\frac{5}{6} + 2\frac{5}{12}$	$8\frac{17}{18} + 1\frac{1}{6}$	$7\frac{7}{24} + 8\frac{7}{8}$	$12\frac{3}{5} + 4\frac{29}{35}$
17.	$4\frac{7}{10} + 6\frac{3}{4}$	$1\frac{8}{9} + 5\frac{7}{12}$	$7\frac{5}{6} + 4\frac{5}{9}$	$4\frac{9}{10} + 3\frac{11}{12}$	$2\frac{7}{20} + 11\frac{11}{12}$

Subtraction of Fractions

Subtract. Write each difference in simplest form.

	a.	b.	c.	d.	e.
1.	$\frac{5}{7} - \frac{1}{7}$	$\frac{14}{15} - \frac{1}{15}$	$\frac{4}{5} - \frac{3}{5}$	$\frac{8}{9} - \frac{1}{9}$	$\frac{4}{13} - \frac{2}{13}$
2.	$\frac{5}{18} - \frac{1}{18}$	$\frac{9}{10} - \frac{7}{10}$	$\frac{20}{21} - \frac{8}{21}$	$\frac{29}{36} - \frac{11}{36}$	$\frac{16}{45} - \frac{7}{45}$
3.	$1\frac{5}{9} - \frac{4}{9}$	$10\frac{5}{6} - \frac{1}{6}$	$2\frac{11}{12} - \frac{7}{12}$	$6\frac{19}{21} - \frac{8}{21}$	$3\frac{17}{24} - \frac{7}{24}$
4.	$5\frac{4}{15} - 2\frac{1}{15}$	$8\frac{5}{11} - 4\frac{1}{11}$	$2\frac{7}{10} - 1\frac{1}{10}$	$4\frac{17}{18} - 3\frac{5}{18}$	$9\frac{23}{28} - 4\frac{9}{28}$
5.	$2 - \frac{1}{7}$	$4 - \frac{1}{8}$	$9 - \frac{1}{10}$	$8 - \frac{5}{12}$	$6 - \frac{11}{15}$
6.	$3 - 1\frac{1}{5}$	$5 - 2\frac{1}{4}$	$7 - 1\frac{4}{7}$	$10 - 2\frac{4}{9}$	$8 - 6\frac{13}{24}$
7.	$4\frac{4}{7} - \frac{5}{7}$	$6\frac{1}{4} - \frac{3}{4}$	$8\frac{5}{8} - \frac{7}{8}$	$5\frac{5}{12} - \frac{11}{12}$	$11\frac{7}{36} - \frac{31}{36}$
8.	$3\frac{1}{6} - 1\frac{5}{6}$	$5\frac{4}{9} - 2\frac{7}{9}$	$9\frac{1}{10} - 1\frac{3}{10}$	$6\frac{7}{15} - 5\frac{13}{15}$	$7\frac{7}{24} - 6\frac{19}{24}$
9.	$\frac{1}{2} - \frac{1}{3}$	$\frac{2}{3} - \frac{1}{5}$	$\frac{7}{9} - \frac{1}{2}$	$\frac{3}{8} - \frac{1}{3}$	$\frac{8}{9} - \frac{3}{4}$
10.	$\frac{7}{12} - \frac{1}{3}$	$\frac{5}{6} - \frac{1}{2}$	$\frac{9}{10} - \frac{2}{5}$	$\frac{13}{18} - \frac{5}{9}$	$\frac{31}{36} - \frac{3}{4}$
11.	$2\frac{3}{8} - \frac{1}{4}$	$6\frac{5}{12} - \frac{1}{3}$	$4\frac{11}{18} - \frac{2}{9}$	$8\frac{7}{28} - \frac{1}{7}$	$10\frac{19}{45} - \frac{2}{5}$
12.	$6\frac{5}{6} - 1\frac{1}{4}$	$8\frac{1}{6} - 2\frac{1}{8}$	$4\frac{1}{6} - 2\frac{1}{9}$	$8\frac{5}{6} - 2\frac{3}{10}$	$11\frac{8}{9} - 2\frac{7}{12}$
13.	$2\frac{1}{4} - \frac{1}{2}$	$4\frac{1}{6} - \frac{1}{3}$	$7\frac{3}{8} - \frac{3}{4}$	$8\frac{2}{3} - \frac{14}{15}$	$3\frac{4}{7} - \frac{20}{21}$
14.	$5\frac{2}{5} - \frac{1}{2}$	$3\frac{1}{3} - \frac{4}{5}$	$1\frac{3}{4} - \frac{5}{6}$	$6\frac{4}{7} - \frac{2}{3}$	$9\frac{2}{9} - \frac{3}{4}$
15.	$2\frac{1}{7} - 1\frac{3}{14}$	$6\frac{1}{4} - 2\frac{5}{8}$	$4\frac{5}{7} - 2\frac{17}{21}$	$8\frac{5}{16} - 2\frac{1}{2}$	$4\frac{2}{9} - 1\frac{11}{45}$
16.	$7\frac{1}{5} - 6\frac{7}{10}$	$8\frac{1}{4} - 6\frac{5}{12}$	$2\frac{5}{18} - 1\frac{5}{6}$	$7\frac{11}{24} - 4\frac{5}{8}$	$10\frac{1}{36} - 4\frac{5}{12}$
17.	$7\frac{1}{9} - 2\frac{1}{6}$	$2\frac{1}{4} - 1\frac{5}{6}$	$5\frac{1}{6} - 4\frac{7}{8}$	$7\frac{1}{8} - 4\frac{3}{10}$	$10\frac{1}{15} - 1\frac{5}{6}$

Multiplication of Fractions

Multiply. Write each product in simplest form.

	a.	b.	c.	d.	e.
1.	$\frac{1}{7} \times \frac{1}{3}$	$\frac{1}{8} \times \frac{1}{2}$	$\frac{2}{3} \times \frac{1}{5}$	$\frac{5}{6} \times \frac{1}{4}$	$\frac{1}{8} \times \frac{3}{4}$
2.	$\frac{2}{5} \times \frac{4}{7}$	$\frac{4}{9} \times \frac{5}{9}$	$\frac{3}{4} \times \frac{3}{5}$	$\frac{5}{6} \times \frac{7}{8}$	$\frac{7}{10} \times \frac{11}{12}$
3.	$\frac{2}{7} \times \frac{3}{4}$	$\frac{3}{5} \times \frac{4}{9}$	$\frac{7}{12} \times \frac{4}{5}$	$\frac{11}{18} \times \frac{2}{3}$	$\frac{8}{11} \times \frac{5}{6}$
4.	$\frac{2}{5} \times \frac{5}{8}$	$\frac{4}{15} \times \frac{5}{6}$	$\frac{4}{7} \times \frac{7}{10}$	$\frac{5}{18} \times \frac{3}{10}$	$\frac{24}{25} \times \frac{15}{32}$
5.	$9 \times \frac{1}{10}$	$\frac{1}{3} \times 2$	$3 \times \frac{2}{7}$	$\frac{4}{9} \times 2$	$4 \times \frac{2}{15}$
6.	$9 \times \frac{2}{3}$	$\frac{3}{4} \times 12$	$\frac{4}{7} \times 28$	$45 \times \frac{8}{9}$	$\frac{11}{18} \times 54$
7.	$7 \times \frac{1}{2}$	$\frac{5}{12} \times 8$	$\frac{3}{4} \times 3$	$9 \times \frac{5}{6}$	$\frac{17}{24} \times 4$
8.	$\frac{1}{5} \times 2\frac{1}{4}$	$1\frac{2}{5} \times \frac{2}{3}$	$1\frac{2}{3} \times \frac{1}{6}$	$\frac{4}{9} \times 1\frac{1}{9}$	$3\frac{1}{8} \times \frac{1}{9}$
9.	$1\frac{3}{8} \times \frac{4}{7}$	$1\frac{2}{9} \times \frac{3}{4}$	$\frac{1}{7} \times 4\frac{1}{5}$	$2\frac{1}{2} \times \frac{1}{5}$	$2\frac{3}{10} \times \frac{5}{12}$
10.	$\frac{1}{2} \times 4\frac{1}{5}$	$2\frac{2}{3} \times \frac{4}{5}$	$\frac{7}{8} \times 1\frac{1}{4}$	$3\frac{1}{12} \times \frac{1}{3}$	$2\frac{1}{3} \times \frac{8}{9}$
11.	$\frac{1}{3} \times 3\frac{3}{7}$	$1\frac{4}{9} \times \frac{3}{4}$	$1\frac{9}{10} \times \frac{5}{6}$	$\frac{8}{21} \times 5\frac{1}{2}$	$\frac{11}{12} \times 2\frac{1}{4}$
12.	$6 \times 2\frac{2}{3}$	$5\frac{1}{2} \times 4$	$6\frac{3}{4} \times 12$	$15 \times 2\frac{4}{5}$	$3\frac{5}{6} \times 12$
13.	$1\frac{2}{9} \times 6$	$9 \times 1\frac{7}{12}$	$2 \times 3\frac{3}{10}$	$2\frac{3}{8} \times 10$	$1\frac{5}{18} \times 2$
14.	$1\frac{1}{8} \times 5\frac{1}{3}$	$1\frac{2}{7} \times 2\frac{1}{3}$	$3\frac{1}{3} \times 4\frac{1}{2}$	$9\frac{1}{3} \times 3\frac{3}{4}$	$2\frac{1}{10} \times 4\frac{2}{7}$
15.	$1\frac{1}{2} \times 2\frac{1}{2}$	$1\frac{2}{3} \times 2\frac{1}{2}$	$1\frac{1}{3} \times 1\frac{2}{5}$	$2\frac{1}{5} \times 1\frac{2}{7}$	$1\frac{5}{6} \times 5\frac{1}{2}$
16.	$3\frac{1}{3} \times 1\frac{3}{5}$	$2\frac{1}{2} \times 1\frac{1}{10}$	$2\frac{1}{6} \times 2\frac{4}{7}$	$5\frac{1}{3} \times 1\frac{4}{5}$	$1\frac{7}{9} \times 5\frac{3}{4}$
17.	$1\frac{7}{20} \times 4\frac{1}{6}$	$3\frac{1}{5} \times 2\frac{1}{12}$	$6\frac{1}{4} \times 1\frac{7}{15}$	$2\frac{1}{12} \times 1\frac{1}{35}$	$4\frac{9}{10} \times 1\frac{5}{21}$

Division of Fractions

Write a multiplication expression for each of the following.

	a.	b.	c.	d.	e.
1.	$\frac{1}{7} \div \frac{5}{6}$	$\frac{2}{3} \div \frac{1}{2}$	$\frac{4}{5} \div \frac{6}{7}$	$\frac{1}{9} \div \frac{1}{9}$	$\frac{9}{10} \div \frac{4}{11}$
2.	$\frac{2}{5} \div 7$	$4 \div \frac{2}{3}$	$\frac{4}{7} \div 9$	$7 \div 4$	$\frac{9}{10} \div 10$
3.	$\frac{5}{6} \div 1\frac{1}{4}$	$2 \div 2\frac{2}{3}$	$2\frac{8}{9} \div 4$	$1\frac{1}{6} \div 2\frac{1}{3}$	$6\frac{3}{4} \div 5\frac{5}{8}$

Divide. Write each quotient in simplest form.

	a.	b.	c.	d.	e.
4.	$2 \div \frac{1}{3}$	$4 \div \frac{1}{4}$	$8 \div \frac{1}{2}$	$10 \div \frac{1}{5}$	$11 \div \frac{1}{7}$
5.	$2 \div \frac{3}{5}$	$11 \div \frac{2}{3}$	$12 \div \frac{5}{6}$	$10 \div \frac{6}{7}$	$11 \div \frac{4}{5}$
6.	$\frac{3}{4} \div \frac{1}{4}$	$\frac{5}{6} \div \frac{1}{6}$	$\frac{9}{10} \div \frac{3}{10}$	$\frac{8}{15} \div \frac{4}{15}$	$\frac{22}{35} \div \frac{2}{35}$
7.	$\frac{3}{14} \div \frac{2}{7}$	$\frac{2}{15} \div \frac{5}{6}$	$\frac{5}{8} \div \frac{11}{16}$	$\frac{1}{4} \div \frac{5}{8}$	$\frac{5}{12} \div \frac{11}{18}$
8.	$\frac{3}{5} \div \frac{1}{4}$	$\frac{2}{7} \div \frac{1}{5}$	$\frac{5}{6} \div \frac{5}{9}$	$\frac{8}{15} \div \frac{1}{10}$	$\frac{16}{21} \div \frac{2}{7}$
9.	$1\frac{3}{4} \div \frac{7}{12}$	$1\frac{3}{8} \div \frac{1}{16}$	$3\frac{2}{3} \div \frac{1}{9}$	$4\frac{2}{5} \div \frac{11}{15}$	$3\frac{4}{7} \div \frac{5}{21}$
10.	$1\frac{2}{5} \div \frac{1}{6}$	$1\frac{1}{3} \div \frac{1}{2}$	$1\frac{1}{8} \div \frac{2}{3}$	$1\frac{1}{2} \div \frac{2}{7}$	$1\frac{5}{6} \div \frac{3}{5}$
11.	$\frac{1}{2} \div 8$	$\frac{3}{5} \div 3$	$\frac{8}{15} \div 3$	$\frac{10}{21} \div 2$	$\frac{2}{11} \div 7$
12.	$1 \div 1\frac{1}{2}$	$3 \div 3\frac{1}{2}$	$4 \div 5\frac{2}{3}$	$2 \div 2\frac{1}{7}$	$1 \div 2\frac{3}{5}$
13.	$3 \div 1\frac{5}{6}$	$4 \div 1\frac{1}{4}$	$3 \div 2\frac{1}{3}$	$7 \div 2\frac{3}{4}$	$8 \div 2\frac{1}{7}$
14.	$2\frac{5}{8} \div 7\frac{1}{2}$	$1\frac{3}{5} \div 2\frac{2}{5}$	$1\frac{1}{3} \div 6\frac{6}{7}$	$1\frac{3}{5} \div 11\frac{1}{5}$	$2\frac{1}{9} \div 5\frac{1}{3}$
15.	$2\frac{4}{5} \div 1\frac{2}{5}$	$3\frac{4}{9} \div 1\frac{1}{9}$	$6\frac{1}{4} \div 2\frac{1}{4}$	$3\frac{1}{8} \div 1\frac{3}{8}$	$5\frac{5}{9} \div 1\frac{7}{9}$
16.	$5\frac{3}{5} \div 4\frac{1}{5}$	$2\frac{4}{7} \div 1\frac{1}{2}$	$10\frac{2}{7} \div 3\frac{5}{7}$	$4\frac{9}{10} \div 1\frac{13}{15}$	$3\frac{1}{21} \div 1\frac{21}{35}$

Fractions, Decimals, and Percents

Change each fraction to a decimal.

	a.	b.	c.	d.	e.	f.
1.	$\frac{2}{5}$	$\frac{1}{4}$	$\frac{7}{10}$	$\frac{3}{20}$	$\frac{4}{5}$	$\frac{17}{20}$
2.	$\frac{1}{3}$	$\frac{1}{6}$	$\frac{2}{3}$	$\frac{1}{9}$	$\frac{5}{6}$	$\frac{2}{9}$
3.	$\frac{3}{7}$	$\frac{1}{12}$	$\frac{5}{7}$	$\frac{7}{12}$	$\frac{11}{12}$	$\frac{2}{7}$
4.	$\frac{7}{8}$	$\frac{5}{16}$	$\frac{3}{8}$	$\frac{1}{16}$	$\frac{5}{8}$	$\frac{11}{16}$
5.	$\frac{4}{3}$	$\frac{9}{4}$	$\frac{14}{9}$	$\frac{35}{6}$	$\frac{53}{12}$	$\frac{15}{8}$

For each of the given fractions, write an equivalent fraction with a denominator of 100.

6.	$\frac{1}{2}$	$\frac{1}{5}$	$\frac{1}{4}$	$\frac{1}{10}$	$\frac{1}{50}$	$\frac{1}{20}$
7.	$\frac{3}{10}$	$\frac{3}{4}$	$\frac{4}{5}$	$\frac{2}{5}$	$\frac{9}{10}$	$\frac{7}{10}$
8.	$\frac{17}{20}$	$\frac{3}{25}$	$\frac{9}{20}$	$\frac{9}{50}$	$\frac{7}{25}$	$\frac{41}{50}$
9.	$\frac{9}{2}$	$\frac{11}{5}$	$\frac{7}{4}$	$\frac{14}{2}$	$\frac{27}{5}$	$\frac{19}{4}$
10.	$\frac{67}{10}$	$\frac{25}{20}$	$\frac{69}{50}$	$\frac{72}{10}$	$\frac{49}{25}$	$\frac{152}{50}$

Change each fraction to a percent.

11.	$\frac{3}{100}$	$\frac{6}{100}$	$\frac{5}{100}$	$\frac{9}{100}$	$\frac{7}{100}$	$\frac{8}{100}$
12.	$\frac{10}{100}$	$\frac{50}{100}$	$\frac{30}{100}$	$\frac{49}{100}$	$\frac{80}{100}$	$\frac{90}{100}$
13.	$\frac{38}{100}$	$\frac{94}{100}$	$\frac{62}{100}$	$\frac{40}{100}$	$\frac{76}{100}$	$\frac{25}{100}$
14.	$\frac{500}{100}$	$\frac{360}{100}$	$\frac{125}{100}$	$\frac{650}{100}$	$\frac{265}{100}$	$\frac{496}{100}$
15.	$\frac{162\frac{1}{2}}{100}$	$\frac{412\frac{1}{2}}{100}$	$\frac{342\frac{6}{7}}{100}$	$\frac{266\frac{2}{3}}{100}$	$\frac{183\frac{1}{3}}{100}$	$\frac{271\frac{3}{7}}{100}$

Fractions, Decimals, and Percents

Change each decimal to a percent.

	a.	b.	c.	d.	e.	f.
1.	0.3	0.7	0.9	0.6	0.8	0.5
2.	0.12	0.65	0.39	0.04	0.09	0.27
3.	0.385	0.706	0.928	0.009	0.065	0.004
4.	1.45	3.8	1.05	5.4	2.06	6.9
5.	5.409	9.365	8.021	4.077	14.084	26.303

Change each fraction to a decimal. Then change the decimal to a percent.

6.	$\frac{1}{8}$	$\frac{1}{16}$	$\frac{1}{40}$	$\frac{3}{8}$	$\frac{5}{16}$	$\frac{9}{40}$
7.	$\frac{64}{50}$	$\frac{17}{10}$	$\frac{70}{25}$	$\frac{189}{50}$	$\frac{69}{20}$	$\frac{258}{50}$
8.	$\frac{23}{16}$	$\frac{17}{8}$	$\frac{71}{40}$	$\frac{19}{16}$	$\frac{57}{40}$	$\frac{37}{16}$
9.	$\frac{2}{3}$	$\frac{1}{6}$	$\frac{4}{9}$	$\frac{5}{12}$	$\frac{4}{7}$	$\frac{3}{11}$

Change each percent to a decimal.

10.	8%	2%	7%	5%	3%	9%
11.	11%	99%	32%	67%	40%	55%
12.	23.4%	62.8%	37.5%	80.1%	92.7%	28.9%
13.	155%	206%	460%	100.5%	605.1%	407.3%

Change each percent to a fraction or mixed numeral in simplest form.

14.	3%	7%	41%	19%	23%	99%
15.	15%	35%	50%	25%	80%	10%
16.	118%	216%	345%	430%	274%	522%
17.	$33\frac{1}{3}\%$	$37\frac{1}{2}\%$	$44\frac{4}{9}\%$	$28\frac{4}{7}\%$	$7\frac{1}{2}\%$	$83\frac{1}{3}\%$
18.	$155\frac{5}{9}\%$	$466\frac{2}{3}\%$	$662\frac{1}{2}\%$	$316\frac{2}{3}\%$	$214\frac{2}{7}\%$	$542\frac{1}{2}\%$

Ratios and Rates

Write each of the following as a rate.

	a.	b.	c.
1.	4 goals in 5 tries	1 pizza for 5 subs	5 wins in 11 games
2.	8 records for 5 tapes	2 hits in 7 at bats	6 laces for 3 shoes
3.	5 grams in 2 liters	10 meters in 3 seconds	55 miles in 1 hour
4.	90 m in 1 h	$48 for 30 g	100 kg in 6 s
5.	47 mL in 5 s	52 g in 1 L	420 m for 20 g
6.	$1.20 for 500 g	$3.60 for 8 kg	$24.50 for 9 L

Write each rate as a unit rate.

7.	$\frac{\text{16 meters}}{\text{8 seconds}}$	$\frac{\text{15 kilograms}}{\text{5 hours}}$	$\frac{\text{95 grams}}{\text{19 days}}$
8.	$\frac{\text{190 kg}}{\text{10 L}}$	$\frac{\text{720 m}}{\text{60 s}}$	$\frac{\text{76 g}}{\text{9.5 mL}}$
9.	$\frac{\$19}{\text{38 h}}$	$\frac{\$8}{\text{80 km}}$	$\frac{\text{4.5 kg}}{\text{15 L}}$
10.	$\frac{\text{3.5 g}}{\text{1.4 mL}}$	$\frac{\text{8 g}}{\text{5 h}}$	$\frac{\$15}{\text{10 m}}$
11.	$\frac{\$5.94}{\text{6 mL}}$	$\frac{\text{28 ml}}{\text{80 s}}$	$\frac{\text{34 m}}{\text{40 g}}$
12.	$\frac{\$51}{\text{12 h}}$	$\frac{\$3.06}{\text{2 h}}$	$\frac{\$188}{\text{16 h}}$

Write each of the following as a unit rate.

13.	6 m in 3 s	81 km on 9 L	90 km in 45 m
14.	80 g in 20 mL	90 m in 2 h	750 km in 10 h
15.	950 m in 9.5 s	50 g in 0.05 kg	140 g in 14 mL
16.	$6.50 for 13 kg	7 kg in 35 L	0.9 g in 3 mL
17.	$5.00 for 2 kg	$6.40 for 4 L	$6.30 for 2 h
18.	5 g in 4 L	6 L in 24 km	72 km in 32 min
19.	7.65 kg in 0.9 L	1.5 kg in 0.4 m	59.4 g in 36 h

Proportions

Use cross products to determine whether the ratios are equivalent. Write yes or no.

	a.	b.	c.	d.	e.	f.
1.	$\frac{1}{2}, \frac{2}{4}$	$\frac{1}{3}, \frac{2}{6}$	$\frac{1}{5}, \frac{2}{11}$	$\frac{1}{10}, \frac{2}{5}$	$\frac{1}{8}, \frac{3}{24}$	$\frac{1}{7}, \frac{4}{28}$
2.	$\frac{2}{5}, \frac{4}{9}$	$\frac{3}{4}, \frac{6}{8}$	$\frac{2}{3}, \frac{3}{9}$	$\frac{2}{7}, \frac{6}{21}$	$\frac{4}{5}, \frac{15}{20}$	$\frac{5}{6}, \frac{15}{18}$
3.	$\frac{4}{9}, \frac{12}{27}$	$\frac{6}{15}, \frac{12}{45}$	$\frac{8}{21}, \frac{4}{10}$	$\frac{11}{24}, \frac{33}{72}$	$\frac{15}{32}, \frac{30}{62}$	$\frac{19}{40}, \frac{96}{150}$
4.	$\frac{7}{4}, \frac{2.1}{1.2}$	$\frac{8}{2}, \frac{3.2}{1.5}$	$\frac{11}{10}, \frac{2.2}{2}$	$\frac{16}{7}, \frac{4.9}{2.1}$	$\frac{27}{1.4}, \frac{81}{4.2}$	$\frac{29}{1.8}, \frac{145}{9}$

Solve each proportion.

	a.	b.	c.	d.	e.	f.
5.	$\frac{1}{4} = \frac{a}{8}$	$\frac{1}{2} = \frac{n}{6}$	$\frac{3}{4} = \frac{m}{12}$	$\frac{4}{7} = \frac{x}{14}$	$\frac{2}{9} = \frac{z}{27}$	$\frac{3}{10} = \frac{b}{30}$
6.	$\frac{1}{8} = \frac{2}{d}$	$\frac{1}{9} = \frac{5}{w}$	$\frac{2}{5} = \frac{4}{c}$	$\frac{5}{12} = \frac{10}{y}$	$\frac{8}{15} = \frac{16}{p}$	$\frac{11}{14} = \frac{33}{q}$
7.	$\frac{h}{6} = \frac{2}{12}$	$\frac{u}{12} = \frac{3}{36}$	$\frac{x}{6} = \frac{15}{18}$	$\frac{d}{11} = \frac{28}{44}$	$\frac{y}{18} = \frac{10}{36}$	$\frac{t}{24} = \frac{44}{96}$
8.	$\frac{1}{v} = \frac{9}{27}$	$\frac{2}{e} = \frac{8}{12}$	$\frac{3}{k} = \frac{18}{24}$	$\frac{3}{m} = \frac{9}{15}$	$\frac{7}{r} = \frac{21}{48}$	$\frac{7}{f} = \frac{42}{72}$
9.	$\frac{4}{11} = \frac{12}{x}$	$\frac{b}{9} = \frac{28}{36}$	$\frac{5}{7} = \frac{t}{21}$	$\frac{a}{15} = \frac{55}{75}$	$\frac{13}{w} = \frac{26}{36}$	$\frac{16}{21} = \frac{m}{84}$
10.	$\frac{5}{2} = \frac{p}{4}$	$\frac{7}{q} = \frac{28}{16}$	$\frac{c}{9} = \frac{55}{45}$	$\frac{12}{5} = \frac{36}{h}$	$\frac{a}{12} = \frac{34}{24}$	$\frac{25}{4} = \frac{z}{12}$
11.	$\frac{8}{a} = \frac{48}{18}$	$\frac{15}{11} = \frac{x}{22}$	$\frac{28}{5} = \frac{84}{d}$	$\frac{s}{12} = \frac{136}{96}$	$\frac{31}{24} = \frac{y}{72}$	$\frac{h}{30} = \frac{102}{60}$
12.	$\frac{2}{3} = \frac{0.8}{n}$	$\frac{0.4}{5} = \frac{a}{10}$	$\frac{4.2}{x} = \frac{7}{12}$	$\frac{b}{4.9} = \frac{3}{7}$	$\frac{0.9}{z} = \frac{3}{5}$	$\frac{1.6}{x} = \frac{14}{21}$
13.	$\frac{0.6}{1.1} = \frac{y}{6.6}$	$\frac{1}{1.7} = \frac{5}{c}$	$\frac{f}{7.5} = \frac{1.9}{5.7}$	$\frac{0.4}{k} = \frac{2}{4.5}$	$\frac{m}{0.4} = \frac{0.9}{3.6}$	$\frac{2.1}{x} = \frac{0.9}{1.2}$
14.	$\frac{4}{7} = \frac{4.92}{d}$	$\frac{t}{8.03} = \frac{6}{11}$	$\frac{4.77}{v} = \frac{3}{8}$	$\frac{1}{9} = \frac{x}{7.74}$	$\frac{7}{12} = \frac{1.68}{a}$	$\frac{5.78}{b} = \frac{2}{5}$
15.	$\frac{5.6}{9.8} = \frac{n}{28}$	$\frac{45}{m} = \frac{23.4}{28.6}$	$\frac{p}{36} = \frac{11.76}{35.28}$	$\frac{8.64}{12.24} = \frac{24}{a}$	$\frac{9.57}{13.05} = \frac{b}{15}$	$\frac{n}{48} = \frac{5.22}{13.92}$
16.	$\frac{a}{3.45} = \frac{8}{5.52}$	$\frac{10}{2.4} = \frac{n}{2.64}$	$\frac{25.27}{7} = \frac{m}{2}$	$\frac{85.8}{c} = \frac{70.2}{9}$	$\frac{30}{6.18} = \frac{40}{d}$	$\frac{0.6}{1.1} = \frac{m}{8.47}$

Finding the Percent of a Number

Solve each proportion.

	a.	b.	c.
1.	$\frac{P}{60} = \frac{10}{100}$	$\frac{P}{84} = \frac{25}{100}$	$\frac{P}{40} = \frac{110}{100}$
2.	$\frac{P}{90} = \frac{8}{100}$	$\frac{P}{180} = \frac{48.5}{100}$	$\frac{P}{220} = \frac{20.5}{100}$
3.	$\frac{P}{50} = \frac{115}{100}$	$\frac{P}{20} = \frac{323}{100}$	$\frac{P}{25} = \frac{198}{100}$
4.	$\frac{P}{32} = \frac{37\frac{1}{2}}{100}$	$\frac{P}{168} = \frac{66\frac{2}{3}}{100}$	$\frac{P}{243} = \frac{44\frac{4}{9}}{100}$

Solve each of the following using the proportion $\frac{P}{B} = \frac{r}{100}$.

5.	____ is 80% of 450	____ is 37% of 420	____ is 9% of 960
	$\frac{P}{450} = \frac{80}{100}$	$\frac{P}{420} = \frac{37}{100}$	$\frac{P}{962} = \frac{9}{100}$
6.	$12\frac{1}{2}$% of 16 is ____	$33\frac{1}{3}$% of 63 is ____	$11\frac{1}{9}$% of 81 is ____
	$\frac{P}{16} = \frac{12\frac{1}{2}}{100}$	$\frac{P}{63} = \frac{33\frac{1}{3}}{100}$	$\frac{P}{81} = \frac{11\frac{1}{9}}{100}$

Solve.

7.	10% of 60 is ____	25% of 84 is ____	6% of 150 is ____
8.	50% of 24 is ____	20% of 40 is ____	90% of 160 is ____
9.	____ is 5% of 140	____ is 75% of 52	____ is 10% of 290
10.	____ is 8% of 40	____ is 11% of 20	____ is 17% of 50
11.	____ is 25% of 16.8	____ is 40% of 9.6	____ is 30% of 28.5
12.	4.1% of 200 is ____	16.5% of 300 is ____	42.8% of 150 is ____
13.	400% of 2.5 is ____	300% of 6.2 is ____	500% of 3.7 is ____
14.	110% of 40 is ____	205% of 22 is ____	485% of 180 is ____
15.	____ is $16\frac{2}{3}$% of 48	____ is $83\frac{1}{3}$% of 150	____ is $41\frac{2}{3}$% of 420
16.	____ is $112\frac{1}{2}$% of 536	____ is $266\frac{2}{3}$% of 561	____ is $416\frac{2}{3}$% of 546

Finding What Percent One Number Is of Another

Solve each proportion.

	a.	b.	c.
1.	$\frac{5}{10} = \frac{r}{100}$	$\frac{11}{44} = \frac{r}{100}$	$\frac{12}{60} = \frac{r}{100}$
2.	$\frac{840}{700} = \frac{r}{100}$	$\frac{90}{40} = \frac{r}{100}$	$\frac{770}{308} = \frac{r}{100}$
3.	$\frac{8.7}{15} = \frac{r}{100}$	$\frac{1.4}{1.6} = \frac{r}{100}$	$\frac{0.12}{0.25} = \frac{r}{100}$
4.	$\frac{16}{48} = \frac{r}{100}$	$\frac{2.6}{23.4} = \frac{r}{100}$	$\frac{1.1}{6.6} = \frac{r}{100}$

Solve each of the following using the proportion $\frac{P}{B} = \frac{r}{100}$.

5.	____% of 40 is 16	____% of 500 is 55	____% of 71 is 17.04
	$\frac{16}{40} = \frac{r}{100}$	$\frac{55}{500} = \frac{r}{100}$	$\frac{17.04}{71} = \frac{r}{100}$
6.	23 is ____% of 69	12 is ____% of 96	130 is ____% of 156
	$\frac{23}{69} = \frac{r}{100}$	$\frac{12}{96} = \frac{r}{100}$	$\frac{130}{156} = \frac{r}{100}$

Solve.

7.	8 is ____% of 32	9 is ____% of 45	11 is ____% of 22
8.	15 is ____% of 75	13 is ____% of 130	33 is ____% of 660
9.	120 is ____% of 800	57 is ____% of 95	713 is ____% of 3100
10.	____% of 96 is 38.4	____% of 895 is 53.7	____% of 28.4 is 9.372
11.	____% of 47 is 10.34	____% of 655 is 537.1	____% of 66.25 is 2.65
12.	____% of 45 is 90	____% of 85 is 102	____% of 705 is 2538
13.	56 is ____% of 16	18.5 is ____% of 2.5	354.04 is ____% of 334
14.	266.8 is ____% of 58	987 is ____% of 940	3.96 is ____% of 0.45
15.	____% of 93 is 62	____% of 40 is 25	____% of 756 is 168
16.	____% of 153 is 170	____% of 21 is 28	____% of 82.4 is 298.7

Finding a Number When a Percent of It Is Known

Solve each proportion.

	a.	b.	c.
1.	$\frac{5}{B} = \frac{10}{100}$	$\frac{75}{B} = \frac{50}{100}$	$\frac{34}{B} = \frac{85}{100}$
2.	$\frac{121}{B} = \frac{220}{100}$	$\frac{808}{B} = \frac{101}{100}$	$\frac{135}{B} = \frac{675}{100}$
3.	$\frac{6}{B} = \frac{80}{100}$	$\frac{4.2}{B} = \frac{80}{100}$	$\frac{6.64}{B} = \frac{16}{100}$
4.	$\frac{168}{B} = \frac{87\frac{1}{2}}{100}$	$\frac{82}{B} = \frac{66\frac{2}{3}}{100}$	$\frac{2.1}{B} = \frac{17\frac{1}{2}}{100}$

Solve each of the following using the proportion $\frac{P}{B} = \frac{r}{100}$.

5.	30% of ____ is 15	65% of ____ is 26	44% of ____ is 37.4
	$\frac{15}{B} = \frac{30}{100}$	$\frac{26}{B} = \frac{65}{100}$	$\frac{37.4}{B} = \frac{44}{100}$
6.	20 is $12\frac{1}{2}$% of ____	108 is $33\frac{1}{3}$% of ____	45 is $55\frac{5}{9}$% of ____
	$\frac{20}{B} = \frac{12\frac{1}{2}}{100}$	$\frac{108}{B} = \frac{33\frac{1}{3}}{100}$	$\frac{45}{B} = \frac{55\frac{5}{9}}{100}$

Solve.

7.	20% of ____ is 12	30% of ____ is 21	25% of ____ is 75
8.	45% of ____ is 162	45% of ____ is 72	3% of ____ is 18
9.	85 is 68% of ____	117 is 26% of ____	738 is 72% of ____
10.	0.9 is 6% of ____	6.82 is 11% of ____	165.3 is 57% of ____
11.	18.27 is 29% of ____	0.891 is 99% of ____	0.804 is 67% of ____
12.	105% of ____ is 630	485% of ____ is 291	440% of ____ is 132
13.	124% of ____ is 7.44	1050% of ____ is 121.8	792% of ____ is 67.32
14.	110% of ____ is 4.95	216% of ____ is 22.68	198% of ____ is 50.49
15.	32 is $66\frac{2}{3}$% of ____	770 is $87\frac{1}{2}$% of ____	3.825 is $37\frac{1}{2}$% of ____
16.	122 is $152\frac{1}{2}$% of ____	525 is $233\frac{1}{3}$% of ____	237 is $658\frac{1}{3}$% of ____

Percent

Solve.

	a.	b.	c.
1.	20% of 15 is ____	10% of 190 is ____	5% of 200 is ____
2.	4 is ____% of 8	2 is ____% of 10	16 is ____% of 64
3.	50% of ____ is 6	10% of ____ is 11	20% of ____ is 6
4.	9 is 25% of ____	8 is 40% of ____	72 is 30% of ____
5.	____% of 200 is 70	____% of 300 is 99	____% of 920 is 92
6.	____ is 50% of 142	____ is 25% of 80	____ is 25% of 56
7.	____% of 140 is 116.2	____% of 231 is 207.9	____% of 858 is 386.1
8.	____ is 70% of 94	____ is 16% of 8	____ is 95% of 450
9.	32.3 is 19% of ____	24.12 is 67% of ____	53.9 is 35% of ____
10.	127% of 180 is ____	200% of 12 is ____	140% of 200 is ____
11.	134.4 is ____% of 84	33 is ____% of 30	19.5 is ____% of 6.5
12.	171% of ____ is 147.06	180% of ____ is 117	105% of ____ is 420
13.	108% of 50 is ____	155% of 68 is ____	490% of 7 is ____
14.	131% of ____ is 26.2	115% of ____ is 87.4	285% of ____ is 239.4
15.	140 is ____% of 80	98.1 is ____% of 90	80.5 is ____% of 25
16.	____% of 36 is 24	____% of 40 is 1	____% of 96 is 36
17.	____ is $33\frac{1}{3}$% of 6	____ is $12\frac{1}{2}$% of 16	____ is $16\frac{2}{3}$% of 36
18.	85 is $62\frac{1}{2}$% of ____	21 is $7\frac{1}{2}$% of ____	48 is $42\frac{6}{7}$% of ____
19.	623 is $77\frac{7}{9}$% of ____	31 is $33\frac{1}{3}$% of ____	18.6 is $66\frac{2}{3}$% of ____
20.	____% of 171 is 76	____% of 672 is 576	____% of 252 is 224
21.	____ is $14\frac{2}{7}$% of 21	____ is $11\frac{1}{9}$% of 126	____ is $87\frac{1}{2}$% of 232
22.	40.5% of 120 is ____	12.4% of 15 is ____	10.8% of 20 is ____
23.	5.6 is ____% of 32	20.4 is ____% of 150	4.24 is ____% of 16
24.	93.5% of ____ is 74.8	7.5% of ____ is 7.2	48.5% of ____ is 77.6

Squares and Approximate Square Roots

N	N^2	$\sqrt{N}$	N	N^2	$\sqrt{N}$
1	1	1.000	51	2601	7.141
2	4	1.414	52	2704	7.211
3	9	1.732	53	2809	7.280
4	16	2.000	54	2916	7.348
5	25	2.236	55	3025	7.416
6	36	2.449	56	3136	7.483
7	49	2.646	57	3249	7.550
8	64	2.828	58	3364	7.616
9	81	3.000	59	3481	7.681
10	100	3.162	60	3600	7.746
11	121	3.317	61	3721	7.810
12	144	3.464	62	3844	7.874
13	169	3.606	63	3969	7.937
14	196	3.742	64	4096	8.000
15	225	3.873	65	4225	8.062
16	256	4.000	66	4356	8.124
17	289	4.123	67	4489	8.185
18	324	4.243	68	4624	8.246
19	361	4.359	69	4761	8.307
20	400	4.472	70	4900	8.367
21	441	4.583	71	5041	8.426
22	484	4.690	72	5184	8.485
23	529	4.796	73	5329	8.544
24	576	4.899	74	5476	8.602
25	625	5.000	75	5625	8.660
26	676	5.099	76	5776	8.718
27	729	5.196	77	5929	8.775
28	784	5.292	78	6084	8.832
29	841	5.385	79	6241	8.888
30	900	5.477	80	6400	8.944
31	961	5.568	81	6561	9.000
32	1024	5.657	82	6724	9.055
33	1089	5.745	83	6889	9.110
34	1156	5.831	84	7056	9.165
35	1225	5.916	85	7225	9.220
36	1296	6.000	86	7396	9.274
37	1369	6.083	87	7569	9.327
38	1444	6.164	88	7744	9.381
39	1521	6.245	89	7921	9.434
40	1600	6.325	90	8100	9.487
41	1681	6.403	91	8281	9.539
42	1764	6.481	92	8464	9.592
43	1849	6.557	93	8649	9.644
44	1936	6.633	94	8836	9.695
45	2025	6.708	95	9025	9.747
46	2116	6.782	96	9216	9.798
47	2209	6.856	97	9409	9.849
48	2304	6.928	98	9604	9.899
49	2401	7.000	99	9801	9.950
50	2500	7.071	100	10000	10.000

TRIGONOMETRIC RATIOS

Angle	sin	cos	tan	Angle	sin	cos	tan
0°	0.0000	1.0000	0.0000	45°	0.7071	0.7071	1.0000
1°	0.0175	0.9998	0.0175	46°	0.7193	0.6947	1.0355
2°	0.0349	0.9994	0.0349	47°	0.7314	0.6820	1.0724
3°	0.0523	0.9986	0.0524	48°	0.7431	0.6691	1.1106
4°	0.0698	0.9976	0.0699	49°	0.7547	0.6561	1.1504
5°	0.0872	0.9962	0.0875	50°	0.7660	0.6428	1.1918
6°	0.1045	0.9945	0.1051	51°	0.7771	0.6293	1.2349
7°	0.1219	0.9925	0.1228	52°	0.7880	0.6157	1.2799
8°	0.1392	0.9903	0.1405	53°	0.7986	0.6018	1.3270
9°	0.1564	0.9877	0.1584	54°	0.8090	0.5878	1.3764
10°	0.1736	0.9848	0.1763	55°	0.8192	0.5736	1.4281
11°	0.1908	0.9816	0.1944	56°	0.8290	0.5592	1.4826
12°	0.2079	0.9781	0.2126	57°	0.8387	0.5446	1.5399
13°	0.2250	0.9744	0.2309	58°	0.8480	0.5299	1.6003
14°	0.2419	0.9703	0.2493	59°	0.8572	0.5150	1.6643
15°	0.2588	0.9659	0.2679	60°	0.8660	0.5000	1.7321
16°	0.2756	0.9613	0.2867	61°	0.8746	0.4848	1.8040
17°	0.2924	0.9563	0.3057	62°	0.8829	0.4695	1.8807
18°	0.3090	0.9511	0.3249	63°	0.8910	0.4540	1.9626
19°	0.3256	0.9455	0.3443	64°	0.8988	0.4384	2.0503
20°	0.3420	0.9397	0.3640	65°	0.9063	0.4226	2.1445
21°	0.3584	0.9336	0.3839	66°	0.9135	0.4067	2.2460
22°	0.3746	0.9272	0.4040	67°	0.9205	0.3907	2.3559
23°	0.3907	0.9205	0.4245	68°	0.9272	0.3746	2.4751
24°	0.4067	0.9135	0.4452	69°	0.9336	0.3584	2.6051
25°	0.4226	0.9063	0.4663	70°	0.9397	0.3420	2.7475
26°	0.4384	0.8988	0.4877	71°	0.9455	0.3256	2.9042
27°	0.4540	0.8910	0.5095	72°	0.9511	0.3090	3.0777
28°	0.4695	0.8829	0.5317	73°	0.9563	0.2924	3.2709
29°	0.4848	0.8746	0.5543	74°	0.9613	0.2756	3.4874
30°	0.5000	0.8660	0.5774	75°	0.9659	0.2588	3.7321
31°	0.5150	0.8572	0.6009	76°	0.9703	0.2419	4.0108
32°	0.5299	0.8480	0.6249	77°	0.9744	0.2250	4.3315
33°	0.5446	0.8387	0.6494	78°	0.9781	0.2079	4.7046
34°	0.5592	0.8290	0.6745	79°	0.9816	0.1908	5.1446
35°	0.5736	0.8192	0.7002	80°	0.9848	0.1736	5.6713
36°	0.5878	0.8090	0.7265	81°	0.9877	0.1564	6.3138
37°	0.6018	0.7986	0.7536	82°	0.9903	0.1392	7.1154
38°	0.6157	0.7880	0.7813	83°	0.9925	0.1219	8.1443
39°	0.6293	0.7771	0.8098	84°	0.9945	0.1045	9.5144
40°	0.6428	0.7660	0.8391	85°	0.9962	0.0872	11.4301
41°	0.6561	0.7547	0.8693	86°	0.9976	0.0698	14.3007
42°	0.6691	0.7431	0.9004	87°	0.9986	0.0523	19.0811
43°	0.6820	0.7314	0.9325	88°	0.9994	0.0349	28.6363
44°	0.6947	0.7193	0.9657	89°	0.9998	0.0175	57.2900
45°	0.7071	0.7071	1.0000	90°	1.0000	0.0000	∞

Glossary

absolute value (227) The number of units a number is from zero on the number line. The symbol for absolute value is two vertical lines. $|^{-}4| = 4$

acute angle (117) An angle that has degree measure between 0 and 90.

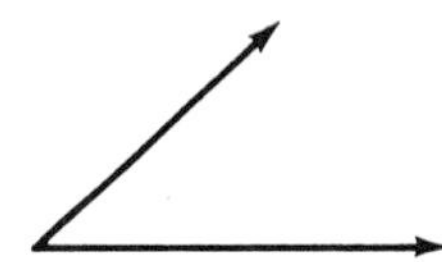

adjacent angles (118) Angles that have a common side, the same vertex, and do *not* overlap. $\angle CDW$ and $\angle WDB$ are adjacent.

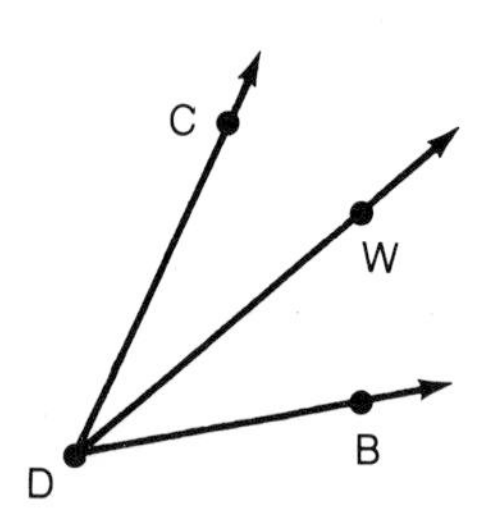

angle (116) Two rays with a common endpoint. Angle DEF is symbolized $\angle DEF$.

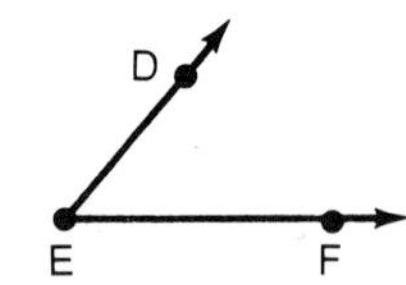

arc (136) Part of a circle.

area (280) The number of square units that covers a surface.

Associative Properties (8) The way in which addends or factors are grouped does *not* change the answer.

$$(20 + 30) + 40 = 20 + (30 + 40)$$
$$(6 \times 7) \times 3 = 6 \times (7 \times 3)$$

average, *see* mean

axes (340) The two perpendicular number lines in a coordinate system. The horizontal number line is called the *x-axis*. The vertical axis is called the *y-axis*.

base (of an exponent) (6) The number that is used as a factor in a power. In 4^3, the base is 4.

BASIC (388) A computer language.

bisect (129) To separate a figure into two congruent parts.

Celsius temperature (°C) (248) The temperature scale used in the metric system. Water freezes at 0°C and boils at 100°C.

chord (136) A line segment with both endpoints on a circle.

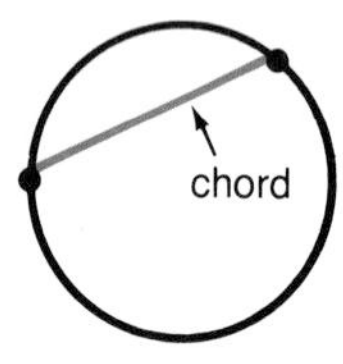

circle (136) A figure in the plane formed by all points that are the same distance from a given point called the *center*.

circumference (284) The distance around a circle.

common factor (66) A whole number that is a factor of two or more given whole numbers. 3 is a common factor of 6 and 9.

common multiple (67) A whole number that is a multiple of two or more given whole numbers. 36 is a common multiple of 6 and 9.

Commutative Properties (8) The order in which numbers are added or multiplied does *not* change the answer.

$$8 + 5 = 5 + 8$$
$$2 \times 30 = 30 \times 2$$

complementary angles (118) Two angles are complementary if the sum of their degree measures is 90.

complex fraction (107) A fraction that has fractions in the numerator, denominator, or both.

$$\frac{\frac{1}{2}}{\frac{4}{5}} \qquad \frac{3\frac{2}{3}}{2} \qquad \frac{4}{\frac{4}{7}}$$

composite number (64) A whole number that is *not* prime. A composite number has more than two factors.

computer program (390) A series of statements that give directions to a computer.

cone (288) A solid with a circular base and one vertex.

congruent figures (122) Figures that have the same size and shape.

coordinate (340) Each point on the coordinate system has an x-coordinate and a y-coordinate. The coordinates of each point are named as an ordered pair.

coordinate system (340) The number plane formed by two perpendicular number lines. Ordered pairs of numbers are graphed on the coordinate system. Point M is the graph of the ordered pair $(3, {}^-2)$.

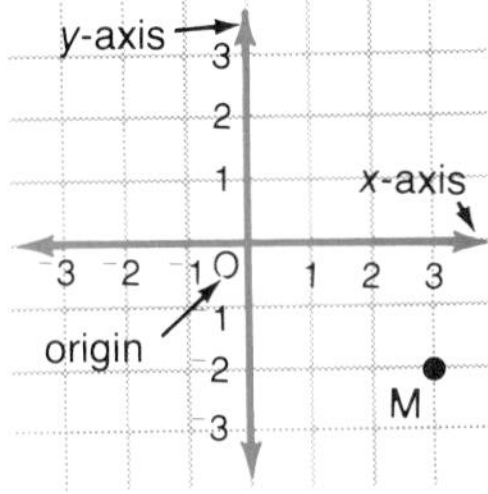

cosine (376) The ratio of the measure of the side adjacent an acute angle in a right triangle to the measure of the hypotenuse.

cross products (174) In the proportion $\frac{3}{6} = \frac{4}{8}$, the cross products are 3×8 and 6×4.

customary system (268) A system of measurement used in the United States. Some common units are foot, pound, quart, and degrees Fahrenheit.

cylinder (288) A solid that has two parallel and congruent circular bases.

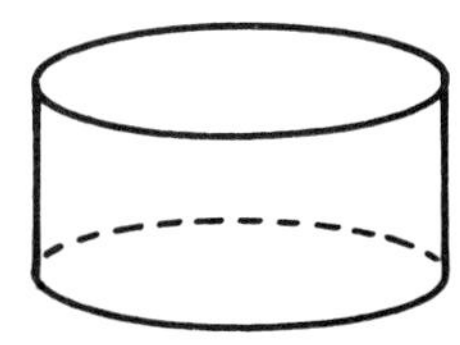

data (318) Numerical information.

decagon (124) A polygon with ten sides.

decimal (decimal fraction) (33) A way of expressing fractions that have denominators of 10, 100, 1,000, and so on.

$$0.3 = \frac{3}{10} \qquad 8.71 = \frac{871}{100} \text{ or } 8\frac{71}{100}$$

degree (116) A common unit of measure for angles.

dependent events (310) Two events in which the outcome of the second event is affected by the outcome of the first event.

diameter (136) A chord of a circle that contains the center of the circle.

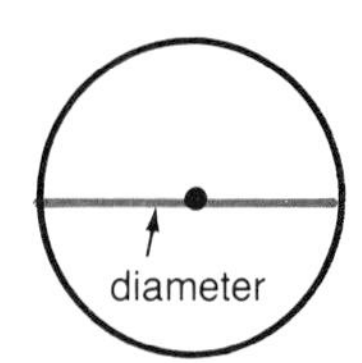

Distributive Property of Multiplication over Addition (9) The product of a number and a sum is equal to the sum of the products.

$$2 \times (4 + 3) = 2 \times 4 + 2 \times 3$$

divisible (63) A number is divisible by another if, upon division, the remainder is zero. 15 is divisible by 5.

equation (149) A mathematical sentence with an equals sign.

$$25 - 17 = 8 \qquad c + 3 = 9$$

equilateral triangle (126) A triangle that has three congruent sides.

equivalent decimals (34) Decimals that have the same value. 0.4, 0.40, and 0.400 are equivalent decimals.

equivalent equations (150) Equations that have the same solution. $x + 3 = 7$ and $x = 4$ are equivalent equations.

equivalent fractions (72) Fractions that name the same number. $\frac{4}{8}$, $\frac{5}{10}$, and $\frac{180}{360}$ are equivalent fractions.

error of measurement (259) The difference between the true length of an object and the measurement of the object.

evaluate (143) To find the value of an expression.

expanded form (7) A form of a number that shows the place value of each digit. There are three ways to write the expanded form of 916.

$916 = 900 + 10 + 6$
$916 = (9 \times 100) + (1 \times 10) + (6 \times 1)$
$916 = (9 \times 10^2) + (1 \times 10^1) + (6 \times 10^0)$

exponent (6) A number used to tell how many times the base is used as a factor. In 10^2, the exponent is 2.

factor (63) Any one of two or more numbers that are multiplied. Since $3 \times 2 = 6$, the factors of 6 are 3 and 2. When you divide a whole number by one of its factors, the remainder is zero.

Fahrenheit temperature (°F) (248) The temperature scale used in the customary system. Water freezes at 32°F and boils at 212°F.

flowchart (394) A diagram used to plan the steps of a problem.

formula (146) A mathematical statement that shows the relationship between certain quantities.

frequency table (318) A table for organizing numbers or items in a set of data. The frequency column gives the number of times each number or item occurs.

gram (g) (260) The basic unit of mass in the metric system.

greatest common factor (GCF) (66) The greatest number that is a factor of each of two or more given numbers. The GCF of 4, 10, and 14 is 2.

greatest possible error (259) One-half the unit of measure used in making a measurement.

hexagon (124) A polygon with six sides.

histogram (318) A vertical bar graph with bars next to each other. A histogram is used to show frequency of numbers or items in a set of data.

hypotenuse (361) The side opposite the right angle in a right triangle.

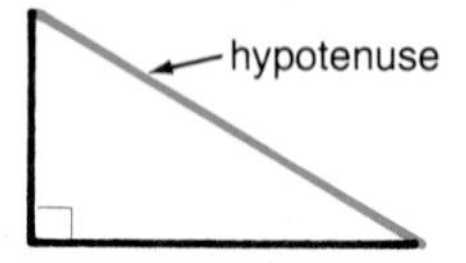

Identity Property of Addition (8) When zero is added to a number, the sum is that number. $213 + 0 = 213$

Identity Property of Multiplication (8) When a number is multiplied by one, the product is that number. $65 \times 1 = 65$

improper fraction (74) A fraction that has a numerator that is greater than or equal to the denominator.

independent events (310) Two events in which the outcome of the second event is *not* affected by the outcome of the first event.

inequality (338) A mathematical sentence that contains a symbol such as $<$, $>$, $\leq$, $\geq$, or $\neq$.

$7 < 8 \qquad 14 \geq x - 1.5 \qquad 0.5 \neq \frac{1}{3}$

inscribed polygon (136) A polygon in which each of its vertices lie on a circle.

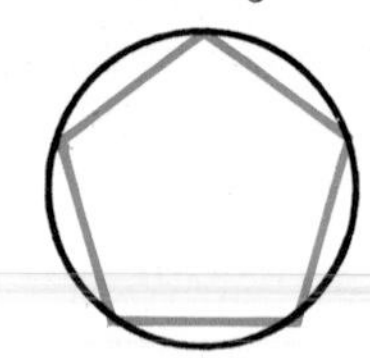

integers (225) The whole numbers and their opposites.

..., $^-3$, $^-2$, $^-1$, 0, 1, 2, 3, ...

irrational number (336) A number that can be named by a nonterminating, nonrepeating decimal.

isosceles triangle (126) A triangle that has at least two congruent sides.

least common denominator (LCD) (78)

The least common multiple of the denominators of two or more fractions. The LCD of $\frac{5}{6}$ and $\frac{5}{8}$ is 24.

least common multiple (LCM) (67) The least whole number, other than zero, that is a multiple of two or more given numbers. The LCM of 14 and 4 is 28.

leg of a right triangle (361) Either of the two sides opposite the acute angles of a right triangle.

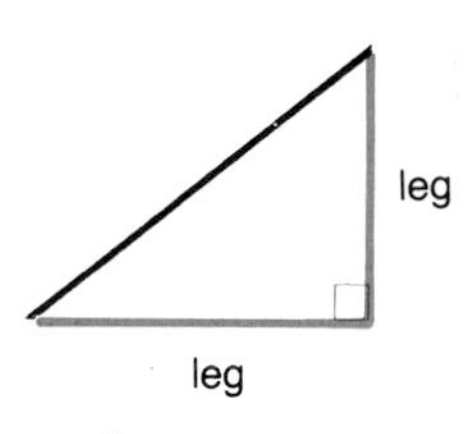

line (115) All the points in a never-ending straight path. Line ST is symbolized $\overleftrightarrow{ST}$.

S
T

line of symmetry (123) The line drawn through a figure so that the figure on one side is a mirror image of the figure on the other side.

line segment (115) Two endpoints and the straight path between them. Line segment PQ is symbolized $\overline{PQ}$.

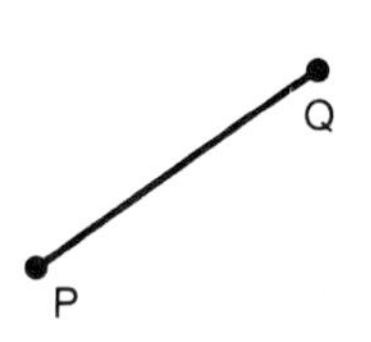

liter (L) (260) The basic unit of capacity in the metric system.

mean (324) The mean, or average, of a set of data is the sum of the numbers divided by the number of addends.

median (324) The middle number in an ordered set of data. When there are two middle numbers, the median is the mean of those two numbers.

meter (m) (253) The basic unit of length in the metric system.

metric system (253) A system of measurement using the following basic units: meter for length, gram for mass, liter for capacity, and degrees Celsius for temperature.

midpoint (131) The point that bisects a line segment.

mixed numeral (74) A numeral that indicates the sum of a whole number and a fraction. $4\frac{5}{7}$ is a mixed numeral.

mode (324) The number that appears most often in a set of data.

multiple (67) A number that has a given number as a factor. The multiples of a number are found by multiplying the number by 0, 1, 2, 3, and so on. The multiples of 3 are 0, 3, 6, 9, 12, and so on.

multiplicative inverse, *see* reciprocal.

negative number (225) Any number to the left of zero on a number line.

obtuse angle (117) An angle that has degree measure between 90 and 180.

octagon (124) A polygon with eight sides.

odds (314) The ratio of the number of ways an event can occur to the number of ways the event cannot occur.

opposites (225) Two numbers that are the same distance from 0 on the number line. The opposite of 7 is $^{-}7$ and vice versa.

ordered pair (340) A pair of numbers in a specific order that names the coordinates of a point in the coordinate plane.

origin (340) The point in the coordinate system where the axes intersect. The ordered pair for the origin is (0,0).

outcome (305) A possible result.

parabola (352) A curved graph of an equation such as $y = 2x^2$.

parallel lines (120) Lines in the same plane that do *not* intersect.

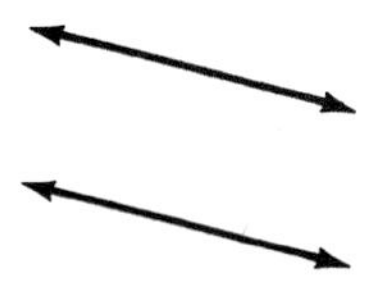

parallelogram (127) A quadrilateral with two pairs of parallel sides.

pentagon (124) A polygon with five sides.

percent (186) An expression of hundredths using the percent symbol (%).

$$23\% = \frac{23}{100} = 0.23$$

perfect square (336) The square of an integer. 64 is a perfect square since $64 = 8 \times 8$.

perimeter (279) The distance around a polygon.

perpendicular bisector (133) A line perpendicular to a line segment that also bisects the line segment.

perpendicular lines (120) Two lines that intersect to form right angles.

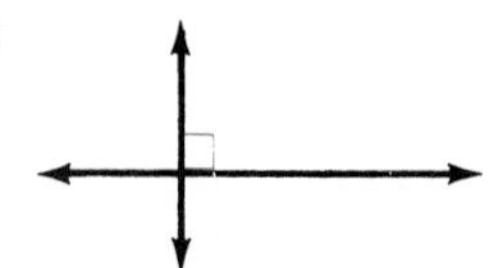

pi (π) (284) The ratio of the circumference of a circle to its diameter. An approximation for π is 3.14.

place value (3) A system for writing numbers. In this system, the position of a digit determines its value.

plane (115) A never-ending flat surface with no boundaries.

point of symmetry (135) A point in a figure so that if the figure is rotated 180° about the point the same figure results.

polygon (124) A closed plane figure formed by line segments.

polyhedron (286) A solid with flat surfaces called *faces*.

positive number (225) Any number to the right of zero on a number line.

power (6) A number that is expressed using an exponent.

precision (258) The precision of a measurement depends on the size of the unit of measure. A measurement to the nearest centimeter is more precise than a measurement to the nearest meter.

prime factorization (65) An expression of a composite number as a product of prime numbers. The prime factorization of 28 is $2 \times 2 \times 7$.

prime number (64) A whole number that has exactly two factors, the number and 1. Some prime numbers are 2, 3, 5, 7, and 11.

prism (286) A polyhedron with two parallel congruent bases that are shaped like polygons. The other faces of the prism are shaped like parallelograms.

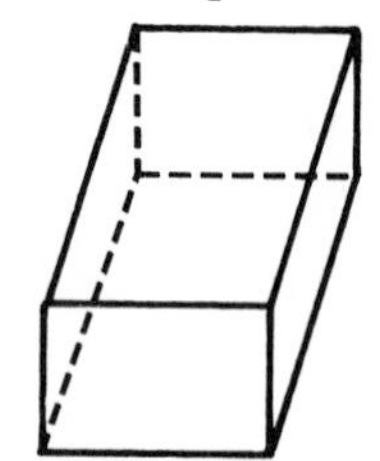

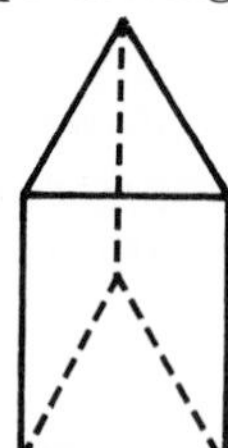

probability (308) The ratio of the number of ways an event can occur to the total number of possible outcomes.

proper fraction (74) A fraction that has a numerator that is less than the denominator.

proportion (174) An equation that states two ratios are equivalent. $\frac{5}{6} = \frac{10}{12}$

pyramid (286) A polyhedron with one base that is shaped like a polygon. The other faces of the pyramid are triangular.

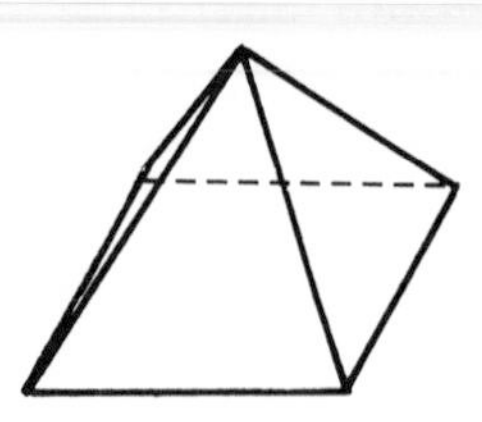

Pythagorean theorem (362) In a right triangle, the square of the length of the hypotenuse is equal to the sum of the squares of the lengths of the other two sides.

quadrant (340) One of four regions formed by the axes in a coordinate system.

quadrilateral (124) A polygon with four sides.

radius (136) A line segment whose endpoints are the center of a circle and a point of the circle.

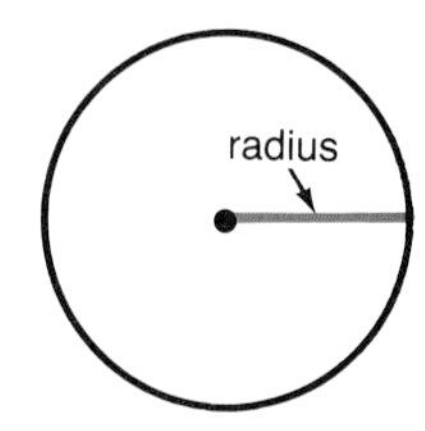

range (324) The difference between the greatest number and the least number in a set of data.

rate (178) A ratio of two measurements having different units.

$\frac{5 \text{ km}}{2 \text{ min}}$ 8 m/h

ratio (172) A comparison of two numbers. The ratio of 2 to 3 can be stated as 2 out of 3, 2 to 3, 2:3, or $\frac{2}{3}$.

rational number (225) Any number that can be expressed as a quotient of two integers, when the divisor is not zero.

ray (115) One endpoint and a never-ending straight path in one direction. Ray GH is symbolized $\overrightarrow{GH}$.

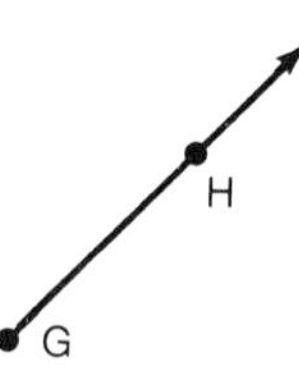

real number (336) Either a rational number or an irrational number.

reciprocals (104) Two numbers whose product is 1. Since $\frac{3}{4} \times \frac{4}{3} = 1$, $\frac{3}{4}$ and $\frac{4}{3}$ are reciprocals of each other. Reciprocals are also called *multiplicative inverses.*

rectangle (127) A parallelogram with four congruent angles.

reflection (342) When a figure is the mirror image of another figure.

regular polygon (124) A polygon in which all sides are congruent and all angles are congruent.

repeating decimal (76) A decimal whose digits repeat in groups of one or more. The decimals equivalent to $\frac{2}{3}$ and $\frac{5}{11}$ are repeating decimals.

$$\frac{2}{3} = 0.6666... \text{ or } 0.\overline{6}$$
$$\frac{5}{11} = 0.4545... \text{ or } 0.\overline{45}$$

rhombus (127) A parallelogram with four congruent sides.

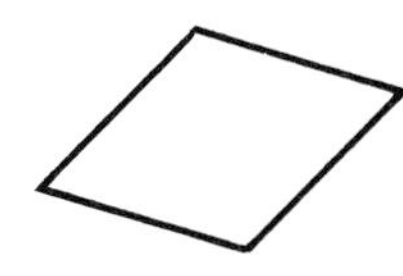

right angle (117) An angle that has a degree measure of 90.

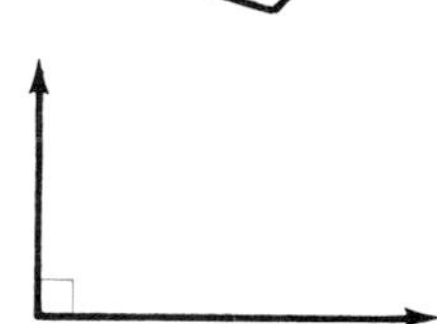

right triangle (126) A triangle that has a right angle.

sample (322) A small group chosen at random from a larger group. Predictions about the larger group are made by studying the sample.

scale drawing (182) A representation of something that is too large or small to be conveniently drawn actual size.

scalene triangle (126) A triangle that has *no* congruent sides.

scientific notation (246) A way of expressing numbers as the product of a number between 1 and 10 and a power of 10. $1{,}017{,}000 = 1.017 \times 10^6$

sequence (164) A list of numbers in a certain order.

arithmetic sequence: 0,2,4,6,8,...
geometric sequence: 1,2,4,8,16,...

similar figures (368) Figures that have the same shape.

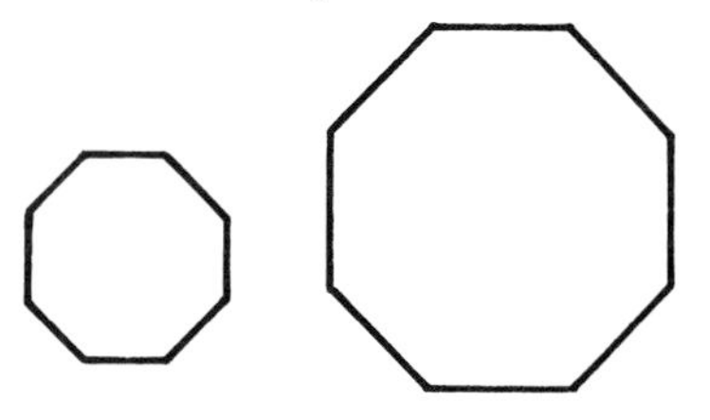

simplest form (73) A fraction is in simplest form when the greatest common factor of the numerator and denominator is one.

sine (376) The ratio of the measure of the side opposite an acute angle in a right triangle to the measure of the hypotenuse.

skew lines (120) Lines in space that neither intersect nor are parallel.

solution of an equation (150) A replacement for the variable that makes an equation true. The solution of the equation $y + 2 = 7$ is 5.

solve (150) To find the number(s) that make an equation or inequality true.

square (127) A parallelogram with four congruent sides and four congruent angles.

square number (square) (332) A number that is the product of two equal factors. 6.25 is the square of 2.5.

square root (333) One of the two equal factors of a number. 7 is the square root of 49 since $49 = 7 \times 7$. $\sqrt{49} = 7$

standard form of a number (6) The simplest place-value form of the number. The standard form for one hundred twenty-eight is 128.

statistics (318) A branch of mathematics that involves collecting, analyzing, and presenting data.

supplementary angles (118) Two angles are supplementary if the sum of their degree measures is 180.

surface area (286) The sum of the areas of the surfaces of a solid.

tangent (376) The ratio of the measure of the side opposite an acute angle in a right triangle to the measure of the side adjacent.

terminating decimal (76) A decimal whose digits end. The decimals equivalent to $\frac{1}{4}$ and $\frac{3}{8}$ are terminating decimals.

$$\frac{1}{4} = 0.25 \qquad \frac{3}{8} = 0.375$$

translation (342) The movement of a figure in one direction.

transversal (121) A line that intersects two or more lines. $\overleftrightarrow{JK}$ is a transversal.

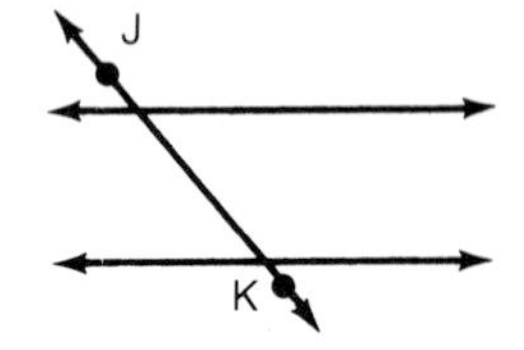

trapezoid (127) A quadrilateral with exactly one pair of parallel sides.

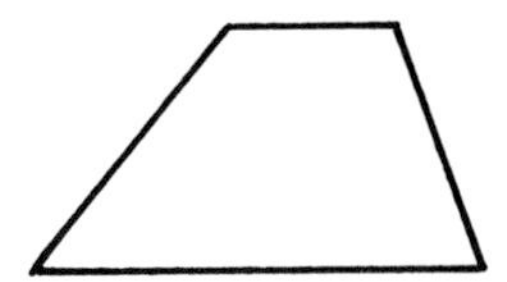

tree diagram (305) A diagram that shows the possible outcomes of an event.

triangle (124) A polygon with three sides.

unit rate (178) A rate with a denominator of one.

variable (144) A symbol, usually a letter, that is used to stand for some number. In the expression $d + 3$, the variable is d.

vertex (116, 124) The common endpoint of the rays forming an angle. The point where line segments meet in a polygon.

vertical angles (119) Angles formed by two intersecting lines. $\angle 1$ and $\angle 3$ are vertical angles. $\angle 2$ and $\angle 4$ are vertical angles.

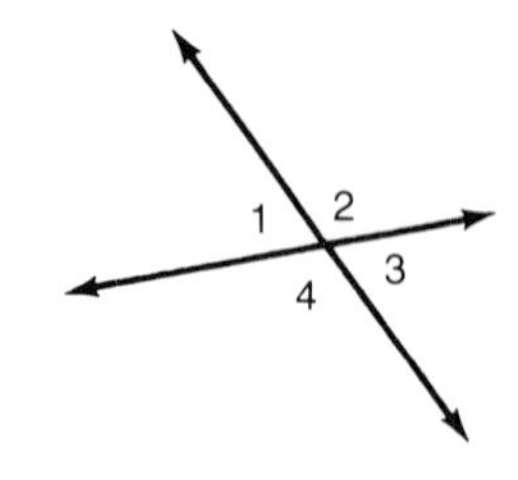

volume (292) The amount of space that a solid contains.

Mathematical Symbols

$=$	is equal to
$\neq$	is not equal to
$>$	is greater than
$<$	is less than
$\approx$	is approximately equal to
$\overleftrightarrow{AB}$	line AB
$\overline{AB}$	line segment AB
$\overrightarrow{AB}$	ray AB
$\triangle$	triangle
$\angle$	angle
$\cong$	is congruent to
$\sim$	is similar to
$\perp$	is perpendicular to
$\parallel$	is parallel to
$^\circ$	degrees
π	pi
$\sqrt{\ }$	square root
%	percent
$^+4$	positive four
$^-4$	negative four

Formulas

$A = lw$	area of a rectangle
$A = b \times h$	area of a parallelogram
$A = \frac{1}{2} \times b \times h$	area of a triangle
$A = \frac{1}{2} \times h \times (a + b)$	area of a trapezoid
$A = \pi r^2$	area of a circle
$c = \pi d$	circumference of a circle
$V = lwh$	volume of a rectangular prism
$V = \frac{1}{3}lwh$	volume of a pyramid
$V = \pi r^2 h$	volume of a cylinder
$V = \frac{1}{3}\pi r^2 h$	volume of a cone
$I = p \times r \times t$	interest

Metric System of Measurement

Prefixes kilo (k) = thousand
hecto (h) = hundred
deka (da) = ten
deci (d) = tenth
centi (c) = hundredth
milli (m) = thousandth

Length 1 centimeter (cm) = 10 millimeters (mm)
1 meter (m) = 100 centimeters or 1,000 millimeters
1 kilometer (km) = 1,000 meters

Mass 1 gram (g) = 1,000 milligrams (mg)
1 kilogram (kg) = 1,000 grams
1 metric ton (t) = 1,000 kilograms

Capacity 1 liter (L) = 1,000 milliliters (mL)
1 kiloliter (kL) = 1,000 liters

Customary System of Measurement

Length 1 foot (ft) = 12 inches (in.)
1 yard (yd) = 3 feet or 36 inches
1 mile (mi) = 1,760 yards or 5,280 feet

Weight 1 pound (lb) = 16 ounces (oz)
1 ton = 2,000 pounds

Capacity 1 cup = 8 fluid ounces (fl oz)
1 pint (pt) = 2 cups
1 quart (qt) = 2 pints
1 gallon (gal) = 4 quarts

Index

A

Absolute value, 227
Accuracy, 277
Acute angle, 117
Acute triangle, 126
Addition, 4
customary system, 270
decimals, 38
estimation, 10, 54
fractions, 87-89
mixed numerals, 90
probabilities, 312
properties, 8
rational numbers, 228
solving equations, 152
time, 266
whole numbers, 12
Adjacent angles, 117
Alternate exterior angles, 121
Alternate interior angles, 121
Altitude, 141
Angles, 116
acute, 117
adjacent, 118
alternate exterior, 121
alternate interior, 121
complementary, 118
constructions, 130-131
corresponding, 121
measuring, 116
obtuse, 117
right, 117
supplementary, 118
vertex, 116
vertical, 119
Area, 280
changing units, 281
circles, 285
parallelogram, 280
problem solving, 296
rectangle, 280
surface, 286, 288
trapezoids, 282
triangles, 282
Arithmetic sequences, 164
ASA rule, 123
construction, 134
Associative properties, 8
Average, 48
see mean

B

Bar graphs, 19, 49, 320
making, 265
100%, 211
Base
percent proportion, 199
powers, 6
Base two (binary), 31
BASIC, 388
DATA statement, 390
END statement, 390
flow charts, 394
IF-THEN statement, 392
input and output, 390
LET statement, 390
loop, 392
order of operations, 389
PRINT statement, 390
programs, 390
writing, 396
READ statement, 390
RUN command, 390
Bisect, 129
angles, 131
line segments, 131
paper folding, 129

C

Calculators, 55, 151, 285, 334, 345
Calendars, making, 155
Capacity
customary system, 269
metric system, 260
volume and mass, 295
Careers
see Mathematics and Careers
Celsius, 248
Center, circle, 136
Centimeter, 253
Certificate of deposit (CD), 356
Chapter Review, 29, 59, 81, 111, 139, 169, 193, 221, 249, 275, 299, 329, 357, 383
Chapter Test, 30, 60, 82, 112, 140, 170, 194, 222, 250, 276, 300, 330, 358, 384
Checking account, 17
Chord, 136
Circle graphs, 13, 109, 203, 321
making, 205
Circles, 136
area, 285
center, 136
chord, 136
circumference, 284
circumscribed, 141
diameter, 136
inscribed, 141
radius, 136
Circumcenter, 141
Circumference, 284
Circumscribed circle, 141
Commission, 200
Common factors, 66
Common multiples, 67
Commutative properties, 8
Compass, 130
Complementary angles, 118
Complex fractions, 107
Composite number, 64
Computers, 267, 274, 388-397

Conditional, 113
Conditional probability, 311
Cones
surface area, 288
volume, 294
Congruent figures, 122
constructions, 130
SSS, SAS, ASA rules, 123
Congruent triangles
constructions, 134
Constructions
angles, 130-131
bisecting, 131
circumscribed circles, 141
congruent triangles, 134
golden rectangle, 138
inscribed circles, 141
inscribed polygons, 136-137
irrational numbers, 365
line segments, 130-131
parallel lines, 133
perpendicular lines, 132
regular polygons, 136
Consumer mathematics
see Mathematics and Consumers
see percents
Coordinate system, 340
Corresponding angles, 121
Corresponding sides
similar triangles, 368
Cosine, 376
Credit card, 217
Cross products, 174
Cumulative Review, 16, 44, 70, 98, 128, 154, 184, 210, 232, 264, 290, 316, 344, 374
Customary system
capacity, 269
length, 268
operations, 270
weight, 269
Cylinders
surface area, 288
volume, 294

D

Data, 318
range, 324
DATA statement, 390
Decagon, 124
Decimals, 33
addition and subtraction, 38-39
annexing zeros, 34
comparing, 34
division, 46-47, 50-53
equivalent, 34
estimation, 54
expanded form, 245
and fractions, 33
to fractions, mixed numerals, 77
multiplication, 40-43, 50-51
ordering, 35
percents, 186-187, 190-191
place value, 33
repeating, 76
to fractions, 171
rounding, 36
terminating, 76
zeros in multiplication, 42
Degree, angle measure, 116
Density, 298
Density property, 241
Dependent events, 310
Diameter, 136
Dilations, 385
Discounts, successive, 223
Distance formula, 147
Distributive property, 9
rational numbers, 251
Divide-and-average, 345
Divisibility, 63,65
Division, 4
customary system, 270
decimals, 46-47, 50-53
estimation, 10, 54
fractions, 105
mixed numerals, 106
powers of ten, 50
rational numbers, 236
rounding quotients, 47, 53
short, 23
solving equations, 156
whole numbers, 22-25

E

Earning statement, 220
END statement, 390
Enrichment, 31, 61, 83, 113, 141, 171, 195, 223, 251, 277, 301, 331, 359, 385
Equations, 149
equivalent, 150
graphing two, 350
problem solving, 160
solving
percents, 200
rational numbers, 238-241
two-step, 162
using addition, 152
using division, 156
using multiplication, 158
using subtraction, 150
two-step
with rationals, 240
two variables, 346
writing, 349
Equilateral triangle, 126
Equivalent
decimals, 34
equations, 150
fractions, 72
simplest form, 73
ratio, 174
Error
percent of, 277
relative, 277
Error of measurement, 259
greatest possible, 259
Estimation
calculators, 55
decimals, 54
whole numbers, 10
Euclidean algorithm, 83
Even numbers, 64
Events, 308
dependent, 310
independent, 310
odds, 314
Expanded form, 7
decimals, 245
Exponents, 6
integers, 244

Expressions, 143
  variables, 144

F

Factorial, 307
Factors, 63
  common, 66
  greatest common (GCF), 66
  problem solving, 68
Factor trees, 65
Fahrenheit, 248
Fibonacci sequence, 195
Figurate numbers, 71
Finance charge, 58
Flowcharts, 394
Focus on Problem Solving
  see problem solving
Formulas
  area, 280, 282, 285, 294
  circumference, 284
  density, 298
  distance, 147
  electricity, 146
  home loans, 168
  horsepower, 147
  interest, 216
  involving square root, 337
  surface area, 301
  temperature, 248
  using, 163
  volume, 292, 293, 301
Fractions
  addition, 87-89
  comparing, 78
  complex, 107
  decimals, 33
  to decimals, 76
  division, 105
  equivalent, 72
  improper and proper, 74
  least common denominator (LCD), 78
  multiplication, 100
  ordering, 79
  percents, 188-191
  problem solving, 96
  ratios, 173
  reciprocals, 104
  simplest form, 73
  subtraction, 92
Frequency table, 318

G

Geometric sequences, 165
Geometry
  angles, 116
    relationships, 118
  basic terms, 115
  congruent figures, 122
  constructions, 130-138, 141
  parallel lines, 120
  perpendicular lines, 120
  polygons, 124
  reflections, 342
  translations, 342
Goldbach's conjecture, 64
Golden rectangle, 138
Gram, 260
Graphs
  bar, 19, 49, 211, 265, 320
  circle, 13, 109, 203, 205, 321
  equations with two variables, 348
  histogram, 318
  inequalities, 338
  line, 11, 39, 233, 320
  ordered pairs, 341
  parabolas, 352
  pictograph, 21, 99, 320
  problem solving, 321, 354
  scattergrams, 331
  slope and *y*-intercept, 359
  of two equations, 350
Greatest common factor (GCF), 66
  Euclidean algorithm, 83
Greatest possible error, 259
Gross pay, 220

H

Hexagons, 124
  inscribing, 136
Histogram, 318
Hypotenuse, 361

I

Identity properties, 8
IF-THEN statement, 392
Improper fraction, 74
Incenter, 141
Income tax, 28
Independent events, 310
Indirect measurement, 370
Inequalities, 338
  graphs, 338
  solving, 339
  with two variables, 351
Inflation, 203
Input, 390
Inscribed circle, 141
Inscribed polygon, 136
Installments, 58
Integers, 225
  as exponents, 244
  number line, 225
  see rational numbers
Interest, 216, 217
Interpolation, 379
Inverse, multiplicative, 239
Irrational numbers, 336
  construction of, 365
Isosceles triangle, 126

K

Kilogram, 260
Kiloliter, 260
Kilometer, 253
Kilowatt-hours, 192

L

Latitude, 382
Least common denominator (LCD), 78
Least common multiple (LCM), 67
Legs, 361

Length
customary system, 268
measuring, 254
metric system, 253-259
LET statement, 390
Line graphs, 11, 39, 233, 320
Lines, 115
parallel, 120
perpendicular, 120
skew, 120
of symmetry, 123
transversal, 121
Line segment, 115
constructions, 130-131
Liter, 260
Logic, 113
Longitude, 382
Loop, 392

M

Magic squares, 93, 157
Markup, 214
Mass, 260
volume and capacity, 295
Mathematics and Careers, 58, 168, 328
Mathematics and Computers, 274
Mathematics and Consumers, 17, 28, 45, 80, 110, 192, 220, 356
Mathematics and Geography, 382
Mathematics and History, 138
Mathematics and Science, 248, 298, 337
Mathematics Lab, 71, 99, 129, 155, 185, 211, 233, 265, 291, 311, 345, 374
Mean, 324
Measurement
accuracy, 277
angles, 116
customary system, 268-271
indirect, 370
metric system, 253-263
precision, 258
relative error, 277
time, 266
Median
data, 324
triangle, 141
Meter, 253
Metric system
changing units, 256-257, 261, 281
length, 253-259
mass and capacity, 260
problem solving, 262
Mileage chart, 27, 80
Milligram, 260
Milliliter, 260
Millimeter, 253
Mixed numerals, 74
addition, 90
comparing, 78
to decimals, 76
division, 106
multiplication, 102
ordering, 79
percents, 188-191
problem solving, 96
subtraction, 94
Mode, 324
Modular arithmetic, 61
Multiples, 67
common, 67
least common (LCM), 67
problem solving, 68
Multiplication, 4
counting outcomes, 306
customary system, 270
decimals, 40-43, 50-51
estimation, 10, 54
fractions, 100
mixed numerals, 102
powers of ten, 50
probabilities, 310
properties, 8
rational numbers, 234
solving equations, 158
whole numbers, 18-21
zeros in, 42
Multiplicative inverse, 239

N

Negative numbers, 225
Net pay, 220
Normal curve, 319
Number lines
integers, 225
rational numbers, 226
Numbers
composite, 64
even and odd, 64
Fibonacci, 195
figurate, 71
integers, 225
irrational, 336
negative, 225
positive, 225
prime, 64
rational, 225
real, 336

O

Obtuse angle, 117
Obtuse triangle, 126
Octagon, 124
Odd numbers, 64
Odds, 314
Opposites, 225
Ordered pairs, 340
graphs, 341
Order of operations, 143
BASIC, 389
Origin, 340
Outcomes
multiplication, 306
tree diagrams, 305
Output, 390
Outstanding checks and deposits, 17

P

Palindromes, 151
Parabolas, 352
Parallel lines, 120
construction, 133
Parallelograms, 127
area, 280
Pascal's triangle, 309
Pentagonal numbers, 71
Pentagons, 124

Percentage, 199
Percentiles, 325
Percents, 186
business, 214
commission, 200
computer programs, 396
decimals, 186-187, 190-191
discount, successive, 223
equations, 200
of error, 277
find a number when a percent of it is known, 204
fractions and mixed numerals, 188-191
of increase or decrease, 206
inflation, 203
interest, 216
markup, 214
of a number, 199-201
one number is of another, 202
problem solving, 208
proportions, 199
taxes, 212
Perfect squares, 336
Perimeter, 279
problem solving, 296
Perpendicular lines, 120
constructions, 132
Pi (π), 284, 291
Pictographs, 21, 320
making, 99
Place value
base two, 31
decimals, 33
metric system, 253
whole numbers, 3
Plane, 115
Point, 115
coordinate system, 340
of symmetry, 135
Polygons, 124
inscribed, 136
perimeter, 279
regular, 124
Polyhedrons, 286
Positive numbers, 225
Powers, 6
Powers of ten
division, 50
multiplication, 50
Precision, 258
Prime factorization, 65
Prime meridian, 382
Prime number, 64
PRINT statement, 390
Prisms, 286
surface area, 286
volume, 292
Probability, 308
addition, 312
conditional, 311
counting outcomes, 305-307
experiments, 317
multiplying, 310
Problem solving
choose the operation, 26
Focus on, 56, 108, 166, 218, 272, 326, 380
fractions and mixed numerals, 96
graphs, 321
indirect measurement, 370
multi-step problems, 48
proportions, 176
Pythagorean theorem, 364
right triangles, 372
tangent, sine, and cosine, 378
using equations, 160
using factors and multiples, 68
using graphs, 354
using metric measurements, 262
using percent, 208
using perimeter, area, and volume, 296
using rates and proportions, 180
using rationals, 242
using statistics, 322
Programs, computer
writing, 396
see BASIC
Proper fraction, 74
Proportions, 174
cross products, 174
percents, 199
problem solving, 180
scale drawings, 182
similar triangles, 368
solving, 175
using, 176
Protractor, 116
Pyramids, 286
surface area, 286
volume, 293
Pythagorean theorem, 362
problem solving, 364
Pythagorean triples, 363

Q

Quadrants, 340
Quadrilaterals, 124
parallelogram, 127
rectangle, 127
rhombus, 127
square, 127
trapezoid, 127

R

Radius
circle, 136
sphere, 301
Range, 324
Rates, 178
percent, 199
problem solving, 180
unit, 178
Rational numbers, 225
absolute value, 227
addition, 228
comparing, 226
density property, 241
distributive property, 251
division, 236
multiplication, 234
number line, 226
opposites, 225
problem solving, 242
solving equations, 238
subtraction, 230
two-step equations, 240
Ratios, 172
equivalent, 174
fractions, 173

rates, 178
tangent, sine, and cosine, 376
Ray, 115
READ statement, 390
Real numbers, 336
Reciprocals, 104
Rectangles, 127
area, 280
golden, 138
Reflections, 342
Regular polygons, 124
constructions, 136
Relative error, 277
Relatively prime, 66
Repeating decimals, 76
to fractions, 171
Rhombus, 127
Richter scale, 244
Right angle, 117
Right triangles, 126
hypotenuse, 361
legs, 361
problem solving, 372
30°-60°, 366
Roots, square, 333
Rounding
decimals, 36
quotients, 47, 53
whole numbers, 3
Rule of 78, 110
RUN command, 390

S

Sales tax, 212
Sample, 322
SAS rule, 123
construction, 134
Scale drawings, 182
making, 185
Scalene triangle, 126
Scattergrams, 331
Scientific notation, 246
Sequences, 164
arithmetic, 164
Fibonacci, 195
geometric, 165
Short division, 23
Sides
angle, 116
Significant digits, 259
Similar triangles, 368
indirect measurement, 370
Simplest form, 73
Sine, 376
Skew lines, 120
Skills Review, 15, 27, 43, 57, 69, 79, 97, 109, 127, 137, 153, 167, 183, 191, 209, 219, 231, 247, 263, 273, 289, 297, 315, 327, 343, 355, 373, 381
Skills Test, 84-85, 196-197, 302-303, 386-387
Slope, 359
Solving
equations, 150, 152, 156, 158, 162
proportions, 175
Spheres
surface area, 301
volume, 301
Square numbers, 71
Square of a number, 332
perfect, 336
Square roots, 333
approximating, 334
divide-and-average, 345
Squares, 127
inscribing, 137
SSS rule, 123
construction, 134
Stadia, 375
Standard form, 6
Statements
conditional, 113
truth value, 113
Statistics
average, 48
data, 318
frequency table, 318
graphs, 320-321
histogram, 318
mean, 324
median, 324
mode, 324
normal curve, 319
percentiles, 325
problem solving, 322
range, 324
sample, 322
scattergrams, 331
Stock market, 233
Subtraction, 4
customary system, 270
decimals, 39
estimation, 10, 54
fractions, 92
mixed numerals, 94
rational number, 230
solving equations, 150
time, 266
whole numbers, 14
Supplementary angles, 118
Surface area, 286
cones, 288
cylinders, 288
prisms, 286
pyramids, 286
Symmetry
line of, 123
point of, 135

T

Tangent, 376
Taxes
percent, 212
sales, 212
withholding tax, 213
Temperature formulas, 248
Terminating decimals, 76
30°-60° right triangles, 366
Time, 266
24-hour notation, 267
Time card, 45
Time zones, 125
Translations, 342
Transversal, 121
Trapezoids, 127
area, 282
Tree diagrams, 305
Triangles, 124
acute, 126
altitude, 141
area, 282
circumscribed and inscribed circles, 141

congruent, 123
constructions, 134
equilateral, 126
isosceles, 126
median, 141
obtuse, 126
Pascal's, 309
right, 126
scalene, 126
similar, 368
Triangular numbers, 71
Truth value, 113
Twin primes, 64
Two-step equations, 162
with rationals, 240

U

Unit rates, 178
Universal Product Code (UPC), 274
Utility bills, 192

V

Variables, 144
equations with two, 346
inequalities with two, 351
using, 148
Venn diagrams, 326
Vertical angles, 119
Volume, 292
capacity and mass, 295
cone, 294
cylinder, 294
prism, 292
problem solving, 296
pyramid, 293

W

Weight, 269
Whole numbers
addition, 12
basic operations, 4
division, 22-25
estimation, 10
expanded form, 7
factors, 63
multiplication, 18-21
place value, 3
rounding, 3
standard form, 6
subtraction, 14
Windchill factor, 227
Withholding tax, 213

X

x-axis, 340
x-coordinate, 340

Y

y-axis, 340
y-coordinate, 340
y-intercept, 359

Z

Zero power, 6
Zeros
annexing, 34
in multiplication, 42

Photo Credits

Cover Photo: *Ken Akers*

2, *Tom Stack/Tom Stack & Assoc.;* **5,** *MARTA;* **7,** *Ted Rice;* **8,** *Texaco, Inc.;* **10,** *Zimmerman/FPG;* **12,** *David Germon;* **18,** *Paul Brown;* **20, 23,** *Tim Courlas;* **32,** *Zimmerman/Alpha;* **34,** *United States Olympic Committee;* **37,** *T. Carroll/Alpha;* **38,** *Elaine Comer;* **40,** *Gerard Photography;* **43,** *Doug Martin;* **47,** *Kevin Fitzsimons;* **51,** *Elaine Comer;* **53,** *Aerial Photo by Collier/Condit;* **54, 56,** *Eric Hoffhines;* **62,** *Tim Courlas;* **64,** *Steve Lissau;* **67,** *Ward's Natural Science Establishment;* **73,** *David M. Dennis;* **74,** *John Youger;* **77,** *USDA:* **78,** *Elaine Comer;* **86,** *Ruth Dixon;* **88,** *Thomas Russell;* **93,** *Tim Courlas;* **94,** *Frank Balthis;* **97,** *Tim Courlas;* **100, 104,** *Thomas Russell;* **106,** *Hickson-Bender Photography;* **108,** *USDA;* **114,** *Doug Martin;* **119,** *Richard Brommer;* **122,** *Russ Lappa;* **125,** *Tim Courlas;* **126,** *Eric Hoffhines;* **131, 132,** *Larry Hamill;* **135,** *Doug Martin;* **136,** *Roger K. Burnard;* **142,** *Elaine Comer;* **144,** *Tim Courlas;* **146,** *Doug Martin;* **148,** *Elaine Comer;* **150,** *Doug Martin;* **153,** *Morgan Photos;* **156,** *Hickson-Bender Photography;* **160,** *Bill and Joan Popejoy;* **162** *(all), Larry Hamill;* **164,** *Tim Courlas;* **172, 174,** *Doug Martin;* **178,** *Ken Van Dyne;* **181,** *NASA;* **187,** *Doug Martin;* **189, 190, 192,** *Hickson-Bender Photography;* **198,** *Ken Van Dyne;* **200, 203,** *Doug Martin;* **204,** *Ken Van Dyne;* **207,** *Elaine Comer;* **208,** *Jim Howard/FPG;* **212,** *Elaine Comer;* **215,** *Doug Martin;* **216,** *Elaine Comer;* **218,** *Ken Van Dyne;* **224,** *Larry Hamill;* **226,** *Doug Martin;* **230,** *Richard Alley;* **234,** *Roger K. Burnard;* **237,** *Ruth Dixon;* **238,** *Ohio Agricultural Research and Development Center;* **240,** *Frank Balthis;* **244,** *Aerial photo by Collier/Condit;* **246,** *Tracy Borland;* **252,** *Tim Courlas;* **257,** *Larry Hamill;* **260,** *File Photo;* **262,** *Tim Courlas;* **266,** *Doug Martin;* **268,** *Roger Burnard;* **271,** *Tim Courlas;* **272,** *Doug Martin;* **278,** *Hickson-Bender Photography;* **280,** *Aerial Photo by Collier/Condit;* **285,** *Gerard Photography;* **286,** *USDA;* **288,** *A. Upitis/FPG;* **294,** *Hickson-Bender Photography;* **296,** *Cheryl Blair;* **304,** *Doug Martin;* **306,** *Susan Marquart;* **311, 312,** *Tim Courlas;* **314,** *Doug Martin;* **318,** *Tim Courlas;* **322,** *Marty Pardo;* **326, 332,** *Tim Courlas;* **334,** *Ward Allan Howe/FPG;* **337,** *File Photo;* **338,** *Tim Courlas;* **341,** *Elaine Comer;* **342,** *James N. Westwater;* **346,** *Susan Marquart;* **350,** *Tracy Borland;* **352,** *Tim Courlas;* **353,** *Larry Hamill;* **354,** *Tim Courlas;* **360,** *Steve Lissau;* **362,** *Betty Medsger;* **367,** *Eric Hoffhines;* **368,** *Ken Van Dyne;* **370,** *James N. Westwater;* **372,** *Tim Courlas;* **380,** *Doug Martin.*